Books by
  Raymond R. Camp

Hunting Trails

A Sportsman's Treasury

Hunting Trails

A Sportsman's Treasury

Edited by

RAYMOND R. CAMP

APPLETON-CENTURY-CROFTS, INC. • NEW YORK

Acknowledgments

For arrangements made with various authors, their representatives and publishers, where copyrighted material was permitted to be reprinted, and for the courtesy extended by them, the following acknowledgments are gratefully made:

Holt, Rinehart & Winston, Inc., for "The Plural of Moose is Mise" by Irvin S. Cobb, in *Field & Stream* Magazine, copyright 1921 by Henry Holt & Company, Inc.; "The Alaskan Grizzly" by Harold Mc-Cracken, in *Field & Stream* Magazine, copyright 1941 by Henry Holt & Company, Inc.; "Algonquin" from *Algonquin: The Story of a Great Dog* by Dion Henderson, copyright 1953 by Holt, Rinehart & Winston, Inc.

H. G. Pickering, for "Merry Xmas, Mr. Williams, 20 Pine Street, N. Y." copyright 1935 by H. G. Pickering.

Coward-McCann, Inc., for "White Deer Are Bad Luck" from *Where Flows the Kennebeck* by Arthur R. MacDougall, Jr., copyright 1947 by Arthur R. MacDougall, Jr.

Charles Schlessiger, % Brandt & Brandt, for "Two Eyes that Shone as One" from *The One-Eyed Poacher of Privilege* by Edmund Ware Smith, copyright 1936 by Edmund Ware Smith.

Outdoor Life Magazine, for "Three Men and a Buck" by William A. Miles, copyright 1940 by Popular Science Publishing Co., Inc.; "With Slashing Tusks" by F. D. Duncan, copyright 1942 by Popular Science Publishing Co., Inc.

Rufus King, for "The Case of the Seven Good Hunters" by Rufus King, copyright 1941 by *Redbook* Magazine.

Appleton-Century-Crofts, Inc., for "The Best Wingshot in the U. S." from *To Hell With Hunting* by Ed Zern, copyright 1946 by Ed Zern.

A. S. Barnes and Company, Inc., for "The Wrong Gobbler" from *Hunter's Choice* by Archibald Ruteledge, copyright 1947 by The Countryman Press.

Charles Scribner's Sons, for "Mollie" from *The Glorious Mornings* by Paul Hyde Bonner, copyright 1954 by Lilly M. Bonner; "The Green Hills of Africa" from *Green Hills of Africa* (pp. 216–244) by Ernest Hemingway, copyright 1935 by Charles Scribner's Sons.

Nash Buckingham, for "Broccoli" from *Ole Miss* by Nash Buckingham, copyright 1937 by Derrydale Press, Inc., 1946 by Nash Buckingham.

J. B. Lippincott Company, for "The Huntsman at the Gate" from *The Huntsman at the Gate* by Almet Jenks, copyright 1952 by Almet Jenks.

Chilton Co.—Book Division, for " 'Possum Up de 'Simmon Tree" from *Tales of Quails 'n' Such* by Havilah Babcock, copyright 1951 by Chilton Books, Philadelphia and New York.

Marguerite Harper, for "Royal Elk" by Verne Athanas, copyright 1961 by Verne Athanas.

Alfred A. Knopf, Inc., for "Hungarian Partridge and Prairie Chicken" from *Nip and Tuck* by Ray P. Holland, copyright 1939, 1946 by Alfred A. Knopf, Inc.; "Blue Ghosts of the Moraine Hills" from *Hunting and Fishing in Alaska* (Chapter XII) by Russell Annabel, copyright 1948 by Russell Annabel.

G. P. Putnam's Sons, for "Grizzly Bear" from *Hunting with the Bow and Arrow* by Saxton Pope, copyright 1947 by G. P. Putnam's Sons.

Farrar, Straus and Cudahy, Inc., for "In the Land of the Sladang" from *Shikar and Safari* by Edison Marshall, copyright 1947 by Edison Marshall.

Oxford University Press, Inc., for "The Bachelor of Powalgarh" from *Man-Eaters of India* by Jim Corbett, copyright 1957 by Oxford University Press, Inc.

Harper & Brothers, for "Clients, Brave and Otherwise" from *Hunter* by J. A. Hunter, copyright 1952 by J. A. Hunter.

Doubleday & Company, Inc., for "Killers in Africa" from *Killers in Africa* by Alexander Lake, copyright 1953 by Alexander Lake.

Contents

INTRODUCTION

There are seasons when the most avid hunter must seek his favorite sport vicariously, or not at all. Hence, this collection of hunting tales. Reading them, some hunters will, as I did, close their eyes and remember the odor of heather, of evergreens, of a tidal marsh or even of peat smoke.

You will find that some of the writers have familiar names. Others you will encounter for the first time and want to meet them again. But you will find few selections by those of literary magnitude. This may require an explanation, and I am pleased to give it.

The basis for the final selection was three-fold: authenticity, interest and diversification. Only a few of our literary lights, past or present, have turned to the hunting tale. The works of those who did are generally familiar to hunter and non-hunter alike, and many of them are disappointing—especially to the former. There are, of course, a few exceptions. These I include in the belief that if they have been read they are worth rereading. At least I found them so.

The lot of an anthologist is a pleasant one, but it has its harrowing moments, most of them at the end. Having assembled a wealth of material, he faces the task of reducing it to about one-fourth its original bulk. Then he discovers he has four magnificent stories, all dealing with the same phase of the sport. Three of them must go. But which three?

When the idea of a hunting anthology is first considered there seems to be an overpowering volume of wonderful material in prospect. But when you reread long-remembered tales you discover it was the idea you remembered, not its presentation. Then there are stories you recall in such detail that you believe you could almost rewrite them from memory. But what was that author's name?

One such circumstance brought me sleepless nights. I realized that I could not complete the book with satisfaction unless this particular story was included. One day at lunch I discussed the problem with a friend who, so far as I knew, had never read a line on the subject. I outlined the plot to him, urging that he query any of his friends who were interested in this phase of hunting, hoping that one of them might have read the story. His response left me sagging in my chair.

"It's a magnificent story and beautifully handled. I have the book at home and will bring it in tomorrow."

In arriving at the final selection I accepted the fact that most hunters are interested only in one or two phases of the sport. I have attempted to go around rather than over this obstacle by selecting stories, fiction and nonfiction, that possessed some interest over and above the subject itself. I shall never know how well I succeeded in this effort, but I enjoyed trying.

RAYMOND R. CAMP

IRVIN S. COBB

The Plural of Moose Is Mise

The average hunter does not take kindly to writers who find something humorous in his favorite sport, and only a master can write in this vein and make it stick. Cobb has accomplished this. He has, at the same time, provided an answer to the plural of "moose" that has disturbed pedants as well as hunters for many years. Having read this story we spent considerable time in exhaustive and exhausting research in an effort to determine whether Damon Runyon—a member of the hunting party—had written a record of the event. We were unsuccessful, so the narrative of this psychopathic safari must rest with Cobb.

A t the outset, when our expedition was still in the preparatory stages, we collectively knew a few sketchy details regarding the general architectural plan and outward aspect of the moose. One of us had once upon a time, years and years before, shot at or into—this point being debatable—a moose up in Maine. Another professed that in his youth he had seriously annoyed a moose with buckshot somewhere in Quebec. The rest of us had met the moose only in zoos with iron bars between us and him or in dining halls, where his head, projecting in a stuffed and mounted condition from the wall, gave one the feeling of dining with somebody out of the Old Testament. Speaking with regard to his family history, we understood he was closely allied to the European elk—the Unabridged told us that—and we gathered that, viewed at a distance, he rather suggested a large black mule with a pronounced Roman nose and a rustic hatrack sprouted out between his ears. Also, through our reading upon the subject, we knew that next to the

1

buffalo he was the largest vegetarian in North America and, next to a man who believes in the forecast of a campaign manager on the eve of an election, the stupidest native mammal that we have. By hearsay we had been made aware that he possessed a magnificent sense of smell and a perfectly wonderful sense of hearing, but was woefully shy on the faculty of thought, the result being that while by the aid of his nose and his ear he might all day elude you, if then perchance you did succeed in getting within gunning range of him he was prone to remain right where he was, peering blandly at you and accomodatingly shifting his position so as to bring his shape broadside on, thereby offering a better target until you, mastering the tremors of eagerness, succeeded in implanting a leaden slug in one of his vital areas.

But, offhand, we couldn't decide what the plural of him was. Still if the plural of goose were geese and the plural of mouse were mice it seemed reasonable to assume that the plural of moose should be mise. Besides, we figured that when we had returned and met friends and told them about our trip it would sound more impressive, in fact more plural, to say that we had slain mise rather than that we had slaughtered moose. In the common acceptance of the term as now used, moose might mean one moose or a herd of them, but mise would mean at least a bag of two of these mighty creatures and from two on up to any imaginable number.

One mentally framed the conversation:

"Well, I hear you've been up in Canada moose hunting." This is the other fellow speaking. "Kill any moose?"

"Kill any moose? Huh, we did better than that—we killed mise."

So by agreement we arranged that mise it should be. This being settled we went ahead with plans for outfitting ourselves against our foray into the game country. We equipped ourselves with high-powered rifles, with patent bedding rolls, with fanciful conceits in high boots and blanket overcoats. We bought everything that the clerk in the shop, who probably had never ventured north of the Bronx in all the days of his sheltered life, thought we should buy, including wicked-looking sheath knives and hand axes to be carried in the belt, tomahawk fashion, and pocket compasses. Personally, I have never been able to figure out the exact value of a compass to a man adrift in a strange country. What is the use of knowing where north is if you don't know where *you* are? Nevertheless, I was prevailed upon to purchase a compass, along with upward of a great gross of other articles large and small which the clerk believed would be needful to one starting upon such an expedition as we contemplated.

On my account he did a deal of thinking. Not since the fall of 1917, when we were making the world safe for the sporting-goods dealers of America, could he have spent so busy and so happy an afternoon as the afternoon when I dropped in on him.

By past experience I should have known better than to permit myself to be swept off my feet by this tradesman's flood of suggestions and recommendations. Already I had an ample supply of khaki shirts that were endeared to me by associations of duck-hunting forays in North Carolina and chill evenings in an Adirondack camp and a memorable journey to Wyoming, where the sage hen abides. I treasured a pair of comfortable hunting boots that had gone twice to European battlefields and down into the Grand Canyon and up again and across the California desert, without ever breeding a blister or chafing a shin. Among my most valued possessions I counted an ancient shooting coat, wearing which I had missed quail in Kentucky, snipe on Long Island, grouse in Connecticut, doves in Georgia, and woodcock in New York State. Finally, had I but taken time for sober second consideration, I should have recalled that the guides I have from time to time known considered themselves properly accoutered for the chase when they put on the oldest suit of store clothes they owned and stuck an extra pair of wool socks in their pockets. But to the city-bred sportsman half the joy of going on a camping trip consists in getting ready for it. So eminent an authority as Emerson Hough is much given to warning the amateur sportsman against burdening himself with vain adornments, and yet I am reliably informed that the said Hough has a larger individual collection of pretty devices in canvas and leather than any person in this republic.

That clerk had a seductive way about him; he had a positive gift. Otherwise I suppose he would have been handling some line which practically sells itself, such as oil stocks or mining shares. Under the influence of his blandishments I invested in a sweater of a pattern which he assured me was being favored by the really prominent moose hunters in the current season, and a pair of corduroy hunting pants which, when walked in, gave off a pleasant swishing sound like a soft-shoe dancer starting to do a sand jig. I was particularly drawn to these latter garments as being the most vocal pants I had ever seen. As I said before, I bought ever and ever so many other things; I am merely mentioning some of the main items.

We assembled the most impassive group of guides in the whole Dominion—men who, filled with the spirit of the majestic wilds, had never been known publicly to laugh at the expense of a tenderfooted stranger. They did not laugh at Harry Leon Wilson's conception of the proper equipment for a man starting upon such an excursion as this one. Wilson on being wired an invitation to go on a hunt for moose promptly telegraphed back that to the best of his recollection he had not lost any moose, but that if any of his friends had been so unfortunate or so careless as to mislay one he would gladly join in the quest for the missing. He brought along an electric flashlight, in case the search should be prolonged after nightfall, a trout rod and a camera. The guides did not laugh at Colonel Tillinghast Houston's unique notion of buying an expensive rifle and a hundred rounds of ammunition and then spending his days in camp sitting in a tent reading a history of the Maritime Provinces in two large volumes. They did not laugh at Colonel Bozeman Bulger's overseas puttees or at Damon Runyon's bowie knife, or at Major McGeehan's eight-pound cartridge belt— it weighed more than that when loaded; I am speaking of it, *net*— or at Frank Stevens' sleeping cap or at Bill MacBeth's going-away haircut—the handiwork of a barber who was a person looking with abhorrence upon the thought of leaving any hair upon the human neck when it is so easy to shave all exposed surfaces smooth and clean from a point drawn across the back of the head at the level of the tops of the ears on down as far as the rear collar button. He must have been a lover of the nude in necks, that barber.

The guides did not laugh even at my vociferous corduroys, which at every step I took, went *hist, hist,* as though entreating their wearer to be more quiet so they might the better be heard.

By a series of relay journeys we moved up across the line into Quebec, thence back again below the boundary and across the state of Maine, thence out of Maine into New Brunswick and to the thriving city of St. John, with its justly celebrated reversible falls which, by reason of the eccentricities of the tide, tumble upstream part of the time and downstream part of the time, thence by steamer across that temperamental body of water known as the Bay of Fundy, and so on into the interior of Nova Scotia. If anywhere on this continent there is a lovelier spot than the southern part of Nova Scotia in mid-fall I earnestly desire that, come next October, someone shall take me by the hand and lead me to it and let me rave. It used to be the land of Evangeline and the Acadians; now it is the land of the apple. You ran out of the finnan-haddie belt in and around Digby into the wonderful valley of the apples. On every hand are apples—on this side of the right-of-way, orchards stretching down to the blue waters of one of the most beautiful rivers in America, on that side, orchards climbing up the flanks of the rolling hills to where the combing of thick timber comes down and meets them; and everywhere, at roadside, on the verges of thickets, in pastures and old fields, are seedlings growing singly, in pairs and in clumps. They told us that the valley sceni- cally considered is at its best in the spring after the bloom bursts out upon the trees and the whole countryside turns to one vast pink and white bridal bouquet, but hardly can one picture it revealing itself as a more delectable vision than when the first frosts have fallen and every bough of every tree is studded with red and green and yellow globes and the scent of the ripened fruit rises like an in- cense of spices and wine.

The transition from the pastoral to the wilderness is abrupt. You leave Annapolis Royal in a motor car—that is, you do if you follow in our footsteps—and almost immediately you strike into the big game country. Not that the big game does not lap over into the settlements and even into the larger towns on occasion, for it does. It is recorded that on a certain day a full-grown moose—and a full-grown moose is almost the largest full-grown thing you ever saw—strolled through one of the principal streets of St. John and sought to enter—this being in the old sinful times—a leading saloon. A prominent lawyer of the same city told me that some four weeks before our arrival a woman client of his, living some two miles from the corporate limits, called him on the telephone at his office to ask his professional advice as to how legally she might go about getting rid of a bull moose which insisted on frequenting her orchard and frightening her children when they went to gather pippins. She felt, she said, that a lawyer was the proper person to seek in the emergency that had arisen, seeing that the closed season for moose was still on and it would be unlawful to take a shot at the intruder, so what she particularly desired to know was whether she couldn't have him impounded for trespass or something of that nature.

But such things as these do not happen every day. Probably a man could spend months on end in St. John without seeing the first of the above-mentioned animals rambling down the sidewalk in the manner of a young moose-about-town and trying to drop into the place where the saloon used to be, only to back out again, with chagrin writ large upon his features, upon discovering that the establishment in question had been transformed into a hat store.

To meet the moose where frequently he is and not merely where occasionally he is, one must go beyond the outlying orchards and on into the vasty expanse of the real moose country—hundreds of hundreds of miles of virgin waste, trackless except for game trails and portages across the ridges between waterways. It is a country of tamaracks and hemlocks, of maples and beech and birch, of berries and flowering shrubs, of bogs and barrens and swampy swales, of great granite boulders left behind by the glaciers when the world was young and thawing, of countless lakes and brawling white rapids and deep blue pools where, in the spawning season, the speckled trout are so thick that the small trout have to travel on the backs of the larger ones to avoid being crushed in the jam. I did not see this last myself; my authority for the statement is my friend the veracious lawyer of St. John. But I saw all the rest of it—the woods wearing the flaunting war-paint colors of the wonderful Canadian Indian summer—crimson of huckleberry, tawny of tamarack, yellow of birch, scarlet of maple; the ruffed grouse strutting, unafraid as barnyard fowl and, thanks be to a three-year period of protection, almost as numerous as sparrows in a city street; the signs of hoofed and padded creatures crossing and crisscrossing wherever the earth was soft enough to register the foot tracks of wild things.

And if you want to know how interior New Brunswick looked after Nova Scotia, you are respectfully requested to reread the foregoing paragraph, merely leaving out some of the lakes and most of the boulders.

On a flawless morning, in a motorboat we crossed a certain lake, and I wish I knew the language that might serve to describe the glory of the colors that ringed that lake around and were reflected, to the last flame-tipped leaf and the last smooth white column of birchen trunk in its still waters, but I don't. I'll go further and say I can't believe Noah Webster had the words to form the picture, and he had more words than anybody up to the time William J. Bryan went actively into politics. As for myself, I can only say that these colors fairly crackled. There were hues and combinations of hues, shadings and contrasts such as no artist ever has painted and no artist will care to paint, either, for fear of being called a nature faker.

The scene shifts to our main camp. We have met our guides and have marveled at their ability to trot over steep up-and-downhill portages carrying, each one of them, upon his back a load which no humane man would put on a mule, and have marveled still more when these men, having deposited their mountainous burdens at the farther end of the carry, go hurrying back across the ridge presently to reappear bearing upon their shoulders upturned canoes, their heads hidden inside the inverted interiors and yet by some magic gift peculiar to their craft, managing somehow to dodge the overhanging boughs of trees and without losing speed or changing gait to skip along from one slick round-topped boulder top to another.

Now we are in the deep woods, fifty miles from a railroad and thirty miles from a farmhouse. We sleep at night in canvas lean-tos, with log fires at our feet; we wash our faces and hands in the lake and make high resolves—which we never carry out—to take dips in that same frosty water; we breakfast at sun-up and sup at dusk in a log shanty set behind the cluster of tents, and between breakfast and supper we seek, under guidance, for fresh meat and dining-room trophies.

We have come too late for the calling season, it seems. In the calling season Mr. Moose desires female society, and by all accounts desires it mightily. So the guide takes a mean advantage of his social cravings. Generally afoot, but sometimes in a canoe, he escorts the gunner to a likely feeding ground or a drinking place and through a scroll of birch bark rolled up in a megaphone shape, he delivers a creditable imitation of the call of the flirtatious cow moose. There are guides who can sound the love note through their cupped hands, but most of the fraternity favor the birchen cornucopia. The sound—part lonely bleat, part plaintive bellow —travels across the silent reaches for an incredible distance. Once when the wind was right there is record of a moose call having been heard six miles away from where it was uttered, but in this case the instrumentalist was Louis Harlowe, a half-breed Micmac Indian, the champion moose caller of Nova Scotia and perhaps of the world.

In the bog where he is lying, or on the edge of the barren where he is feeding, the bull hears the pleading entreaty and thereby is most grossly deceived. Forgetting the caution which guides his course at other times, he hurries to where the deceiver awaits him, in his haste smashing down saplings, clattering his great horns against the tree boles, splashing through the brooks. And then when he bursts forth into the open, snorting and puffing and grunting, the hunter beholds before him a target which in that setting and with that background must loom up like a grain eleva-tor. Yet at a distance of twenty yards or thirty, he has been known to miss the mark clean and to keep on missing it, while the vast creature stands there, its dull brain filled with wonder that the expected cow should not be where he had had every vocal assur-ance that she would be, and seemingly only mildly disturbed by the crashing voice of the repeater and by the unseen, mysterious things which pass whistling over his back or under his belly as the gun quivers in the uncertain grasp of the overanxious or mayhap the buckague-stricken sportsman.

Once though he has made up his sluggish mind that all is not well for him in that immediate vicinity, he vanishes into deep cover as silently as smoke and as suddenly as a wink.

The mating time comes in mid-September and lasts about a month, more or less; and since the open season does not begin until October the first, it behooves the hunter who wishes to bag his moose with the least amount of physical exertion to be in camp during the first two weeks of October, for after that the bull moose is reverting to bachelorhood again. He may answer the call, but the chances are that he will not.

A little later on, after the snows have come, one may trail him with comparative ease. Besides, he is browsing more liberally then and consequently is moving pretty consistently. But between the time when the leaves begin to fall and the time when the snow begins to fly he is much given to staying in the densest coverts he can find and doing the bulk of his grazing by night.

So he must be still-hunted, as the saying goes, and it was still-hunting that we were called upon to do. The guide takes his birch-bark horn along each morning when he starts out, carrying it under one arm and an axe under the other, and upon his back a pouch containing the ingredients for a midday lunch and the inevitable fire-blackened teapot, which he calls by the affectionate name of "kittle." He never speaks of stopping for lunch. When the sun stands overhead and your foreshortened shadow has snuggled up close beneath your feet like a friendly black puppy, he suggests the advisability of "biling a kittle," by which he means building a fire and making tea. So the pack between his shoulders is necessary but the moose call is largely ornamental; it is habit for him to tote it and tote it he does; but mainly he depends upon his eyes and his ears and his uncanny knowledge of the ways of the thing we aim to destroy.

Yes, they call it still-hunting and still-hunting it truly is so far as Louis Harlowe, the half-breed, or Sam Glode, the full-blooded Micmac, or Charley Charlton, the head guide, is concerned, as he goes worming his way through the undergrowth in his soft-soled moccasins, instinctively avoiding the rotted twig, the loose bit of stone and the swishy bough. But the pair of us, following in his footsteps, in our hard-bottomed, hobnailed boots, our creaky leather gear and our noisy waterproofed nether garments, cannot, by the wildest latitude in descriptive terminology, be called still-hunters. Carrying small avalanches with us, we slide down rocky slopes which the guide on ahead of us negotiated in pussyfooted style; and we blunder into undergrowth; and we trip over logs and we flounder into bogs and out of them again with loud, churning sounds. Going into second on a hillside we pant like switch engines. I was two weeks behind with my panting when I came out of Canada and at odd times now I still pant briskly, trying to catch up.

Reaching level ground we reverse gears and halt to blow. Toward mid-afternoon, on the homebound hike, our weary legs creak audibly at the joints and our tired feet blunder and fumble among the dried leaves. We create all the racket which, without recourse to bass drums or slide trombones, it is humanly possible for a brace of overdressed, city-softened sojourners to create in deep woods. And still our guide—that person so utterly lacking in a sense of humor—speaks of our endeavor as still-hunting. If an ethical Nova Scotian guide—and all professional guides every-where, so far as I have observed, are most ethical—were hired to chaperon Sousa's band on a still-hunt through the wilderness and on the way Mr. Sousa should think up a new march full of oom-pahs and everything, and the band should practice it while cruising from bog to barren, the guide, returning to the settlements after the outing, would undoubtedly refer to it as a still-hunt.

In our own case, I trust that our eagerness in some measure compensated for our awkwardness. At least, we worked hard—worked until muscles that we never knew before we had achingly forced themselves upon our attention. Yes, if for the first day or two our exertion brought us no reward in the shape of antlered frontlets or great black pelts drying on the rocks at the canoe land-ing or savory moose steaks in the frying pan; if it seemed that after all we would have to content ourselves with taking home a stuffed guide's head or so; if twilight found us reuniting at the supper table each with tales of endless miles of tramping to our credit but no game, nevertheless and notwithstanding, the labor we spent was not without its plenteous compensations.

To begin with, there was ever the hope that beyond the next thicket or across the next swale old Mr. Sixty Inch Spread would be browsing about waiting for us to come stealing upon him with all the stealthy approach of a runaway moving van and blow him over. There was the joy of watching our guide trailing, he reading the woods as a scholar reads a book and seeing there plain as print what we never would have seen—the impress of a great splayed hoof in the yellowed moss, the freshly gnawed twigs of the moose wood, the scarred bark high up on a maple to show that here a bull had whetted his horns, the scuffed earth where a bear had been digging for grubs, the wallow a buck deer had made at a crossing. And when he told us that the moose had passed this way, trotting, less than an hour before, but that the deer's bed was at least two nights old, while the bear's scratching dated back for days, we knew that he knew. Real efficiency in any line carries its own credentials and needs no bolstering affidavits. There may be better eyes in some human head than the pair Louis Harlowe owns or than that equally keen pair belonging to Harry Allen, the dean of New Brunswick guides, but I have yet to see their owner, and I am quite sure that for woodcraft there are no better equipped men anywhere than the two I have named.

We couldn't decide which was the finer—the supper at night with a great log fire chasing back the dense shadows, and the baked beans and the talk and the crisp bacon and the innocent lies passing back and forth or the midday lunch out in the tangy, painted forest, miles and miles away from anywhere at all, with the chickadees and the snowbirds and the robins flittering about, waiting their chance to gather the crumbs they knew we would leave behind for them, and with the moose birds informally dropping in on us before ever the kettle had begun to sing.

Naturalists know the moose bird, I believe, as the Canada jay and over the line in the States they call him the venison hawk, but by any name he is a handsome, saucy chap, as smart as Satan and as impudent as they make 'em. The first thin wisp of your fire, rising above the undergrowth, is his signal. For some of the denizens of the wilderness it may be just twelve o'clock, but to him it's feeding time. Here he comes in his swooping flight, a graceful, slate-blue figure with his snowy bib and tucker like a trencherman prepared. And there, following close behind him, are other members of his tribe. There always is one in the flock more daring than the rest. If you sit quietly, this fellow will flit closer and closer, his head cocked on one side, uttering half-doubtful, half-confident cheeps until he is snatching up provender right under your feet or even out of your hand. His preference is for meat—raw meat for choice, but his taste is catholic; he'll eat anything. Small morsels he swallows on the spot, larger tidbits he takes in his bill and flies away with to hide in a nearby tree crotch. His friends watch him, and by the time he has returned for another helping they have stolen his cache, so that chiefly what he gets out of the burden of his thriftful industry is the exercise. I do not know whether this should teach us that it is better to strive to lay something against a rainy day and take a chance on the honesty of the neighbors or to seize our pleasure when and where we find it and forget the morrow. Aesop might be able to figure it out, but, being no Aesop, I must continue to register uncertainty.

Campfire suppers and high noon barbecues and glorious sunrises and shooting the rapids in the rivers and paddling across the blue lake, scaring up the black duck and the loons from before us, and all the rest of it, was fine enough in its way, but it was not killing the bull moose. So we hunted and we hunted. We dragged our reluctant feet through moose bogs—beaver meadows these are in the Adirondacks—and we ranged the high ground and the low. Cow moose we encountered frequently and calves aplenty. But the adult male was what we sought.

We had several close calls, or perhaps I should say he did. One of our outfit—nameless here because I have no desire to heap shame upon an otherwise well-meaning and always dependable companion—had been cruising through thick timber all day without seeing anything to fire at. Emerging into an open glade on a ridge above Little Red Lake, he was moved to try his new and virgin automatic at a target. So he loosed off at one of the big black crows of the North that was perched, like a disconsolate undertaker, with bunched shoulders and drooping head, on a dead tamarack fifty yards away. He did not hit Brother Corbie but he tore the top out of the tamarack snag. And then when he and the guide had rounded the shoulder of the little hill and descended to a swamp below they read in certain telltale signs a story which came near to moving the marksman to tears.

Moving up the slope from the other side the guide had been calling, a bull moose—and a whaling big one, to judge by his hoof marks—had been stirred to inquire into the circumstances. He had quitted the swamp and had ambled up the hill to within a hundred yards of the crest when—as the guide deduced it—the sound of the shot just above caused him to halt and swing about and depart from that neighborhood at his very best gait. But for that unlucky rifle report he probably would have walked right into the enemy. My friend does not now feel toward crows as he formerly felt. He thinks they should be abolished.

An experience of mine was likewise fraught with the germs of a tragic disappointment. In a densely thicketed district, my guide, with a view to getting a view of the surrounding terrain above the tops of the saplings, scaled the steep side of a boulder that was as big as an icehouse and then beckoned to me to follow.

But as a scaler I am not a conspicuous success. By main strength and awkwardness I managed to clamber up. Just as I reached the top and put my rifle down so that I might fan breath into myself with both hands, my boot soles slipped off the uncertain surface and I slid off my perch into space. Wildly I threw out both arms in a general direction. My clutching fingers closed on a limb of a maple which overshadowed the rock and I swung out into the air twelve feet or so above the inhospitable earth, utterly unable to reach with my convulsively groping feet the nearermost juts of granite. For an agonized moment it seemed probable that the only thing that might break my fall would be myself. But I kept my presence of mind. I flatter myself that in emergencies I am a quick thinker. As I dangled there an expedient came to me. I let go gradually.

And then as I plumped with a dull sickening thud into the herbage below and lay there weaponless, windless and jarred I saw, vanishing into the scrub not a hundred feet away, the black shape of a big and startled moose. I caught one fleeting glimpse of an enormous head, of a profile which might have belonged to one of the major prophets, of a set of horns outspreading even as the fronded palm outspreads itself, of a switching tail and a slab-sided rump, and then the shielding bushes closed and the apparition was gone, and gone for keeps. For my part there was nothing to do but to sit there for a spell and cherish regrets. Under the circumstances, trailing a frightened bull moose would have been about as satisfactory as trailing a comet, and probably not a bit more successful as to results.

For the majority of the members of our troupe the duration of the hunt had a time limit. On the afternoon of the last day in camp two of the party strolled into the immediate presence of a fair-sized bull and, firing together, one of them put a slug of lead in a twitching ear which he turned toward them. It must have been his deaf ear, else he would have been aware of their approach long before. But one moose was singular and the achievement of the plural number was our ambition. So four of us crossed back into New Brunswick, where, according to all native New Brunswickers, the moose grow larger than they do in the sister province, Nova Scotians taking the opposing side and being willing to argue it at all times.

With unabated determination the gallant quartet of us hunted and hunted. Three big deer died to make holiday for us but the moose displayed a coyness and diffidence which might be accounted for only on the ground that they heard we were coming. Indeed they could not very well help hearing it.

Each morning under the influence of the frost the flaming frost colors showed a dimming hue. Day before yesterday they had been like burning brands, yesterday there were dulled embers, today smoldering coals; and tomorrow they would be as dead ashes. Each night the sun went down in a nimbus of cold gray clouds. There was a taste and a smell as of snow in the air. The last tardy robin packed up and went south; the swarms of juncos grew thicker; wedge-shaped flights of coot and black duck passed overhead, their bills all pointing toward the Gulf of Mexico. Then on the last day there fell a rain which turned to sleet and the sleet to snow—four inches of it—and in the snow on that last day the reward which comes—sometimes—to the persevering was ours.

To know the climactic sensation which filled the triumphant amateur you must first of all care for the outdoors and for big-game shooting, and in the second place you must have known the feeling of hope deferred, and in the third place you must have reached the eleventh hour, so to speak, of your stay in these parts with the anticipation you had been nurturing for all these weeks since the trip was first proposed still unrealized in your soul.

You and your camp mate and your guide were on the last lap of the journey back to camp; the sun was slipping down the western wall of the horizon; the shadows were deepening under the spruces; you rounded the shoulder of a ridge and stood for a moment at your guide's back looking across a fire-burned barren. He stiffened like a pointer on a warm scent and pointed straight ahead. Your eye followed where his finger aimed, and two hundred yards away you saw a dark blot against a background of faded tamarack—a bull standing head-on. You shot together, you and your companion. Apparently the animal swung himself about and started moving at the seemingly languid lope of the moose, which really is a faster gait than you would suppose until you measure the length of his stride. You kept on firing, both of you, as rapidly almost as you could pull the triggers of your automatics. Twice he shook himself and humped his hindquarters as though stung, but he did not check his speed. You emptied your magazine, five shots. Your mate's fifth shell jammed in the chamber, putting him out of the running for the moment. In desperate haste you fumbled one more shell into your rifle, and just as the fugitive topped a little rise before disappearing for good into the shrouding second growth you got your sight full on the mark and sent a farewell bullet whistling on its way. The black hulk vanished magically.

"That'll do," said your guide, grinning broadly. "You got 'im. But load up again before we go down there. He's down and down for keeps, I think, judgin' by the way he flopped, but he might get up again."

But he didn't get up again. You came on him where he lay, still feebly twitching, with two flesh wounds in his flanks and a third hole right through him behind the shoulders—a thousand pounds of meat, a head worth saving and mounting and bragging about in the years to come, a pelt as big as a double blanket and at last the accomplished plural of moose was mise.

So then you did what man generally does when language fails to express what he feels. You harked back sundry thousands of years and you did as your remote ancestors, the cave dweller, did when he slew the sabretoothed whatyoumaycallhim. About the carcass of your kill you executed a war dance; at least you did if you chambered the emotions which filled the present writer to the choking point.

And then the next day, back in the settlements, when you reunited with the two remaining members of the outfit who had been in camp eight miles away from the camp where you stayed, and when you learned that now there was a total tally of three deceased beasties, the war dance was repeated, only this time it was a four-handed movement instead of a solo number.

H. G. PICKERING

"Merry Xmas, Mr. Williams, 20 Pine Street, N. Y."

Many writers of great candlepower are hidden beneath the ob-scure bushel of private printing. Such is the case with the literary efforts of H. G. Pickering, whose creations are intended solely for the diversions of his friends. Pure chance, plus the kindness of an individual known to angling purists as Sparse Grey Hackle, led to my discovery of this duck hunting narrative. All of us who seek out the marshes, sloughs and rock blinds have met men like "Baldy". But how many of us have had the ingenuity to devise a scheme that would cut him down to average size?

A good hardworking duck hunter has to get some fun out of life, and I'd be the last man to begrudge him a little amuse-ment. But when he seeks escape from the rigors, hardships, and disappointments of his avocation by indulging in practical jokes he ought to employ at least enough of his gunning technique to refrain from pointing his jibe promiscuously about the landscape and letting it go off in the face of an innocent gunning partner.

Baldy was the target, and the gunner scored a hit, but the jibe was so carelessly discharged as to nick my face with the edge of the pattern. Perhaps the circumstance that it was my face, which is little if any improved by suddenly growing red, warped my view-point until it was a bit on the bias. But now that years have erased the scars of disillusionment, which come of learning that there are limits to the trust and confidence which you can repose in friends, I look back on the episode with equanimity and find it at least mildly amusing.

Baldy, Harry and I, along with any given number of others, are partners. I want to avoid at least any appearance of advertising, because in this business of ours, which once was a profession, the accepted ethic perhaps no longer requires any more than just that —avoiding any appearance of advertising. So Harry and I will remain anonymous, but it is necessary to identify Baldy. His surname is Williams—Mr. Wilyums, as Will calls him, and his office address is 20 Pine Street, New York, N.Y.

Baldy and I having arranged to shoot together, I picked him up early, if not quite bright, and we started for Stuyve's country place at Hampton Bays all hope and expectation. On the morrow the law would be off the duck, in Frank's expressive vernacular, and the doughty knights of St. George were to gather at Stuyve's today to open the season by opening a couple of bottles, and thus, in a manner of speaking, wetting their duck calls.

As we drove along, two simple and unsuspecting souls, we began blithely enough to discuss our choice of blinds for the next day. If first choice for the morning fell to our lot, my suggestion was that we take a blind in the cove—north or south, depending on the wind. Baldy knew in his heart that I was right about it. But the cove affords only broadbill shooting, and Baldy would almost rather wait all day for a shot at a couple of blacks than to get his limit of broadbill in an hour. So even on the hypothesis of first choice he was tempted to pick a black duck pond in the bush. But no one does that. First choice in the morning means last choice in the afternoon, and with the full membership on hand last choice simply takes what is left, and that isn't much. Hence, every first choice does the obvious, stakes everything on the forenoon shoot by taking the blind that is surest to offer opportunity—in the cove.

Once Baldy's predilections were overcome our first decision was very simple. We agreed on the cove. However, that barely scratched the surface of our problem. A multitude of more difficult decisions still faced us. Suppose we drew last choice. Well, that would be luck, because it becomes first choice after lunch. Baldy clung to the contemplation of that possibility—Woods Hole, with black duck pitching in about midafternoon! But second, third or fourth. Ah me! Those were possibilities to worry about. It should have occurred to two old heads like us that to worry is less than wise. Either the thing you envisage never comes to pass or something worse, and either event leaves you looking frightfully foolish. But worry we did, and so were left looking frightfully foolish.

With so many contingencies to struggle with in laying our plans, it was not until the last Long Island village was behind us and we were approaching Hampton Bays that our every problem was solved, and by then we were weary with our anserine worry and mental effort and looking forward to a bit of diversion ourselves.

You just can't imagine the trials, tribulations and vexations which beset the pitiable duck hunter. If you could, you too might understand what even then was beginning to dawn on me, a mere neophyte. It simply comes down to the proposition that a good hardworking duck hunter has got to take his fun where he can find it. And now that it has come home to me, in the maturity of experience and long contact with the game and the fraternity, I am able to take a more charitable view of the fateful events of the day that was then about to dawn, and I can understand that the boys were merely trying to put a little fun into their gunning.

There was no trouble finding the byroad into Stuyve's. Not with Baldy along. He is as proud of his skill as a pathfinder as he is of his goose gunning. Up to now his pride in one was quite as justifiable as in the other, on the basis of performance and a goodly portion of his unfailing luck, and he guided me in to the byroad with all the certainty of a pinboy dropping a bowling ball onto the track for its return trip to the top rail.

When we pulled into Stuyve's about midafternoon several of the lads—I always try to be considerate in matters of age—were already there. Dan and Harry were playing tennis. It beats the devil what some duck hunters will do to take their minds off their work. Personally, as a duck hunter seeking diversion, I only go in for a couple of sports that I don't do very well—pheasant shooting and angling. But some of the boys run the whole gamut of athleticism, probably because they faintly remember that they were good at this or that at Harvard or Yale. However, that's their business. I live my own life, except for being a bit bridal-broken—an event the anniversary of which is duly celebrated as though it were something for both sides of the house to be proud of. So I observed the amenities and was an excited and interested spectator of the epoch-making match. Maybe it was good. I wouldn't know.

From remarks passed by Wally and the Colonel I take it the game wasn't above criticism. This was clear enough from Wally's wisecracks, but in the Colonel's case I had to make allowance for the caution in his comments. After all he is vulnerable. His diversion is pheasant shooting, and while it may serve him well as an escape from the exactions of duck hunting, certainly his technique lays him wide open to reprisals. When the Colonel goes berserk in the pheasant lot, running a cock to earth two gunshots ahead of his dog, the myth of the seven-league boots is rendered commonplace. No doubt he was conscious of the fact that Dan and Harry, having witnessed such a performance, wouldn't abide caustic coaching from the sidelines with any degree of complacency and accordingly he was circumspect in his remarks.

Stuyve stood about clad in his camel's hair greatcoat. For some unaccountable reason he was without his big beaver cap which is his crowning glory as we chug down the river to the blinds. I believe he occasionally indulged in mild applause as the game progressed, gracious and genial host that he is, but if, despite that, he was a bit inattentive to the game it is pardonable, because he had his duties as a host to engage him. Although the S.O.S. was functioning perfectly, and refreshments appeared as if by magic, who was there but Stuyve to seek and find the missing opener, and to remember who had put the corkscrew where?

I don't know just what Stuyve does to find release from the stress and strain of his duck hunting. Certainly he takes it seriously. Most of the time, to look at him, you'd think he was playing poker. He has a sort of strained aspect as though he were waiting for that tense moment when kings full on queens (three drakes and a pair of hens, to put it another way) will drop in. However, I have it on the authority of Bob Morgan that once, on the last day of the season and at ten seconds to four, having knocked down the last duck of his limit, he broke out of the blind, threw his beaver cap in the air and hallooed until the Montauk lighthouse rocked on its foundations. I don't doubt it. I don't criticize it. As I say, I live my own life except . . . and I can forgive any man one indiscretion. As a matter of fact, every man is entitled to at least one, only it ought to be more fun than just throwing his hat in the air.

Well, the tennis game was called on account of darkness, and the others having arrived we retreated to Stuyve's sitting room, which was closer to the base of supplies, and thus we minimized the hazard of losing liaison after nightfall.

There on the mantel of the great stone fireplace were thirty-odd beautifully carved and perfect replicas of various waterfowl in miniature. Almost before he'd touched a drop, the Colonel challenged any man in the room to name each one of them. The Colonel himself accepted the challenge—after two drops—and he accomplished the feat of naming the birds with neatness and dispatch. That is, he named all but one, or two if you'll have it that way. But the second was hardly an error. It was bait for Baldy, as I now know.

As the Colonel picked up each of the little wooden ducks, examined it and called its name I checked it on the key list. If I hadn't been so busy marveling at his precise performance, I might have begun to suspect something. But it was all over my head. He went swiftly but unerringly down the line of ducks about half way with no trouble at all. Suddenly he stopped. He turned the little image over in his hand and the bewilderment registered in his face was genuine. He simply said: "I don't know this one." I've forgotten now which one it was, and in the interest of accuracy I recently asked the Colonel about it. He said he didn't remember, and I told him I thought it was something with a reddish head. That was the wrong thing to say. He fairly shouted at me over the phone: "You don't mean to tell me that I mistook anything with a red head!" I hastened to assure him that I was merely testing my recollection and must be entirely mistaken about the whole business.

"No! No!" said he. "I did miss one. I don't remember what it was. It must have been a rare and comparatively unknown species. It might have been a harlequin. They're almost extinct and practically no one has ever seen one."

So we'll put it down as a harlequin. At any rate, it was a clean miss. But what is more to the point, the Colonel immediately capitalized it. He hesitated on the next one, said he couldn't think of it right then and would come back to it. He quickly called off the remaining ducks, and returning to the one he had passed by tried vainly to simulate the bewilderment that had put him back on his heels when he had picked up the harlequin. The simulation wasn't as apparent to me then as it is now, but there it was for keen eyes, an alert brain, and a sophisticated and suspicious mentality. I didn't take it in. Right there and then I fumbled the tipoff.

The Colonel lolled against the fireplace and muttered, half audibly. He propped up his drooping head by resting an elbow on the mantelpiece and cupping his cheek in his hand. With his other hand he picked up the diminutive wooden bird and slowly turned it about in the glow of the firelight, apparently wracking his brain to identify the most easily identifiable bird in the lot. Gradually his mutterings became articulate. "Now I ought to know that bird; I ought to know that bird."

After a few moments his face lighted up and he turned expectantly to Baldy. (It really was a rather good act.)

"Now, I know what this bird is," he said, "I just can't think of the name of it. Hey, Baldy, you know this one. You saw one last year in the moonlight or something. What is it?"

Baldy chuckled, as only a f——, I mean a jolly well-built, man can chuckle. "Saw *one*," said he. "You fellows are still jealous. I saw four of them fly across the full moon, and Dan and I got 'em the next day. You can take an old goose gunner's word for it, that's a Canada goose."

"By jove! You're right," said the Colonel. "I ought to have known it."

Ought to. He did know it. It was part of the build-up. He set out, as I know now, to inveigle Baldy into reminding himself and the rest of us of his extraordinary performance of a year ago and to glow with pride in the telling of it. Baldy told, and Baldy glowed.

It was just the year previous, at the same place and the same hour, or a bit later, that Baldy had stepped out on the lawn to size up the weather. There he saw four geese winging their way across the face of the full moon, boasted that he would bag them the next day, drove twenty-five miles at dawn, went into a blind with Dan and came out at the end of the day with a limit of duck and four geese.

This fatuous prophecy and its fabulous fulfillment left the rest of the members—not cold, nor yet precisely hot, but certainly a bit clammy under their collars. They were really sporting about it, and the lucky gunners were showered with praise and congratulations. But it may be that a good sport is neither more nor less than a chap who keeps the whip-hand over his innate envy, and even the best of the lot, perhaps, doesn't always feel quite as sporting as his poise, conduct and countenance would seem to indicate.

So, I imagine that right there by the rustic arbor at the clubhouse door, as we stood in the cold and looked on Baldy's bag with its four great geese, some evil sprite suggested to someone's subconsciousness that something be done about Baldy. It seems plausible, for the field was fertile for the devil's handiwork. Just a subtle suggestion, and there was opened up the vision of a brief release of suppressed emotion and a flash of fun to relax the rigors of duck hunting. Biding their time for a whole year to have it out would seem to indicate that the suppressed emotion might be characterized as vindictive, but by the way of extenuation, it should be remembered that these gunners were facing an insufferable situation. They had to do with a gunning partner, passably good to be sure but certainly no Colonel Hawker, who not only had become psychic of a sudden, but had called his shots. After all, that's a bit thick.

Had I given any thought to it at the time I must have sensed an undercurrent of mild rancor beneath the plaudits and congratulations. I can't see that it would have stood me in any stead, however, unless it be that it might have deterred me from having a little fun over the episode on my own. What I did was to write up the story. Derrydale printed it, and I gave it a limited currency, just among friends. And that gives me an idea, now that I am wondering how it happened that a year later my face got in the way of the carelessly—or artfully—discharged jibe. Perhaps in the story I treated Baldy too kindly. Perhaps I made him out a hero. Perhaps in portraying other club members in their several roles in this and related episodes I was too authentic. I don't want to be dogmatic about it. I'm just scouting the possibilities. Now I can see that it is possible that the sportive Machiavellis meant to "have me on" as well as Baldy; yet it is equally possible that they merely neglected to take me into account and at the last minute had to deal with me as expediency dictated. At any rate, whichever it was the result was the same. When that mild rancor, which sometimes smolders beneath the placid and polite exterior of your sporting gentleman, finally burst into a devastating explosion, I was accorded all the amenities which are the proverbial lot of the innocent bystander.

I will never know precisely what happened in the year that intervened; nor will Baldy. Vague rumors have come to me of egg buying, selecting a brooding hen, wet nursing, scientific feeding and what not, but all I know is what happened at, from and after the moment when the Colonel betrayed Baldy into reminiscing about the geese of the year before.

The Colonel had done his work not only well but timely. As we strolled into the dining room and took our seats the conversation was all of Baldy the goose gunner, and Baldy was goaded into boasting that, given a break in the draw, he would pick himself a goose pond and turn up with another brace of geese this year.

The first order of business, as usual, was for our patriarchal president, Stuyve, to repeat to us Frank's report on the season's prospects. Frank ran the Club for us. Over in England I suppose they would call him a "keeper" or some such thing; and a grand keeper he was. He knew ducks, their habits and their eccentricities. His competence and his loyalty earned him the confidence of his gunners, and we came to know that he would get us a day's shoot-ing, if one were to be had. He continued to do just that as year after year the changes in the law made it more and more difficult, for back in the easy days of baiting and live decoys he had accumu-lated a wealth of knowledge and experience which enabled him to keep up with the game as it got tougher. What he had learned in staking out live decoys where their irresistible call would best lure ducks to death made it so much the easier for him when only blocks were permitted. Which is by way of saying that he still could turn the trick. And turning the trick, Frank and his gunners were able to forget for a time that the gods play a like game better, luring us on by their quaint devices from one bayou of life to another. Though not long after this night there was occasion for remembering when Frank, answering the call of Death's decoy, pitched into life's last haven.

But as yet Frank was very much alive, and the report which he had sent to us by Stuyve was full of promise. Having cheered us with so great good news, Stuyve rose to perform the sacred and traditional rite of the Club. Grasping the leathern pill bottle he shook it till the rhythm of the plastic pills incited everyone to a state of hopeful expectancy. Who would draw first choice of blinds? But just as the little lopsided pills were rolling themselves into an ecstatic frenzy, he suddenly stopped agitating them, set the pill bottle down, and as the pellets settled into a state of innocuous quietude, the gunners followed suit.

Calmly surveying the assembled gunners, Stuyve said: "There are eleven of us, and nobody wants to gun alone. Why don't some-body volunteer to go third in a blind. I suppose most of you have already paired off, so let's find out who's shooting with who before we draw."

Being the newest member of the Club, I had a feeling that I should be the one to volunteer. But Baldy had asked me to shoot with him. More than likely Baldy didn't want to shoot three in a blind. Nor was it at all clear just what Stuyve wanted. Did he want the odd man to volunteer? Seemingly, Baldy didn't know and he hesitated. I was on the spot and I hesitated. Hesitating, both were lost.

An emphatic bellow broke the silence: "Well, I'm gunnin' with Baldy."

This was a startling announcement. I couldn't believe my ears. Slowly it dawned on me that it was Dan who had spoken. Again silence, and more questions presented themselves to my tortured mind. Had Dan spoken to Baldy about shooting? Was Baldy on a spot? I looked at Baldy, hoping for a sign. Baldy looked non-plussed and gave no sign. One by one the other pairs announced themselves, and I was out on a limb.

The Club's perennial president pre-empted the floor again: "I think somebody ought to volunteer to go third in a blind. Nobody wants to gun alone."

That's what he thought. But at this juncture I was quite sure that more than anything in the world I did want to gun alone. Did anyone want to shoot with me anyway? Much less two of them! Why didn't Stuyve ask for some pair to volunteer to take on a third man instead of the other way 'round? That would make sense.

But Stuyve's suggestion evoked no comment, and things got so bad that somebody had to say something. So Stuyve, with a sort of air of being sorely hurt, said: "Well my suggestion don't seem to go over, so I suppose we might as well draw."

Again the pellets rattled forth their crazy music, but this time rolled out of the bottle one by one and came to a stop. Baldy turned up with first choice, but he reserved his election until he could give an eye to the weather in the morning.

These dinners at Stuyve's are bright spots in the lives of men who have gone off the deep end and taken up duck hunting seriously. But this particular dinner bid fair to leave me in a dither. Was I shooting on the morrow, and if so where and with whom? I was not left long in doubt because Dan is not the man to let a fellow sufferer suffer. Oh no! By the time I was edging into the poker game that was getting under way he had resolved all of Baldy's doubts and uncertainties. Next, turning his blandishments on me, he cajoled me into thinking that it had been ordained from the beginning of time that he and Baldy and I were to shoot together on opening day. The prospect was pleasing, life seemed lovely again, and I turned unsuspectingly to the poker game, hopeful of coming out of it with my gun and a couple of shells and quite indifferent to the fate of pants and shirt.

The gunners awoke in a gay and loquacious mood. Lost in the spirit of the occasion and the aroma of a sumptuous huntsman's breakfast, I still mistook life to be lovely and untroubled. But when, after an hour's ride, we arrived at the Clubhouse, my misgivings returned. Frank was on hand to greet us, assure us the blacks were using the ponds, and that the broadbill were in the cove. But his wonted helpful interest was lacking. Usually he dispensed information as to the number of ducks using this or that pond and how the broadbill were leading, and gave the gunners the benefit of his weather wisdom to aid in the choice of blinds. But this morning, after a brief and meager report, he and Dan disappeared into the johnny and engaged in audible but inarticulate whispering. Nor were the other gunners by any means single-minded and assiduous in getting into gunning clothes and getting guns together. Harry and Wally retired to the kitchen, for no ostensible purpose, and talked under their hats. Stuyve and the Colonel went into a huddle behind a locker door. Gould, our best-dressed gunner, always meticulously correct in his attire, responding to Ray's invitation, communicated by a wink and a crooked forefinger, dashed out into the chill November air without stopping to tuck his shirt into his pants. Treasurer Bill probably can be exonerated of complicity. He sat on the edge of a bed, within earshot of Stuyve and the Colonel, who obviously were unrestrained by his presence, shoving a pudgy leg into a reluctant boot. He seemed only to be collecting his thoughts. With the dues all paid I suppose there was nothing better to collect. As for me, I wondered whether I should hand in my resignation or wait till it was asked for. Only in retrospect, and then for the first time, did I note that Baldy, too, was an outcast. Clothed and geared long before the sub rosa gaggling was over, he strode about in his bottes sauvages, whistling, as he had done the year before, what might pass for "The Parade of the Wooden Soldiers," enraptured with visions of geese in gun range and quite oblivious to the skulduggery afoot.

Eventually we were off to the blinds. Baldy reluctantly chose the North Cove blind for himself, Dan and me, and the others chose, in due order, various posts on pond and river. Baldy's choice was a wise one, as I told him it would be. The broadbill were in, and the north blind was a lodestone. Baldy's shooting was good, though he didn't get three with one barrel as he came to do a couple of years later. Dan was somewhat preoccupied, rather left the easy ones to me and knocked down several hard ones after they had scorned the stool and were high over the corner of the blind. By noon we had sixteen ducks. I didn't lay claim to any, and Baldy and Dan went as far as they could when they said that swinging on the leading duck of a flock I had ticked the tail of the rearmost. They even swore they had noticed a feather fall from that lesser scaup as he scurried away.

Doc and Wally were absent as we gathered at lunch. We wondered at their tardiness. We grew restive. We cursed them for overshooting their allotted time. We worried. At long last they arrived, faces drawn and haggard. They said they had been pinched —guns and game confiscated. We laughed. They didn't. Finally we were in a mood to accept their story at face value, and taking their faces into account that was an all-time low. It seemed that some four Federal Ogpus had gone into hiding in the swamp about Big Fish Pond at three o'clock of a very clammy and uncomfortable morning. No doubt they had expected to find someone shooting before seven A.M. Doc and Wally not having appeared until about eight, the Ogpus might have swallowed their disappointment, but it was so thoroughly congealed in the frigid air of the swamp that they couldn't do it. So they spitted it on the hearthstone of their torrid spite and undertook to make it hot for somebody. Thus, when the unsuspecting gunners emerged from the blind at eleven-thirty they were faced with trumped-up charges of shooting over live decoys and other ill-founded and indefinite accusations. They surrendered guns and game and were ignominiously dragged off to Patchogue to face the chief. Now it seemed that they were due to appear forthwith, under duress, at the United States Court House in Brooklyn. Forgotten was the phenomenal string of pheasants the Colonel had run down and brought in. Gone was the exultation over a grand morning's shoot. And you might think that gone too were the sinister designs of the plotters. But, no! Nothing could come between Baldy and his fate. In fact this very untoward event served only to set the stage for it. The honor of the Club being at stake, the Colonel and Harry, learned in the law and lore (vocally the same in Brooklyn) of gunning since the days of Queen Anne and her forbears, volunteered to go along and see that injustice was done and the gunners returned to the bosoms of their families. And they were off, the four of them.

Well, that's four. Four from eleven leaves seven. Seven divided into pairs is three and a half. Still an odd man, but that's only me. Four men out of luck. But four men's poison is five men's meat, leaving Baldy and me out of the picture. I'm only leaving us out for purposes of calculation. Actually we were right under the klieg lights. And don't remind me that I started out talking about the stage, and that now I'm babbling of meat and poison and pictures and klieg lights. If I want to mix my metaphors that's my business. Who's writing this book anyway?

But what I really want you to understand, and I hope I haven't made it too difficult, is that with only two to choose before him, Baldy, with his penchant for black duck shooting, mightn't sell designing Dan down the river. And he didn't!

The boys were somewhat taken aback at the sad turn of events and it was seriously proposed to abandon shooting for the day. However, at last it was concluded that no laws having been broken they should carry on. No doubt, at some future day the unbiased judgment of history will be that had they been free from ulterior motives they would have suspended shooting for the day out of deference to their falsely accused and martyred brothers, and that they carried on, not by virtue of their fortitude, but only because the will properly to humble one of their own number was greater than their sympathy. At any rate they carried on.

Stuyve and Bill took Woods Hole. Gould and Ray took Big Fish Pond. Baldy hemmed and Dan hawed. Baldy thought, as I did, that there was nothing left but Little Fish Creek and the river blinds. But Dan had news for us. Lyon's Hole was rigged up with a fine new blind, stools and a boat, and according to Dan, it was the place for black duck.

Forgetting ulterior motives for the moment, Dan could recommend Lyon's Hole with a clear conscience. Since it fell to my lot to see it on this lamentable day I can testify that it is a deceivingly likely pond, and has all the earmarks of a black duck haven. But it isn't.

Remembering ulterior motives for the moment, other factors loom larger. Lyon's Hole had not been shot in any prior year. (And I may interpolate, it has not been shot in any year since.) Oddly enough, it lies just in the fringe of the bush and next to the marsh, and is the only pond you can drive right up to in a car. It also has other exclusive features, as compared with the other club ponds. It does not lie in a swamp. The brush about it is not impenetrable and you can circumnavigate its shore line afoot, so to speak.

It was a perfect setup, and yet without rhyme or reason. Suppose Baldy, with last choice for the afternoon, had been forced to take us back to the river, where the only approach to the blinds is by motorboat passing in full view. Suppose his only recourse had been a brush blind surrounded by swamp, with only one approach, and that open to detection. Suppose either of these alternatives and the trick just wouldn't have come off. But don't bother about supposing, because the fickle winds of fate buffeting poor mortals about without apparent discrimination blow ever gently upon the doers of evil. And it's a foul wind that fails the funster. Think of it! Well laid and long thought out as the plans were, complete failure was avoided only by the coincidence of circumstance. The thing just couldn't come off unless somehow they could get Baldy (and me?) at Lyon's Hole. Baldy and I never could have gone to Lyon's Hole if he hadn't drawn first choice for the morning, and by the same token last for the afternoon, if Doc and Wally hadn't got pinched, thus depleting the number of gunners to choose blinds, and if Baldy hadn't had a passionate preference for black duck shooting. Which simply goes to prove that it doesn't pay to live right, and that Lady Luck showers her favors on those who are knavishly disposed. Thus, the way things stood when Fate had dealt the last card and the betting was open, all Dan had to do was to say that Lyon's Hole was the best bet for blacks. Baldy called the bet and chose Lyon's Hole.

Now, if I haven't diverted you too much, you will remember that Baldy, Dan and I were shooting together—or had been. But, of a sudden, Dan conceived an aversion for shooting three in a blind. It seemed, also, that he wasn't so keen for black duck. He wanted to get out in the open marsh, where anything was apt to come along. With four gunners gone, Little Fish Creek was open and Danny chose to go there and shoot all by his lonesome. But he is a friendly soul, and reminded us that Little Fish was a right neighborly spot, just beyond the fringe of brush and within a stone's throw of Lyon's Hole. So he suggested that if he heard us shooting our heads off, and there was nothing doing at Little Fish, that he would come up and join us, and urged that if conditions were reversed that we drop down and join him. It was all too perfect for argument and Baldy and I accepted the arrangement.

By two o'clock we were ensconced in Lyon's Hole blind. By three o'clock the bleak breezes blowing through the brush of the blinds—if you don't mind having it that way—had chilled us to the marrow, and we had our several chills for our pains. As the afternoon wore on we listened enviously to the steady barking of Dan's gun at Little Fish. Mindful of Dan's thoughtful suggestion we did an Alphonse and Gaston from two-thirty to three, each urging the other to join Dan. Had I gone, the story would have been different; had Baldy gone there wouldn't have been any story, because Little Fish Blind lies out in the open marsh, inaccessible by road and the whole world open to view. But neither went. We were just kindly, courteous, simple folk, born to be taken in.

Finally, through chattering teeth, Baldy began to make conversation: "You know what I'd like?"

"Sure."

"I'll bet you don't."

"I'll bet I do," I chattered back, but it seemed best to let Baldy give expression to his own obvious thoughts.

"I'd like to see a big fat old Canada goose come flappin' in here and give the old goose gunner a shot at him."

"You'd shoot him," said I, "if he were the goose that laid the golden egg."

"He?"

"Well, she, and I hope you freeze to death before I do."

At three-ten a black pitched in and was deftly dispatched by Baldy. At three-fifteen there was a "halloo" from behind the blind, and Baldy gladly seized the opportunity to step out and greet the visitor. It was Frank. Frank said he was just going the rounds to see how his gunners were doing, checking up and what have you. Nothing could have been more disarming. It was Frank's wont to do just that. Nor was it his wont to deceive or to lend himself to deception. Of course he may not always have been quite himself—Frank, that is—with game wardens, which is altogether another matter. But certainly there had been nothing in his previous conduct which would have warranted our entertaining the least suspicion on the present occasion, and if the fact that the denouement followed suddenly upon his departure is circumstantially suspicious, I can only say that Frank enjoyed a bit of fun himself and couldn't resist aiding his guns in their deviltry.

Be all that as it may, we responded cordially to Frank's friendly inquiry, assured him that we were quite comfortable (liars!), had plenty of shells, and that everything was fine. Frank disappeared into the brush in the direction of the road and we disappeared again into the blind. Shortly after Frank had gone, but so shortly that perhaps he had not gone at all, there came a startling "Gwank! Gwank!" seemingly in the brush back of my end of the blind.

"Sufferin' catfish, what's that?" I exclaimed.

"Sounds like my Canada geese," said Baldy.

"Are they ground runners?" I asked.

"No, they ought to come flyin' high and swoop in."

"At least you wouldn't expect them to be swooping about in the thick brush back there," I agreed.

"No."

"Gwank! Gwank!"

"Then what the hell is it?"

"Probably an old shitepoke on the edge of the pond," said Baldy.

Our observations on the matter were sound. You wouldn't expect geese to be waddling around in brush and briar. That is, unless someone, emulating Little Boy Blue in disposing his toy soldiers, "had kissed them and put them there."

When I asked our editor to verify this quotation, she said: "But you aren't going to put that in your book, surely."

I replied: "I can use it nicely."

"Why you can't either," said she. "You know that is a very sad little story."

I put on my very best sneer and cynically asserted: "And so what."

But at the third "Gwank! Gwank!" we forgot all about shitepokes and sprang to our feet, guns at the ready. As we stood up a great Canada goose winged itself lazily across the pond. Baldy let loose with his right barrel and missed. He let loose with his left barrel and the goose fell fairly into the pond. I was petrified with astonishment. Baldy turned to me jubilantly and was about to say something, but suddenly the look of triumph faded from his face and gave place to one of—well, a different one.

"There's another! On your side! On the dam!"

I looked to my left and saw another goose waddling slowly, sedately and unsuspectingly across the dam. I went on looking, still petrified.

"Shoot him," shouted Baldy.

"On the ground?" I asked.

"Sure! Shoot a goose any way you can get him."

I brought my gun up and fired. I missed. But I was unpetrified now, and with the second barrel the poor goose fell floundering.

"My goose is outside the wire," I said. "I'd better go pick him up." The wire net, if you must know, is stretched around ponds to prevent cripples from getting away. In rigging up Lyon's Hole specially for this year they had even wired it—and I don't like the implication.

Now Baldy's goose had dropped fairly in the pond. It was inside the wire, though at the far end to be sure, and could no more get away crippled than dead. But the old goose gunner was taking no chances. As I strode back across the dam, carrying my trophy by the legs, my astonished gaze fell on Baldy hotfooting it around the pond. He clambered over the wire, but one botte sauvage didn't quite make it, and a somewhat plump Baldy plopped headlong into the muck and mire. He picked himself up, and tough as the going was he mushed his way through to the goose, seized it by the legs and floundered back with it to the blind.

Seated again in the blind, Baldy and I gloated over the game at our feet. Baldy glowed. His enthusiasm generated a warmth that tempered the bleak breezes blowing through the blind.

"Well! Did it again," said he. "You just can't beat the old goose gunner."

"I guess not," I said, "but my goose is banded. How about yours?"

"Yes, mine's got a funny thing on his leg too."

I had noticed that the funny things on the legs of the geese were not machine made bands customarily used by the Biological Survey, but were crude makeshift things of tin wound on and attached with rusty wire. My misgivings returned again, this time accompanied by a sick sensation in the pit of my stomach. Turning to Baldy I said: "Maybe we'd better look at them."

"Sure," said Baldy, "probably banded up in Canada last spring."

I picked up my goose, unwound the wire, unwrapped the ragged piece of coffee-can tin and smoothed it out over my knee. On it was pricked a legend, which I read to myself, and all the puzzling events of the last twenty-four hours began to straighten themselves out. I could see it all now. All the fuss and bother about the draw, the call for a volunteer to go third in a blind and Dan's announcement that he was shooting with Baldy. Stuyve probably had countenanced such chicanery with reluctance. The Colonel perhaps thought it inimical to the traditions of the "regiment," but he might wink at it. Colonels, now and then, are human. Diabolical Dan, without a shadow of doubt, had had nothing to do with it. That is, not much. Frank had probably participated with delectable reluctance, and I'm glad he had the fun of it.

As I thought it through, Baldy's glow glimmered, the bleak breezes blowing through the blind were chill again, and Baldy's teeth resumed their chattering.

"W-w-wh-what does it say?"

"Well, goose gunner, read it for yourself."

And Baldy read:

MERRY XMAS

MR. WILLIAMS

20 PINE ST. N.Y.

A. R. MacDougall,
Jr.

White Deer Are Bad Luck

To the sportsman who reads of hunting when he can't, Dud Dean is as real as his creator, and if you do much hunting along the margin of Maine's Kennebec you will certainly encounter the reality of MacDougall. Move along the fringe of a few Kennebec cedar swamps or drop a fly on one of its quiet pools and you are almost certain to meet someone like George, who could have lifted himself standing in a bushel basket if the handles hadn't let go. MacDougall's characters are not unreal; you just have to spend a bit of time in Maine to find them.

The teeth of early winter bit at a man's ears. The November sky was wind-blown and implacable. I was waiting on the station platform for the northbound train. That train was late.

Joseph Danner was due. There was a telegram in my pocket that said so. Danner is a man of the world, a sophisticated metropolitanite. But he was born in a story-and-a-half house that squats in forlorn abandonment beside a narrow road that long since forgot the way out. The Danners are all gone, but the little house, grim and neglected in its afteryears, is evidence that their roots go far back in the Maine soil.

I sat on my full pack and wondered how much of an alien this last of the Danners had become.

Mat Markham was with me—that is, in a detached way. He sat on the off edge of the platform and smoked a corncob pipe. And his face was as blank of emotion and expectancy as a beaver bog in the midwinter moonlight.

Mat is the only successful guide I know who is the epitome of mirthlessness. But Mat is also a crafty, careful, and skillful guide. As a cook among the old guides, he has but one equal, Dud Dean, who is his lifelong friend, although two men could not be less alike. Mat's cream of tartar biscuits are light, luscious masterpieces. And if there is time, and a suitable oven, Mat makes pies that are as good as those Mother made. And as for his bean-hole beans, are they not famous from Bingham to the border?

But Mat had come with me not as a professional guide but as a friend and fellow hunter. "I'd like to git me a deer," he had said, when I had suggested the project on a wage basis, "but I'm all done guidin' fer the year. Let folks wait on themselves."

When I had said that I was anxious that Danner have a pleasant week, and that he get his deer, Mat had said, "Thar's deer enough, but the woods is so dry that a deaf owl c'ud hear a deer mouse wiggle his ears. Can this Danner shoot?"

Danner had written me that he had not fired a rifle for ten years.

"Now, ain't that jist like them Babylonians? They hardly know which end of a gun is loaded, but they'll strike off fer the woods, expectin' all they need to do is pull a trigger, an' then all the wild things will fall out of the trees an' lay around with broken necks, er sunthin'."

So we sat there, Mat and I, waiting for the train to pull into Bingham. Down the track a whistle blew. Then we heard the engine's bell at the crossing.

There were only four passengers for Bingham, and Danner was one of them.

"Hey there, Mak," he called. "It's good to see you again. The last time was at the Lawyer's Club—a nice place for a parson! How are the prospects? Got one salted? I remember an uncle of ours who always baited them that way. He claimed that such methods expedited business."

We shook hands. Mat reached out a paw, which Danner grasped, when they were introduced.

"How do you do?" he said to Mat.

"I do jist as I dang please, part of the time," said Mat.

"What do you do the rest of the time?" asked Danner, with a tone of levity that Mat would detect and dislike, as he had the formal, "How do you do?"

"I guide," replied Mat.

In those days the train came in to the lower station at Bingham, waited, backed out, and went on up to Kineo. By the time we had carried our duffle inside the coach, the train was leaving.

Danner and I talked. I don't think that Mat listened. At Moxie Station there was a group of men and women, and manifest excitement. Mat got off to ask questions. He came back to us when the train started.

"It was jist as I guessed," he said. "Somebody got hurt—shot in the neck."

"Dangerously hurt?" asked Danner.

"We-el, the doctor they've sent fer ain't got thar yit. It was Joe Pratt. They lugged him out from in back of Bald Mountain. If I was goin' to pass jedgment, I'd say that Joe was back from his last trip."

"How did it happen?"

"Somebudy didn't wait—took him fer a deer. An' a man on his hind legs looks erbout as much like a deer as a deer looks like a stepladder."

"Did the poor devil who did the shooting come in with him?"

"Yup. He's thar. He's takin' on like a woman with her best hat lost in the wind, but that don't do Joe no good. They've got a feller from The Forks who can stop blood, but Joe's lost a lot of it. If they don't git a doctor purty quick, it'll stop all right."

"What do you mean by a fellow who can stop blood?"

"Why, I d'know. Never knew. Some does. It's a verse in the Scripture, er sunthin'. Anyway, it's a secret amongst them that know it. A man can only pass it on to a woman. A woman can only tell a man. Them that knows it, an' has faith, can stop bleedin'. At least, so I've hear'n tell. No, dang it! They *can!*"

Danner turned to me. "There's some more of it. I remember that, too. Folks believed it when I was a small boy. My uncle did."

To my surprise, Mat made a genuine effort to lighten our mood induced by the unhappy event at Moxie.

"So far as Joe's consarned," he said, "that's the way of all flesh: born slow, die quick. Joe had it comin' to him."

"Coming to him!" exclaimed Danner. "What do you mean?"

"I don't mean anything against Joe," Mat made haste to say, "but last week he was foolish e-nough to shoot a white doe deer. That's the surest way to invite the blackest luck in the world: to shoot a white doe deer. Matter of fact, I never heard of a person who shot a white deer that didn't come to some v'ilent end, er at least to black trouble. It never fails."

"Oh," said Danner. "I remember now. The curse of the white

deer. There was such a superstition when I was a boy. My uncle believed it. And there were many who shared it in those days. But as a matter of fact, superstition is common to all primitive and isolated societies."

"If ye'll excuse me," said Mat, "I want to go up front. See a feller up thar who borrowed five dollars of me last summer. He can't remember none too good."

Danner watched Mat, as the older man walked up the aisle. "My uncle," he said, "has been dead for thirty years. And I thought he was the last of men like that. Do many persons up here believe such nonsense?"

At Forsythe Siding, we left the train and shouldered our packs. A man with a packsack on his back is a symbol of other days and other ways than those of urbanity. Once out of the train, and facing the wild lands, Mat became almost cheerful. This was his country, where he was at ease and at home.

"We hain't packin' enough grub to see us through the week," he said. "So we either shoot some meat, er we go ga'nt."

"That's businesslike," said Danner.

"Better keep it in mind," said Mat.

On the way to camp—the camp Mat had chosen for our head-quarters—Danner talked as a man would want to if he had been away a long time but felt, even patronizingly, that he belonged. I answered when necessary. But Mat maintained an Abnaki silence, except for one utterance: "The deer are wilder'n hell's bells."

And they were. The ground was frozen. The leaves were dry. We needed snow. And through the next day, and the following, we hunted without sight of a deer. But the night of the third day, Mat reported that he had seen a white deer. The incident was startling, because white deer are rare.

"Was he a big one?" asked Danner.

Mat laid aside the hot buttered biscuit that he had been lifting to his mouth. That was the sort of question Mat would answer with ponderous consideration.

"Wa-al, maybe I've seen bigger bucks—white deer don't usually live to git real big—but I never did see a bigger *white* deer 'n this 'un."

"How many points, would you guess?"

"Don't need to guess. I had plenty of time to look him over, same as he did me. All white deer are foolish, I reckon. He's got twelve p'ints, an' he w'ud dress off a hundred an' eighty pounds, maybe."

"Man!" exclaimed Danner. "That was a good one. Did you miss him?"

The question was tactless. Men like Mat fit their guns. And when they shoot, they kill. Furthermore, Mat had already made plain how he felt about the shooting of white deer.

But Mat patiently restated his position. "Young feller, I don't ever plan to shoot any *white* deer."

"Surely you do not mean that you forfeited the chance to shoot at a head like that, because the animal happened to be a sport! What is a white deer? Answer, it's a freak dropped by a normal doe. You would shoot at its dam or sire, why presume that this oddly marked offspring is attended by supernatural accruements?"

Mat's blue eyes squared away at Danner's. There was no anger in them, but a pity.

"Listen," he said ponderously. "I knew a feller by the name of George Sands. George was inclined to be sure of his own powers, an' talked erbout them. So some of the young fellers bet George a dollar that he c'udn't lift hisself in a bushel basket. An' the durn fathead tried it. He lifted until he was red in the face an' pooched. Then the ash handles let go, pulled out from the rim. 'Thar!' says George. 'Yer see I c'ud have done it, if these danged handles had held.'

"What I mean is that a man can't lift hisself in a basket. We're mortals. A college eddication don't alter that by one hundredth of an inch. If thar's anythin' that a college sh'ud learn a man, it's that he don't come out an inch taller. But you city squirts want to come up here an' tell us folks that has learned things the hard way that what we *know* is true hain't so. An' then, like damfools, ye're surprised if we don't swallow it. Crotch!"

Danner stared at Mat. "Oh, well, heck," he said, "let it go at that. You make the best biscuits I ever ate."

It was wise to change the subject. But the incident spoiled the evening. We could feel Mat's glumness.

During the next day, when I met Mat, he said, "Do yer really think this perfessor Danner w'ud shoot that white buck if he was to see him? If yer do, thar hain't no two ways erbout it. An' I'm goin' home. Don't want no truck with unasked trouble, myself."

"Danner is a lawyer, not a professor," I said. "I don't think that you need to worry about him shooting the white buck."

"Becuz, I'll be condemned if I didn't jump that critter ag'in this forenoon," explained Mat. "Yer really don't think this perfessor w'ud be sech a punkinhead, eh?"

"I am confident he wouldn't," I said. But I was wrong.

That day, when we were returning to camp, the white buck and a normal doe jumped from the cover of a patch of young fir.

Danner's 30-06 hit his shoulder, and he fired before Mat could bellow, "Don't do it!"

"Missed him!" said Danner, with obvious disappointment.

Mat was angry and agitated, and he did not attempt to hide those emotions. "Yer better thank God, er your own foolishness, that yer did miss him," he said. "An' I am done—goin' home. Crotch, I w'udn't even consider shootin' that natural doe, becuz of her comp'ny. An' you blaze away at the *white* buck!"

I knew that Mat had made a masterly effort not to overindulge in adjectives, and that he was profoundly moved and disturbed.

"Oh, come now," said Danner. "That was a handsome creature. Its legs and ears are standard. And there's a big brown patch on his ribs. At least, that's only half bad luck!"

"That buck," said Mat, "is as white as they usually come. I never see but one pure white deer, an' I hain't sure she warn't ancestral. [Mat meant spectral.] As fer *shootin'* this one, if ye'd hit him, it's likely that we'd all have run right plum inter bad luck. Even shootin' at him may be e-nough to bring it on."

Mat looked like an earnest, if not brilliant, prophet. Even Danner sensed the man's utter concern and alarm.

"Mat," he said, "I'm sorry. Let's talk it over when we have eaten and rested. We're on edge now."

Mat grunted. "Thar's nothin' to talk," he said. "All is, if yer pro-pose to shoot at *white* deer, yer can count me out of your comp'ny, right now."

Danner looked at me. I could only shake my head. In the first place, I had been provoked at my own stupidity which had led me to stare at the departing white buck when I should have shot at the doe, for we needed meat at camp. Now, however, I was relieved that both the buck and his little doe had gone free.

The day had been cold and gray. There was the promise of snow in the sky and in the wind. The camp was pleasant with its smells of good warm food, the purring of the hardwood burning in the stove, and the lamplight, which is not so much a light as the presence of a color.

But to my disappointment, Danner provoked more talk about white deer. Taciturn Mat became evangelistically determined to convince the hard, unimaginative, and skeptical lawyer. It was the only time in all the years I have known Mat when his astringent vocabulary was overworked. Once started on the project, he told incident after incident, all illustrating the curse of the white deer.

Danner threw in words such as bosh, taboo, totemism, and the like.

I was uncomfortable, as a man always is in the presence of genuine conviction pitted against skepticism. I would cheerfully have given ten dollars for more light in that little cabin than the small oil lamp achieved. And all my efforts to change the subject were ignored by the zealot on each side of the debate.

At last, Mat grew weary of his own unaccustomed loquaciousness. "Mak," he said, "I wish this friend of your'n had more *sense*."

Danner laughed. "I'll sleep on that," he said.

Mat pulled a cap down over his ears and went outside to inspect the weather. We heard him knock the ashes out of his pipe. When he returned to the camp, he seemed to have rid himself of the perturbed mood.

"Fellers," he said, "whatever 'it' is, it's spittin'. I sh'udn't wonder if it snowed enough to make good trackin' tomorrow."

So we went to bed—nothing settled, nothing achieved. I resolved to talk to Danner in the morning. Mat felt too profoundly about the ill omen and its aftermaths to be ignored. And if I had to choose between the friendship of Mat or Danner, the latter could go to New York. There was no doubt in my mind about that!

The next sound I heard was Mat's voice, mournfully reminding me that it was almost noon. But morning was still in obeisance, bowing the knee to the night. And the bit of earth I saw from the doorway was cold, white, and uninviting.

Breakfast waited while we washed, and Mat went after another pail of water.

"Joe," I said, "this may seem to be an unusual and even unreasonable request, but I must ask you not to shoot at that white deer again, should you see him today."

Danner gurgled in the pan of ice water, grabbed a towel, and looked up at me. He was amused.

"Why should one listen to you? After all, it seems to me that you are a neutral, not belonging to either school of thought about freakish deer."

"Mat feels this business too earnestly," I said. "After all, there are deer enough."

"Did you mean that?" demanded Danner.

"I did. And I do."

"Well, for gosh sakes. I give you my word. Far be it from me to disturb the peace of the upper Kennebec!"

I liked Danner more than ever before for that speech.

We partook of Mat's good breakfast, closed the camp for the day, and followed Mat into the shivering world. A great horned owl flew like a shadow out of a gaunt, naked tree.

Mat halted. "That is a crotchly bad sign," he said.

Danner said, "To heck with the signs and the seasons. Today, I'm out to shoot anything that comes along on all fours, except a blue ox, and that white deer of yours, Mat."

"He sartinly hain't *mine*," said Mat, with a sober haste.

I hated that cold, sticky morning—it laid clammy hands on a fellow, and I looked back at the warm camp we had left, like the lady from Gomorrah, while I marveled at Mat and Danner, who had accepted the weather as if it were not.

Furthermore, I didn't know where we were, after we had walked for a half hour. And I suspected that Mat did not know, because of the dull light and the rapidly falling snow.

At last we came upon the edge of a little wild meadow, a dry bog. There in the open the large, squashy snowflakes fell in an endless, whispering confusion.

Mat turned to me and whispered, "B'crotch, I can't rec'lect this place—can you?"

So we stood there watching and pondering our situation. It was Danner that heard the deer. There was a curling line of alders near the center of the meadow. And a deer was feeding there but was half concealed in the alders, and somewhat blotted out by the snow. It stood broadside to us. There was no doubt that it was a deer, or that it was a normal, brown creature.

This was our last day. We had come to it without so much as the chance to shoot a deer, unless one counted Danner's wild shot at the white buck, which Mat would not do, of course. Therefore Mat was anxious.

"Make it quick," he said to Danner.

Danner raised his heavy rifle, aimed, and fired. In spite of that dim light and the blurring snow, Danner's lead had been deadly. The deer slumped as if it had been knocked between the eyes.

"Good on your head!" said Mat. But it was only said, when we saw a deer leap to its feet—no, not leap, for it seemed to rise, and to get off at top form and speed.

Danner appeared to be possessed by astonishment—unable to

act. I slammed my own rifle to the shoulder, but Mat was seconds ahead of me. His .30-30 sounded like a dull thud in the snow-blanketed country. The running deer plunged forward, came up again, but went down when Mat fired a second shot.

"Thar!" said Mat, as excited as a grocer weighing out half a pound of prunes. "Thar, I reckon we got that 'un, if we did have to shoot up the whole landscape to do it."

Danner was ashamed. "I thought," he explained, "that he had gone down for keeps, after I fired."

"So did I," said Mat, as we walked out into the little opening.

And of course Mat would go first to the spot where the deer had stood, when Danner fired, for there the story began.

"Ju-das priest!" he exclaimed when he reached the spot, a few steps in front of Danner and me.

There lay a doe—dead where it fell, hit cleanly in the heart—dead beside that black ribbon of a small brook within the alders.

"Judas an' the priest," said Mat, turning from the dead doe to a spot where there was no snow on the gray-brown meadow grass. "Thar's where another one bedded down."

"Then I did get mine," said Danner.

"Yes," said Mat, "but what in the devil have I shot?"

And he left us to follow the second deer's tracks. When he came to an abrupt halt, Danner shouted, "Got him?"

Mat was slow to reply. At last, he said, "B'crotch, Mak, I've gone an' shot that *white* buck—killed him, deader'n a stun heap."

Danner stared at me. Then he sat down, or collapsed, in the slush.

"Oh, mygosh! This is comedy, Greek comedy undefiled. Oh, mygosh!"

I went to Mat. I think that I ran. Sure enough, there lay the white buck. The last shot had smashed its heart. Mat had removed his cap. His stiff gray hair was awry, and on his face was the expression of an extrovert shipwrecked on the foam of perilous seas, in fairy lands forlorn.

"Wa-al," he said, "what's done is done, an' who in God's world can undo it? If I had only waited a min-it, but, no, I had to shoot b'fore thar was time to look it over. So I've gone an' killed that *white* buck."

With that speech finished, Mat got out a jackknife and began to dress the white buck of the Forsythe country. Once he looked up to Danner and me. "I wish you fellers w'ud unload your guns," he said, "becuz if I've got to be shot, I w'ud rather it 'ud be done by strangers."

Knowing that Mat meant what he said, I unloaded my rifle. Danner unloaded his.

"While ye're erbout it," said Mat, "unload mine."

"How would you like to have that nice, fat doe of mine?" asked Danner. "I would like to trade deer with you."

Mat was impressed. He looked searchingly at Danner. But his mind added up two and two and then stuck to it that the result was four.

"Danner," he said, "that's a handsome offer, but it w'udn't come to no good fer either of us. This is a danged deceitful world, where a feller with the best of intentions is apt to be led astray. But a man has to take his own consequences. *I* shot this white buck."

I have made my report. Now you know how it happened. Mat Markham shot a white buck—a big white buck with twelve points. Mat sold that buck for fifty dollars. An out-of-state hunter who had more money than fortune at deer hunting went home with that beautiful creature. I saw Mat pocket the money as if in a daze.

"Not that it'll ever do me any good," he said.

That was twenty years ago. I am sure that the fifty dollars have not changed hands since then. Moreover, Mat has enjoyed robust health and enough good fortune to satisfy a citizen in this good land that the Lord God gave to us. But Ecclesiastes is still the sum of Mat's conclusions concerning the lot of mortal man in this vale of tears. And to this day, he insists that it is p'ison bad luck to shoot a white deer.

WILLIAM A. MILES

Three Men and a Buck

Any collection of hunting stories that neglected the "farm-fringe" big game hunter would be favoring the exotic and ignoring the familiar. In the course of my aimless wanderings with a gun and a typewriter over most of the country, I arrived at the conclusion that just about every state has its "Catskill" deer hunters. It is not easy to capture the spirit of such groups, but Miles has managed to do it. It could be that you will find this story so real it hurts.

The whole thing happened because Doc had a friend who owned a farm in upstate New York, in the foothills of the Adirondacks. Here he had retired to the placid life of reading and checker playing. That is, most of his time was spent that way. The rest of the day was spent chasing deer out of his young orchard. That's the way the story came to us.

Now the mere mention of venison seems to rouse the sporting instinct. The pulse quickens; the fountain of youth starts bubbling. Even the most serene individual will prick up his ears. It's like a bugle call to an old war horse. Must be a throwback to our pioneer forbears.

Anyway, it was the origin of the most incongruous foursome that ever responded to the call of the wild. There was Jim, a surgeon of great repute in the greatest city; Joe, a dentist who asked and received better than ten dollars an hour for his labors; Sam, an undertaker, who, contrary to tradition, was fat and jolly and as full of jokes as a hound dog is of ticks. And a magazine publisher. I was the publisher.

How we ever got together for a deer hunt remains a mystery to this day. We had nothing in common. We were, indeed, members of the same club—but all for different reasons. However, just the suggestion of venison seems to make strange bedfellows.

Jim started it all at the round-table lunch at the club when he passed around a letter from his retired friend in the Adirondacks. It wasn't much of a letter, as I recall. Merely the suggestion that Jim come up and help dispose of some of the deer that were chewing up the young fruit trees. So the four of us looked at one another and asked: "Why not?" Sam, the undertaker, was more candid. He still maintains that he went along solely for business reasons.

The outfits that were lugged aboard the Adirondacks Special at Grand Central Terminal a couple of weeks later were just as much mismated as we were. That is, all but Sam's. All he brought was an overnight bag, which held a gallon jug and a change of underwear. Sam said the jug contained embalming fluid. It did. It was four-year-old applejack—also known as Jersey lightning. It has other names too, that are just as apt as the drink is effective.

The treasure in Jim's outfit was a sheep-lined trench coat that reached below his knees—just the right length to entangle the leg action. Joe simply brought his oldest clothes and a borrowed Winchester. My rig was fairly complete, with duffel bag, hunting togs, shoepacs with no heels. The shoepacs were a mistake. My gun was an 8 mm. Sauer-Mauser that immediately got a lot of examining and required a lot of explaining.

When we tumbled out of the sleeper on a cold November morning, the temperature was well below freezing. There was nothing in sight but the platform and a horse-drawn stagecoach. Funny how some Adirondack villages are located so many miles away from the railroad, and use train stops in the wilds. The ten-mile ride before breakfast over slippery mountain roads took a couple of hours, and during the ride Sam's supply of embalming fluid was appreciably lowered. State troopers stopped us en route to check our licenses, which luckily were in order, though one of the troopers took plenty of time to examine the Sauer-Mauser.

It was still early in the morning, according to city standards, when we arrived at the farm. Just seven o'clock. Breakfast was waiting, for we were expected. Now, if you've never sat down to an Adirondack farm breakfast on a cold November morning after a two-hour ride—man, you've missed something. That meal alone was worth the price of the whole trip. Fried cakes (flapjacks to you), real maple sirup, country sausage homemade from home-grown pigs, fried eggs by the dozen, sizzling bacon, fried ham, and country-fried potatoes—and coffee in what looked like a lumber-camp coffeepot.

That was the assortment. The quantity was even larger. But it wasn't too much. Four healthy appetites can do wonders to such a meal. But what a far cry it was from our usual orange juice, toast, and coffee, with which we started the day's work back in the city!

Even the irrepressible Sam finally called quits, though he did try to kiss Sally, the dusky cook, from sheer gratitude. He stopped only when she said: "Ah declares, Mistuh Sam, ef yuh don't quit dat monkeyin', Ise gonna souse yuh with dis yere dishwater." But she was pleased by his enthusiasm just the same. From then on, he was her favored "chile."

The two natives who were to do the "guidin" arrived shortly after breakfast. They were an odd pair. Lou was about six feet four, looking a lot as Lincoln must have in his rail-splitting days, and with just as dour a countenance. Jules, his partner, a French-Canadian, was at least a foot shorter, and as round and chubby as Lou was tall and lean.

We were late in getting started. Much too late, as we found out afterward. But then we found out lots of other things too. Sam decided that he would stay at the farm, and no amount of persuasion would make him change his mind. "Nope," he said, "I'm tired already, and it's too soon after eating. I'll just wait here until you fellows get back—one way or another. You may need me. Besides, Sally's going to bake me an apple pie."

That was that. The three of us got off finally, sometime after nine o'clock, with the two guides leading the way. There was a bit of misgiving, however, for Sam's remarks, jokingly made as they were, stuck in our minds. The pace set by Lou and Jules should have been warning enough. But we were all mature men in fair physical trim. We had knocked around plenty—and had taken plenty of knocks. So the pace was a challenge which we accepted. It never occurred to any of us then that we were getting the works. But we were. The snow was just a couple of inches deep —just a fine tracking snow, according to Lou. The first mile or so across the pasture that led to the edge of the woods, passed without any particular discomfort, though it wasn't exactly a Sunday stroll.

It was not until we were in the woods, headed up the mountain, that the first sign of trouble appeared. Jim's knee-length sheep-lined coat began to get in its fine work. If there was any trail, it had been carefully avoided. Climbing through down timber is a tough job at the best. In such a rig, Jim had trouble aplenty. He was sweating profusely and cussing more profusely—when he had breath enough to cuss. I offered to take his gun, but he wouldn't hear of it. It was just as well. My heel-less shoepacs worked satisfactorily crossing the flat pasture land. Upgrade in the woods was another story, and I found myself slipping back two steps for every one I advanced. They were of no help climbing in and out of ravines, of which there seemed to be plenty.

Somewhere up ahead, Lou and Jules had disappeared. It was an easy matter to follow their trail, but we were falling far behind the pace. I lost count of the number of times we stopped for a breather, but there were many of them. Joe, the dentist, wasn't doing so badly in his outfit of old clothes. His footgear was most unorthodox, for a well-rigged Nimrod—just a pair of overshoes or arctics over his city shoes—but they were mighty effective and I would gladly have swapped my shoepacs for them.

It was nearly noon when we reached the ridge from which we were to hunt. It wasn't much of a mountain, according to Western standards—just a mere three or four thousand feet. For us it was too much, particularly as we had found every ravine and had climbed over or under every piece of fallen timber on the way up. Lou and Jules were waiting for us, calmly smoking their pipes, their backs resting comfortably against a tree trunk. Apparently it had been just a nice morning jaunt to them. They eyed us speculatively but said nothing. We gave it right back to them with suspicion added, but we too, said nothing. We couldn't. There wasn't breath enough.

Maybe fifteen minutes passed in silence. Darn taciturn, these natives. Then Lou outlined the plan of campaign. It was simple enough, and sounded logical. The three of us were to be placed on separate stations or posts about a quarter of a mile apart, where each of us could get a good view down each side of the ridge. Lou and Jules were to separate, each taking a side of the mountain and working up again from the bottom. The idea was, that any deer lurking in the thickets would be jumped by one or the other of them and would head up the mountain, crossing our line of posts, so that one of us might get a shot. Yes, it seemed logical enough then. None of us figured that the noise we'd made coming up the ridge had probably scared every deer—if there ever were any—clear into the next county. All we had to worry about was not to take a shot at each other.

So off we went with Lou to take our respective posts. Joe was dropped first, by a nice round stump, and with a clear view in all directions. Jim was next. He drew an outcrop of rock that also gave him an unbroken view. On we went up the ridge to the very end. Below was an almost sheer drop of several hundred feet. This was my station—also with a nice rock outcrop. South of me were my two companions, perhaps a quarter and half a mile away respectively. They were in plain sight when they stood up. If they sat down there was nothing but the mountain ridge with its sparse covering. Off in the distance were more ridges, more ravines, and more mountains.

Lou left me without a word and departed down the mountain. No final word of instruction. No warning of any kind. No suggestion of when he'd be back. He just went. And then silence. Nothing moved or made a noise except as a vagrant breeze occasionally rustled a dead leaf. I slipped the cartridge clip into the Mauser and waited. Fifteen minutes passed—then a half hour. Nothing happened. Nothing stirred.

To the south, I could see Jim and Joe, equally alert, like two sturdy outposts ready to go into action at the first opportunity. And so we passed the first hour. That was about as long as the alertness lasted. I found a sheltered nook against the rock outcrop and settled down with my back against it. I wanted to smoke, but didn't dare, for fear the tobacco aroma would reach the keen nostrils of some soft-footed deer. That was all I remembered for some time. The utter stillness covered me like a blanket—and I slept.

When I awoke the sun was well down in the southwest. My wristwatch said three-thirty, so I got up and stretched. Not a sign of Jim or Joe. I tried a cautious yell to attract Jim's attention. No response. That was too much. Picking up my rifle, I made my way to Jim's post. He was there right enough, but sound asleep. The snow was littered with cigarette butts. If he had thought the tobacco odor might reach the deer, he didn't care about it. I stirred him with my foot. He roused with a sleepy "Hello—what's up?"

Joe popped up on his stump and we waved for him to join us. He hadn't been asleep, he said, and produced a nicely carved cane whittled from a handy bush as proof. So we held a council of war. The sky was thickening fast. Clouds had come up from nowhere, and the sun had disappeared. It was colder. There was a distinct smell of snow in the air.

Whatever decision we might have reached eventually was postponed by a bedlam of noise from down the mountain—loud yells and much baying of hounds. Lou and Jules had jumped a deer. Jim lost his lethargy immediately, as Joe and I sprinted for our opposite posts. At last we were to get some action. Back at the rock outcrop I waited. If I examined the action of my Mauser once, I did a dozen times. I wondered if I would get buck fever.

The noise was getting closer, but the baying of the hounds had stopped except for an occasional yelp. It was beginning to get dark, and the snow started—big flakes, they were, that made for poor visibility. But I was all set for a quick snap shot if necessary.

Suddenly all noise stopped; then from out of the silence came the single sharp crack of a rifle. I looked toward Jim and Joe. They were alert but barely visible. Neither of them had shot—the report was more to the west of them. Lou or Jules. Maybe they had missed, and I might get a running shot. I knew that the deer would be getting away fast, if he could get away at all. So I waited, nerves tense. Nothing appeared. A crashing in the underbrush at my right focused my attention there. It was followed by a loud "hello, thar" that brought my rifle down. Out from the brush came Lou, followed by Jules, who let out a loud bay as he appeared. So Jules was the baying hound. Jules carried a nice plump snowshoe rabbit. So that was the deer!

"Well, too bad you boys didn't get no shootin'. Guess they ain't no deer amovin' today." It was Lou. "Well, we might git one in the swamp on the way out," he continued, "but we gotta git agoin'. It's gittin' dark, and acomin' on to snow." And with no further word he and Jules started off. If the pace had been fast for us coming up the mountain, it was as nothing at all to the rate going down. Lou's long legs just reached out in four-foot strides. Jules, shorter geared, with legs fairly twinkling, looked like a small boy being led to the woodshed by an irate father. We picked up Jim and Joe with a curt "Come on, we gotta git." We did—and how!

But lo—a miracle. Going up that darn mountain we had the toughest kind of going. In and out of ravines, over and under logs and down timber that had pulled our corks. Now Lou had found a perfectly good wood or tote road that was a boulevard by comparison, and down which he fairly flew.

If my shoepacs had given me trouble going up, that trouble was doubled on the way back. I had absolutely no traction. I lost count of the number of times that I sat down, sometimes gracefully like an adagio dancer, but more often suddenly, and with a jar that shook my back teeth. The fast pace set by the guides, the snow, and fast-approaching darkness made it worse. We had been jobbed. I was sure of it. Somehow we reached the bottom.

The ground flattened out and I greeted it with a welcome sigh. Too soon. A little farther along, just as I'd begun to hit my stride, one foot sank down about six inches, and I nearly pitched on my face. A swamp. The rest was nightmare. Every few steps, one foot or the other would sink into the half-frozen bog until it seemed there would be no ending. There was. I fetched up suddenly against the man ahead. Forward progress had ceased. What now? Just a beaver dam to be crossed!

If you've ever crossed a beaver dam in shoepacs, in snow and darkness, carrying a rifle like a balancing pole, it's an experience you won't ever want to repeat. On one side, a pond covered with slush ice and deeper than you cared to think about; on the other side, rocks, and darkness with somewhere a brook trickling. There was little choice. Just a thorough wetting one way, and a broken leg the other. If I had any leaning at all, it was definitely toward the wetting.

Somehow we all made it safely. Lou led the way. He can have that credit for what it's worth. Jules brought up the rear—to fish us out from one side or the other, I suppose. Yes, we made it, but I wouldn't tackle it again for all the deer in the woods.

"You boys did all right," said Lou from somewhere out of the darkness ahead, as we trudged down the road toward the farmhouse, whose lights faintly shone in the distance. Nobody answered. What was there to say? What we thought was something else again. And so we got back to the farm—silently and in single file.

Our entrance into the farmhouse was made with no exuberation. Sam was playing checkers with our host. The half-emptied jug of applejack sat conveniently on the floor by his chair. "All back safe, eh? That's good," he said, as if he didn't mean it. "Any luck?"

Our silence gave him the answer. "Too bad," he continued. "Here, take a shot of apple and you'll feel better."

There was a smirk on his face that I didn't fancy. He had a look like the cat that ate the canary. Was he responsible for our ragging? I wondered, as I reached for the extended glass. But no. That couldn't be. Sam didn't know either Lou or Jules. He'd never seen them before. What was it? Something was in the air.

Then Sally stuck her head in through the kitchen doorway and announced: "Supper's gwine be ready in a shake, gemmun. Yo better git yosef cleaned up." And back she went into the kitchen with a chuckle.

The wash bench was out back of the kitchen. Jim was the first to reach it . . . a wild yell from him brought us all running.

Out back of the woodshed, strung up by his horns, was a nice plump spike-horn buck. So that was the Ethiopian.

Then the story came out. Sally had spied the young buck in the orchard behind the barn. She had told Sam, who quit his checkers and applejack long enough to borrow a rifle from our host, then meandered out and shot the buck—not a hundred yards from the house.

That's all there was to it. But it was too much for Lou and Jules. They disappeared into the darkness with a well-emphasized "GOOD NIGHT!"

Some day, though, I'm going on another deer hunt. And when I do, there'll be no climbing mountains, clambering through ravines, or crossing beaver dams. I'm just going to get a bag, and a jug—and follow Sam's system.

EDMUND   WARE
SMITH

Two Eyes that Shone as One

There are innumerable reprobates cluttering the heart and fringes
of hunting, but certainly none more lovable than the creations
of Edmund Ware Smith. The pages of *The One-Eyed Poacher of
Privilege* are crowded with amazing, but real, characters. Their
reality can be established through the testimony of game wardens
in almost every part of this country. Uncle Jeff Coongate might
well be described as the warden's specter.

Uncle Jeff Coongate was depressed. He sat in a rocker in the
front room of Zack Bourne's cabin, responding gloomily to
Zack's conversation. The origin of Uncle Jeff's mood was, to him,
so hideous and shameful that he hated to think of it. The fact was
that yesterday he had deliberately missed a standing shot at a buck
deer. He had willfully fired his rifle into the air. This act of mercy,
being without precedent in the one-eyed poacher's career, made
him suspect that his mind was going. Even granting that the buck
was a very particular one, Uncle Jeff could neither condone nor
comprehend his own softness. It humiliated and distressed him.
He now lived in constant dread lest Zack discover his chicken-
hearted secret and expose him to ridicule throughout the lake
country.

Zack perched on a bench, his rifle across his lap, his voice
merry with self-esteem. Zack was fitting a wire frame to the re-
ceiver of his rifle. The frame was cunningly designed to hold a
flashlight in position to shine not only the front and rear sights,
but the eyes of a deer in the dark. Come nightfall, Zack, never

49

doubting Jeff's enthusiastic aid, proposed to use the device in laying low the very buck that the one-eyed poacher had spared. To Zack, it was unthinkable that his old comrade might revolt at the idea. Zack monologued blissfully:

"Dang shame a feller couldn't patint a rig like this. I'd call her the Zack Bourne Dead Shot Jacklightin' Frame. We'll test her out tonight on that old buck. Bet he'll dress two hundrid, easy."

At the mention of the buck, Uncle Jeff winced imperceptibly. "You couldn't patint that rig this side of hell," he muttered.

Zack tightened a screw and spoke himself a word of congratulation, while Uncle Jeff's good eye rested sorrowfully on a faded print entitled *The Fiancee,* from a drawing by Edouard Bisson, 1891. The Fiancee was bushel-bosomed. She appeared to be dreaming of dignified passions. A couple of overstuffed cherubim floated in her background. Uncle Jeff snorted, and remarked: "Besides, the chances is I scairt that buck clear'n out of the country yest'dy afternoon."

"Nope," contradicted Zack. "He'll likely hang 'round till a good frost starts him ridge-runnin' after does. How close did you get onto him, d'you say?"

"Right handy," said Uncle Jeff, squirming.

"Can't see how come you to miss him."

"Tripped over a damn root, like I told you," lied the old poacher. "Jest's I pulled the tricker."

"Huh. Well, sir, I'll jest nail him cold tonight. An' I won't trip over no root, neither. I'll lay off shore a ways in my canoe, an' shine him. First blood for the Dead Shot Jacklightin' Frame."

Uncle Jeff Coongate was by now completely miserable. He pushed back his high-crowned felt hat and stroked his forehead with his wrist. He yearned to unburden, to tell Zack the truth and call the whole thing off. But he knew he would never hear the last of it. Truth was, Uncle Jeff could not bring himself to kill the buck. He would even go to dangerous extremes to prevent anyone else killing it. And the reason was that both he and the buck had lost an eye!

The common injury had given Jeff the deer's point of view for the first time in his bloodthirsty career. The shock had unnerved him. But how could he save the deer's life without losing his own reputation?

The old woodsman dismally recalled that he had invited himself to Zack's cabin for the purpose of hunting this very buck. It was to have been a heartwarming reunion, following their recent feud over the chicken shoot at Jumbo Tethergood's.

On that bitter occasion at Jumbo's, Jeff had won both chickens, not so much by superior marksmanship as by means of a pint of Old Flat-Spin rye to which he had introduced Zack an hour before firing time. Onlookers joyously proclaimed that Zack was shooting blanks. Zack himself had asserted that his rear sight looked as big as Yellowhead Pass, and in the notch his front sight towered like a chimbley.

Since Zack was considered by himself and everyone else to be the best offhand rifle shot in the country, he had been furious. For weeks afterward he had not spoken to his old crony. But recently they had met on the main street of Privilege. For a moment, their quarrel still rankling, they had exchanged sulky stares. Then their natures overcame the grudge, and they had charged one another, arms flailing.

"You old tomcat!"

"Why, you danged outlaw, you."

"How's Sarah?"

"Down to her folks. I'm dreadful lonesome."

"Me, too. Ain't seen a real friend for a month."

"Say, was them chickens of Jumbo's any good?"

"Turrible! Scrawniest a man ever set tooth into!"

They had tested their renewed friendship by poking one another in the ribs. Both stood the test. Then Uncle Jeff leaned close to Zack's ear, and whispered: "You got any prime wild meat located uplake? I ain't et a thing but pork an' baloney since them hellish chickens. I'm droolin' for a junk of loin."

Zack had clutched his friend's sleeve: "Jeff, boy—I got my eye on the biggest buck ever this country heard tell of. Been fattin' in the wild medder grass in the cove. Ain't half a mile from my door."

"Dear Lord, leave me at 'im," Uncle Jeff had supplicated, his eye teary with anticipation. "Wait'll I git my rifle."

Later, his rifle barrel down his pants leg, and the stock and fore-arms concealed under his coat, Jeff rejoined his partner. In poker-faced innocence, they had strolled past the game warden's house and on to the canoe landing without attracting official notice.

It was on the following afternoon, in the cedar thicket bordering the wild meadow, that Uncle Jeff and the magnificent buck met eye-to-eye at a distance of ten yards. The buck had been lying down, napping. Startled by the woodsman's approach, the deer had leaped straight into the air and come to earth, legs braced, distended nostrils whistling.

For a long instant Uncle Jeff and the buck had stared at each other. The old poacher's teeth bared in his ruthless kill-grin. "Jest hold quiet another second," he growled, "till I blast you between the eyes!" Then, suddenly noticing the buck's lone eye, Uncle Jeff had begun to tremble. He couldn't understand it. He had always been cool and merciless in the presence of illegal game. He tried to pull the trigger. He couldn't. Here was the standing shot of a lifetime, but it was no use.

"You poor old feller," murmured the one-eyed poacher. "You got on'y one eye, too."

Then he elevated his rifle muzzle, fired into the air, and hissed: "Go to it, boy. Git out of here."

The buck cleared an eight-foot blowdown on the first jump, and by the third was making forty miles an hour in dense cover. Zack was stationed on a stump in an old chopping. He reported subsequently that he had seen nothing but a reddish-white flash as the buck sailed across. . . .

Now, in the cabin, the hot breeze humming in the screens, Uncle Jeff thought tenderly of the buck, while Zack Bourne assembled his deadly jacklighting frame. The seeds of a scheme had sprouted slowly in the one-eyed poacher's mind. If the sprouts flowered, the buck would be spared, or at least its death indefinitely postponed. And Zack never would be the wiser.

Zack taped the flashlight to the frame and sighted along the cabin wall. "She's a humdinger," he declared.

Uncle Jeff coughed, but withheld comment.

"Lines up jest perfick," Zack announced.

Uncle Jeff uttered a low moan, and Zack pricked up his ears. "Say, you got a misery? You been mopin' all mornin'. What ails you? Heat?"

The old poacher bowed his head, as if in agonized embarrassment. "I guess its jest my dang conscience, gnawing at my innards."

"Your what?" asked Zack, astounded.

"Conscience."

"Christ A'mighty, since when . . . ?"

Uncle Jeff held up his hand for silence. "I ain't been square with you, Zack. I been holdin' back on you. After you invitin' me here to share in that buck, too."

"Holdin' back what?" grunted Zack, laying his rifle on the bench at his side.

Uncle Jeff hitched in his chair. He passed his hand across his chin. "I'm scared to tell you, Zack."

"Why?"

"Might mean we'd have to leave that buck go awhile."

"Why so? What you drivin' at?"

Uncle Jeff's head jerked. A jet of Strong Jaw tobacco juice splashed through the lower draft of the cold stove. "Cause in this weather, meat don't keep good. Fly-blows. An' you can't keep no buck deer in Ruffy Dixon's icehouse in September. Too dang risky."

"Who said anything about puttin' our buck in any icehouse?"

The one-eyed poacher winced, as if his conscience had struck him a mortal blow. "No. But you can hang a veal calf in Ruffy's icehouse. All clear an' legal, too."

"Who's got any veal calf?"

"You," said Uncle Jeff contritely. "I practickly stole it from you, too. On'y I couldn't—not after what I done to you at Tethergood's chicken shoot."

Zack was thoroughly perplexed. He was also interested. He loved veal. "You say you stole a veal calf off me that I never had in the first place?"

"Yuh. I dang near did, on'y for my conscience. Tomorrow, after we'd killed that buck, I was goin' down to Jumbo Tethergood's an' win your calf in the big shoot."

Zack was deeply impressed. "Jumbo puttin' up a veal calf?"

"Yuh, tomorrow. An' I never said a word to you about it, 'cause" —Uncle Jeff swallowed noisily—"you're the on'y one in the country can beat me shootin'."

Flattered by his old friend's regard for his marksmanship, and cheered by prospects of tender veal, Zack said: "You're a mighty square friend, Jeff. I'll give you half the meat."

"I couldn't take it from you," Uncle Jeff sighed. "On'y just a little junk of loin. 'Nough for two feeds. I—I feel like I'd ought to pay your entry fee to the shoot, too, Zack."

"Couldn't let you do that."

Zack sat for a time in deep thought. "Maybe," he said at last, "we'd ought to let that one-eyed buck roam for a spell. If we killed him tonight, he'd fly-blow while we was eatin' veal."

"I was a-feared of it," mourned Uncle Jeff. "I hate awful to pass him up, but still an' all"—he sighed heavily—"I see the sense to it. He'd be maggoty in three-four days."

"Well, look. I'll give you a quarter of the veal, Jeff."

"Couldn't take it."

"I'll make you take it!"

"Well, all right," conceded the one-eyed poacher. "Mighty white of you, Zack."

"Which calf is it?" Zack inquired.

"The spotted one. The bull."

Zack rolled his eyes in bliss. "I can smell the gravy now."

"I seen the calf in Ruffy's icehouse. Dressed a hundrid and eighty," informed Uncle Jeff. "Fat as butter. But I'd ruther a loin steak off that buck, any day."

"What? Venison off an old buck, 'stead of veal? You're crazy."

With an air of heavy sacrifice, Uncle Jeff changed the subject: "Maybe, if you're aimin' to appear at Jumbo's shoot, you better unscrew that jacklightin' frame off your rifle. That young game warden Tom Corn's li'ble to be there."

The weather for Tethergood's shoot broke clear and windless. Zack and Uncle Jeff Coongate arrived by canoe about noon, Zack carrying some rope and a bundle of sacking in which to wrap that portion of the prize which, in Dixon's icehouse, he would carve off after the shoot was over.

Sixty-five competitors had paid the one dollar entry fee. Those who knew of Zack's skill moaned when he appeared on the scene. Zack grinned and patted his rifle. "She ain't shootin' blanks today, boys!"

The target, set a hundred yards from the firing line, had a five-inch bull's-eye. Each contestant was allowed ten shots. The competition was keen, but Zack Bourne was determined to wipe out the shame of his performance at the chicken shoot while under the spell of Old Flat-Spin rye. He and Jeff Coongate joyfully watched the targets come in. The only one which was going to bother Zack was Stumpy Coldwillow's. Stumpy had nine shots in the black.

"Beat that, Zack," Stumpy said.

The shoot was practically over. The onlookers crowded close to watch Zack perform. Uncle Jeff stood at his elbow, whispering words of encouragement. Zack settled and began firing. He put ten shots into the black—all of them cleanly save for one, which broke a trifle into the white. Uncle Jeff Coongate whooped with triumph. His one-eyed buck was spared. Zack waved his rifle, kissed its hot barrel, and yelled: "Jumbo! Gimme the key to Ruffy's icehouse. I want my veal."

"Just a minute," Jumbo said. "One more feller to shoot yet."

A small, apologetic man stepped to the firing line. He was a stranger. He wore a curious-looking coat, heavily padded at the elbows. Nothing like it had been seen in the surrounding country. The stranger's rifle, too, seemed odd. It had set triggers. The barrel was very heavy. The caliber was twenty-two, and the sights telescopic. The stranger's ten shots simply cut the center out of the bull's-eye. Zack Bourne got second prize, which was a tub of lard. Uncle Jeff felt so sick that he bought a pint of medicine from Jumbo Tethergood. It was Old Flat-Spin.

On the way down to the canoe landing, he spoke disconsolately to Zack. "Tub of lard, an' nothin' to fry in it."

Zack swore savagely. He gripped his friend by the elbow and snarled: "Looks like you're goin' to have a chance at that one-eyed buck after all. If I can't shoot for veal, I can kill deer. I'd like to kill about six, jest to git even with my feelin's. That buck-ll be jest a starter. Come on!"

Reluctantly, his feet leaden and his heart sad, Uncle Jeff got into the canoe. They reached Zack's cabin after dark. The night was cloudy and dead still—perfect conditions for jacklighting. In the cabin, by the lamp, Zack hummed "The Church in the Wildwood" as he refitted the Dead Shot Frame to his rifle. Jeff took his first gulp of Old Flat-Spin, and choked. "I got the cholery—summer cholery!"

"Take a swallow of kerosene," Zack advised.

"This is stronger," said Uncle Jeff, taking another jolt, "but it don't taste so good."

The whiskey seemed only to intensify Uncle Jeff's sympathy for all one-eyed creatures, especially himself and the buck. As he listened to Zack's plan of strategy the old poacher grieved sorely. Zack was to take his canoe and paddle along the cove, about fifty yards off shore. He was almost certain to shine the eye of the gigantic buck, and almost certain to drill him cleanly when he did. But in case of a miss, the buck would run across the chopping on his regular route. There with the second flashlight, Uncle Jeff was to be stationed. He would hear the buck coming, perhaps stall him with a sudden blaze of light, and get a quick shot.

In the darkness the oldtimers crept down to the canoe. Zack laid his rifle on the floor of the craft.

"Git in," he whispered. "I'll leave you ashore down a ways. No sense walkin' that fer."

Presently Zack sided in to shore. Uncle Jeff got out on a sand spit.

"I'll give you ten minutes to get set in the choppin'," Zack whispered. "Then I'll turn on my light an' start rakin' the shore for his eye!"

The paddle dripped as Zack eased the canoe out into the lake. Uncle Jeff stood alone in the darkness, just inside the seawall growth. He knew the country well. His moccasins felt for the little path used by deer. He didn't use his light. He crept forward, a hand up to fend the branches from his face. He paused and took a mammoth gurgle of Old Flat-Spin. The shock made him close his eye. When he opened it, he saw the long, sharply focused beam of Zack's light. Zack was a considerable distance behind him and coming slowly.

Uncle Jeff intended to jump the deer somewhere close to shore. He did not propose to go anywhere near the chopping. All he wanted to do was frighten the deer, somehow, so that Zack wouldn't get a shot. But Zack was getting closer. He was within hearing. If Uncle Jeff yelled or crashed about in the brush, Zack would be suspicious. If he fired his rifle, Zack would mistrust him, and ask questions as to what he was doing in the shore growth, when he should be a quarter of a mile away by the runway in the chopping. No! The only thing to do was to make Zack fire *his* rifle.

Zack was now so close that his light gleamed occasionally on the undersides of cedar fronds. Uncle Jeff crept a bit nearer shore. He concealed his body behind an old spruce blowdown, and stood to his full height. He moved his head, so that a hemlock branch all but hid his face. Confident that he would be invisible to Zack, Jeff took another slug of whiskey, muttered a prayer, and waited.

Slowly the light beam played along the shore, always a little closer. Once or twice it slanted into the sky, as Zack laid his rifle against a thwart and paddled a few strokes. Now the beam glowed on a birch trunk ten feet away. Behind him, Uncle Jeff heard a branch crackle. His heart pounded. The one-eyed buck was near.

The next instant, from his cover, Uncle Jeff Coongate looked fair into the beam of Zack's light. From out on the lake came a metallic click as Zack cocked his rifle. Uncle Jeff thirsted for one more searing swallow of Old Flat-Spin, but he dared not move a finger. The light beam had steadied.

Zack's rifle shot ripped open the stillness of the night, re-echoing from the steep shores of the lake. Uncle Jeff stooped, clutched his hat, and dodged back, deeper into the forest. He had made but a few yards when he heard a buck whistle. The buck was warned now. He was gone. Safe.

Uncle Jeff slunk back to the cabin. He had just lighted the lamp when Zack came in, his face like a squall cloud.

"I missed him! Shone his eye plumb fair! So help me, it glowed like a 'lectric bulb, an' I missed!"

Uncle Jeff teetered over to the rocking chair and sat down a little off center. "Nope, Zack," he remarked wearily, "you never missed that buck. You missed me."

"I tell you I shined that buck's eye."

"No you didn't, neither," corrected Uncle Jeff. "What you shined was my glass eye."

Zack's lips twitched. "How'd I shine your eye, an' you a quarter mile back there, in the choppin'?"

Uncle Jeff significantly stroked his stomach, and moaned: "I never got to the choppin'. I was took with a turrible cholery cramp, an' had to lay down. Didn't dast yell to you, for fear I'd scare that buck. I must of kind of fainted for a spell. 'Cause when I come to, an' stood up, I was lookin' right into your light. Next thing I knowed you'd fired. Your shot scared the buck, an' he run. Oh, ain't it cruel! Cruel! If he'd of been a few steps nearer the shore, just a little mite sooner, we'd been rollin' out his entr'ls right now."

Zack Bourne's face had turned ash white. He sank down on the bench. "My God! I might of killed you!"

"Well, you didn't. Feller's gen'ally apt to shoot high over a jack-light, I allus say." The one-eyed poacher picked up his hat and stuck his thumbs through the bullet holes in the crown. "You had the line jest perfick," he complimented, showing Zack the holes, "but you was about two inches high. I dunno how many times I've told you to hold down, shootin' over a light."

Zack's forehead had broken out in a cold, glistening sweat. "So help me, I'll never shoot at a one-eyed buck again—never! It might be you!"

"Take a lick of this," said Jeff, offering Zack the whiskey.

Zack accepted the bottle. It rattled against his teeth as he drank. "Look, Jeff," he begged, "can't we leave that one-eyed buck go? Prob'ly be tough as snowshoe fillin' anyways."

"Well," shrugged Uncle Jeff, " 'course if you feel that way, I know where we might shoot a dry doe tomorrow."

"Let's do it. I don't want no more of that buck."

"Jest's you say," sighed the one-eyed poacher. "Guess I'll open a can of beans for us to eat tonight."

MAXIMILIAN
FOSTER

The Conqueror

The wilderness put a firm stamp on Foster at an early age, and his writings (as shown by his correspondence) led many Americans to hunt and fish outside their local boundaries. He was a practical conservationist, which was not common prior to the turn of the century, and although he did everything possible to stir more individuals to take to the outdoors, he urged that bag and creel limits conform to the individual need rather than legal limits, which were overgenerous in those days. In most of his writings he managed to impart instructions in the craft without the reader being aware of it. "The Conqueror" is typical of his work in the sense that it shows his thorough knowledge of the wilderness and its inhabitants.

Away by the head of the forgotten Mamoziekel lies a barren—a gray solitude in the depths of the untraversed woods. Grim hills of mystery look down upon it, and the forest, pausing at its edge, overshadows quagmires working darkly like a witch's pot. Man is seldom there. Its waste is given over to the somber moose and to herds of woodland caribou, stray voyagers of the wilderness who track in from the runways leading to the south, and go unchallenged across its breadth.

There came a wind from the north. It drew down the flank of the mountain, sheeting the landscape with a pall of flying vapor, roared a moment on the forest edge, and swept across the barren. Night was falling. The last daylight glimmered in the west, and hastening clouds streaked the horizon in the van of the coming storm.

On the brink of the black pool at the center of the barren stood a herd of caribou, their heads uplifted, staring. A moment before there had been peace—quietly feeding, they had straggled across the bog. But now battle was in the air. On the flank of the band stood the herding bull—a great, white-maned creature, gray on the flanks, whose crowning antlers upreared over the cows like a guarding weapon. Beyond him pawed the challenger, once tolerated in the herd, but now, with the rut strong upon him, bawling defiance at the leader. They were sire and son. Across the shoulders of each ran a broad, white band, an unusual marking among the caribou. All day the younger had been beating the alders with his horns; now he was wildly eager for the fray. *Ruh-rr-r!* he bellowed gutturally.

The gale had lulled a moment, and in the sudden quiet, the sound volleyed across the interval. An uneasy tremor moved the herd; it bunched in its agitation, the cows huddling about their principal. The swollen neck of the herding bull bristled. Snorting an answer, he breasted the cows aside, his call of war ringing clear across the gathering night. Pawing the sodden earth, he pushed forward, "brattling" in rage. After years of mastery, should his sway be now disputed? Here was the bidding of Nature—once more the struggle for mastery.

Roaring, they crashed together. With a ringing stroke their antlers met, and, heads down, they wrestled across the mossy flooring of the bog. Their breaths whistled stridently, and the ground thudded beneath their quick-flying strokes. Night resounded with the clang of horn on horn. Nervously the cows looked on, or, again, in the lulls of the combat, stamped the bog. Sometimes they trotted to and fro along the flanks of the combat; sometimes they blatted, their staccato complaint urging on the fighters.

Weakness fell upon the herding bull, long time master of the ranges. He felt his power slipping from him. Conqueror in half a hundred battles, he was himself to taste the bitterness of defeat. Against his stout antagonist, whose thews and sinews were an inheritance from himself, his stand was short. His breath failed, and every voice gasped agony as it whistled from his lungs. The younger bull plied on with added fierceness, hurling his bulk against the tottering defense, beating down the swaying head— striking, stabbing as he would. Roaring in frenzy, the older bull upreared, wavered, and crashed backward as the other goaded him with piercing tines. A moment he lay inert; then, tottering to his feet, he fled, his implacable enemy following, driving him from the place.

A sudden flaw swept again across the barren, and the wind hummed among the spruce like a sound of gales upon the sea. The cows had wandered on, and with backs to the gusts, were feeding before the storm, indifferent now to the outcome of the fray. They had passed the pond hole, when across the bog came a rattle of hoofs clicking like a dancer's castanets. They threw up their heads and tried the air. Then they faced the storm, and out of the blinding rain-sheets came the conqueror, his neck still ruffled and his eyes still red from rage. He called once, they answered softly, and they were gone together—fleeting specters vanishing into the gloom. It was but the way of Nature—the survival of the fittest.

With the deepening of the snows, the battling rage of the bull died out. Yet he still held sway over the herd, leading it proudly from range to range. Their old leader was gone—exiled, an outcast. Together the band tracked the wilderness—here one day and gone the next, yet ever returning to the big barren of the Mamoziekel. In broad daylight they kept to the open country, for their lord was not the usual caribou bull, who skulks halting through the bushes. His craft seemed infallible; his nose keen to detect danger in the wind. So he led bravely.

Through the long winter they hovered about the barren. Sometimes, after a heavy wind, they voyaged through the forest to feed on the lichens blown down with broken limbs and treetops, but in the deep snow their usual food was the moss on the big barren. In its center were no drifts, and they pawed away the white covering and fed fatly upon the food beneath. Still wind and weather told. Before the new year had come, their coats were growing streaky yellow, the hair long and heavy, and their round barrels were gradually flattening out.

The bull no longer wore his crest with pride. It seemed a useless burden. He faced the wind with a lowered head, and about the bases of his horns crept an itching soreness. As he straggled into the wracked, distorted depths of a cedar swamp, he struck his antlers against a tree, and one antler dropped to the ground. Then he forged along, lop-eared and lop-headed, a most dejected-looking royalty—for all like a tipsy princeling with coronet askew. But a day later he revived; the other horn followed its mate, and, relieved of the uneven burden, he skipped across the barren at an eager pace, the snow flying in clouds under his cracking hoofs. The cows followed, and working to the northward he crossed the timbered valley, swung up over the ridges, and bore away to Nictau. Through the forest they kept their unbroken gait, their broad hoofs carrying them gallantly over the snowdrifts, and, at length, burst forth on the frozen surface of the lake. The sun shone, the air was crisp and invigorating. Like kittens they gambolled up and down the broad expanse. At night they fed in the black swamp at the eastward, and with the rising of the moon filed again across the ice, bound for a far-away range on the headwaters of the Sisson Branch.

The winter passed, and there was promise in the air. Flights of wild fowl, gossiping high overhead, sped northward to the breeding places; and on the mountain's southern slopes the ground was bursting with new life. The winter uneasiness of the herd had waned; they sought for a summer resting ground, and in swift passages southward drove the bewildered moose floundering from many a winter yard. But, after all the wandering, the herd returned once more to the big barren, and in a thick swamp just at its head cast themselves down to settle for the season.

Domestic affairs occupied their time. The bull's horns had just sprouted, when a heavy cow bore into the world a little awkward stranger. It was an uncouth youngling indeed. Its feet seemed out of all proportion; it was knock-kneed and hardly bigger than a dog. The bull clung about idly while this offspring was delivered into the world, and at dawn slouched into the covert where the mother cow lay huddled, the weakling at her side. He gazed at the calf—the clumsy, spindle-legged creature with the spreading, splay feet—and sniffed as if in scorn. But still the calf was big—a bull, and, like its sire, curiously marked with the band of white across its withers. It shuffled loosely to its knees as he loomed over it, and the cow, reaching forth, steadied it with her head until it stood, with legs far apart, for the first time on its feet.

Seemingly, the calf gave little concern to the bull, for the surly leader had troubles of his own. His head was swollen about the pedicles of the growing horns, and all his attention was required to pick a painless way for himself through the forest arches. Moreover, the flies had come with the first warm weather; life was hardly worth living when they grew attentive, and there was no peace without a lake or mud-wallow handy. Two pads of velvet on the sides of his head showed where the new antlers were sprouting and as they pushed forth he scratched them delicately with the point of his hoof. They were sore—very sore, indeed—and he moved about in moody dignity.

When the weather grew warm in earnest, and the calf was able to frisk about with his fellows, the herd's longing took them tripping from one lake to another. In the clear, cool water they swam and wallowed. Sometimes they fed on the water grasses, but their main food was still lichens. They did not often browse, as the moose do, on the tender sprigs, and when they did, they plucked at the buds instead of nipping them clearly. An Indian, seeing their work, would have known it from the browsing of the moose. "Moose ben here, sartin"—pointing to a clean-cut twig. "Hunh! that caribow feller!"—pointing to a fractured one.

During the day they clung to the heart of the deepest swamps, and at night tracked the shores of the black ponds and pug-holes. There was one mud-pit in an opening on the ridges which they often favored, and here the bull, his cows, and the calves would wallow in pure delight. Garbed with black slime from head to foot, they were a rowdy crew, but the morning dip in the lake made them once more presentable. It was a grand life, and they waxed fat and happy.

One warm afternoon, just after the last snow had vanished from the hollows under the hills, the herd bore down the slope of Bald Mountain, and swung away toward Bathurst. When they struck into the flat lying between, the bull paused and threw up his head. A faint air strayed about the valley, and, as a cross-current swept overhead, the bull caught a warning scent—the rank taint that betrayed the presence of a foe. He sniffed heavily, his nose wrinkling as he sought another gust, and was just tentatively stepping onward, when there was a resounding crash in the bush.

A black form hurled itself upon him. He saw the creature jump —a great hulk of fur—saw its distended jaws and horrid shape. One instant he stood appalled, then with a violent thrill he leaped aside. It was a bear, a lean, ravenous creature, not long from its winter den, and wild with hunger. As the bull jumped the bear shot by, missed its stroke, but by chance gashed a cow cruelly along the shoulder. She was a big one, an anomaly that boasted a small set of horns. Bawling with fear, she wheeled and fled, a flap of skin hanging from her shoulder, and blood streaming along the brown forest. Crashing forward with frantic jumps, the herd cleared the perilous neighborhood, and once free from the peril, dropped into their swinging trot, while from the rear came the bear's long-drawn howl of disappointment.

As they clattered along the back-trail fresh disaster awaited. Beyond the spur of the ridge, they crossed down toward the lake, and were clattering along the game trail at its edge, when the cows halted abruptly, spun about, and fled, the calves shambling at their heels. The bull stopped in wonder. He tried the air, and scented a strong pungent odor—saw a wisp of blue smoke crawling over the treetops, and, for the first time in his life, beheld a man. Cautiously he drew near, vainly trying for a scent. He saw the figure at the fire start up, and then a ripping crash thundered along the forest. The bull jumped. He did not know he had been fired on, and in mild curiosity skipped through the bush and circled the camp. There a sudden suspicion seized him; he plunged about, and in a long, swinging stride took away on the trail of the cows.

On the Bathurst carry he overtook them. The cows and calves were ambling along the open path, still nervous with vague terrors. They had escaped so far, but what was in store? The bull took his place at their head, resolved that peace and quiet must be sought far away from here. As they dipped down over the crest of the divide, and neared an abandoned beaver meadow, he swung out, mindful of his horns, from under a leaning tree trunk that had all the semblance of a windfall. But the cows kept straight on. Crash! The windfall fell thunderously, filling the silent forest with re-echoing noises. The bull leaped as if struck. Beneath the heavy tree lay the leading cow, her back broken, writhing in a last mortal effort. She had walked into the trap, sprung the trigger, and the deadfall had slain her, as its builders had devised. They were the poachers in camp on the lake—bear hunters—and this was their method of getting bait for bruin.

The bull circled about the dying cow, powerless to aid. He sniffed the air, and hung over his stricken mate, trotting to and fro with futile energy. A gust stirred the treetops, and whirling along the ridge, set down toward him. Snorting anew, he threw up his head and looked. He saw two figures running swiftly along the trail—saw them stoop and point forward, and once more the forest resounded with the rifle's deafening noise. The herd broke and ran in every direction, leaving him there alone. Once more there was a loud report, a gush of flame—the man had fired and missed again. But as the lead stirred the hair on the bull's shoulders, he shook himself together from this mad fascination and fled—away from the direful place and the cow heaving in a convulsion of death upon the forest floor.

The herd was gone, and he a wanderer alone. He followed to

the north, searching far and wide. He tried the unknown barrens under the flank of Bald Mountain, swept about the edge of the long ridges, and circled the headwaters of the Mamoziekel. But they were gone, he knew not where. Alone and weary, he kept up the days of weary pursuit, felt the summer slip by, and, with the first frosts, was touched, once more, with the rutting wrath.

They told in the settlements of a caribou bull—a mighty straggler from the herds, bigger than any man had ever seen before. He was using along the great range westward of Nictau, and twice, they knew, he had been fired upon. Once blood had been drawn, but the men on the trail were no match in speed or stamina for this solitary, and had given up the chase after weary miles, convinced that the wound was slight. His antlers were a marvel, they spread like the brown roots of a hemlock windfall, and down the center of his nose ran a brow-palm, as big and broad, almost, as the shovel of a moose. Vainly they sought for a nearer shot, but his craft foiled them. At the first suggestion of danger he was gone, vanishing like a specter.

Fear had taught its lesson to the big bull. He had renounced his first swaggering indifference, and now skulked and treaded as timorously as any creature on the range. He followed the wind keenly, and on the rising ridges looked over for possible foes before revealing himself. He no longer swam the ponds in daylight, and rarely moved except at night. But among the caribou he was still master. He fought from range to range, forever looking for the lost herd, but the snows came again, and he had not found it. Sometimes he forgot his terrors, and ran through the forest, pausing on the ridges to roar a challenge or a call. But it was of no avail, and, at last, in a sudden access of fury, he fell upon the leader of a passing herd, beat him down, and, victorious, thrust his companionship upon the cows.

Year after year he kept on. His rage was masterful. He harried and abused and drove from the hills the bulls that sought to withstand him. He rounded his cows about roughly, hectoring them at every turn. At the beginning of every rut he fell in a fury upon the spike-horn yearlings, and gored cruelly, driving them from the herd. Perhaps he was in mind of how he himself had come into power over his own sire. In this warfare he wandered far from the barren of the Mamoziekel, carrying dismay before him. Yet in his heart there was ever a longing, a desire to return and once more be with the lost herd, to go back to the place of his birth as every caribou goes.

Years passed and he grew old. His horns had increased in size and strength while his vigor held, but now that age was coming, he noted a difference. At last one autumn found him with diminished weapons. In the place of the center palm was only a spindly tine. Moreover, his antlers did not reach so far, nor were they so stout about the beams. Still he felt no relaxing of his ugly humors, no weakening of his might. He held his sway unchecked, and when other bulls came up against him, he forced the conflict to a swift and powerful climax.

His fear of men had become a second nature. He steered wide of ranges where he had heard the rifle speak doom to other caribou. Nor did he relax his vigilance, like the other bulls, when law forbids the shooting. He took no chances, and so survived. Then one day the fit to wander homeward fell upon him. He shacked to his feet, and roared. The cows arose, and, at the sound, another bull came challenging up the slope of the ridges. He was big, and the battle waxed furious. At its height still another bull, an interloper, stole in and drove away the cows. Thus, when the conflict ended, and the challenging bull had been driven crashing through the thickets, he again found himself alone. He stood for a while and called. But there was no answer, no clatter of the brush betokening their return. Darkness fell upon the forest, and turning his head southward, he sped away, homeward—back to the black headwaters of the Mamoziekel and the big barren that still lay unchanged, to the forest where axe never sounded nor rifle spoke. Hope sprung high in his heart—the lost herd would be found.

Into this wild came, the day after, a man. He had followed the long valley of the stream that runs into Nictau, setting a course along the ridges that back up the southern slope of Bald Mountain. He pushed out upon the barren, and halted, studying the tracks that marked the black ooze of the quagmire. Presently he stooped, with wide eyes studying one great track that punctuated the writing of trafficking herds. The slot was big and broad, more than a hand's-breadth across, and, with the twin dots of the accessory hoofs, almost as long. Rising with a gesture of eagerness, he sped along, studying the ground.

Overhead, a skim of dull vapor cast across the zenith, and the wind, moaning fitfully among the tall spires of the pines and spruce, betokened the approach of snow. Abruptly the man turned aside from the trail, plunged into the edge of the forest, and threw down his pack. Pushing aside the bush, he crouched there, his rifle ready.

In a thicket farther up the bog lay the big bull. Here in this retreat he was nursing the wounds of battle—stiff and sore and ugly.

A twig cracked on the hillside. His neck bristled, and he heaved himself to his feet. Across the open he saw a cow steal to the edge of the woods and peep forth. Another followed, then came a pair of skipping calves and two more cows, one a shoulder-scarred creature with small horns. A tremor seized him. He saw the familiar forms, the gray figures of old, the calves band-streaked across the withers—the lost herd! He pushed from the thicket, calling madly, and at the same moment another bull stepped into the open in the train of the advancing cows.

Across the shoulders of the newcomer was that same distinctive mark. His own memory went back to the day when this great, gallant creature was but a weakling come into the world in this same swamp. And now it had grown to this proud estate! Year after year it had clung to the herd. As a yearling it had been tolerated by the usurper who had found the stray herd when they lost their leader in the disaster of the trap. But with its second year and its first long spikes, it had been browbeaten, pushed, and driven about. Still it had kept by the same little family, returning in peace when the rut was past. Again in the third year it had fought and failed; but in the fourth it arose, mighty in strength, well armed and headed, and falling upon the bullying lord of the herd, drove him forth, stricken and cowed.

At a sharp trot the band moved down the wind. Forward stepped the old bull. His head was uplifted with its still mighty crest, and there was a new fire in his eye. He gazed at the cows and at their leader. He stretched his throat and called anew, and at the racketing call, they halted in their tracks.

The younger bull stopped, stamping. The hair on his neck ruffled; he spread his feet and bellowed a challenge. Who was this come to dispute his sway? His petulant hoof pawed the earth, and gutturally he gave the call of war.

The sound rang down the barren, stirring the man crouching in the thicket. At the challenge the old bull tossed his antlers. Before, he had never hesitated; but now he did not rush to battle. Old memories, perhaps, were in his mind, and in his heart peace. But the challenge was renewed; the other was advancing. With lowered head the younger bull stepped along, fire in his eyes. *Ruh-rr-r!* he roared—*ruh!*

They advanced, the old bull half temporizing. He called plaintively, but the other took no notice of the appeal. Nearer he came —nearer and nearer, and the man, crouching in the thicket, cocked his rifle, waiting.

A sudden scurry of hoofs beat upon the bog. With a frenzied effort the younger bull burst upon the other. The big one fell back, unwilling for combat, but once more the young one charged. Startled, the old bull recoiled again, and the younger, breaking through his guard, stabbed him on the flank.

A pang rang through the old caribou's nerves, and a roar escaped him. He forgot all; his wrath, his fear, perhaps, aroused. Once more the blood ran hotly through his veins, and he turned upon his antagonist, mad for the fight.

Their heads shocked together, and the forest threw back the sound in clattering echoes. The torn and trampled moss flew about and blood-streaked froth flecked their heaving shoulders. Again they lunged, the antlers locked—one striving for mastery; the other—knowing it—for life. Once the old bull was forced back upon his haunches, and was all but lost. By a mighty effort he writhed free and recovered. Then he whirled upon the other, and strove to beat down his crest. He was sublime, yet he failed—and terror choked him.

A flurry of snow sped across the bog, the first of the dying year. It wheeled across the landscape for an instant, blotting out the fray. The man, crouching in the thicket, drew a hand across his eyes, almost appalled at the fierceness of this strife. Slipping out upon the barren, he crawled toward them.

The younger bull drew on. With unabated strength he beat and battered at the swaying antlers of his adversary, and inch by inch drove him back. His rage was direful. The cows, trotting up and down the arena, called piteously; yet the strife went on. At last, with an overwhelming effort, the younger bull drove upon the other. He hunched his shoulders, struck with destroying force, and as the old bull staggered for an instant, half-reared, and turned aside, he struck still again, another mighty blow. Down went the old bull, a brow-tine piercing him to the vitals. He struggled once to his knees, turned with a despairing call to the cows, and died.

Back from the forest blew the wind, laden with a terrifying taint. One breath of it sent the cows streaming in every direction. But the conqueror gave no heed. He stood over the dead, lifted his crest, and gave the call. Blood and froth flecked his white mane; the steam spumed from his wide-pressed nostrils.

A moment's silence—then from down the bog streamed a spear of flame. The hills harked back with thundering echoes. Again a shot! High into the air leaped the conquering bull, and fell, kicking spasmodically, across the form of the other.

FRANK FORESTER

Warwick Woodlands

A hundred years ago the sportsman who concentrated on the woods and fields did not have a "rod and gun" writer to help— or hinder—his activities, and there were few periodicals dedicated to these sports. The writer who made the only real effort in this direction, and who gives us the only accurate picture of the hunting and fishing of that day, was Frank Forester. Prolific though they were, his writings were interesting and detailed. A friend of mine compared them, of all things, with beer, pointing out, "There are a thousand brands of beer, none of them bad. Some are just better than others. It's that way with Forester's stories. All of them are good but some are better than others." Forester saw no reason why he should suffer discomfort merely because he sought rather isolated areas for his sport. It is surprising how many modern sportsmen are reaching the same conclusion. At an Adirondack hunting cabin, a few years ago, the first night's dinner included green turtle soup, grilled lobster, English mutton chop and cherries jubilee. The spirit of Frank Forester still lives. So does the Warwick Woodlands, as a book; the actual terrain is somewhat different today.

Our last day's shooting in the vale of Sugar-loaf was over; and, something contrary to Harry's first intention, we had decided, instead of striking westward into Sullivan or Ulster, to drive five miles upon our homeward route, and beat the Long-pond mountain—not now for such small game as woodchuck, quail, or partridge; but for a herd of deer, which, although now but rarely found along the western hills, was said to have been seen already several times, to the number of six or seven head, in a small cove, or hollow basin, close to the summit of the Bellevale ridge.

As it was not, of course, our plan to return again to Tom Draw's, everything was now carefully and neatly packed away; the game, of which we had indeed a goodly stock, was produced from Tom's ice-house, where, suspended from the rafters, it had been kept as sound and fresh as though it had been all killed only on the preceding day.

A long deep box, fitting beneath the gun-case under the front seat, was now produced, and proved to be another of Harry's notable inventions; for it was lined throughout, lid, bottom, sides and all, with zinc, and in the centre had a well or small compartment of the same material, with a raised grating in the bottom. This well was forthwith lined with a square yard, or rather more, of flannel, into which was heaped a quantity of ice pounded as fine as possible, sufficient to cram it absolutely to the top; the rest of the box was then filled with the birds, displayed in regular rows, with heads and tails alternating, and a thin coat of clean dry wheaten straw between each layer, until but a few inches' depth remained between the noble pile and the lid of this extempore refrigerator; this space being filled in with flannel packed close and folded tightly, the box was locked and thrust into the accurately fitting boot by dint of the exertion of Timothy's whole strength.

"There, Frank," cried Harry, who had superintended the storage of the whole with nice scrutiny, "those chaps will keep there as sound as roaches, till we get to young Tom's at Ramapo; you cannot think what work I had, trying in vain to save them, before I hit upon this method; I tried hops, which I have known in England to keep birds in an extraordinary manner—for, what you'll scarce believe, I once ate a Ptarmigan, the day year after it was killed, which had been packed with hops, in perfect preservation, at Farnley, Mr. Fawke's place in Yorkshire!—and I tried prepared charcoal, and got my woodcock down to New York, looking like chimney sweeps, and smelling——"

"What the devil difference does it make to you now, Archer, I'd be pleased to know!" interposed Tom; "what under heaven they smells like—a man that eats cock with their guts in, like you does, needn't stick now, I reckon, for a leetle mite of a stink!"

"Shut up, you old villain," answered Harry, laughing. "Bring the milk punch, and get your great coat on, if you mean to go with us; for it's quite keen this morning, I can tell you; and we must be stirring too, for the sun will be up before we get to Teachman's. Now, Jem, get out the hounds; how do you take them, Tom?"

"Why, that darned Injun, Jem, he'll take them in my lumber wagon—and, I say, Jem, see that you don't over-drive old roan—away with you, and rouse up Garry, he means to go, I guess!"

After a mighty round of punch, in which as we were now departing, one half at least of the village joined, we all got under way; Tom, buttoned up to the throat in a huge white lion skin wraprascal, looking for all the world like a polar bear erect on its hind legs; and all of us muffled up pretty snugly, a proceeding which was rendered necessary by a brisk bracing northwest breeze.

The sky, though it was scarcely the first twilight of an autumnal dawn, was beautifully clear, and as transparent—though still somewhat dusky—as a wide sheet of crystal; a few pale stars were twinkling here and there; but in the east a broad gray streak, changing on the horizon's edge to a faint straw color, announced the sun's approach.

The whole face of the country, hill, vale, and woodland, was overspread by a universal coat of silvery hoar-frost; thin wreaths of snowy mist rising above the tops of the sere woodlands, throughout the whole length of the lovely vale, indicated as clearly as though it were traced on a map the direction of the stream that watered it; and as we paused upon the brow of the first hillock, and looked back toward the village, with its white steeples and neat cottage dwellings buried in the still repose of that early hour, with only one or two faint columns of blue smoke worming their way up lazily into the cloudless atmosphere, a feeling of regret—such as has often crossed my mind before, when leaving any place wherein I have spent a few days happily, and which I never may see more—rendered me somewhat indisposed to talk.

Something or other—it might with Harry, perhaps, have been a similar train of thought—caused both my comrades to be more taciturn by far than was their wont; and we had rattled over five miles of our route, and scaled the first ridge of the hills, and dived into the wide ravine; midway the depth of this the pretty village of Bellevale lies on the brink of the dammed rivulet, which, a few yards below the neat stone bridge, takes a precipitous leap of fifty feet, over a rustic wier, and rushes onward, bounding from ledge to ledge of rifted rocks, chafing and fretting as if it were doing a match against time, and were in danger of losing its race.

Thus we had passed the heavy lumber wagon, with Jem and Garry perched on a board laid across it, and the four couple of stanch hounds nestling in the straw which Tom had provided in abundance for their comfort, before the silence was broken by any sounds except the rattle of the wheels, the occasional interjectional whistle of Harry to his horses, or the flip of the well handled whip.

Just, however, as we were shooting ahead of the lumber wain, an exclamation from Tom Draw, which should have been a sentence, had it not been very abruptly terminated in a long rattling eructation, arrested Archer's progress.

Pulling short up where a jog across the road, constructed—after the damnable mode adopted in all the hilly portions of the interior —in order to prevent the heavy rains from channelling the descent, afforded him a chance of stopping on the hill, so as to slack his traces. "How now," he exclaimed; "what the deuce ails you now, you old rhinocerous?"

"Oh, Archer, I feels bad; worst sort, by Judas! It's that milk punch, I reckon; it keeps a raising—raising all the time like——"

"And you want to lay it, I suppose, like a ghost, in a sea of whiskey; well, I've no especial objection! Here, Tim, hand the case bottle, and the dram cup! No! no! confound you, pass it this way first, for if Tom once gets hold of it, we may say good-bye to it altogether. There," he continued, after we had both taken a moderate sip at the superb old Ferintosh, "there, now take your chance at it, and for Heaven's sake do leave a drop for Jem and Garry; by George now, you *shall not* drink it *all!*" as Tom poured down the third cup-full, each being as big as an ordinary beer-glass. "There was above a pint and a half in it when you began, and now there's barely one cup-full between the two of them. An't you ashamed of yourself now, you greedy old devil?"

"It doos go right, I swon!" was the only reply that could be got out of him.

"That's more a plaguy sight than the bullets will do, out of your old tower musket; you're so drunk now, I fancy, that you couldn't hold it straight enough to hit a deer at three rods, let alone thirty, which you are so fond of chattering about."

"Do tell now," replied Tom, "did you, or any other feller, ever see me shoot the worser for a mite of liquor, and as for deer, that's all a no sich thing; there arnt no deer a this side of Duck-seedar's. It's all a lie of Teachman's and that Deckering son of a gun."

"Holloa! hold up, Tom—recollect yesterday!—I thought there had been no cock down by the first bridge there, these six years; why you're getting quite stupid, and a croaker too, in your old age."

"Mayhap I be," he answered rather gruffly; "maybe I be, but you won't git no deer to-day, I'll stand drinks for the company; and if we doos start one, I'll lay on my own musket agin your rifle."

"Well! we'll soon see, for here we are," Harry replied, as after leaving the high-road just at the summit of the Bellevale mountain, he rattled down a very broken rutty bye-road at the rate of at least eight miles an hour, vastly to the discomfiture of our fat host, whose fleshy sides were jolted almost out of their skin by the concussion of the wheels against the many stones and jogs which opposed their progress.

"Here we are, or at least soon will be. It is but a short half mile through these woods to Teachman's cottage. Is there a gun loaded, Tim? It's ten to one we shall have a partridge fluttering up and treeing here directly; I'll let the dogs out—get away, Flash! get away, Dan! you little rascals. Jump out, good dogs, Shot, Chase— hie up with you!" and out they went rattling and scrambling through the brushwood all four abreast!

At the same moment Tim, leaning over into the body of the wagon, lugged out a brace of guns from their leathern cases; Harry's short ounce ball rifle, and the long single-barrelled duck gun.

" 'T roifle is loaden wi' a single ball, and 't single goon wi' yan of them green cartridges!"

"Much good ball and buck-shot will do us against partridge; nevertheless, if one trees, I'll try if I can't cut his head off for him," said Archer, laughing.

"Nay! nay! it be-ant book-shot; it's no but noomber three; tak' haud on't, Measter Draa, tak' haud on't. It's no hoort thee, mon, and 't horses boath stand foire cannily!'

Scarce had fat Tom obeyed his imperative solicitations, and scarce had Tim taken hold of the ribbands which Harry relinquished the moment he got the rifle into his hands, before a most extraordinary hubbub arose in the little skirt of coppice to our left; the spaniels quested for a second's space at the utmost, when a tremendous crash of the branches arose, and both the setters gave tongue furiously with a quick savage yell.

The road at this point of the wood made a short and very sudden angle, so as to enclose a small point of extremely dense thicket between its two branches; on one of these was our wagon, and down the other the lumber-wain was rumbling, at the moment when this strange and most unexpected outcry started us all.

"What in t' fient's neam is yon?" cried Timothy.

"And what the devil's that?" responded I and Archer in a breath.

But whatever it was that had aroused the dogs to such a most unusual pitch of fury, it went crashing through the brushwood for some five or six strokes at a fearful rate toward the other wagon; before, however, it had reached the road, a most appalling shout from Jem, followed upon the instant by the blended voices of all the hounds opening at once, as on a view, excited us yet farther!

I was still tugging at my double gun, in the vain hope of getting it out time enough for action. Tom had scrambled out of the wagon on the first alarm, and stood eye, ear, and heart erect, by the off side of the horses, which were very restless, pawing, and plunging violently, and almost defying Timothy's best skill to hold them; while Harry, having cast off his box-coat, stood firm and upright on the foot board as a carved statue, with his rifle cocked and ready; when, headed back upon us by the yell of Lyn and the loud clamor of his fresh foes, the first buck I had seen in America, and the largest I had seen anywhere, dashed at a single plunge into the round, clearing the green head of a fallen hemlock, apparently without an effort, his splendid antlers laid back on his neck, and his white flag lashing his fair round haunch as the fleet bitches Bonny Belle and Blossom yelled with their shrill fierce trebles close behind him.

Seeing that it was useless to persist in my endeavor to extricate my gun, and satisfied that the matter was in good hands, I was content to look on, an inactive but most eager witness.

Tom, who from his position at the head of the off horse, commanded the first view of the splendid creature, pitched his gun to his shoulder hastily and fired; the smoke drifted across my face, but through its vapory folds I could distinguish the dim figure of the noble hart still bounding unhurt onward; but, before the first echo of the round ringing report of Tom's shot-gun reached my ear, the sharp flat crack of Harry's rifle followed it, and at the self-same instant the buck sprang six feet into the air, and pitched head foremost on the ground; it was but for a moment, however, for with the speed of light he struggled to his feet, and though sore wounded, was yet toiling onward when the two English foxhounds dashed at his throat and pulled him down again.

"Run in, Tom, run in! quick," shouted Harry, "he's not clean killed, and may gore the dogs sadly!"

"I've got no knife," responded Tom, but dauntlessly he dashed in, all the same, to the rescue of the bitches—which I believe he loved almost as well as his own children—and though, encumbered by his ponderous white top-coat, not to say by his two hundred and fifty weight of solid flesh, seized the fierce animal by the brow-antlers, and bore him to the ground, before Harry, who had leaped out of the wagon, with his first words, could reach him.

The next moment the keen short hunting knife, without which Archer never takes the field, had severed at a single stroke the weasand of the gallant brute; the black blood streamed out on the smoking hoar-frost, the full eyes glazed, and, after one sharp flutter-ing struggle, the life departed from those graceful limbs, which had been but a few short instants previous so full of glorious energy—of fiery vigor.

"Well, that's the strangest thing I ever heard of, let alone see-ing," exclaimed Archer, "fancy a buck like that lying in such a mere fringe of coppice, and so near to the road-side, too! and why the deuce did he lay here till we almost passed him!"

"I know it's been, any heaw," said Jem, who had by this time come up, and was looking on with much exultation flashing in his keen small eye. "Bill Speer up on the hill there told me jist now, that they druv a big deer down from the back-bone clear down to this here hollow just above, last night arter dark. Bill shot at him, and kind o' reckoned he hot him—but I guess he's mistaken—leastwise he jumped strong enough jist neaw!—but which on you was 't 'at killed him?"

"I did," exclaimed Tom, "I did by——!"

"Why you most impudent of all old liars," replied Harry—while at the same time, with a most prodigious chuckle, Tim Matlock pointed to the white bark of a birch sapling, about the thickness of a man's thigh, standing at somewhat less than fifteen paces' dis-tance, wherein the large shot contained by the wire cartridge—the best sporting invention by the way, that has been made since per-cussion caps—had bedded themselves in a black circle, cut an inch at least into the solid wood, and about two inches in diameter!

"I ken gay and fairly," exclaimed Tim, " 'at Ay rammed an Eley's patent cartridge into 't single goon this morning; and yonder is 't i' t' birk tree, and Ay ken a load o' shot fra an unce bullet!"

The laugh was general now against fat Tom; especially as the small wound made by the heavy ball of Harry's rifle was plainly visible, about a hand's breadth behind the heart, on the side toward which he had aimed; while the lead had passed directly through, in an oblique direction forward, breaking the left shoul-der blade, and lodging just beneath the skin, whence a touch of the knife dislodged it.

"What now—what now, boys?" cried the old sinner, no whit disconcerted by the general mirth against him. "I say, by gin! I killed him, and I say so yet. Which on ye all—which on ye all daared to go in on him, wishout a knife nor nothen. I killed him, I say, anyhow, and so let's drink!"

"Well, I believe we must wet him," Harry answered, "so get out another flask of whiskey, Tim; and you Jem and Garry lend me a hand to lift this fine chap into the wagon. By Jove! but this will make the Teachmans open their eyes; and now look sharp! You sent the Teachmans word that we were coming, Tom?"

"Sartin! and they've got breakfast ready long enough before this, anyways."

With no more of delay, but with lots more of merriment and shouting, on we drove; and in five minutes' space, just as the sun was rising, reached the small rude enclosure around two or three log huts, lying just on the verge of the beautiful clear lake. Two long sharp boats, and a canoe scooped out of a whole tree, were drawn up on the sandy beach; a fishing net of many yards in length was drying on the rails; a brace of large, strong, black and tan foxhounds were lying on the step before the door; a dozen mongrel geese, with one wing-tipped wild one among them, were sauntering and gabbling about the narrow yard; and a glorious white-headed fishing eagle, with a clipped wing, but otherwise at large, was perched upon the roof hard by the chimney.

At the rattle of our arrival, out came from the larger of the cottages, three tall rough-looking countrymen to greet us, not one of whom stood less than six foot in his stockings, while two were several inches taller.

Great was their wonder, and loud were their congratulations when they beheld the unexpected prize which we had gained, while on our route; but little space was given at that time to either; for the coffee, which, by the way, was poor enough, and the hot cakes and fried perch. which were capital, and the grilled salt pork, swimming in fat, and the large mealy potatoes bursting through their brown skins, were ready smoking upon a rough wooden board, covered, however, by a clean white table cloth, beside a sparkling fire of wood, which our drive through the brisk mountain air had rendered by no means unacceptable.

We breakfasted like hungry men and hunters, both rapidly and well; and before half an hour elapsed, Archer, with Jem and one of our bold hosts, started away, well provided with powder and ball, and whiskey, and accompanied by all the hounds, to make a

circuit of the western hill, on the summit of which they expected
to be joined by two or three more of the neighbors, whence they
proposed to drive the whole sweep of the forest-clad descent down
to the water's edge.

Tim was enjoined to see to the provisions, and to provide as
good a dinner as his best gastronomic skill and the contents of our
portable larder might afford, and I was put under the charge of
Tom, who seemed, for about an hour, disposed to do nothing but
to lie dozing, with a cigar in his mouth, stretched upon the broad
of his back, on a bank facing the early sunshine just without the
door; while our hosts were collecting bait, preparing fishing tackle,
and cleaning or repairing their huge clumsy muskets. At length,
when the drivers had been gone already for considerably more
than an hour, he got up and shook himself.

"Now, then, boys," he exclaimed, "we'll be a-movin'. You Joe
Teachman, what are you lazin' there about, cuss you? You go with
Mr. Forester and Garry in the big boat, and pull as fast as you can
put your oars to water, till you git opposite the white-stone pint—
and there lie still as fishes! You may fish, though, if you will,
Forester," he added, turning to me, "and I do reckon the big
yellow pearch *will* bite the darndest, this cold morning, arter
the sun gits fairly up—but soon as ever you hear the hounds
holler, or one of them chaps shoot, then look you out right stret
away for business! Cale here and I'll take the small boat, and keep
in sight of you; and so we can kiver all this eend of the pond like,
if the deer tries to cross hereaways. How long is't, Cale, since we
had six on them all at once in the water—six—seven—eight! well,
I swon, it's ten years agone now! But come, we mustn't stand here
talkin', else we'll get a dammin' when they drives down a buck into
the pond, and none of us in there to tackle with him!"

So without more ado, we got into our boats, disposed our guns,
with the stocks toward us in the bows, laid in our stock of tinder,
pipes, and liquor, and rowed off merrily to our appointed stations.

Never, in the whole course of my life, has it been my fortune to
look upon more lovely scenery than I beheld that morning. The
long narrow winding lake, lying as pure as crystal beneath the
liquid skies, reflecting, with the correctness of the most perfect
mirror, the abrupt and broken hills, which sank down so precipi-
tously into it—clad as they were in foliage of every gorgeous dye,
with which the autumn of America loves to enhance the beauty of
her forest pictures—that, could they find their way into its moun-
tain-girdled basin, ships of large burthen might lie afloat within

a stone's throw of the shore—the slopes of the wood-covered knolls, here brown, or golden, and interspersed with the rich crimson of the faded maples, there verdant with the evergreen leaves of the pine and cedar—and the far azure summits of the most distant peaks, all steeped in the serene and glowing sunshine of an October morning.

For hours we lay there, our little vessel floating as the occasional breath of a sudden breeze, curling the lake into sparkling wavelets, chose to direct our course, smoking our cigars, and chatting cozily, and now and then pulling up a great broad-backed yellow bass, whose flapping would for a time disturb the peaceful silence, which reigned over wood, and dale, and water, quite unbroken save by the chance clamor of a passing crow: yet not a sound betokening the approach of our drivers had reached our ears.

Suddenly, when the sun had long passed his meridian height, and was declining rapidly toward the horizon, the full round shot of a musket rang from the mountain top, followed immediately by a sharp yell, and in an instant the whole basin of the lake was filled with the harmonious discord of the hounds.

I could distinguish on the moment the clear sharp challenge of Harry's high-bred foxhounds, the deep bass voices of the Southern dogs, and the untamable and cur-like yelping of the dogs which the Teachmans had taken with them.

Ten minutes passed full of anxiety, almost of fear.

We knew not as yet whither to turn our boats' head, for every second the course of the hounds seemed to vary, at one instant they would appear to be rushing directly down to us, and the next instant they would turn as though they were going up the hill again. Meantime our beaters were not idle—their stirring shouts, serving alike to animate the hounds, and to force the deer to water, made rock and wood reply in cheery echoes; but to my wonder, I caught not for a long time one note of Harry's gladsome voice.

At length, as I strained my eyes against the broad hill-side, gilt by the rays of the declining sun, I caught a glimpse of his form running at a tremendous pace, bounding over stock and stone, and plunging through dense thickets, on a portion of the declivity where the tall trees had a few years before been destroyed by accidental fire.

At this moment the hounds were running, to judge from their tongues, parallel to the lake and to the line which he was running —the next minute, with a redoubled clamor, they turned directly down to him. I lost sight of him. But half a minute afterward, the sharp crack of his rifle again rang upon the air, followed by a triumphant "Whoop! who-whoop!" and then I knew another stag had fallen.

The beaters on the hill shouted again louder and louder than before—and the hounds still raved on. By heaven! but there must be a herd of them a-foot! And now the pack divides! The English hounds are bringing their game down—here—by the Lord! just here—right in our very faces! The Southrons have borne away over the shoulder of the hill, still running hot and hard in Jolly Tom's direction.

"By heaven!" I cried, "look, Teachman! Garry, look! There! See you not that noble buck? He leaped that sumach bush like a race-horse! and see! see! now he will take the water. Bad luck on it! he sees us, and heads back!"

Again the fleet hounds rally in his rear, and chide till earth and air are vocal and harmonious. Hark! hark! how Archer's cheers ring on the wind! Now he turns once again—he nears the edge— how glorious! with what a beautiful bold bound he leaped from that high bluff into the flashing wave! with what a majesty he tossed his antlered head above the spray! with how magnificent and brave a stroke he breasts the curling billows!

"Give way! my men, give way!"

How the frail bark creaks and groans as we ply the long oars in the rullocks—how the ash bends in our sturdy grasp—how the boat springs beneath their impulse.

"Together, boys! together! now—now we gain—now, Garry, lay your oar aside—up with your musket—now you are near enough—give it to him, in heaven's name! a good shot, too! the bullet ricochetted from the lake scarcely six inches from his nose! Give way again—it's my shot now!"

And lifting my Joe Manton, each barrel loaded with a bullet carefully wadded with greased buckskin, I took a careful aim and fired.

"That's it," cried Garry; "well done, Forester—right through the head, by George!"

And, as he spoke, I fancied for a moment he was right. The noble buck plunged half his height out of the bright blue water, shaking his head as if in the death agony, but the next instant he stretched out again with vigor unimpaired, and I could see that my ball had only knocked a tine off his left antler.

My second barrel still remained, and without lowering the gun, I drew my second trigger. Again a fierce plunge told that the ball had not erred widely; and this time, when he again sank into his wonted posture, the deep crimson dye that tinged the foam which curled about his graceful neck, as he still struggled, feebly fleet, before his unrelenting foes, gave token of a deadly wound.

Six more strokes of the bending oars—we shot alongside—a noose of rope was cast across his branching tines, the keen knife flashed across his throat, and all was over! We towed him to the shore, where Harry and his comrades were awaiting us with another victim to his unerring aim. We took both bucks and all hands on board, pulled stoutly homeward, and found Tom lamenting.

Two deer, a buck of the first head, and a doe, had taken water close beside him—he had missed his first shot, and in toiling overhard to recover lost ground, had broken his oar, and been compelled inactively to witness their escape.

Three fat bucks made the total of the day's sport—not one of which had fallen to Tom's boasted musket.

It needed all that Tim's best dinner, with lots of champagne and Ferintosh, could do to restore the fat chap's equanimity; but he at last consoled himself, as we threw ourselves on the lowly beds of the log hut, by swearing that by the eternal devil he'd beat us both at partridges to-morrow.

The sun rose broad and bright in a firmament of that most brilliant and transparent blue, which I have witnessed in no other country than America, so pure, so cloudless, so immeasurably distant as it seems from the beholder's eye! There was not a speck of cloud from east to west, from zenith to horizon; not a fleece of vapor on the mountain sides; not a breath of air to ruffle the calm basin of the Greenwood lake.

The rock-crowned, forest-mantled ridge, on the farther side of the narrow sheet, was visible almost as distinctly through the medium of the pure fresh atmosphere, as though it had been gazed at through a telescope—the hues of the innumerable maples, in their various stages of decay, purple, and crimson, and bright gorgeous scarlet, were contrasted with the rich chrome yellow of the birch and poplars, the sere red leaves of the gigantic oaks, and with the ever verdant plumage of the junipers, clustered in massy patches on every rocky promontory, and the tall spires of the dark pines and hemlock.

Over this mass of many-colored foliage, the pale thin yellow light of the new-risen sun was pouring down a flood of chaste illumination; while, exhaled from the waters by his first beams, a silvery gauze-like haze floated along the shores, not rising to the height of ten feet from the limpid surface, which lay unbroken by the smallest ripple, undisturbed by the slightest splash of fish or insect, as still and tranquil to the eye as though it had been one huge plate of beaten burnished silver; with the tall cones of the gorgeous hills in all their rich variety, in all their clear minuteness, reflected, summit downward, palpable as their reality, in that most perfect mirror.

Such was the scene on which I gazed, as on the last day of our sojourn in the Woodlands of fair Orange, I issued from the little cabin, under the roof of which I had slept so dreamlessly and deep, after the fierce excitement of our deer hunt, that while I was yet slumbering, all save myself had risen, donned their accoutrements, and sallied forth, I knew not whither, leaving me certainly alone, although as certainly not so much to my glory.

From the other cottage, as I stood upon the threshold, I might hear the voices of the females, busy at their culinary labors, the speedily approaching term of which was obviously denoted by the rich savory steams which tainted—not, I confess, unpleasantly—the fragrant morning air.

As I looked out upon this lovely morning, I did not, I acknowledge it, regret the absence of my excellent though boisterous companions; for there was something which I cannot define in the deep stillness, in the sweet harmonious quiet of the whole scene before me, that disposed my spirit to meditation far more than to mirth; the very smoke which rose from the low chimneys of the Teachmans' colony—not surging to and fro, obedient to the fickle winds—but soaring straight, tall, unbroken, upward, like Corinthian columns, each with its curled capital—seemed to invite the soul of the spectator to mount with it toward the sunny heavens.

By-and-by I strayed downward to the beach, a narrow strip of silvery sand and variegated pebbles, and stood there long, silently watching the unknown sports, the seemingly—to us at least—unmeaning movements, and strange groupings of the small fry, which darted to and fro in the clear shallows within two yards of my feet; or marking the brief circling ripples, wrought by the morning swallow's wing, and momently subsiding into the wonted rest of the calm lake.

How long I stood there musing I know not, for I had fallen into a train of thought so deep that I was utterly unconscious of everything around me, when I was suddenly aroused from my reverie by the quick dash of oars, and by a volley of some seven barrels discharged in quick succession. As I looked up with an air, I presume somewhat bewildered, I heard the loud and bellowing laugh of Tom, and saw the whole of our stout company gliding up in two boats, the skiff and the canoe, toward the landing place, perhaps a hundred yards from the spot where I stood.

"Come here, darn you," were the first words I heard, from the mouth of what speaker it need not be said—"come here, you lazy, snortin, snoozin Decker—lend a hand here right stret away, will you? We've got more perch than all of us can carry—and Archer's got six wood-duck."

Hurrying down in obedience to this unceremonious mandate, I perceived that indeed their time had not been misemployed, for the whole bottom of the larger boat was heaped with fish—the small and delicate green perch, the cat-fish, hideous in its natural, but most delicious in its artificial shape, and, above all, the large and broad-backed yellow bass, from two to four pounds weight. While Archer, who had gone forth with Garry only in the canoe, had picked up half a dozen wood-duck, two or three of the large yellow-legs, a little bittern, known by a far less elegant appellative throughout the country, and thirteen English snipe.

"By Jove!" cried I, "but this is something like—where the deuce did you pick the snipe up, Harry—and, above all, why the deuce did you let me lie wallowing in bed this lovely morning?"

"One question at a time," responded he, "good Master Frank; one question at a time. For the snipe, I found them very unexpectedly, I tell you, in a bit of marshy meadow just at the outlet of the pond. Garry was paddling me along at the top of his pace, after a wing-tipped wood-duck, when up jumped one of the long-billed rascals, and had the impudence to skim across the creek under my very nose—'skeap! skeap!' Well, I dropped him, you may be sure, with a charge, too, of duck shot; and he fell some ten yards over on the meadow; so leaving Garry to pursue the drake, I landed, loaded my gun with No. 9, and went to work—the result as you see; but I cleared the meadow—devil a bird is left there, except one I cut to pieces, and could not find for want of Chase—two went away without a shot, over the hills and far away. As for letting you lie in bed, you must talk to Tom about it; I bid him call you, and the fat rascal never did so, and never said a word about you, till we were ready for a start, and then no Master Frank was to the fore."

"Well, Tom," cried I, "what have you got to say to this?"

"Now, cuss you, don't come foolin' about me," replied that worthy, aiming a blow at me, which, had it taken place, might well have felled Goliah; but which, as I sprang aside, wasting its energies on the impassive air, had well nigh floored the striker. "Don't you come foolin' about me—you knows right well I called you, and you knows, too, you almost cried, and told me to clear out, and let you git an hour's sleep; for by the Lord you thought Archer and I was made of steel!—you couldn't and you wouldn't—and now you wants to know the reason why you warn't along with us!"

"Never mind the old thief, Frank," said Archer, seeing that I was on the point of answering, "even his own aunt says he is the most notorious liar in all Orange county—and Heaven forbid we should gainsay that most respectable old lady!"

Into what violent asseveration our host would have plunged at this declaration, remains, like the tale of Cambuscan bold, veiled in deep mystery; for as he started from the log on which he had been reposing while in the act of unsplicing his bamboo fishing pole, the elder of the Teachmans thrust his head out of the cabin nearest to us—"Come, boys, to breakfast!"—and at the first word of his welcome voice, Tom made, as he would have himself defined it, stret tracks for the table. And a mighty different table it was from that to which we had sat down on the preceding morning. Timothy—unscared by the wonder of the mountain nymphs, who deemed a being of the masculine gender as an intruder, scarce to be tolerated, on the mysteries of the culinary art—had exerted his whole skill, and brought forth all the contents of his canteen! We had a superb steak of the fattest venison, graced by cranberries stewed with cayenne pepper, and sliced lemons. A pot of excellent black tea, almost as strong as the cognac which flanked it; a dish of beautiful fried perch, with cream as thick as porridge, our own loaf sugar, and Teachman's new laid eggs, hot wheaten cakes, and hissing rashers of right tender pork, furnished a breakfast forth that might have vied successfully with those which called forth, in the Hebrides, such raptures from the lexicographer.

Breakfast despatched—for which, to say the truth, Harry gave us but little time—we mustered our array and started; Harry and Tom and I making one party, with the spaniels—Garry, the Teachmans, and Timothy, with the setters, which would hunt very willingly for him in Archer's absence, forming a second. It was scarce eight o'clock when we went out, each on a separate beat, having arranged our routes so as to meet at one o'clock in the great swamp, said to abound, beyond all other places, in the ruffed grouse or partridge, to the pursuit of which especially we had devoted our last day.

"Now, Frank," said Harry, "you have done right well throughout the week; and if you can stand this day's tramp, I will say for you that you are a sportsman, aye, every inch of one. We have got seven miles right hard walking over the roughest hills you ever saw—the hardest moors of Yorkshire are nothing to them—before we reach the swamp, and that you'll find a settler! Tom, here, will keep along the bottoms, working his way as best he can; while we make good the uplands! Are your flasks full?"

"Sartain, they are!" cried Tom—"and I've got a rousin big black bottle, too—but not a drop of the old cider sperrits do you git this day, boys; not if your thirsty throats were cracking for it!"

"Well, well! we won't bother you—you'll need it all, old porpoise, before you get to the far end. Here, take a hard boiled egg or two, Frank, and some salt, and I'll pocket a few biscuits—we must depend on ourselves to-day."

"Ay, ay, Sur," chuckled Timothy, "there's naw Tim Matlock to mak looncheon ready for ye 'a the day. See thee, measter Frank. Ay'se gotten 't measter's single barrel; and gin I dunna ootshoot measter Draa—whoy Ay'se deny my coontry!"

"Most certainly you will deny it then, Tim," answered I, "for Mr. Draw shoots excellently well, and you——"

"And Ay'se shot mony a hare by 't braw moon, doon i' bonny Cawoods. Ay'se beat, Ay'se oophaud * it!" So saying, he shouldered the long single barrel, and paddled off with the most extraordinary expedition after the Teachmans, who had already started, leading the setters in a leash, till they were out of sight of Archer.

"They have the longest way to go," said Harry, "by a mile at the least; so we have time for a cheroot before we three get under way."

Cigars were instantly produced and lighted, and we lounged about the little court for the best part of half an hour, till the report of a distant gunshot, ringing with almost innumerable reverberations along the woodland shores, announced to us that our companions had already got into their work.

"Here goes," cried Harry, springing to his feet at once, and grasping his good gun; "here goes—they have got into the long hollow, Tom, and by the time we've crossed the ridge, and got upon our ground, they'll be abreast of us."

* Oophaud, Yorkshire. Anglice, uphold.

"Hold on! hold on!" Tom bellowed, "you are the darndest critter, when you do git goin—now hold on, do—I wants some rum, and Forester here looks a kind of white about the gills, his what-d'ye-call, *cheeroot*, has made him sick, I reckon!"

Of course, with such an exhortation in our ears as this, it was impossible to do otherwise than wet our whistles with one drop of the old Ferintosh; and then, Tom having once again recovered his good humor, away we went, and "clombe the high hill," though we "swam not the deep river," as merrily as ever sportsman did, from the days of Arbalast and Longbow, down to these times of Westley Richards' caps and Eley's wire cartridges.

A tramp of fifteen minutes through some scrubby brushwood, brought us to the base of a steep stony ridge covered with tall and thrifty hickories and a few oaks and maples intermixed, rising so steeply from the shore that it was necessary not only to strain every nerve of the leg, but to swing our bodies up from tree to tree, by dint of hand. It was indeed a hard and heavy tug; and I had pretty tough work, what between the exertion of the ascent, and the incessant fits of laughter into which I was thrown by the grotesquely agile movements of fat Tom; who, grunting, panting, sputtering, and launching forth from time to time the strangest and most blasphemously horrid oaths, contrived to make way to the summit faster than either of us—crashing through the dense underwood of juniper and sumach, uprooting the oak saplings as he swung from this to that, and spurning down huge stones upon us, as we followed at a cautious distance. When we at last crowned the ridge, we found him, just as Harry had predicted, stretched in a half-recumbent attitude, leaning against a huge gray stone, with his fur cap and double-barrel lying upon the withered leaves beside him, puffing, as Archer told him, to his mighty indignation, like a great grampus in shoal water.

After a little rest, however, Falstaff revived, though not before he had imbibed about a pint of applejack, an occupation in which he could not persuade either of us, this time, to join him. Descending from our elevated perch, we now got into a deep glen, with a small brooklet winding along the bottom, bordered on either hand by a stripe of marshy bog earth, bearing a low growth of alder bushes, mixed with stunted willows. On the side opposite to that by which we had descended, the hill rose long and lofty, covered with mighty timber-trees standing in open ranks and overshadowing a rugged and unequal surface, covered with whortleberry, wintergreen, and cranberries, the latter growing only along the course of the little runnels, which channelled the whole slope. Here, stony ledges and gray broken crags peered through the underwood, among the crevices of which the stunted cedars stood thick set, and matted with a thousand creeping vines and brambles; while there, from some small marshy basin, the giant Rhododendron Maximum rose almost to the height of a timber tree.

"Here, Tom," said Harry, "keep you along this run—you'll have a woodcock every here and there, and look sharp when you hear them fire over the ridge, for they can't shoot to speak of, and the ruffed grouse will cross—you know. You, master Frank, stretch your long legs and get three parts of the way up this hill—over the second mound—there, do you see that great blue stone with a thunder-splintered tree beside it? Just beyond that! then turn due west, and mark the trending of the valley, keeping a little way ahead of me, which you will find quite easy, for I shall have to beat across you both. Go very slow, Tom—now, hurrah!"

Exhorted thus, I bounded up the hill and soon reached my appointed station; but not before I heard the cheery voice of Archer encouraging the eager spaniels—"Hie cock! hie cock! pu-r-rh!"—till the woods rang to the clear shout.

Scarce had I reached the top, before, as I looked down into the glen below me, a puff of white smoke, instantly succeeded by a second, and the loud full reports of both his barrels from among the green-leafed alders, showed me that Tom had sprung game. The next second I heard the sharp questing of the spaniel Dan, followed by Harry's "Charge!—down cha-arge, you little thief— down to cha-arge, will you!"

But it was all in vain—for on he went furious and fast, and the next moment the thick whirring of a grouse reached my excited ears. Carefully, eagerly, I gazed out to mark the wary bird; but the discharge of Harry's piece assured me, as I thought, that further watch was needless; and stupidly enough I dropped the muzzle of my gun.

Just at the self-same point of time—"Mark! mark, Frank!" shouted Archer, "mark! there are a brace of them!"—and as he spoke, gliding with speed scarcely inferior to a bullet's flight upon their balanced pinions, the noble birds swept past me, so close that I could have struck them with a riding whip.

Awfully fluttered was I—I confess—but by a species of involuntary and instinctive consideration I rallied instantly, and became cool. The grouse had seen me, and wheeled diverse; one darting to the right, through a small opening between a cedar bush and a tall hemlock—the other skimming through the open oak woods a little toward the left.

At such a crisis thought comes in a second's space; and I have often fancied that in times of emergency or great surprise, a man deliberates more promptly, and more prudently withal, than when he has full time to let his second thought trench on his first and mar it. So was it in this case with me. At half a glance I saw that if I meant to get both birds, the right-hand fugitive must be the first, and that with all due speed; for but a few yards further he would have gained a brake which would have laughed to scorn Lord Kennedy or Harry T——r.

Pitching my gun up to my shoulder, both barrels loaded with Eley's red wire cartridge No. 6, I gave him a snap shot and had the satisfaction of seeing him keeled well over, not wing-tipped or leg-broken, but fairly riddled by the concentrated charge of something within thirty yards. Turning as quick as light, I caught a fleet sight of the other, which by a rapid zig-zag was now flying full across my front, certainly over forty-five yards distant, among a growth of thick-set saplings—the hardest shot, in my opinion, that can be selected to test a quick and steady sportsman. I gave it him, and down he came too—killed dead—that I knew, for I had shot full half a yard before him. Just as I dropped my butt to load, the hill began to echo with the vociferous yells of master Dan, the quick redoubled cracks of Harry's heavy dog-whip, and his incessant rating—"Down, cha-arge! For sha-ame! Dan! Dan! down cha-arge! for sha-ame!"—broken at times by the impatient oaths of Tom Draw, in the gulley, who had, it seems, knocked down two woodcock, neither of which he could bag, owing to the depth and instability of the wet bog.

"Quit! quit! cuss you, quit there, leatherin' that brute! Quit, I say, or I'll send a shot at you! Come here, Archer—I say, come here!—there be the darndest lot of droppins here, I ever see—full twenty cock, I swon!"

But still the scourge continued to resound, and still the raving of the spaniel excited Tom's hot ire.

"Frank Forester!" exclaimed he once again. "Do see now— Harry *missed* them partridge, and so he licks the poor dumb brute for it. I wish I were a spannel, and he'd try it on with me!"

"I will, too," answered Archer, with a laugh; "I will, too, if you wish it, though you are not a spaniel, nor anything else half so good. And why, pray, should I not scourge this wild little imp?

He ran slap into the best pack of ruffed grouse I have seen this two years—fifteen or sixteen birds. I wonder they're not scattered—it's full late to find them packed!"

"Did you kill ere a one?" Tom holloaed; "not one, either of you!"

"I did," answered Harry, "I nailed the old cock bird, and a rare dog he is!—two pounds, good weight, I warrant him," he added, weighing him as he spoke. "Look at the crimson round his eye, Frank, like a cock pheasant's, and his black ruff or tippet—by George! but he's a beauty! And what did you do?" he continued.

"I bagged a brace—the only two that crossed me."

"Did you, though?" exclaimed Archer, with no small expression of surprise; "did you, though?—that's prime work—it takes a thorough workman to bag a double shot upon October grouse. But come, we must go down to Tom; hark how the old hound keeps bawling."

Well, down we went. The spaniels quickly retrieved his dead birds, and flushed some fifteen more, of which we gave a clean account—Harry making up for lost time by killing six cock, right and left, almost before they topped the bushes—seven more fell to me, but single birds all of them—and but one brace to Tom, who now began to wax indignant; for Archer, as I saw, for fun's sake, was making it a point to cut down every bird that rose to him, before he could get up his gun; and then laughed at him for being fat and slow. But the laugh was on Tom's side before long—for while we were yet in the valley, the report of a gun came faintly down the wind from beyond the hill, and as we all looked out attentively, a grouse skimmed the brow, flying before the wind at a tremendous pace, and skated across the valley without stooping from his altitude. I stood the first, and fired, a yard at least ahead of him—on he went, unharmed and undaunted; bang went my second barrel—still on he went, the faster, as it seemed, for the weak insult.

Harry came next, and he too fired twice, and—tell it not in Gath—missed *twice!* "Now, Fat-Guts!" shouted Archer, not altogether in his most amiable or pleasing tones; and sure enough up went the old man's piece—roundly it echoed with its mighty charge—a cloud of feathers drifted away in a long line from the slaughtered victim—which fell not direct, so rapid was its previous flight, but darted onward in a long declining tangent, and struck the rocky soil with a thud clearly audible where we stood, full a hundred yards from the spot where it fell.

He bagged, amid Tom's mighty exultation, forward again we went and in a short half hour got into the remainder of the pack which we had flushed before, in some low tangled thorn cover, among which they lay well, and we made havoc of them. And here the oddest accident I ever witnessed in the field took place—so odd, that I am half ashamed to write to it—but where's the odds, for it is true.

A fine cock bird was flushed close at Tom's feet, and went off to the left, Harry and I both standing to the right; he blazed away, and at the shot the bird sprung up six or eight feet into the air, with a sharp staggering flutter. "Killed dead!" cried I; "well done again, Fat Tom." But to my great surprise the grouse gathered wing, and flew on, feebly at first, and dizzily, but gaining strength more and more as he went on the farther. At the last, after a long flight, he treed in a tall leafless pine.

"Run after him, Frank," Archer called to me, "you are the lightest; and we'll beat up the swale till you return. You saw the tree he took?"

"Aye, aye!" said I preparing to make off.

"Well! he sits near the top—now mind me! no chivalry, Frank! give him no second chance—a ruffed grouse, darting downward from a tall pine tree, is a shot to balk the devil—it's full five to one that you shoot over and behind him—give him no mercy!"

Off I went, and after a brisk trot, five or six minutes long, reached my tree, saw my bird perched on a broken limb close to the time-blanched trunk, cocked my Joe Manton, and was in the very act of taking aim, when something so peculiar in the motion of the bird attracted me, that I paused. He was nodding like a sleepy man, and seemed with difficulty to retain his foothold. While I was gazing, he let go, pitched headlong, fluttered his wings in the death-struggle, yet in air, and struck the ground close at my feet, stone-dead. Tom's first shot had cut off the whole crown of the head, with half the brain and the right eye; and after that the bird had power to fly five or six hundred yards, and then to cling upon its perch for at least ten minutes.

Rejoining my companions, we again went onward, slaying and bagging as we went, till when the sun was at meridian we sat down beside the brook to make our frugal meal—not to-day of grilled woodcock and champagne, but of hard eggs, salt, biscuit, and Scotch whiskey—not so bad either—nor were we disinclined to profit by it. We were still smoking on the marge, when a shot right ahead told us that our out-skirting party was at hand.

All in an instant were on the alert; in twenty minutes we joined forces, and compared results. We had twelve grouse, five rabbits, seventeen woodcock; they, six gray squirrels, seven grouse, and one solitary cock—Tim, proud as Lucifer at having led the field. But his joy now was at an end—for to his charge the setters were committed to be led in leash, while we shot on, over the spaniels. Another dozen grouse, and eighteen rabbits, completed our last bag in the Woodlands.

Late was it when we reached the Teachmans' hut—and long and deep was the carouse that followed; and when the moon had sunk and we were turning in, Tom Draw swore with a mighty oath of deepest emphasis—that since we had passed a week with him, he'd take a seat down in the wagon, and see the Beacon Races. So we filled round once more, and clinked our glasses to bind the joyous contract, and turned in happy.

RUFUS KING

The Seven Good Hunters

It is almost as easy to merge oil and water as it is to combine mystery and hunting and obtain a pleasant blend for the reader. It has been tried on many occasions, but too often the results pleased neither the mystery fan nor the hunter. Here is a hunting mystery you may have missed.

The lake held a heliotrope flush of dawn, and it was very cold, very still. Fragile ice rimmed its edges, tentatively seeking a glaze for the late fall's first imprisonment of the water.

The crack of a single rifleshot came clear, down from westward.

Gertrude Enford woke up. There was no blurred transition from slumber about it. She knew exactly where she was. She knew the day. She knew the time of day. She suspected that the source of her wakening had been a shot.

Gertrude was an odd woman, lean and stringy, tough in her fibers, and indefinably smart, no matter what she wore or how she put it on. There was a great assurance in all of her movements; and her voice (which she never bothered to lower) was decisive, final and clipped. Gertrude's age was forty-seven. Her hair, which she wore rather long, and arranged with an artful simplicity, still excitingly retained its natural deep-auburn tones. She was very rich.

You had to be rich to stay at the Lodge, for its tariff was stiff, and you either paid it and liked it, or else you stayed away. The Jenklins owned it, Jerry and Sara: a rambling estate in the heart of the Adirondack Mountains, having its own lake, four hundred acres, and the best deer hunting in the north country.

Gertrude never minced decisions. In spite of the earliness of the hour, she decided to get up. She had had enough sleep, and her nerves were in excellent condition. She dressed. She looked at herself critically in a mirror. Her face, she decided, was in shape: colorless, ageless, with interesting wide frank eyes and a mouth whose shading held a dash of fuchsia in its red.

She went through the living room of her suite and out into a central hallway, darkly paneled, dark with the obscurity of the day's pale dawn, and down stairs of waxed oak. Lighted candles were somber in the main hall (the Jenklins leaned heavily on atmosphere), and she saw the stranger vaguely, standing before a large open hearth where birch logs flamed.

She said: "I'm Gertrude Enford. When did you get in?"

"I came on the morning train. The one that dumps you out at half-past four. I'm Colin Starr."

"Oh, yes. They said you were coming—but they said next week."

"It's hard for me to arrange anything definitely."

"Yes, I suppose that would be so."

Gertrude stared at Starr openly, taking him all in, his compact tall vigor and brief ugliness of features which gave to his face a curious effect of charm. One of those healthy animals, she thought, who live in the eternal forties, with digestions like clockwork. A server, a good man. A keen, kind, honest man and to hell with him. One who from birth would have lived on the proper emotional side of the tracks, in a lovely house of clear-white glass bricks secure on a foundation of ethics. She thought: "What I need is a couple of cups of strong black coffee."

Gertrude sketchily recalled Dr. Starr's dossier as she had obliquely learned it: his home was in Ohio, in one of those settled small towns which you sometimes see at fairs done in miniature, a well-cleaned, polished microcosm of all that was sturdiest and best in the nation. The name, if she remembered, was Laurel Falls. He was a doctor of considerable repute, a repute that reached beyond any local or state boundaries, a man of wealth, and a man with a strange aptitude for the medico-legal angles of his profession. This, in the sense of his having been instrumental in the unmasking of several apparently natural deaths and stamping them as murder.

"I understand you have been here before, Doctor."

"Yes, several times. Whenever I can arrange to, in fact. The Jenklins are old friends." Starr considered Gertrude's turnout, its severe smartness, the inappropriateness of her shoes. "You're not going out this morning?"

"I don't hunt. I'm here with Jack, my brother, and a friend of his—an intense young thing by the name of Mason Hallway, whose family is involved with soaps. Jack hopes to bag a twelve-point buck. I've no objection to his mounting the heads—we live on Long Island, a little town called Mealand, and his den is littered with antlers—but I do object to his making us eat up the rest of them. Jack thinks it's the only sporting thing to do. Would that be atavism or just a plain obsession, Doctor?"

"Perhaps just a healthy appetite?"

"Well, if it's healthy, it's the—"

The main door opened and Bill, one of the guides, came in: a hardened youngster, leathery, and with deep-blue, vital eyes. Hard running had left him breathless.

He said to Gertrude: "Where's Mr. Jenklin, Miss Enford? Mr. Singmen's been shot. He's bad."

Gertrude's pale long fingers clutched the back of a chair for support, and Starr observed her sudden convulsive trembling, and thought her about to faint.

She said: "Mr. Singmen—Mr. Singmen is dead?"

"No, he ain't dead, but he's near enough to make no difference. They're bringing him in. I got to find Mr. Jenklin. I got to find a doctor."

"I'm a doctor."

Bill looked relievedly at Starr.

"Maybe you can fix him up?"

"Maybe I can."

But he couldn't. Nothing could. Starr knew that when Singmen was brought in and carried up to a bed. Singmen was of medium build, a middle-aged man wearing corduroys, stout boots, a gray hunting jacket and a red cap. He had been shot through the back. There was not, on the gray hunting jacket, much blood, and Starr believed shortly that an internal hemorrhage would make death a matter of minutes or of an hour or so at most.

Singmen's eyes were cloudy and almost absurdly kind. They gave his pleasant face a stricken spaniel look. He said to Starr: "I should have worn my red hunting jacket after all, not that gray one. The red cap wasn't enough."

("There's no use," Starr thought, "in making him preserve his ebbing strength. He might as well talk, and keep his mind occupied. There's nothing at all I can do.")

"Who shot you, Mr. Singmen?"

"I don't know."

"Do you mean to say whoever did it didn't come to your help?"

"Yes. Too frightened, I guess. A couple of the guides found me and brought me in." Singmen sighed gently and closed his cloudy eyes. "It's a funny thing how excited some men will get when they think they see a buck."

"Were you in brush or on a trail?"

"A trail, Doctor."

"Fairly straight?"

"Yes, right along there it was, for almost a hundred yards or so. But you know how it is with buck fever."

"Look here, Singmen, that shot went directly through your back in a straight line. Surely whoever fired must have seen you pretty clearly. Tell me this—"

"I'm very tired, Doctor."

"I know you are. But tell me, of the people who are up here, of the men out hunting this morning, has any one of them anything against you?"

"Me? Lord no, Doctor. I've always been my own worst enemy." Singmen smiled feebly at this feeble airing of the bromide. "Don't get any notion like that in your head."

"Was any one of them using the same trail you were on?"

"No. I did meet Mason Hallway for a minute at the fork, where there's a cross trail of sorts, but he hit on off to the left up toward the ridge. He's that young friend of Jack Enford. Enford has a nice sister, by the way. A very interesting woman. She's staying here. You'll meet her."

"I have. Was Mason Hallway the only man you saw?"

"That's right, Doctor. It couldn't have been he who caused this accident, because he knew the way I was heading. Just how bad am I, Doctor?"

"You are all right." And Singmen was . . . He was dead.

Starr talked with Sara Jenklin while they were waiting for the sheriff. Gray peppered Sara's dark sleek hair, and her animated eyes were heavy with shock and worry.

Seven hunters (Sara said) were out that morning, including Singmen, who was dead. None of the others had as yet returned, including Mason Hallway, whom Singmen had met at the fork and who had branched off to hit it up for the ridge. No concerted drive had been set for the morning. Each man had started off on his own. The guides were out now, bringing them in.

"Tell me, Sara, something about Singmen."

"There isn't much, Colin. He was a widower. No children. His wife was Alice Dobbs. Alice and I went to school together, which is how Arthur started coming up here."

"What did he do?"

"Arthur? Nothing. He had a good income, and more or less budgeted it. He owned a co-operative apartment in New York, just a good, plain fine one with nothing bizarre about it—old stuff, old silver. He kept a place on the beach at Miami." Sara looked at Starr earnestly. "He couldn't have been a kinder man, or more harmless."

"You're puzzled, Sara, too?"

"Naturally I'm puzzled. I know the place in the trail where he was shot. There's a good clear view for quite a stretch back. Anyhow, every man who went out this morning is experienced. I just can't believe that any one of them would get buck fever."

"What of Mason Hallway, Sara?"

"I don't know, except that I like him. It's his first time here. He came with the Enfords. I've known them, of course, for several years. Jack met him sometime last spring, I understand, when both of them were applying for the Reserve Corps. Each was turned down for some reason or other, and it seemed, well, to form a bond. They became quite friendly."

"Did Hallway know Singmen?"

"Only in the sense of their having met two days ago."

Starr thought back upon Gertrude Enford's convulsive trembling, the sharp clutch of her fingers upon the chair when the guide had told them about Singmen having been shot. It had struck him as far too sharp a reaction at news concerning a stranger, no matter how shocking. There was a connection with Singmen, he felt, either through Hallway or through the Enfords themselves.

"Tell me about Jack Enford. I've met his sister."

Sara thought for a while, staring contemplatively at Starr with her dark-gray animated eyes.

"Jack's all right."

"That suggests reservations."

"Yes, I know it does. Jack's the type of man whom all sorts of things are said about. But nothing's ever proved. I feel sorry for him because you know how that sort of thing goes. How it spreads. He's a magnet for innuendoes."

"Unpleasant ones?"

"Some. Very."

"Moral? Ethical? Financial?"

"Oh, they run the whole list. His job's promoting things. Sometimes they come off; more frequently they don't—leaving a lot of bag-holders."

"Including, perhaps, Singmen?"

"No; I'm sure about that. Jack and his sister only met Arthur two days ago, too."

"I've still a feeling that there's some connection. I gathered that from Miss Enford's reaction to the news."

Sara leaned forward and said earnestly: "Colin, Arthur Singmen never harmed anyone in his life. There's not even anyone I know of left who will gain by his death. He told me last season that he was leaving his money to charity. Now if it had been Jack—" She bit her lip, and stopped abruptly.

"Yes, Sara?"

"I'm doing exactly what I've just complained about in others. Going in for innuendoes. You see, with the exception of Arthur and Mason Hallway, Jack knows the other men who were out this morning fairly well. And I mean by that, of course, that they know him. Frankly, they don't like him. And to be still more frank about it, I think that each has been bitten by one or another of his promotion schemes."

"Deeply enough to want to take a pot-shot at him?"

Sara hesitated.

"Who can ever tell about that? But it wasn't Jack who was shot; it was Arthur."

"Did you see them when they left this morning, Sara?"

"Yes."

"What sort of hunting jacket was Jack Enford wearing?" Starr asked.

"His regular red one."

"Then that knocks out that thought. Singmen's was gray."

They were sitting in Sara's living room: a pleasant clear place of pickled pine, with casement windows having a magnificent view across a valley that was flooding with the rising sun. A maid came in without knocking. She said to Sara: "It's Miss Enford, ma'am. I think she's got hysterics. Anyhow, she's screeching awfully."

Gertrude had them, all right. Severely. And there was little that

Starr could do but give her an opiate to knock her out. He observed the usual disjointed mélange of sense and nonsense to her ravings: a mélange of fears and remembrances, all uprooted from the sable caves of her subconscious mind, and brokenly shrieked out.

He felt strongly disturbed, more so even than was usual with him during such exhibitions. He thought: "She thinks that it was murder, all right. Her brother's on her mind like an obsession. It must be that she thinks that the shot was meant for her brother—as Sara did."

Sara stood watching Gertrude quiet down; then a man stepped into the room very softly. His face was deadly pale, and stamped with a weak prettiness that contrasted oddly with his large, rangy build.

He said to Starr: "Oh, you're the doctor, aren't you?"

"Yes."

"I'm her brother. How is she?"

"She has had a bad shock, Mr. Enford."

"Yes, I know. Look here—nothing will happen to her, will it?"

"No, she'll get over it."

Jack felt sweat on his forehead. He found it distasteful, and wiped it away petulantly.

"Awful thing. Awful thing about Arthur Singmen."

"Very."

"You were with him, weren't you? I mean when he died."

"Yes."

"Well—did he say anything?"

"He did speak of having met your friend Mr. Hallway along the trail. He mentioned a fork."

"Yes? He didn't imply—I mean he didn't seem to feel that Mason was responsible, did he?"

"No, on the contrary. He felt strongly that Mr. Hallway could not have been."

"It's funny that whoever did fire the shot didn't come forward—right away—and help Singmen. I suppose it was panic at the accident."

"I suppose it was."

"It makes it awkward."

"Awkward, Mr. Enford?"

"Sure, for the rest of us."

"Your sister seemed to feel—I don't know exactly how to put

this, but I got the impression that she, well, has her own rather strong ideas about this business."

"Yes?"

Both of them stared down at the bed, at Gertrude with her lips a little parted over sharp white teeth, with her breath coming through them in the first deep plunge into the opiate sleep.

"Your sister—I almost gathered that she was inclined to consider it murder, but that the bullet wasn't meant for Singmen."

"Gertrude? She said that?"

"Not in so many words. I felt it implied, rather, in her hysteria."

"Look, Doctor, that's all that it was. Just hysteria. I know Gertrude, and she gets that way. She's highly strung. She goes right off her bat sometimes just over trifles." Jack's hand was petulant again with sweat. "It isn't only Gertrude. Our family has always been that way. I am myself sometimes. High-strung."

"Was that why they rejected you for the Reserves last spring, Mr. Enford?"

"Well, not entirely." Jack smiled. There was some syrup on the smile's deprecatory sweetness. "I believe they just considered me as temperamentally unfit."

"I understand that Mr. Hallway was rejected at the same time, that that was how you met. Was he rejected on the same grounds?"

Jack suddenly stopped being pleasant.

"Why do you harp on him? Singmen gave him a clean slate, didn't he? Well, isn't that good enough for you?"

"Sorry, Mr. Enford."

"That's all right. So am I. I told you that I—that it ran in the family. Forget it, Doctor."

Four men stood in the main hall.

Welford, a banker from Boston, dominated the others in appearance: strikingly silver-haired, thin, and tall to the point of gauntness, with sharply chiseled ears and nose and lips. They gave him (as he very well knew) the patrician look. He also knew its value to him in business, even though it amused him considerably when he considered his private vices, which were pigs' knuckles, Western novels, and gin mixed with plain water and no ice.

He observed Jack Enford coming into the room with a stranger. He did not see the stranger very clearly, because his fine bold eyes were concentrating so sharply on Enford. Their expression was not pleasant. He thought: "You wait!"

Burkell stood beside Welford. Denwood Burkell was a novelist of a brief repute whose flair lay in calling soil *soil*. He was a little man, barely five feet two inches in his lifts, and still he publicized himself amazingly as a sportsman: big fish, big game. Secretly it bored him stiff, but his agent thought it useful with his public and for his press. The hours were the things that "got his goat." It irked him constantly that no animal of the slightest publicity value could, apparently, be bagged at noon.

Haskell Fortescu was on Welford's other side. He was a corporation counsel for a general-utilities outfit in the South: a stout man, rotund all over, with limpid little eyes and a merry mouth. People thought him famously jolly. His reaction to Enford was a little smile.

The fourth man, Hallway, was very much the intense young thing that Gertrude had called him. You got that from the deep burning look in his dark eyes rather than from his build, which was medium and placid enough. But his eyes were extraordinary and Starr read in them, as he shook hands, a hint of emotionalism, the suggestion of the dreamer or the fanatic, say in the sense of a hero-worshiper who would let his god or enthusiasm of the hour go to good lengths before admitting even the possibility of any feet of clay.

Starr met them and noted that they wore, to a man, hunting jackets of assorted reds. He acknowledged the usual perfunctory generalities: *"Terrible. . . . Fine man, Singmen. . . . Can't understand it. . . . Happens every year—terrible. . . . You would think that by now . . . Buck fever—you might expect it in a novice, but not one of us—terrible!"* Then he went into a small lounge room where he saw Jerry Jenklin.

Jerry, Sara's husband, seemed lethargic when you first met him, which wasn't so. He was like an animal that way, slipping from a lounge into the most fluid physical sort of activity without any consciousness on the part of anyone watching him of the transition. Everything about him looked sleepy and somewhat sultry and slow. You expected him to scratch himself and continuously yawn.

He said to Starr: "You've still got to meet McDuff."

"The seventh hunter?"

"Yes. He'll be along soon. Well?"

"Well?"

Jerry continued to slouch and look sleepy. He offered Starr a cigarette, lit one himself, and let it dangle.

"This is bad, Colin. It's murder. And there's one thing that makes it pretty convincing that Singmen was meant to be the victim. He's the only one of the lot who wore a gray hunting jacket. They all must have known that, because they started out together. Still, you've been talking with Sara. I can only emphasize what she told you, that there's no sane reason why anybody here or anywhere else would want to kill Singmen—but someone did. So that leaves us what?"

"It leaves us with Miss Enford in hysteria."

"Yes, Sara told me that, too. Jack's at the bottom of that. She's pretty blind about him, but she can't be so utterly blind as not to realize what a more rational victim he would have made than Singmen. Or than anybody else who's here."

"She seems quite a good deal older."

"She is. She's always dominated him. She brought him up."

"From childhood?"

"Nearly. He was eleven when their parents died. Gertrude was going on nineteen. She made a fine mess of it, if you ask me." Jerry leisurely turned his head. "That's McDuff now. Hey, McDuff!"

McDuff came in. He was a huge, raw-boned, beef-skinned, red-nosed man and, Starr realized, full of Scotch. He was dour. He walked with precise care. He shook hands with Starr, and lowered himself into a chair, and said: "I've been up all night." His eyes looked it. They were as red as his hunting jacket. "You're the doctor. Why couldn't you pull old Singmen through?"

"It was too late."

McDuff turned to Jerry.

"Who was the fool who got buck fever?"

"No one's saying."

"He will." McDuff stuck a bony finger out at Starr. "You know that, Doctor. No man can escape from a consciousness of guilt."

"I'm afraid they've been known to, Mr. McDuff. Sometimes it has to be smoked out."

Starr sent a wire. He sent it to the proper department of the Reserve Corps at which Enford and Hallway had applied. He wanted to know on what grounds the two men had been rejected. He wanted to know whether there was any record on the files about a man named Arthur Singmen. As a right to the courtesy of this information, he referred to himself as a friend of the Adjutant General.

It was, he felt, an arrow shot into the air but it was impossible to get rid of the belief that Jack Enford was a focal point in the case.

It was impossible to forget that Jack's friend Mason Hallway had met and talked with Singmen just before the shot was fired. It seemed of pressing importance to get all of the information about Enford and Hallway and Singmen that he could.

The sheriff was starting to spread out his bag of tricks in the main hall. Starr joined the group and was introduced. He liked the sheriff for his air of plain forthrightness, and the healthy color of his skin, and (in spite of the air of forthrightness) his political ability to skate with dexterity over these assembled surfaces of human importance and considerable wealth. He followed the sheriff's casual but pertinent questions carefully.

"Well, gentlemen," the sheriff said in conclusion, "I think it's murder, all right; and because of any seeming lack of motive, I think that Mr. Singmen was murdered by mistake. Now there's only one thing that made him look different from the rest of you at any distance away in the woods, and that was his gray jacket. All the rest of you had on some shade of red. The point as I see it is this: was that Mr. Singmen's jacket? Was it the one he wore habitually, or did he borrow it from somebody else?"

McDuff aroused.

"That gray jacket was mine. I was up all night and saw Singmen when he came down this morning. He had ripped the sleeve of his own jacket yesterday and was looking for one of the maids to sew it. I suggested he leave it and borrow that gray one of mine. Gentlemen—I sent that man to his death."

"No, I'd hardly say that, Mr. McDuff. The question seems to be, did you sometimes wear that gray jacket yourself?"

"Certainly. I wore it every day last week. I'd ordered a red one, but it only came through last night."

The sheriff was pleased.

"Well, now we seem to be getting some place."

McDuff, who was not so pleased, began to get the impact of the drift.

"Me? That shot was meant for me?"

"After all, Mr. McDuff, it was aimed at the only gray jacket in camp."

Starr thought: "Wait—this is wrong; you've gone off the track somewhere. They all started off together this morning; they would have known that Singmen was wearing the gray jacket, not McDuff." Then he felt a presence behind him, and turned, and saw Gertrude Enford in the doorway. She was looking at the sheriff with her wide, frank eyes. Then she turned them on McDuff. Then she started to laugh hysterically.

The answering wire came toward late afternoon.

No one by the name of Arthur Singmen, Starr read, was listed or known. Mason Hallway rejected under suspicion of an incipient psychopathological trend. Jack Enford rejected for deuteranopia, but recent experiments in the detection of camouflage made it desirable Enford apply again.

Starr thought carefully for a long while. So it was like that.

He folded the telegram and put it in his pocket. He looked up the sheriff. He looked up Bill, the guide who had found Singmen that morning. He asked Bill to take them over the trail which Singmen had followed. The sun was sinking below the top of the range. Pine and balsam needles offered a silent, pungent strip of carpeting for their steps, while Starr talked with the sheriff.

It was, Starr said to the sheriff, one of the oddest cases he had ever come upon. At least he thought so. He asked the sheriff to take the five protagonists: a kindly man who was dead; a local, easy-going character who had loaned the kindly man a gray hunting jacket; an idealist who touched on being a zealot and who was thought to have a psychopathological trend; a weakling, and a woman who feared desperately for this weakling whom she herself had brought up. The case should, he thought, be speedily cleared up. For he believed that there was danger still.

They came to the "cross trail of sorts" which Singmen had mentioned, and where there was a definite fork to the left. It was here that Singmen had met and spoken briefly with Hallway. They stood at the fork and Starr explained to the sheriff his theory of what could have occurred.

He suggested that they observe the trail along which they had just come: it was a winding one, and masked by a turn as closely as ten yards back.

They observed the "trail of sorts" which Hallway had used that morning. It too was tortuous, and from their viewpoint briefly obscured.

He indicated then the trail which forked to the left, the one which Hallway had taken after his chat with Singmen: he pointed out that you could not see any farther than several yards along it at the most.

On the other hand, the right fork, which Singmen had continued upon, held a straight and unobstructed stretch through the woods for possibly a hundred yards; and therein, Starr suggested to the sheriff, could lie the answer to the case.

He suggested that they return to the Lodge. He suggested that the sheriff put some pressure to bear upon young Hallway. . . . He suggested that they borrow seven coats.

Gertrude decided on a jade-green net. It offset her hair. She fixed her face carefully so the jade didn't also offset her skin. Pretty good. They'd have to get out of here on the morning train. Get right out and away from here, if that milk-fed sheriff didn't force them to stay. Nice guy, the sheriff. A he-man. With a whittler's delicate touch. And, no doubt, a rattler's fang. Tooth? No, fang. She felt that every hour they stayed there spelled, for Jack, the most desperate sort of danger. . . . Gertrude shuddered.

She'd been shuddering a lot all through the day, and even seven old-fashioneds hadn't soothed the jitters. She clasped an emerald necklace about her throat. What would an eighth old-fashioned do? Well, what would it do?

She went downstairs, a smart, flowing shaft of jade.

All right. Why not? If he wanted to sit beside her and watch her down her eighth, let him.

"Sit down, Doctor Starr. I'm thinking of a cocktail. I'm still on the first today—the first dozen.—Jane!"

"Miss?"

"An old-fashioned."

"Yes, miss. And you, sir?"

Starr would, he said, have an old-fashioned too.

"I missed you this afternoon, Doctor. I haven't thanked you yet for your kindness this morning."

"Not at all, Miss Enford. Any St. Bernard in a storm."

"I go off that way all the time. People get so they supply other house-guests with that stuff you stuff in your ears to keep out street noises."

"Haven't you ever done anything about it?"

"Of course I have. I've been to every psychiatrist in town. My major reaction was that most of the psychiatrists needed *me*. Honestly, Doctor, there was one man who had the infernal nerve to ask me how I would handle the situation if the *Normandie* started sailing up Broadway."

"Of course you told him?"

"Explicitly. After I got home, I sent him a bill for twenty-five dollars." (*I wish that old-fashioned would come. I can't keep this up much longer. I'll start shuddering again.*) "Tell me—you've been talking with the sheriff; has he found anything out?"

"About Singmen?"

"About his murder."

Starr looked evasive.

"I'm afraid the case is in his hands."

"Oh—then there is a case?"

"He thinks so. He plans to conduct a little experiment."

"Really? Of what nature, Doctor?"

"I understand it has to do with the selection of a hunting jacket."

"Are you being serious?"

"Very serious, Miss Enford."

"The maid is taking a wretched time with those old-fashioneds."

Gertrude looked toward the door hopefully, on the last outpost of her nerves. There were people coming in, but there were no old-fashioneds, and there was no maid. The sheriff came first carrying, amazingly, some hunting jackets on his arm. The six men left from the morning hunt trailed him. They grouped, with awkward reticence, near the blazing hearth. The Jenklins, with odd formality, came in and sat on a settee near the doorway.

It's like a tableau, Gertrude thought: *stilted. Jack looks terrible. I wish he'd look at me.* She examined Hallway. *He's worse off than Jack*, she decided. A chill ran through Gertrude and she thought, still covertly examining Hallway: *He's talked. He's spilled it.* Then the future became a tunnel through which she was entering into bitter darkness.

The sheriff was folding the hunting jackets lengthwise and placing them side by side on a lounge. Odd—six of them were in different shades of red, ranging from maroon to vivid scarlet, but the seventh one was gray. The sheriff was speaking, and Gertrude listened with a feverish impatience to this prelude which, from the look on Mason Hallway's tortured face, she had already discounted.

"—defalcation," the sheriff was saying, "—outright theft of a good many thousands of dollars, nearly two hundred, to be exact —a swindle perpetrated by Mr. Enford and achieved partly through the influential and trusted position of his friend Mr. Hallway. There was no doubt but that Mr. Hallway had been completely deceived as to the transaction, but Mr. Hallway had ultimately discovered its criminal nature and had insisted that the miserable business be exposed, even though he himself would also be subject to prosecution and disgrace. Mr. Hallway was that kind of man—an idealist."

(*Yes,* Gertrude thought, *we know all that. Get on with it. Get through with it.*)

There was, the sheriff said, a curious angle about the matter which gave it a classic touch: the strange power of domination which Miss Enford held over her young brother, who all of his life had been a moral weakling. It was a power, in Doctor Starr's opinion, analogous to that exercised over her husband by Lady Macbeth, in the sense that Miss Enford had planted in her brother's mind the seed of murder. A seed which she had then nurtured into fruition.

(Gertrude thought: *Give us your proof. It was still a hunting accident, and nothing can make it come out differently.*)

Mr. Hallway had admitted to him, the sheriff said, that he had agreed to accompany Miss Enford and her brother on this hunting trip, so that they could all talk things over. Miss Enford had pleaded that her own disgrace at her brother's exposure would be as deep as theirs. She had begged Mr. Hallway not to force her into social ostracism. She had insisted that a reasoned discussion of the disgraceful affair would show them some honorable way out. That, of course, was nothing but a lure. Mr. Hallway had been deliberately brought up here to be "accidentally" shot and killed—to silence him and his zealous moral qualms. Mr. Singmen had unhappily been shot instead. Perhaps Doctor Starr would offer his conclusions about that?

Starr was nervously depressed. It affected him this way—the end of a chase, and any psychological trick devised to cause a suspect to crack. He sensed the virulence in Gertrude, her fierce mental intention to make her brother look at her so that she could control him. Starr spoke to her directly, forcing her to attend to him.

"Miss Enford, your brother followed Mr. Hallway this morning, staying at a careful distance behind. By the time your brother reached the fork, Mr. Hallway had completed his brief talk with Mr. Singmen and was already lost to view behind the first turning of the trail that leads up to the ridge. On the other hand, Mr. Singmen was still in view, say a hundred yards or more away, at the farther end of the clear stretch of the right-hand trail. Your brother took it for granted that Mr. Singmen was Mr. Hallway and followed him. He shot him. His mistake was a natural one, because of all the men who were out hunting this morning only Mr. Singmen and Mr. Hallway had similar builds."

Gertrude's head was shot with sharp pain. Her eyes, in memory, compared Singmen's body with Mason's. All right. That much was true. Both were of medium build, whereas the others grouped by the fire were a varied assortment of gaunt, of small, of large size, of fat. And still all right. She looked at Jack. That was true, too. He was a weakling, and a flash of honesty made Gertrude admit that perhaps it was she who had made him one. Then the hunting jackets neatly lined up on the lounge began to fascinate her.

She said desperately: "You're wrong, Doctor. Mason wore a red hunting jacket, whereas Mr. Singmen's jacket was gray. No matter what the distance, no matter what the similarity in their builds, Jack would have noticed that. He would have known by the jacket alone that Mr. Singmen couldn't have been Mason."

Starr crossed to the hearth.

He said: "Mr. Enford, there are six coats on that lounge of varying shades of red. There is one coat there that is gray. Will you indicate the gray one, please?"

Sweat was unpleasant on Jack's face. His lips felt abominably loose, and he was terrified at the thought that he was about to cry. One chance in seven. Like that ordeal-by-fire stuff, and other tests for guilt or innocence of the Middle Ages. It suddenly didn't matter—nothing. Singmen, he remembered absently, had given several convulsive twists before he had fallen. Even Gertrude seemed a long distance away.

He pointed to the end jacket on the left.

He said: "That's the gray one."

Gertrude looked at him for a breathless second; then she screamed.

"*No,* Jack—that one is red."

Starr held her firmly by the shoulders.

"Not to your brother, Miss Enford. I suppose his vanity prevented him from ever telling you. He's color-blind, you see. He *knows no red.*"

The Best Wingshot in the United States

Only the man who composed *To Hell With Fishing* and its companion, *To Hell With Hunting,* would be capable of providing a vignette of Frank King, one of the few individuals in this world whose factual existence gives the lie to fiction. Having known the estimable Frank for almost thirty years, I want to join Ed Zern in widening the circle of his acquaintances; there are so few like him.

Back in Frank King's market-hunting days, he was somehow appointed one of the assessors for the township—probably because he knew every inch of it thoroughly, and if his respect for property lines was not highly developed, his knowledge of them was unsurpassed.

It happened that a portion of an immense private shooting preserve, owned by a wealthy New York sportsman named Milford, lay within the township boundaries, and also that a great many of the deer and grouse Frank shipped to market came from within its closely patrolled confines.

In pursuance of his official duties, Frank learned that Milford was present at the main lodge one day, and so he put on his best bib and tucker, carefully picking off any stray partridge feathers that adhered thereto, and drove over to discuss the property's assessment with the owner.

The owner explained to Frank that he kept the place merely as a shooting preserve, primarily for the large numbers of grouse it harbored, and politely inquired whether Frank ever did any bird-shooting. Frank looked at the city man suspiciously, but when it seemed clear that the question was asked out of prime innocence, Frank allowed that he sometimes fooled around with a scattergun, and knew a grouse from a groundhog.

The owner then went on to remark that he considered himself the best wingshot in the United States. Frank pricked up his ears, and allowed that the United States was a pretty big country. "I know it's a big country," said the owner, "but I've shot birds from one end of it to the other, and always with the best wingshots in the area, and I've yet to meet a man I couldn't outshoot. And the same holds true for England and Scotland.

"Of course," he explained, "I *ought* to be the best wingshot in the country. I've never done anything else since I was a youngster, except fish for salmon. Got my first English shotgun as a gift on my twelfth birthday, and been shooting upland and lowland ever since."

"Well now," said Frank, "mebbe you *are* the best wingshot in the United States. Like you say, you *ought* to be. But if you're the best, I figure I'm a real close *second*-best."

"Really?" said the owner. "Well, Mr. King, I'll tell you what. I'll wager one hundred dollars that we can shoot grouse over the same dog for one day, and I'll grass two birds to your one. How does that strike you?"

"It strikes me fine," said Frank. "When would you like to settle this here wager?"

"How does Saturday suit you?" Milford said. "I've a fine grouse dog up with me that needs a workout, and we'll make a day of it."

Thus the next Saturday morning found Frank and Milford setting out from the lodge with a good English setter, and it was a matter of minutes before the dog came to point on birds.

"How do you want to work this, Mr. Milford?" Frank asked. "If we're shooting alternate points, you take the first one."

"None of that, Mr. King!" chuckled the owner. "I'm not going to do you any favors, and I don't want you to do any for me. When those birds flush, you shoot as many as you can, and I'll do the same. This is every man for himself."

"Suits me," Frank said. (Afterwards Frank said, "That's where that feller made his mistake. For ten years back I hadn't never let a ruff fly more than eight—ten feet, and mostly I hit 'em less than five.")

When three grouse flushed, Frank doubled on the two that came

up on Milford's side while Milford was still bringing his gun up—
and by eleven o'clock Frank had killed twenty-seven birds to
Milford's three.

"It looks like you've won yourself a hundred dollars, Mr. King,"
Milford said. "Let's go back and have lunch. And may I say that
this has been one of the most disconcerting days of my life, and
that you, sir, are beyond the slightest shadow of doubt the greatest
wingshot in the world."

"You'd better not tell that to nobody around these parts," said
Frank. "Some of these Sullivan County boys can *really* shoot."

After lunch, Frank took the hundred dollars, thanked his host
for a pleasant morning's shoot, and drove home. That afternoon
the head gamekeeper of the preserve appeared at the lodge in a
black fury, and announced his resignation.

"What's the matter?" Milford asked his usually mild-mannered
minion.

"Matter?" screamed the enraged bailiff. "Yesterday I hired two
extra watchmen to keep Frank King off this place—and today you
invite him in!"

Once a year thereafter, until his death, Milford (which isn't his
name, of course) invited Frank to the lodge for a day of compan-
ionable (and noncompetitive) shooting. "It's the only way I can
give the watchmen a day off," he explained one time to Frank, and
they both chuckled.

DION HENDERSON

Algonquin

This is one of the most unusual hunting dog stories I have ever read. Had space permitted, there would be justification for providing every chapter of *Algonquin,* rather than the concluding few, although the real muscles of the small volume are flexed only in the section presented here. There may be stories in which the essential character of a dog is presented as clearly, but I have not read them. You could pay tribute to Algonquin; but could you love him? I could not decide. Perhaps you can.

Whatever it was that you had to put into a dog to make him great, and wherever you had to take it from, my Uncle Ovid did it. As I remember the judgment of my elders, there was no doubt about Algonquin. Afterward, men who had seen him measured the excellence of other dogs by saying: "There is one who looks like Algonquin." And you then could pick out the ones who really had known Algonquin. I mean, known him well, because they would look at each other then and smile and shake their heads because there never was a dog like Algonquin.

But you heard such things only occasionally, and on days of great enthusiasm, when a very good dog in a very lucky heat would accomplish climactically just that once what Algonquin did always, and easily, and with reckless abandon.

The main thing I remember was how it seemed a pity to ask any common dog to run against him, because he was more than a dog inside, more than any dog ought to be, and you'll have to decide for yourself what it was that made him that way. It was a feeling you had after first watching him, and after you knew him a while it was stronger, but it changed, too, so that you began to feel it was a pity to ask any common man to handle a dog against him as well.

Not that he was any trouble. He was not sullen, nor mean, nor bad-hearted. He was not like Muscle Shoals Jake, who was so thorough about not liking things that they had to put the livestock up in trees when he came by. No, Algonquin was as merry as any trial judge could ask, but it was a devilish gaiety, and the fuel he drew on to keep it bright came from that wonderful glittering inexhaustible cold thing that sort of frosted you whenever you looked into his yellow eyes.

I had a very difficult time expressing what I thought, even to myself, until one day after we had watched him Grandsir said as much to himself as to me, "Behold the consuming rage, and the rest is ashes."

This was another of the things Grandsir said that confused me and although I did not understand exactly what he meant, I knew I must cling desperately to that phrase, because it would mean something eventually.

Right then, I knew it meant Algonquin hated something. The thing was, you did not know what it was he hated. At different times it seemed different things, and just when you were about sure, you advanced a little in your understanding of him and realized that you had been entirely wrong and this was another thing he did not really hate, but he hated something, all right.

At first a lot of men thought he hated people, because he looked at them with curdling contempt and looked past them as though they were not there. Some of them were hurt, and some were angry, but they needn't have been because he did not really hate people. It was that he knew the things men wanted, and the things they did, and what they were worth, maybe, but he couldn't help them and they couldn't help him, no one at all could help him so he did not pay any attention to people any more.

Then after the first of the big trials there was a good deal of talk about how he hated the other dogs, how he wanted to destroy them, and how that was the reason that he very nearly did destroy several of them—not directly, of course, but with his impeccable and relentless way of destroying them little by little in the field by obliterating the self-respect that a winner must have.

You put him down with a dog and the first part of the heat he spent finding out just what the other dog's limit was, in speed and range and sight and wind. And after that he did everything just a little bit beyond the other dog's utmost ability and did it in a way you knew was breaking the other dog's heart. When he had done that, and made his brace-mate into a broken and dispirited trailer hardly going through the motions any more, he took his graceful farewell and went out ahead to his main performance for the two judges and the gallery.

In the bylaws of many field clubs, the championship is to be awarded to the Open-All-Age dog who on a certain day most closely approaches the ideal of a shooting dog for purposes of actual hunting under similar field conditions. That is a noble precept in some eyes, and progressively closer adherence to it in the years of my time is why we have seen emerge the unlovely concept of the meat dog, and the even less savory emphasis on birds by the pound. It also probably is why no one cares so much about dogs any more. For in the time before my time, bird dogs were brought to a very high pitch, and the people who produced them knew it and provided a shooting-dog stakes in which the shooting dogs were run and judged as you judge any other workman's effectiveness at his trade.

But in that time, when everyone held an ideal of perfection in his mind, and a great many people cared a very great deal about dogs, an Open-All-Age dog was a different thing. There were no rigid definitions of what he should do, but only of the effect he should create. That was because poetry fits very loosely in formal regulations, and an Open-All-Age dog was a thing of poetry. He was sort of a wisp of pure splendor given momentary substance within a frame of ritual like a sonnet or the decathlon or the Order for Burial of the Dead.

We make many parables in our world now to keep our love of beauty from ourselves. An Open-All-Age bird dog was one of the first and most open of them, and learning to appreciate the genius of his spirit was one of the most difficult and desirable attainments of a mysterious and almost vanished culture. He was a little like a virtuoso with a violin, doing many fabulous things and showing you while he was doing them why you would never see it done in just such a way again. Perhaps he was even more like a great conductor, because he dominated a whole orchestra of parts, he mastered the formal environment of the trial, and he used the acoustics of emotion to make his song. He bent the participants to his will and he drew passages out of even the mediocre that could not be equaled again under any circumstances, and put upon the best of them a little of his own magic before he turned to another movement of his program and mercifully allowed the spotlight to be drawn from their exhausted faces.

That was Algonquin, and if you ever saw him, you know what I mean. You saw that he did not hate the other dogs, and a famous judge, who was very old, even then, was one of the first to see it. After the heat he rode around and said to Uncle Ovid, "The dog is very gallant, sir; I think perhaps he would pity his brace-mates if he were not enough of a nobleman to know they would rather die than be pitied."

When you saw how just and reasonable that was, you knew that the other dogs were not what he hated, because he did his best for them, too. He was letting them show their best, because he could not help what he had to do to them afterward. It was not his fault that they were so much less than he that the comparison sickened even them, and it was the pride he had in himself that made him do the same things himself so beautifully and arrogantly and with something so splendid in the air around him that the other dog could not endure it, but broke in tragic disgrace, and for the rest of the heat went around pointing meadowlarks because that way Algonquin would stay away from him.

And most certainly he did not hate the birds. He had the feeling for the birds that they all have, that is the foundation of their art. The birds are the medium of a bird dog, and he must be united with them in his heart, and understand them, and be trusted by them, and speak through his artistry and control them with the power of his genius or he has lost the frame of ritual, he no longer fulfills the fiction of convention, he is adrift and nothing.

The birds were where Algonquin was unmatched. He spoke to them in the immortal and universal language that all men and all dogs understand, and the galleries would hush to hear the rolling periods of his classic declamation. When you saw him swinging wide, burning whitely across the birdfields with that blazing speed to come down on a full wild covey in a locked and statuesque point that skidded him ten yards, pin-wheeling across the stubble on braced legs, lofty as a king acknowledging the presence of other royalty, you knew that you had seen what painters see in their hearts but seldom put on canvas.

But it was the other times, the rare and unexpected times when circumstance called upon the resources of his originality that you felt the hush come down on the gallery and even the horses paused. It was like this when his brace-mate was very lucky very early, and made a splendid find, and Algonquin came to back him, and backed him with that high-stationed pride, saluting the other dog's work in a tribute so fine that the white light of magic descended on him and blinded you and you could not remember afterward what the other dog had done but you remembered Algonquin.

There was the time when the gallery was very eager to watch him, and followed much too closely on the judges. Uncle Ovid spoke to the marshal, and the marshal turned them, but some riders were so eager they pulled away to one side and galloped along a little ridge and that was where the course turned and they were in the path of the coursing. The dog who was down with Algonquin accepted the error and turned away from the horses, but Algonquin went into them and through their groups and with them all around he made game. One of the judges said something very sharp and began to spur his horse toward Algonquin, but there was no haste.

There, with the uneasy horses and embarrassed riders pulling back, Algonquin moved in on his bird, tenderly. The judges rode in and looked at him very seriously, then motioned to Uncle Ovid, and Uncle Ovid dismounted and walked in.

No bird rose and the gallery groaned just a little, a sighing sound of disappointment, but Uncle Ovid stooped over and picked up a cock quail that was very calm and unalarmed because Algonquin had spoken to him as no dog ever spoke before. Uncle Ovid walked a little way and held up his hand and Bob White came back from the far land where he had been resting his spirit and was very frightened suddenly, and flew wildly and desperately out through the line of horses, and there was the long hiss of breath through the gallery that meant more than the applause coming afterward.

There was another time when the judge first said, "Let them go!" and the brace went as they always go when they have the terrible energy bottled up in them and it is released, and Algonquin stretched out ahead and suddenly cart-wheeled as though something had reached up from the ground and caught him by the head, and it had. A find on barren ground is a wonderful thing but most handlers fear it because it is so shocking that it may jar the artist in a bird dog out of place and for just a moment he is all dog. That is where you see handlers smoking their dogs to hold them, or slapping their crops pointedly against their boots walking in, and those things are not very nice either. But Algonquin made the point in full stride and his brace-mate who was running very desperately, trying to catch up, came through too fast and blasted the stray single out and hardly recovered in time to steady at wing, but Algonquin stood there.

This was the quality of his manners in the presence of game, and afterward men who knew him used it as a measure, so you can see whatever it was he hated, it was not the birds.

I have told you these were the great days. I guess we hit most of the trials. That doesn't matter. Even though I was only a boy, I realized it did not matter whether I remembered the names because there are more important things to remember about great days. If it is only the names you want, and the performance records, you can stay at home and read them in a book and you will know all there is to know about them except the part that really matters. Grandsir did not have to tell me about that because when you are a kid you know it better and have more confidence in knowing it than you will again until you are very old and wise and have experimented with the other ways.

It is the being there that matters, being full of hot grits and side meat, and so cold that the rest of you is jealous of the belly being warm, so you sit on the horse and shiver until you think maybe you better hang on to the saddle but that isn't dignified, and the dew on the handlers' boots and the jingle of harness and the horses moving a little restlessly and the electric feeling before a brace is cast off even if they are not very good dogs. Of course, on the circuit they all are very good dogs, but they do not always have very good days. Field-trial performances depend on many things; they depend on the brace-mate you draw, and the time of day, and whether there was a good dew, and whether you are working over a section where other dogs were put down previously so that the coveys are scattered and scared. These things all are important, and sometimes they make a great deal of difference, but Algonquin did not care about them. Of course, when he was lucky, too, and drew an early heat and the dew and several big coveys and a fine brace-mate, those were the really magnificent days when everyone on the field knew they were witnessing an event.

Those days affected me very strongly, and at the end of them I felt drained and exhausted, and even though I was not such a little boy any more, I felt fretful and might have wept easily if there were anything definite to weep about. One time, I remember, I went to sleep in the saddle and the horse kept moving and Grandsir came after me and I woke up when he took hold of my bridle.

"You're very tired, boy, aren't you?"

"Yes, sir," I said sleepily.

"But now we have started this and we must see it through," Grandsir said. "Just remember, some day all this will seem very long ago."

"We," Uncle Ovid said, always "we."

That meant he was speaking of Algonquin and himself. He did not say "I" any more, nor "he" but only "we." It was a thing you didn't notice at first, then it insinuated itself into your attention and you tried to ignore it but you noticed it even more intensely then, straining your senses for new manifestations of it, and dreading to find them. In the field you saw it work; the tall old man and the white dog did not need any apparent communication. More than once I have seen Algonquin carrying a cast to the outermost limit of judgment and be turned as though you turned him by force when my uncle did not even gesture, much less whistle, but willed that he should turn.

And once I was close enough to see how at the end of a heat, when a handler may call upon a famous champion to finish with a mighty final sweep against the odds of time and fatigue, my uncle stood still and closed his eyes and his whole body tensed in a gathering motion and the veins swelled on his forehead with the effort, but not for himself. Instead, when he let his breath out explosively, it was Algonquin, a quarter-mile away, who hurtled forward in a climactic drive as memorable as the falling of a star.

And time after time I saw them, in the gray light of morning, the man kneeling beside the dog with the bizarre head, at the hour when during the long campaigns a champion feels the universal mortality of all flesh, and his blood runs slow and the throat is thick and the fire of the spirit is banked with sheer weariness. I have seen Uncle Ovid, his face gray as the dawn, kneel beside the dog on the line and speak to him softly and the dog would look at him hardly caring. But my uncle would talk rapidly and tenderly and the dog would change slowly under the effect not of the language, but of the man's determination, and the increasing glow of mockery and bitterness would rise in his chilling yellow eyes, the cold light of rage would puff into life and blaze higher, and the power would surge through the gaunt body again, and when the hoarse voice cut through the expectant hush saying: "Cast them off, gentlemen," Algonquin would go just as he always went, more dog than any dog should ever be, tireless and unrelenting.

But Uncle Ovid would not be that way. Even in the beginning

he would come back slowly from the line and his feet would drag wearily as though it were late afternoon instead of morning, and during the heat he would stoop and the lines would deepen in his face as though he were running it himself instead of the tall, white dog. There was a time when he still kneeled when the dogs were hunting their way far out, and Grandsir started forward because it did not seem my uncle would rise to his feet unaided.

"Never mind, Charleton." Uncle Ovid's voice would be weak, but you could see him summoning up new reserves of strength. "Never mind. See how we already are on the horizon."

He meant Algonquin was there.

Then by night Uncle Ovid would be very pale and weak. You get to know the other handlers of big-time dogs. They live in a little world alone, and because Uncle Ovid was very old and had been very famous when most of them were little boys, they were kind. Of course, he was an owner, too, and that made some difference, but even without that he was very impatient. There was nothing wrong with him that being kind could help, he said. Mostly, he wanted to rest. Grandsir would sit and talk to him until he went to sleep and the white dog slept on the floor beside him. Sometimes my uncle would stir in his sleep and mutter and the white dog would raise that head with the chilling, sleepless eyes and look at him, not loving, nor sentimental, nor even as though he gave a damn, but knowing the desperate extent of their alliance.

Grandsir would tiptoe away then and shake his head and say something I could not understand because it started out ’Ω ξεῖν, ἀγγέλλειν —

Once Uncle Ovid heard him and wakened abruptly.

"What's that, Charleton?" He propped himself on his elbow and repeated, "What did you say?"

"I did not really say it." Grandsir hardly ever was sharp with Uncle Ovid now. Mostly he was sort of waiting.

"I heard you," Uncle Ovid said. "Quoting Simonides, you were. 'Tell them in Lakedaemon, passer-by, that here obedient to their word we lie.' "

Grandsir did not say anything and after a moment Uncle Ovid relaxed again.

"You do not have to worry, Charleton. Maybe we have gone out one time too many. Maybe we will use up the last mysterious supplies of our mutual time." He gave a peaceful kind of sigh here and said, "But you remember, Charleton, I was very wasteful in my youth. We can go back and gather up the fragments of courage and strength discarded then, and we will last them out, we will last all right."

Grandsir sounded as though he would rather not say it but had to.

"Until when, Ovid?"

"That's a very good question, Charleton," he said, and folded his hands on the cover and went back to sleep.

I might have been considerably more worried about the latter part of that conversation if I had not been stalled over the first part. To begin with, I was astonished that Uncle Ovid recognized the Greek, and knew what it was, and I wondered if maybe he did not know a great many things like that but did not want to admit knowing them. And I wondered also what it was in a man which made him deprecate his own knowledge because goodness knows, no matter how much you have it amounts to very little.

Then I thought about Algonquin, and how they talked about what he was and how he got that way, and something kept bothering me, and I wondered whether it is not possible that when you are very old and very wise and know so very much, that you might have forgotten just a little. There is something in a boy, an instinct that trusts in sorcery and spells and unspoken prophecies, and the something that is gone before a boy becomes a man had spoken to me in the night, that night Algonquin came alone out of the fire then turned and desired to go back in, and I thought perhaps Algonquin had been the way he was before they knew what he would be. I wondered whether the rage that was in him came from their stopping him when he wanted to go back into the fire, but I could not imagine how that might be possible, and I thought also in a confused and feverish way that I would know, if I could remember whether that buried light had been in his yellow eyes before, or only after.

Sitting there half asleep I reached that point and jumped in fright, and turned my head. Uncle Ovid was asleep and Grandsir was sunk in meditation, but Algonquin was watching me with that unspeakable stare, and I swear I thought he would laugh and the laugh would be too full of rage and bitterness for anyone to bear.

But of course he didn't, and Grandsir stirred and glared at me, and made me go to bed where I belonged.

After it was over no one remembered when it started. A dog in competition has his own flesh and blood to contend with, and it is very hard because of the demands he makes. His feet get so hard they are like sole leather, so tough you could hardly cut them with a knife, but he wears his nails so short sometimes they bleed after a long run on hard ground, and of course the brambles always are there, cutting fine gashes across the loins and under the forelegs. It gets so a dog's muzzle is bare and nearly raw between nose and eyes, just from hitting cover, and the hair is all worn off around the eyes. Then the weed seeds get in his ears and eyes, and sometimes you don't get them all washed out with the borax water at night, and then there is trouble. Or the seeds and pollen and things like that are so heavy some days, and he gets his nose and throat clogged with them and has to cough every little while, only he won't take time to do it while he's running, but saves all the coughing and wheezing for afterward until you think he's going to die any minute. It is a hard life and it is not mastered by qualities you teach to any dog. He has it bred into him for thousands of years by elimination and for several hundred additionally, on purpose, and either it comes down to him strongly enough so nothing stops him, or it does not; and there's no use trying to teach him any more than it is trying to make him forget it if you do not want to have it.

These hardships came to Algonquin just as they happen to any trial dog. He did not care, he not even notice, and he seemed to sneer at us when we took care of his cuts and injuries. That's why it was so hard afterward to tell when the cough started.

It was nothing at first; you did not notice. There was a regional championship, as I remember. It was a hot day and they put the money dogs down in a three-hour heat which is the same long grind they have in the final series of the Free-for-All and the National. Algonquin was down with a bitch who was middling fair, but was very smart and figured things out for herself very quickly. After that she ran as though she had drawn a bye and worked busily on whatever he left her, and although, as I said, she was middling fair, Algonquin was so wide and so fast and so sure that it looked like she was misplaced and ought to be running in the foot stakes with the Irish setters and the Brittanies. Of course, he did not put on his performance for nothing. He took what he had and brought it out and it was just that he had so much to give that illuminated it with the authenticity of being so much to see.

At the end of the heat there was a long hill and the judges were waiting off at one side and the marshal was at the end with a handsome roan horse, and Uncle Ovid called on him for one more long cast, the finish everyone waited for. He made it, a flat-racing, white sickle curving across the field of sedge in that wonderful symmetrical pattern he had, soaring like the last four bars of a symphony and loud with the timpani that each man heard for himself in the pulse thudding in his own ears.

But when Uncle Ovid brought him back to the wagon, he was coughing, a dry, hard, hacking cough and you noticed it then, all right.

No one said anything; no one dared mention it. The next day instead of waiting for the rest of the braces we went out alone and Uncle Ovid put him down again. This time, without the competition to fire him, it did not take so long. The cough frightened me dreadfully; I did not know anything about it, but I was very frightened because it seemed I could feel how it hurt; and the way his ribs heaved through the tight skin as though he could not breathe and worst of all the way he looked afterward, the eyes yellow and malevolent with rage that had burst into flower and was there in the open now for anyone to see. You could see the object of his hate there now, indistinct, but coming closer now, closer to the surface, and evil, evil, as though he were getting ready for what he had known all along was coming, and which now was very near.

We did not even wait to get the trophy and have Algonquin's picture taken with it, and mark down the names of the men who wanted to get pups by him when the time came. We went right on to the next city because Uncle Ovid did not want to start talk that getting a local veterinarian would do.

In the city Uncle Ovid and Grandsir and Algonquin went into the vet's place and left me waiting in the office. I must have sat there all morning, alone, watching people with sick dogs come in and wait, and tire of waiting, and go out. After a while another doctor came in hastily and went where Uncle Ovid and Grandsir and Algonquin were. Then still later I heard Uncle Ovid shouting something terrible, a long way down the halls, and one doctor came out looking mad and a little disheveled, and a new one came in from outside.

But I guess all the shouting in the world couldn't help. You could see that, by looking at Uncle Ovid and Grandsir.

They looked like two men who had lived too long and done too many things and were too exhausted to do whatever there was left for them to do. I understood why Uncle Ovid was that way, sick.

But Grandsir did not care so much about dogs any more so he must have been sick of something else.

No one ever told me any more about what happened there. We loaded up and started on the road and I knew we were going home. Mostly Grandsir and Uncle Ovid were very polite to each other, and very gentle to me, and were kind of not there at all the rest of the time. Mr. Washington and I did whatever needed to be done and by the time we were settled back at the Old Place I was about as old as Mr. Washington was when we started out, and Grandsir and Uncle Ovid were only a little bit younger than God.

At the Old Place, it was late winter. There still was snow on the north sides of the shelter-belt evergreens, and ice in the pools where the river overflowed during thaws, but during the middle of the day the ground was soft and the second day I found a pasque-flower on the bar, and the day after that I was lifted right out of my bed just at dawn by the trumpet call of geese.

Around the house for a few days I walked on tiptoe because I did not want to make any noise and disturb Uncle Ovid and Grandsir who appeared to be listening very hard for something.

But presently it seemed that you couldn't hold your breath any more and for a little while Uncle Ovid and Grandsir did not listen so hard. One night it turned cold and froze the puddles and the drenched grass, and afterward it snowed.

In the morning Mr. Washington went out and stocked his bird feeder, the one that stood on a stump cut high for the purpose, so you could see it from the window beside the fireplace. For a long time there were no birds. Then a cardinal cock swooped down to it, looking like a flame against the snow. Two bluejays came along, conducting a transient quarrel, saw the cardinal in the feeder, and promptly began shouting, "Thief! Thief!" in unison, even though they knew the cardinal would leave all the suet for them.

I focused the glass on him to see whether he was the same bird Uncle Ovid banded after an accident three years before. He wasn't. A new cardinal was cock of the hill now. The bluejays were in good voice. Then I saw a downy woodpecker which was in-specting the hickory tree beside the stable. The jays attracted him and he came over to see what they were shrieking about. When he landed on the roof of the feeder and tuned up with a couple of preliminary rattles, the brightest sparrow of them all gave up and flew away. So did the downy, back down the hill where the poison ivy grew, and which Uncle Ovid once had spent all spring cutting back so the downies could reseed it from the berries they loved in the winter. The poison ivy had gotten fierce in the last couple of years, though.

The birds made me feel better. They reminded me that outside our house the world was busy, and the end of certain personal great days comes with the same kind of a sunset that ends any other day. It even made me think that in some ways it was a good thing that the great days did not last forever, because no one would appreciate them then, nor understand them, nor maybe even be able to stand them, because you are not conditioned to endure great days forever. Possibly not at all.

The snow around the feeder was marked by tracks, bird tracks. What kind of tracks would they be, I wondered, if there were no birds? That made me smile a little to myself, because if I had said it aloud Grandsir's eyebrows would have wrenched into a comical slant, and he would have allowed that either I was a very backward boy, or else I was very bright and likely should grow up to be a conspicuously bad poet.

Anyway, it was time to go outside and walk in the snow. Grandsir put on his coat and came along, because there is a feeling you get in fresh snow and that was going to be the last snow of the winter. There is no use wasting anything like that. We did not go out the front of the house because out there where the wintering ground and the marsh used to be, the land looked naked and desolate even under snow. The snow healed the scars made by the bulldozers and covered the welts of ditches, but it was like a cemetery just the same and you have to be in a certain kind of a mood before you go wandering around in snow-covered cemeteries.

Instead, we left Uncle Ovid sitting in the chair in front of the wall where the windows were curtained now, so you did not need to look out and see how the end of something marched across the prairie at you, and went out in back. We crossed the grove of oaks, making our own tracks in the snow, and along the edge of the woods looked for other tracks. There was a brush pile and when I jumped on it a rabbit burst frantically from the far side and dashed headlong into the woods, throwing little divots of snow spray behind him. Farther along, there was a set of tracks like rabbits with bare feet only there was a tail sometimes making a series of dents like maybe the owner had a complaint or two to make and emphasized them with his tail. We followed the tracks to where their owner had dug a nut out of a hollow stump and gone back up a tree. He sputtered indignantly after we passed and I thought how if all the squirrels were gone, the woods would lose many qualities that at first glance do not seem to have to do with squirrels.

On the edge of the pasture there was a belt of standing hay, and snow had bowed it over and the miniature mountain range of grass was cobwebbed with the complicated tunnels of field mouse engineers arising early.

We encountered the long trail of a venturesome mouse surveyor aiming at the woods. Here was a tail to be reckoned with, furrowing between the birdlike tracks. We followed him as he made his tour, bent on some microtomic research, and observed how he had been set upon by fate. We tracked him from clump to clump, losing him once in a while where he'd dawdled and backtracked around a ragweed stalk, to the ambush where the weasel had lain in wait. The weasel's body had melted a depression behind his screen of grass, and I imagined him licking his villainous chops at the prospect of fresh mouse steaks.

There was a climax where the weasel sprang, and the traces of a flurry in the snow. But it was all right. The next mouse tracks were a good three feet away and kept going, wide-spaced with haste and lacking the dalliance of tail marks. The weasel tracks followed, but didn't catch up. Our adventurer had made it the ten feet to the rock pile. Many weasel tracks and angry scratches testified to his safety.

"Well," Grandsir said. "It is not always the same story. This one turned out to have a happy ending."

"Not for the weasel," I said.

Grandsir stopped and rubbed his face thoughtfully.

"That is a rare thing, boy; that is one of the things a boy is so clever about, but that a man is afraid to face."

We started back to the house and after we had walked halfway, Grandsir shook his head again and said, "Yes, indeed, boy, a basic truth. Every time a mouse escapes, a weasel goes hungry; therefore, what is a happy ending?"

"I don't know," I said. "I was just asking."

That is a thing about snow. You go out in it, and if you look about you, it is easy to become involved with many of your neighbors in the wild community; you become interested, and even concerned, and presently you realize that what you are seeking is, truly, a morsel of comfort in animal analogues, that you want reassurance of your own mighty fate from the small fates of field mice.

Then either you are embarrassed and stop looking so closely, or you are not embarrassed and then you had better be careful. Because if you keep looking, sooner or later you may be forced to admit that the prophecies of nature are written very brutally in bloodstains on the snow, and proclaim how many must die so some may live, making mercy a temporary waste, and power eventually vain. Then you might as well go where there is no snow any more, to save yourself from brooding, unless you like to brood.

But after the walk in the snow Grandsir and I came in and cleaned our boots and started into the other room, but could not get by because Algonquin was lying in the doorway, his head down on his forepaws. The yellow eyes were open and glowing with the rage that had begun to ripple and boil on the surface lately, and while we stood there thinking about stepping over him, his flews curled savagely and contemptuously, but he was not looking at us, those tortured eyes were looking into another time.

"He still sneers," Grandsir said. "The mutinous spirit, knowing it must die."

"Will he die, Grandsir?"

"Yes," Grandsir said. "But so must we all. It is a thing you have to get used to, boy."

"I guess maybe he knew it all along," I said.

"Be that as it may," said Grandsir. "Then he knew as much as any man. There is a scriptural injunction, that you must be ready at any time to render up your stewardship and present an accounting of your term."

"Sir," I said. "What is it that no one is supposed to know about dying?"

Grandsir really looked at me now.

"Not the day, nor the hour, nor the manner of it, boy."

"Then that is what he knew," I said and I knew when I said it that my voice was shaking a little with hysteria. "He knew it all along, and so did I."

"Well, now," Grandsir put his hand on my shoulder and let his breath out so it was loud. "And how did you know, boy?"

"You told me," I said, and he had, although he did not remember; he had told me when he spoke the names of great dogs, when he described the bond between men and dogs; he had told me in the lines of sadness on his face when everyone else was flushed with triumph; he had told me by knowing more about men and dogs than he would ever tell; he told me by not telling. I could not possibly explain, but he had told how it would be, and when, in intimate detail: the story of the life and death of great Algonquin, in a parable concerning how everything is for nothing, and worth every bit of it.

Spring came on quickly that year. Sometimes it seemed that Algonquin was all right, around the house and in the yard, but he could not work any more without bringing on the cough, and that was such a terrible thing to see that after it happened once or twice accidentally, everyone was very careful to see that it should not happen any more.

No one said anything about the trials, from the time we came home. I marked off the days in my mind, and the day the Free-for-All started I knew it, but around the Old Place it was as though there was no place like Shuqualak, and no state like Mississippi, and no such thing as a bird dog any more.

Two weeks later was when the travelers would be converging on Grand Junction, the fine dogs and the famous handlers and the owners and the people who wanted to be owners or tried to be handlers or had that strange yearning inside of them that made them look at bird dogs. By that time, though, I had convinced myself the days would pass unnoticed, and I went to bed as usual.

Then suddenly someone was shaking me awake, and it was Uncle Ovid. The lamp he held flickered from the draft, but I could see he was dressed in his fine boots and breeches and the split coat with the velvet lapels, his mustaches trimmed and his face flushed. I was all confused from being asleep and dreaming and I blubbered something incoherent, but Uncle Ovid smiled and said gaily, "Rise and shine, boy. In two hours they put down the first dogs in the National."

I was very bewildered and not sure even whether I was awake or still dreaming. Sitting up in bed I stammered out a question about whether he thought Algonquin was going to win after all.

"Why, boy," Uncle Ovid said fiercely," he never lost at nothing and he isn't going to start now." He left me the lamp and went downstairs. I dressed quickly, because we were five hundred miles from Tennessee, and Algonquin could not run a hundred yards. But Uncle Ovid said so, and looked so, and when I started downstairs I could smell the ham and potatoes and coffee that meant a field breakfast was ready. Mr. Washington was working busily over the range like in the old days when he was between wives, and Algonquin lay on the quilt beside the couch, sprawled carelessly and watching us. He looked nearly as good as ever, as strong and confident and he was breathing all right except for a little catch that stirred his ribs once in a while, but he looked different too, although I could not tell right away why.

Uncle Ovid was sitting at the table getting his first cup of coffee, and, my goodness, he looked fine. I could just barely remember him looking that way, long ago when I first came to visit him. His face was all pink and shining behind the white mustaches, and his shirt was very white and the coat with the padded right shoulder was brushed and there was a shine on his boots that reflected the lamplight like a mirror. He was very cheerful and kept making little jokes and Mr. Washington slid my breakfast in front of me, and all of a sudden I felt fine, too.

The kitchen was warm from the stove, and familiar and comfortable by the old yellow lamplight, and the ham made everything smell wonderful. Mr. Washington kept on working at the range and Uncle Ovid told me about other Nationals he had seen, like in 1902 when Sioux was returned the winner for the second time after running the National's greatest heat in three hours of freezing sleet. Mr. Hochwalt was there, Uncle Ovid said, and had written about it so I might read how it was, but he was there to tell me it was splendid. And he told me about La Besita, the last Llewellin to win, and how she ran in the ice with Brunswick Countess to find nine coveys and three singles. I sat there fascinated and Uncle Ovid said happily, "This is just like old times, isn't it, boy?"

"Yes, sir," I said, happily too, and right then is when it stopped being like anything.

Algonquin coughed.

The cough started tearing at him and he would not give in to it, but the immense cage of his ribs heaved and shuddered, and something in his throat made a choking sound, but Uncle Ovid did not look up, nor stop chuckling at a little joke he had just made. I stopped eating and turned myself to stare at the dog with some terrible premonition that he was looking straight at Uncle Ovid, and then I knew what was different. It was his eyes, not bitter any more, not mocking nor full of hate, but aflame with triumph, *triumph.* The frigid spell cast over his heart all these years was burned away by the bright flame of victory, and the dark shadows were lighted up and there was no more need for fury; the hard times were almost over and he had made it safely, nothing could hurt him any more, and you could see by the way he looked at Uncle Ovid that they had entered a fatal pact.

I put my hands over my face with a frantic gesture and cried out something. Mr. Washington turned around from the range and I saw in horror that his eyes were swollen and bloodshot and the tears had made long clean streaks down his whiskery face. Then my grandfather came into the kitchen, tall and formal and austere and as coldly distant as a mountaintop, and no one had to tell me after that what was going to happen.

Uncle Ovid stood up and I said, "I don't want to go."

"You got a right," Uncle Ovid said. "He was your dog, away back from the beginning. He was your dog by right and you got to stand by him."

"I don't want to go," I said. "Do I have to, Grandsir?"

Maybe he didn't hear me. He had buttoned his coat and was pulling on his gloves and saying names to himself like he was calling a roll. In the silence I heard them, the magic rolling sound of the fabulous roster, conjuring up visions of triumphs in the past: High Valor and Stanford Lad and Blue Dan and Riptide and Roanoke and Prime Minister and all the rest, all slain before their time.

"All right," I said. "All right, then."

And when I got up I said bitterly in a way I never had talked to my elders before, "If you don't want to leave me anything."

Uncle Ovid did not seem to hear. Anyway, it was a foolish thing to say, because doing it this way he left me everything and did not keep any of it for himself.

There were only three horses, so Mr. Washington walked with the dogs, his own old setter and Algonquin, walking slowly for Algonquin's sake. Grandsir rode with the reins folded in his gloved hands, and Uncle Ovid rode a little ahead, smiling straight into the coming sunrise and holding before him the shotgun Lou Smith's daddy made for him, the lovely graceful gun, with the gold and silver all over it.

When we got as far as we were going, Uncle Ovid reined up, but he did not dismount and go to the dog and talk to him and put into him the reserves of his strength because he needed them all himself, all there was left, and Algonquin didn't, not ever any more. He just motioned and Mr. Washington cast the old setter away and Algonquin went out all right without coughing.

Mr. Washington's bitch did not move well any more, she was breaking down behind and Algonquin went away out wide, but she kept on after him. Then on the ridge Algonquin had to stop and cough, it was awful even from that far away, and the old bitch with her limp caught up to him and with him standing there retching she moved past. You could see his head turn and his eyes show the yellow flame as she went by and Uncle Ovid gave a ghastly choking kind of cry, but Algonquin would not let it be this way. He stopped coughing and plunged out, for ten seconds looking like he used to, high and wide and so handsome it made your throat ache. The bitch was making game, a little tentatively, and Algonquin swept up to her so fast I thought he would slam into her but he didn't. He had the wonderful gallantry even when time was running out and he bathed her in that spotlight of his own greatness to make her proud and happy. But she stumbled and the bird flushed wild. Then he went on past her in an absolutely scorching burst of speed and fifty yards further on he hit the covey, moving with that almost footless velocity that swung him in a long graceful pin wheel when the scent stopped him. The sun was just fairly up beyond the hills and there was not much color, just the blue sky and the spring-brown fields and Algonquin silhouetted on the hill, majestically in that one moment all that he ever was.

I tried to lag behind but they waited until my horse came up even.

"There, boy," Uncle Ovid said. "You want to remember that. He has come all the way, and no dog ever touched him or came near to him, and there never was anything like that out there right this minute, because there never was a dog like Algonquin."

He did not have to tell me, no one had to tell me anything about Algonquin. He was my dog, my first dog, and I knew more about him than anyone else dared know. He stood there and he knew how it was. I could tell from the way he stood that he was speaking to the birds for the last time now. They were alarmed by the feeling in the air, but he was pouring out the final eloquence of his genius, saying: *Fare thee well, little brothers; be thee beautiful for me one time more, and be at peace, for it is not thee who shall be slain today; put out the candles of thy alarm and look upon me one time more—thou shalt not see my like again, little brothers, not like me who loved thee. Look one time more into my eyes, then say farewell, and rise together and fly strongly in a pattern that makes a unity of all of us; of earth and sky and men, and thee and me.*

And my Uncle Ovid dismounted then, and I looked straight ahead crying and he walked up to where Algonquin was on point. My God he was splendid, and the birds burst beautifully like a skyrocket and instead of shooting them he shot Algonquin in the head.

Afterward, he picked up the dog and the shotgun lay there, the one Lou Smith's daddy made with all the gold, and I wouldn't touch it, and Grandsir wouldn't even look at it so it was just left there and all the way back Uncle Ovid carried the dead dog and I walked behind him weeping and the horses followed us and Grandsir rode off across the field with the old setter following him and Mr. Washington walked behind all of us saying over and over in a strong calm voice, "Now I lay me down to sleep, I pray the Lord my soul to keep."

On the way home, we did not talk much until the train was away from the prairie country, and safely into the moraine where the hills are very abrupt and there are many lakes, all hard, dark-blue-colored, and the marshes stretch away between the hills for miles, but the grain fields are very small and tidy. We changed trains in the city and there was a while between, so Grandsir and I walked up the ramp from the depot and looked around. A man wearing golden earrings was selling balloons on the corner and across the street in a park the kids were playing baseball.

"Well, boy," Grandsir said. "Now you know."

"Yes, sir," I said.

"A man has only so much time," Grandsir said. "He has a right to make up his own mind how to spend it."

"Yes, sir," I said.

"Presently," Grandsir said, "we will go out and find a puppy. Maybe an Irish setter."

"Irish setters don't win field trials, do they?" I asked. "I mean, you are not running much danger of getting a great dog, are you?"

Grandsir pursed his lips a moment.

"No," he said. "Not much danger."

"Then an Irish setter would be nice," I said.

The man who wore golden earrings began to sing in a liquid tenor voice.

Grandsir asked, "Do you know anyone who maybe would rather have a new bicycle or something, when we get home?"

I said, "No, sir. Bicycles are for young boys."

"Yes," Grandsir said after a moment. "To be sure."

Then we were home and because no one mentioned those times again I became busy with other things. I went back to school and settled down with youngsters my own age again, the familiar, city kind of youngsters who never would have to worry about what I had worried about, and did not know anything about that kind of a life, so I was spared explaining anything. Most of them were wonderfully ignorant about the important things, and hardly any of them knew anything about bird dogs, or cared, because they were spending all their time finding out about athletics and training rules and girls. It was a great relief and after a while I forgot very easily many of the things I had learned so hard, but I did not ever get another bicycle.

It could not have been past midsummer that I came home, though, and found Grandsir glaring at a handful of letters and looking very stern and worried. I asked him if they were about Uncle Ovid, but Grandma said, "Tend to your own knitting, sir."

She talked that way a considerable part of the time, but I had heard her enough to know when she wasn't fooling and this was one of the times. As I said, though, I was very busy and did not actually think about it very much until Grandsir packed his bag quite suddenly one day and got on a train for the Old Place. As I said, it was the middle of the summer and there wasn't any shooting or anything. That was what puzzled me at first, then I settled down enough to figure it must be about Uncle Ovid. I was just stubborn enough to want to go along, but he wouldn't let me.

At the station, Grandsir said something to Grandma about how it was time someone took the old man in hand. I guess, though, that it must have been a little past time, because Grandma heard from Grandsir by telegram just a day or two afterward and was very upset. I asked her was something wrong with Uncle Ovid and Grandma started to get a certain expression on her face, then paused, and instead her face became very soft and gentle and she said, "Ovid is all right now, boy."

At first, they would not let me go to the funeral, but when the time came I did. They thought perhaps I might not be very good when I saw Uncle Ovid that way in the church, but they couldn't fool me, that wasn't Uncle Ovid there. I knew better, but they fooled a lot of people.

When we came back from the church the house was full of people, not from our town, but from all the distant places, with the soft sound of travelers in their voices, men I had always seen with their eyes squinted against the sun, with whistles in their hands and fresh dust on their boots, looking new and strange, now, in the black suits.

They were a little uneasy with the womenfolks around, especially Grandma, from the way they kept bowing and making flowery compliments, but when they drifted away from the parlor into the library they relaxed and looked at the pictures standing there in their frames above the bookcases, and one of them said he allowed it was a pity and a shame for a man to break his heart that way over a dog.

"That's purely the truth," said another, "and I reckon the only thing keeps it such a seldom sin is that not many of us have that kind of a dog, nor that kind of a heart."

There was a picture of Algonquin in the library now, opposite the one of High Valor, and he was splendid in it, tall and white and proud, proud, proud, with the dark head turned a little and the yellow eyes looking out, not at you, but beyond you, forever, lighted with the cold, white light that always glowed around him and was the color of grief and victory.

"Now they have all passed away," the first man said. "And we are safe, finally. The judge is right, how no one cares that much about dogs any more."

And I guess he was.

Anyway, we didn't go west that year, nor the next year, and finally I asked Grandsir if perhaps we could not go back.

"You can," he said and looked at me from beneath those bushy brows. "But if you are wise, you'll wait until you are a little older."

I did not see why it mattered; I could always go back again.

"No," Grandsir said. "Just one time more."

That was a strange thing for him to say. We were in the library and suddenly I became conscious of the old feeling, of the power and magic, and I looked up at the picture of Algonquin and the sweat started wet in my clenched hands, because I felt I was very close to something for maybe the last time.

"Sir," I said, "why did my uncle always live alone?"

There was a silence that stretched out interminably, and I thought for a moment that Grandsir would not answer me. But at length he said, "As a young man, Ovid was disappointed in love."

I did not say anything at all.

Grandsir said, "Nothing is left now, not of the house, nor the grounds, nor the trees, nor anything. Except the stone. Did you know?"

"No," I said.

"It is real marble, like you buy for your kinsmen. Ovid had them carry it from Italy so that the man who carved angels might come and cut upon it the word that was a name."

I said, "Algonquin."

"That's all," Grandsir said. "Nothing else is left."

ARCHIBALD
RUTELEDGE

The Wrong Gobbler

You can count on the fingers of one hand the American outdoor
writers who have attained the stature of Ruteledge. It can hardly
be said that he is a writer first and a hunter next, for the two are
so combined that the result can only be described as unusual.
Every phase of hunting, along with the small, often hidden things
that make the sport what it is, are part and parcel of his tales.
Making a selection from his writings was not easy.

You may remember that my good Negro Steve has a favorite
prayer that I have fallen into the habit of using myself, and
its beauty and all-inclusive nature are best understood if one will
remember how Negro cabins have a habit of staggering when they
attempt to stand. Says Steve feelingly, "O Lord, prop me up in
all my leaning places!" I find myself repeating this prayer whenever I get in a tight spot, especially in the big woods, as I did on
that memorable February morning when I found myself amid a
disconcerting number of wild turkeys.

It's a man's job at any time to handle skilfully one wild turkey;
but when they start simultaneously coming to you from every
direction, calling at every step, as if you were some fatal siren and
they were poor human beings, why, I say it's being in a jam for
sure. It almost makes a hunter feel that, instead of being after
them, they are after him.

The afternoon before, on the advice of Steve, I had gone with
him to Hampton Island, a wild area of some six hundred acres
that is a part of my plantation. As it is little more than waste rice-
fields and overgrown banks, and little better than a watery wilder-

ness, I rarely visit it. One reason why I am not keen about this hunting territory is because it is infested, at all seasons, with cottonmouth moccasins, and these truculent devils take much of the sport out of hunting. But wild turkeys are on the island, and when food is plentiful they never leave it. So perfectly do they adapt themselves to that marshy and semi-submerged waste land that they may be said to have become semi-aquatic, for often they spend the entire day in the reedlands and tawny morasses, returning to the timbered ridges only to roost.

During the late hunting season, so uniformly unsuccessful had I been with wild turkeys that I had set my dusky woodsman on their trail. If they are in the land of the living, Steve will find them; moreover, as they pay small attention to him, he never really scares them. It is a fact, at least in my country, that wild game is invariably less afraid of a Negro than it is of a white man.

Steve shambles amiably along, and deer and turkeys consider him harmless; he is, except that he relays news of their presence to me. It was so on this occasion. He said that he had been hunting hogs on the island (anybody's hogs) and had come across fresh turkey tracks in the old rice-field mud.

Here on the Carolina coast, along the great delta of the Santee, vast areas of former rice-lands are overgrown to white marsh, duck-oats, wampee, wild rice, smartweed, and other aquatic foods. In almost impenetrable cover like this most of our turkeys spend the day. In addition to the foods supplied by the natural growths, they get a lot that is drifted in by the tides. In the late winter, when most of the acorns and other seeds are gone, they feed much on the young green of springing plants. I have killed a gobbler of the marsh in late February that had in his crop nothing but young marsh blades and wampee leaves.

Hopefully Steve and I ranged the island that afternoon, and I did see all the turkey sign a man could wish for. There were tracks innumerable, droppings under the great cypresses and water-oaks, and on some of the ridges and banks whole acres of dead leaves were raked up in long windrows. For two hours we sat still, trying to roost a bird. But we neither saw nor heard a thing except countless gray squirrels and thousands of mallards coming in to the marsh to feed during the night.

At dim dusk we pushed our boat across the river and landed on the old Wambaw Bank, a huge earthen structure of pre-Revolutionary days, still strong and intact, and now grown to trees of immense size. We had hardly left the boat for our walk home when, right over my head, from out of a towering moss-shrouded cypress a gobbler pitched. He was closely followed by another. I did not see either one; but there was no mistaking what they were, and we could tell what direction they had taken.

I knew they would not fly far, and I knew they would alight in trees rather than on the ground, for when flushed from the roost at twilight a wild turkey usually makes an absurdly short fly and never alights on the ground. He may alight in a bare tree, presumably because he can see the branches. I have known a whole flock of sixteen, disturbed at dark, to fly not more than seventy-five yards. Taking Steve's arm, I whispered to him not to say a word, and we tiptoed away from the place. Under such circumstances, a hunt at daylight is the thing.

Let me add that, as far as my observation goes, of late years the turkeys are roosting more warily than they used to. Heretofore I often found them in comparatively bare trees, with perhaps a little mistletoe or moss in them; but now, for their abode for the night, they appear to choose the most densely shrouded cypresses and yellow pines, trees so heavily hung with moss that I have repeatedly stood under one of them, knowing a turkey to be above me, yet also being unable to make him out. I believe our turkeys travel considerable distances to discover trees suitable to their taste for roosting.

When we had gone far enough to make it safe to talk, I told Steve that by daybreak we should be back under the tree from which the two gobblers had been flushed. Thus it was that, while we got home with empty hands, we had a lot of hope in our hearts.

We left the house at five-thirty that mild February morning to walk the mile and a half to the magic spot we had in mind. There should be, I knew, more than those two turkeys that we had flushed. It was still, warm, and very beautiful in the woods, which were awakening to light and to life. I spend much of my time abroad in the wilderness at this hour and at twilight, for one can see and hear things then that he will never see or hear during the garish hours of sunlight.

In the dim swamp that sloped away from the old wooded bank toward the river I began to look for a suitable place for calling. Such a place is hard to find. I mean that the turkey caller should not be too much in the open (so much, for example, that even a slight movement on his part will be detected by an approaching turkey) yet not so hidden that he has a difficult time seeing what is coming. It is important which way he faces, for if one of these great birds is headed your way the slightest noise or movement will make him suddenly and radically change his mind.

At last I decided to sit at the base of a huge cypress, with my back to it, and about thirty yards from the tree on which the gobblers had gone to roost the night before. Steve, who had been shambling stealthily behind me, nodded approval of my selection of a stand, and eased off into the gross swamp. I had to smile when I saw him sit down against a black pine stump, a background that rendered him practically invisible.

Immediately before me was a thin screen of wild blackberry canes, with shielding moss draped over them. Just behind this screen was a small hardwood ridge. Behind me was a muddy swamp, densely grown to willows and alders. I know that it is sometimes bad policy to sit with one's back against a tree, but in this case I decided to face toward the place where the two gobblers had flown.

By the time I got settled, day began to dawn, all pearly and pink through the silent swamp, gradually tingeing everything with a roseate fairy light. Then, curiously, I heard a whippoorwill, for that bird is excessively rare here in the spring. Cardinals awoke, and Carolina wrens gave their rollicking calls; marsh hens cackled raucously from across the river, and chickadees began to radio their companions. Light was coming fast.

Taking out my beloved call, Miss Seduction, I touched her gently. Thinking at that time that I heard a slight noise behind me, I eased up cautiously to look. As I did so a masterly gobbler flew out of the cypress against which I had been leaning! He had been there all the time, camouflaged by the heavy moss, but I had not suspected his presence.

Especially in the dusk of the morning, a wild turkey will sometimes let you walk up under him; and this is commonly true if he thinks he is pretty well hidden. A wild thing enjoys as much as a human being a sense of security; give him this, and he will not rush away at your coming. I have walked within fifteen feet of an old buck curled up in dense brush.

Well, I thought, there are three big boys in this vicinity. I heard this latest gobbler come to ground far behind me; and, believe me, a big one can sometimes make a lot of racket doing that. I did not know whether I had disturbed him or whether he had come down of his own accord. As soon as he was on the ground I called again, at the same time looking at my watch. It was six-forty. I glanced off to my right and happened to see good old Steve, silent and inscrutable, trusting me. I must try not to disappoint him.

At that moment a thunderous sound came from the island—a long, low roar. The mallards and black ducks were leaving the marshes for a day in the salt creeks and bays down the river. For several minutes this little earthquake continued. Then all was still. Suddenly, behind me and a good way up the creek bank on my left, I heard a turkey. I answered softly, cajolingly. Oh, man! The whole country was full of turkeys! I heard them on every side of me. And they just happened to be in the right mood for calling.

I knew at once that this must be a good-sized flock, of which I had seen but three. The calm morning, the still wilderness, their own slight and unalarmed separation—all these conspired to make them loquacious. Suddenly, from across the river, a gobbler came straight for me. But he was flying well above the tall treetops, and I did not want to spoil everything by risking a most uncertain shot at him. But he was a grand sight, sailing high through the red dawn on those wide and splendid wings of his. He went over my head and alighted on the Wambaw Bank in a high water-oak, about two hundred yards behind me.

I heard four or five calling from the river bank on my left. Two were calling from the island immediately across from me. I heard one far behind me. Then one tuned up right in front of me. There were too darned many turkeys!

I glanced at Steve. The whites of his eyes were slowly rolling. Gently and coaxingly I touched Miss Seduction. I felt certain of an early chance to shoot. But in hunting this great bird almost everything is unpredictable. I have known a wild turkey to give a hunter a chance by making a stupid break; but he would be a foolish man who counted on his bronzed majesty's making a mistake. When it comes to blundering, a wild turkey isn't in a class with a man.

As soon as the gobbler in front of me began to call softly yet clearly, and I heard the turkey in the tree behind me calling him, I decided to quit my cajoling. I would concentrate on the one coming straight for me. It's all right to call a turkey; but if you really want one to come, let another of his kind call him for you. I knew that the turkey in front of me was coming right out to me, and might step from the shelter of the swamp at any minute.

I put up my gun. At such a time a man should have his gun at his shoulder; for if he waits to make that motion until the great bird is in sight, things may happen to make the hunter kick himself all the way home. For one thing, a wary gobbler is almost certain to vanish before the hopeful hunter can shoot—or at least before he can shoot with the accuracy essential in killing this finest of all game birds of the world.

So there was the layout: Old Steve rolling his eyes like a drunken gorilla; some six or seven birds now calling behind me—two across the river on my left; one straight in front of me—and all their yelps indicated that Miss Seduction had them in her power. They were closing in on me from every direction. And there was I, sitting flat, my call beside me, my gun up and ready for action.

I knew well enough that if I shot, the whole business of calling would be over for a long time. I only hoped that the rajah of the river bottoms was the bird coming straight for me. I had it all arranged very nicely. As soon as he showed himself I would collect him and go home in serene triumph. But weird things happen in the big woods, things which, years later, the hunter remembers with an "ouch."

While I was concentrating on the ridge before me, without a sound to warn me, a gobbler walked up behind me, right up to my tree, and started to walk past me—not an inch farther than three feet from me, and on my right. He had come through the swamp on the soft mud, and he hadn't made a sound.

Turkeys make a lot of noise when they are in the water—almost as much as deer—but the approach of this bird had been noiseless. The first thing I knew of his presence was his great head stuck around the tree; then, "Kut! Kut!" in wild alarm. And just as I saw him out of the corner of my right eye I made out a black shape ahead of me, but dimly outlined in the fringes of marsh that lined the swamp edges. He was the gobbler on which I had designs, but this other old boy had broken into the picture. And I knew that one "Kut!" of his would change the whole aspect of things.

As soon as he saw me he jerked back and then made a prodigious leap that was half flying. He didn't run and didn't fly; but he made a marvelous slashing high jump that took him back and away to the left toward the creek bank. Meanwhile the gobbler ahead of me had vanished; and any man who knows turkeys knows that my chances of seeing that gentleman again were slight.

But the big bird that had, as you might say, been eating out of my right-hand pocket stopped within range, though partly shielded by stout alder stems. So silent and spectral he stood that if I had not seen him go there I would hardly have been able to make him out. Without lowering my gun, I swung it slowly around until I got the ivory bead on him. Since he had sounded the alarm, I was not counting on seeing any other turkeys. I touched the trigger, and one of the old monarchs of Wambaw was down to stay.

Of the ten or twelve other turkeys near me when I shot, I heard not a sound. After I had retrieved my grand bird, a twenty-pound bird of the purest wild stock left in North America, Steve and I began our triumphant march homeward just as the rising sun was turning the broom-sedge into a field of gold.

Said Steve, "Sometimes it is harder to kill a turkey when there is a plenty than when there is only one."

As I looked at the old strategist of the wilds slung over Steve's broad and patient shoulders I was satisfied, even though I had killed the wrong gobbler. The one that was coming straight for me will never know how close a call he had, nor how it happened that one of his own mates saved his life.

P A U L H Y D E
B O N N E R

Mollie

This was selected as the most different quail shooting story ever encountered. It is by a writer who is recognized for the excellence of his novels as well as his short stories. Drawn from his *Glorious Mornings,* a collection of hunting and fishing tales from a wide area, it has some of the flavor of "Rajah's Rock," a salmon fishing story laid in Ireland. Bonner can make the possible quite probable, which you will admit after reading "Mollie."

It was not until the season had closed on March fifteenth that Purvey began to realize the change that had come over Mollie. The very first day out with the plow he had noticed that she was not pulling her weight. It was on the twenty-acre piece that he had figured on switching from corn to tobacco because it lay in low ground along the branch where there was always good drainage and the soil was a mixture of rich dark loam and sand. He could tell at once by the way her traces sagged and he had to lean on the right handle to keep the share-cutting straight. He had slapped her with the reins for three lengths of the field, then he had cut a nice limber sucker from a sweetgum in the woody copse that followed the course of the branch and given her a good smart lick with it every time her traces were not as taut as Mike's.

When he had bought Mike and Mollie from a dealer up at Andrews three years before, his neighbors had shaken their heads and clucked their tongues. Pretty looking, yes, they had said down at the store, but too small, too neat and fancy for mules that have to be plowing and hauling and doing a day's work. Purvey had not argued. He had known what he was doing. That pair was just what he had been looking for—strong enough to work his land, which was so full of sand it turned soft and easy, and small enough so that the gentlemen whose quail leases he looked after could mount into the saddle without him having to give them a leg up. He used to have horses for the gentlemen, horses he rented for the season, but they never worked out right. There would always be one that was skittish and shied at every shoat, or one that was so lazy on its feet that it stumbled into every stump hole. And the gentlemen were always complaining and saying, Purvey, why can't you get us some decent nags to ride? Why, hell, mules would be better than these bucking bronchos.

That had given him the idea, and it had worked out just fine. He had paid Mr. Fletcher, the dealer, two hundred and forty dollars for the pair, which was a bargain because nobody wanted mules that size even though they were perfectly matched, sound as two new-minted dollars, and only four years old. Mr. Jessup had been the first of the gentlemen to shoot that season. He had come down in early December and brought a friend with him. When he had gotten out of the car at the little church for colored folks where they always met to shoot the Rutledge property, he had slapped Purvey on the back and let out a whoop like a schoolboy. That's the slickest pair of mules I ever laid my eyes on, he had said, patting Mollie's shining neck. Don't ever let the Duke of Alba see that pair. He'd give a thousand dollars for them.

Purvey had no idea who the Duke of Alba was, nor why he would fancy mules enough to pay big money for them, but he was pleased by the reception. He had had to admit to Bessie, his wife, when he had ridden off that morning, he on his little gray mare, leading Mollie and Mike, that they looked as pretty as anything in the circus. He had curried and brushed them until their smooth mahogany coats shone like patent leather. Nor had Mr. Jessup's enthusiasm waned after a day in the saddle. They had turned out to be quick, careful walkers who cutely dodged every stump hole and delicately picked their feet over fallen logs. When the dogs had a point, there was no need to tie them up or carry the reins for Purvey to hold. Just dismount and leave them and they would stand there, stanch and immobile.

When, later on in the season, Mr. Dodge and Mr. Weatherby, the two other members of the syndicate, came down for their shooting, they were prepared to admire, for Mr. Jessup had written them glowing accounts of Mollie and Mike. And it had gone on like that for two seasons, everybody happy about the mules and complaints reduced to the behavior of the dogs, which could not be blamed on Purvey as the gentlemen supplied their own and all he had to do was feed and kennel them from Thanksgiving to March fifteenth. Of course Purvey also handled them in the field. He was good with dogs, talking to them mostly and never beating them real hard when they jumped a covey. Just a light whack or two on their hind quarters and a real sharp scolding while they lay in the grass and cringed. Dogs knew when they had done wrong, just as well as people, and it often wasn't their fault. Coming down fast on the lea of a covey, they sometimes wouldn't get the scent until they were right on one of the outlying birds, and when he flushed the whole covey was sure to follow.

There were only two out of the six that were what you could call real downright reliable bird dogs. They were Brownie, a small rangy pointer who was three-quarters covered with liver-colored spots that made it difficult to keep an eye on him in the high broomsedge, and Tess, a big white setter bitch with a black patch over one eye that made her look like Lew Douglas or the Hathaway shirt man. The others were temperamental, sometimes flashy, sometimes messing everything up.

Of course all three of the gentlemen wanted to hunt Tess and Brownie every day. But Purvey was stubborn on that point. Even though it was their leases and their dogs, as long as he was guide and handler all six dogs had to take their half-days in rotation, so they wouldn't get tuckered out and lame and not be able to get through the season. But no matter how often he explained this to them in his soft voice, they would always say to Bessie when they stopped by at the farm to pick up the pair for the morning, what's the matter, Mrs. Gourdine? Why aren't we taking Brownie and Tess? Because Purvey says it's to be Jack and Sunset, Bessie would tell them, because Brownie and Tess was out yesterday and they ain't due to go hunting again until after tomorrow. They grumbled a bit, but they knew that Purvey was right and they respected him for it.

The business with Mollie was all the fault of Mr. Christie. He was the new member who had taken Mr. Weatherby's place in the syndicate when Weatherby had had to give up quail shooting because of a stroke. He had come down for the first time in the early part of February, after Mr. Jessup and Mr. Dodge had had their quota of days in the field and had gone back to Cleveland where they both were something big in the steel industry. This Christie wasn't a Clevelander. He was a New York lawyer, who, according to what he said, handled some legal matter for Jessup and Dodge. He brought his wife down with him, a well-set-up blonde woman he called Gertrude who could ride and shoot as well as any man Purvey had ever guided. They put up at a motel near Georgetown and motored over every day for the two weeks they were down, that is, every day but Sundays.

Purvey took a fancy to the Christies from the start. There was no fuss and feathers about them the way there is about some of the northerners who come to hunt quail in the Low Country of South Carolina during the winters. They were full of beans and fun, liked to horse around and say silly things, kidding and sassing each other, and Purvey. And they were both real smart with a gun— quick and deadly. They used double-barreled sixteens which they said they had had made to measure in England. With those four barrels they could kill more birds in a day than Jessup and Dodge with their automatics could kill in a week. Maybe there was something to that made-to-measure business. More times than not there were four birds to pick up after a covey rise.

It was because he liked Christie that Purvey felt so mean about Mollie. For it was Mr. Christie who had ruined her, made a trollop out of a good steady mule. If he hadn't given her to Christie on that very first day, all might have been well. He had given Mike to Mrs. Christie because Mike's saddle holster was newer and nicer looking. Well, that was the big mistake. He had not known then that Christie was one of those city fellows who just can't help spoiling animals. Anything with four legs made him go soft. He just couldn't bring himself to cross that mule on one little thing. If Mollie wanted to go around a tree to the right, he let her go to the right. If Mollie stopped and ate cane, fine. If Mollie looked longingly at a streamer of Florida moss that was hanging out of her reach, Mr. Christie would reach it for her and lean over in the saddle so that she could take it in her dainty, gunmetal lips. He brought a pocketful of sugar every day to feed her, and gave her half his lunch. No Duke of Alba was ever more stuck on a mule than Mr. Christie was on Mollie. It got to be so that Mrs. Christie would look disgusted and say, why Dan, anyone would think you were in love with that mule, and Christie would whoop and shout, love her? I adore her. Don't I, my sweet little Mollie?

By the time March first had come around and the Christies had said good-bye and Christie had kissed Mollie on the nose, she was the most ornery, stuck-up mule in Williamsburg County. She wouldn't work. She wouldn't eat unless there was some cane in the hay, and she treated Mike like she'd never been in harness with him. Let him swing his nose over towards her and her ears would go back and one of those little black hooves on her back feet would flash out so fast you couldn't follow it with your eye.

"Look, Bessie," Purvey Gourdine said to his wife one evening in late April when the tobacco was all set out and he was resting up to plant the cotton. "There ain't nothin' to it, I jes got to get rid of Mollie. She's ruint, plum ruint. She won't work. She's ornery. Kicks Mike or any other animal gets near her. It's all right havin' a mule that the gentlemen likes to ride huntin', but I didn't buy that pair jes for the saddle. From March to November they got to do their share of the work around the farm. I ain't in no position like Jake Ferrier over to the Longleaf Plantation who ain't got nothin' to do the year round but plantin' lespedeza and shootin' hawks when he ain't takin' the gentlemen out huntin'. I ain't paid on that basis. I got my farm to run if you and me and the kids ain't goin' to starve. Jake's got horses in the barn that never carries nothin' but a saddle, but my mules has got to work when there's work to be done."

"Mebbe you could trade her with Mr. Fletcher for another the same size," Bessie suggested as she cut a piece of denim from a pair of old overalls which was going to patch another, less old pair.

"Yeah, well mebbe I could," Purvey said, with doubt in his voice.

"Mollie's a right pretty lookin' mule," Bessie commented, having noted her husband's hesitancy.

"But she ain't got a good reputation," Purvey said.

Bessie Gourdine looked up from her sewing and smiled at Purvey. "I do believe you're carryin' on like Mr. Christie, talkin' about Mollie havin' a reputation jest as if she were some slut of a girl."

"Things like that gets around," Purvey said, moodily.

"Shucks, Purvey," Bessie said impatiently, "who-all knows about Mollie not workin' right except you and me and our kids and old Jim?"

"They're laughin' about it down to the store," Purvey said sorrowfully. "I heard 'em. They was sayin' how Mr. Christie has ruint her for work."

"Tst, tst," Bessie clucked, "You reckon the story's got as far as Andrews?"

"I reckon it has. Seems like it's some kind of big joke on me. Mr. Fletcher's likely to be laughin' fit to burst his collar."

There was a long silence while Purvey sucked on his pipe and Bessie sewed on the patch.

"Maybe Jake Ferrier might use her over to Longleaf Plantation," Bessie said finally.

"I done spoke to him a'ready. He says his gentlemen ain't ridin' no mules."

"My, oh my!" Bessie murmured and sighed.

That summer seemed the longest that Purvey Gourdine could remember. Though his son Harry, a strapping boy of eighteen, and old Jim, the colored hand, were willing, they could be of little help except to work Mike alone or run the pick-up truck. Mollie would not work for them at all, and if neither of them came near her, she just kept turning her rear artillery in their direction. Purvey was the only one who could get her to move, and to do that he had to keep after her every minute with a stout, limber switch. You might have thought she would come out of it, forget about Mr. Christie and his sugar and his patting, but not Mollie. She had a long memory and she knew well that, come the first frost of November, she'd have that saddle on again and would be lazing her way across the savannahs, through the longleaf saplings, snipping dainty bits here and there when the fancy took her, and smelling the sweet scent of warm dead partridge in her saddle bag. Those were the days she waited for in her pettish, ornery, feminine way.

Sure enough, the day Purvey and his son came back from Monks Corner with the six crates of bird dogs in the pick-up and set them loose in the kennels, Mollie trotted across the small field where she and Mike and the gray mare were pastured with her big ears up and forward like twin bayonets. She stuck her head over the wire fence and started a song that was half bray and half whinny. From that moment she was a redeemed animal, sweet and gentle as a kitten. Anyone, Harry or old Jim, could walk up to her in the field and toss a halter over her head. And she took to nuzzling Mike again, something she hadn't done since March. But Purvey was not fooled. He knew that the change of heart would only last as long as the bird season, that next spring she would be worse than ever.

When Mr. Dodge and Mr. Jessup came down together in early December, Purvey could hardly wait to tell them his sad tale. They met at the Simons farm on the first day. Because Purvey knew that there were at least ten coveys using there, he started them off with Brownie and Tess. The day was bright and sunny, with a scattering of fleecy clouds blowing high from the west, and the night dew had been heavy enough to leave a good scent. Everything was perfect for a good day's sport except the state of Purvey's mind.

As they rode out through the back gate of the farm into a broad savannah, Purvey turned in his saddle and spoke to Mr. Jessup, who was behind him on Mollie. "That mule you're ridin' like to ruin my summer," he said with feeling.

Mr. Jessup chuckled. "Mollie? Why, what's she been up to?"

"She won't do a lick of work no more, and she's got so ornery she'll kick anyone who gets in range of her."

"She was as gentle as a lamb when I mounted her," Mr. Jessup said, patting Mollie's neck reassuringly.

"Sure, she's all right now, now that the huntin' season's on. She likes you gentlemen fine, and following the dogs suits her, but she's got it into her mind she's too good to pull a wagon or a plow."

Mr. Jessup roared with laughter and turned in his saddle to Mr. Dodge who was following on Mike. "Did you hear that, Jerry?" he said. "Purvey says that Mollie has delusions of grandeur. She only likes to go shooting with us. Won't work anymore."

"I always said that was a damn smart mule," Mr. Dodge said, and they both laughed loud and long.

"Next year she'll be wanting to spend the summer at Newport," Mr. Jessup said, wiping the tears from his eyes.

Purvey was disturbed. No one wanted to take his problem seriously. It was just a big joke, and he was the butt of it. "With me it ain't so funny as it sounds, Mr. Jessup," he said earnestly. "I've got me a farm to run. I can't afford to feed no mule as thinks she's too good to work. If she cuts up next spring the way she did last, I'm goin' to find me another mule."

Mollie stopped to pluck a bunch of laurel leaves. Mr. Jessup jerked her head up and kicked her with his heels, but she did not move until the branch was secure in her mouth. "Come on, Mollie," Mr. Jessup commanded, "no feminine temperament. You're out hunting now."

Purvey shook his head. "You see what I mean, Mr. Jessup."

But they never really did believe the story of her wickedness. How could they, when she was always so docile, so clever on her feet, so stanch when the guns were firing and she was left alone? They put it down to Purvey's natural pessimism, the pessimism of a man who spends his life in a struggle with Nature. It delighted them that Mollie had the instincts of a lady and preferred the sporting life to the drudgery of the farm. It was a story they would tell and retell back home on Shaker Heights.

Purvey's gloom persisted in spite of fine days with many coveys found. The gentlemen were happy even though they fired four shells for every bird killed. It was the pines against the blue and the dogs racing back and forth in the wind-billowed broomsedge that thrilled them as much as the shot fired. But poor Purvey knew that in another two weeks Mr. and Mrs. Christie would arrive and that would be the end of any chance to retrieve Mollie from her path of glory.

How right he was! The morning the Christies arrived, as they stepped out of their station wagon at the colored church, Mollie, who was tethered to the fence under the chinaberry tree, lifted her head, her ears forward, and gave forth with her combination bray-whinny.

"Mollie, sweet Mollie!" Mr. Christie called, and forgetting his wife and the yelping dogs in the back of the car, rushed across the yard and flung his arms around Mollie's neck. The mule pushed at his pocket with her nose. "Oh, it's sugar you want, my Mollie-O." He pulled out a lump and she picked it daintily from his palm. "What a mule! What a memory! Did you see that, Gertrude? Did you hear her call to me? She knew me the minute I stepped out of the car. Oh, Mollie, if you could only talk." Mollie let out a low snort. "By God, Purvey, she understands me. She tried to answer."

Purvey Gourdine, who was slipping the guns into the saddle holsters, grunted. "I reckon she knows what you're sayin' aw right. That's the trouble with that mule, she knows more'n is good for her."

Mrs. Christie laughed. "Now don't tell me she gossips, Purvey."

Purvey walked over to the station wagon, opened the rear window and let the dogs out. They were Flotsam and Blitz, a pair of fast, unreliable pointers. He was saving Brownie and Tess for the next day when they would be shooting the paper company lease where there were at least twelve coveys using. Purvey watched the dogs race around the church yard. He was worried. He liked the Christies. They were nice, kindly folk, and they shot like masters. Yet they, that is, he, was the cause of all the trouble. He hated to disappoint him after that greeting with Mollie, but it was no use, he had to tell him sooner or later, and it might as well be now.

"Ma'am," he said to Mrs. Christie, "that mule is doin' the last bit of huntin' she's ever goin' to do on my property. She's so spoilt she won't do a lick of work outside of ridin' gentlemen after birds. When the season's over, I'm gettin' rid of her. I jes can't afford to own a mule that won't do her share."

"What's that? What's that?" Christie asked in astonishment. "You're going to get rid of Mollie?"

"Yes, sir, Mr. Christie," Purvey said firmly. "She's gettin' too smart for her own good."

"Now listen, Purvey," Christie said genially. "Let's not talk about this now. Gertrude and I have come down for a pleasant two weeks of sport and we don't want any sorrows hanging over it. Just give Mollie another chance for the moment. Let me talk to her. Then if she doesn't behave, you can have a second look at the problem."

"Jest as you say, Mr. Christie," Purvey said skeptically. "Only I'm warnin' you, and—" he nodded toward Mollie—"her too, that she's got to pull that plow and keep her hind feet on the ground or else."

As usual Flotsam and Blitz ranged so wide that they were out of sight half of the time. Purvey did not worry so much about Blitz, who he knew would hold stanch if he did find a covey, which was not too often as he preferred to range the cotton fields and corn stubble where quail are seldom found. It was Flotsam he was not sure of. He had a suspicion that this dog liked to get out of sight for the express purpose of flushing coveys. More than once he had seen birds flying from a direction where Flotsam had been heading. He told the Christies to keep an eye on Blitz while he trotted off to see what Flotsam was up to.

Christie and his wife had ridden on a hundred yards or so, whistling for Blitz whom they could see far off on the right, racing across a plowed field as if he were a sweepstake greyhound, when Mollie lifted her head, shot her ears forward, and gave a little rattling snort with her nostrils.

"She's worried about Purvey and the grey mare leaving us," Gertrude Christie said.

Christie patted Mollie's neck. "Never mind, old girl," he said, "they'll be back in a minute."

Mollie stopped, her head still high, her nostrils still fluttering. Christie paid no attention. He was intent on getting Blitz out of the plow and back to the feed patch of lespedeza which was just ahead. He put the whistle between his lips again and blew two long sharp blasts. Blitz must have heeded finally, for they could see him turn sharply, bound the low hedge that bordered the plow, and come racing towards them.

"Come on, Mollie," Christie said, giving her a gentle tap with his heels.

Gertrude Christie reined in Mike and turned in her saddle. "What's got into Mollie?" she asked. "What's she looking at?"

"I can't imagine," her husband replied. "She seems to be watching Blitz."

When Blitz was about fifty yards from them, bowling along, he suddenly jammed on his brakes and froze. The point was a solid one. Every muscle of the dog was petrified into the final attitude of stopping, his front feet thrust forward, his head down, his tail rigid as a bent stick.

"Down we get," Christie said to his wife, excited. "This is it. No stink bird this time."

They both slid out of the saddles, pulled the guns out of the holsters and loaded.

"I think we had better lead the mules around behind Blitz so they won't be facing us when the birds get up," Mrs. Christie said.

Christie pulled on Mollie's bridle. "Come, girl," he urged. But she did not move. Her head was still high, her ears still forward. She was as frozen as Blitz. Christie gave the bridle a yank. "Come on! What are you frightened of?" It was useless. He might as well have tried to move a bronze statue. "She's not going to move," he said to his wife.

"Well, leave her, then," Gertrude Christie said impatiently. "If she gets a pellet in her hide, it's her own stubborn fault. I'm beginning to see what Purvey was talking about."

The Christies took a wide circle and came up behind Blitz, who had never moved a muscle. Christie came well forward on the left side of the dog in the hope of making the birds break away from the direction of the mules. When a lone cock quail rose at Gertrude's feet, she nailed it. Then the whole covey exploded and Gertrude dropped another, while Christie missed with his first shot and killed one with his left barrel. They both stood where they had fired, intently watching to mark where the birds would settle.

Christie tried to call in Blitz to retrieve the dead birds, but he found it hopeless. The overexcited dog was racing in circles like a chicken with its head cut off. So he and Gertrude did their own picking up, which was not too difficult on the sparse ground.

Mollie was eating grass when Christie came up to her, carrying the three dead birds. "You know, Gertrude," he said, "I wonder if Mollie was pointing that covey."

"Don't be an idiot," Mrs. Christie said crossly.

Christie dangled the birds in front of Mollie. She lifted her head and sniffed them deeply, then ruffled their feathers with her prehensile lips. "Did you smell 'em, Mollie?" he asked. "Did you get that point? Was Blitz only backing you up?"

Purvey came riding up with Flotsam running behind him. "I seen where some of your birds lit," he said. "I got 'em marked good. How many did you get?"

"The little lady got two, but I muffed my right barrel. Too excited," Christie said, and mounted into the saddle. "Okay, let's go. I want to get that bird I missed."

They rode over to a spot where the pines grew closer together, Purvey keeping the dogs in at heel. Finally Purvey halted and told them to dismount. "They're right in there by them saplin's," he said, pointing to a cluster of young longleaf pines that looked like green brooms up-ended. Purvey dismounted too, walking between them, talking to the dogs, cautioning them to take it easy and hunt close. Christie and his wife went forward cautiously, guns ready, as the dogs worked back and forth in front of them, noses to the ground. Flotsam was the first to get a point and Christie took it. A single bird rose up, curled, and flew back over their heads. Christie wheeled and killed it high and far out. He was surprised to see that it dropped near Mollie. Then he realized that she had moved, that she had left Mike and the grey mare and had wandered fifty yards to the right. That was unlike her. Never before had she budged from the spot where he had left her. He walked over to pick up the dead bird and Blitz followed him.

He was about to scold Mollie when he saw that she had again assumed the rigid, watching posture, with her head high and her ears forward. Blitz galloped up beside her and froze to a point. Christie turned to Purvey and his wife. "Look at that!" he called excitedly. "Mollie's pointing a single and Blitz is backing her up again."

"More'n like she smells a snake," Purvey said.

"Do be careful," Gertrude warned.

"Blitz he's pointin' your dead birds," Purvey said.

"No he isn't," Christie said, walking forward. "That bird of mine is right here," he stooped down and picked it up. "Blitz ran right over it." Stuffing the bird quickly into his pocket he moved forward cautiously, edging between Mollie and Blitz, his eyes on the ground, fearing it might be a snake after all.

When the quail flushed, Christie took his time and killed it neatly, then he turned and came up to Mollie whose ears were drooping mulewise now. He put his cheek on her soft nose. "Mollie, my lass, you're the wonder of the age," he crooned. "You found a covey and you found a single. And those dumb people wouldn't believe you. They thought you were just ornery. They thought you were seeing snakes. Well, we'll show 'em who's the best damn quail hound in South Carolina. Come on, Mollie."

He walked in the direction of the dead bird, Mollie coming along behind him, nuzzling the pocket where he kept the sugar. Stopping a few yards from the spot where the quail had fallen, he pointed. "Now fetch it, Mollie," he said. "Fetch dead and you get your lump of sugar."

Mollie looked at him, then punched her nose hard against his pocket.

Christie shook his head. "No, Mollie, not until you fetch that bird."

Mollie hesitated, then out of the corner of her eyes she saw Flotsam running over to the spot where the dead bird lay. With a spring she jumped forward, pushed the dog away with her head and picked up the quail in her lips. Tossing her head as if in triumph and snorting through her nostrils, she brought it back to Christie. He took it with his left hand and offered her a lump with his right.

"Nobody's going to sell you down the river," he whispered to her, stroking her sleek neck.

Mrs. Christie and Purvey had come up, looking bewildered.

"This is weird," Mrs. Christie said. "It's fantastic!" She turned to Purvey. "Tell me, did you ever hear of a mule pointing birds?"

Purvey shook his head. "No, ma'am, I can't rightly say as I have. It don't look to me as if it's quite natural."

"You saw it, didn't you?" Christie asked.

"Yes, sir, I saw what looked like it," Purvey admitted.

"And, Gertrude, you saw her point the covey, didn't you?" Christie asked his wife.

"I suppose I did, but I still think I dreamt it," Gertrude said.

"What did you pay for Mollie, Purvey?" Christie asked.

"I give Mr. Fletcher two hundred and forty for the pair," Purvey replied.

"Well, you can keep Mike, I'm giving you three hundred dollars for Mollie this very day," Christie said, with the smile of a man who has acquired a masterpiece. "And what's more, I'm paying you for her feed and keep." He turned to Mollie. "No more bloody plowing for you, my Mollie-O."

"It's sure kind of you, Mr. Christie," Purvey said, embarrassed, "but I don't reckon there is a mule on earth worth . . ."

"Says you!" Christie shouted with a whoop at the end. "Wait till the Duke of Alba hears about Mollie. He'll pay anything to get her for his partridge shoot in Andalusia."

"Yeah?" Purvey said skeptically, taking off his cap and scratching his head. "Mr. Jessup was speakin' about that Dook. He must be powerful fond of mules."

NASH BUCKINGHAM

Broccoli

The duck hunting stories of Nash Buckingham have, in the fullness of time, become accepted as the true classics of this phase of
the sport. They attained this stature not merely through time,
but by comparison with other writings on the subject. I not only
reread the offerings from *Game Bag, De Shootinest Gent'man,
Mark Right* and *Tattered Coat,* I re-reread them. I came up with
"Broccoli" because I like it—for countless reasons which you may
discover.

Because that stand at the head of Long Pond is where I was
permitted to make my first solo duck hunt, it is my favorite
of all such delectable spots I have ever known. A comprehensively
final statement, in view of the fact that my later wildfowling days
have rounded the compass. Perhaps the head of Long Pond isn't
or never was the one best duck-shooting spot on the continent. But
to my certain knowledge there have been few better during the
past fifty years. Besides, sentimental factors of a most engaging
nature bolster my attachment to the place. For even before I was
allowed to gun without Dad or Mister Arthur, I had come to know
all the favorite blinds encircling famous old Aconapaw Club,
Willow Poles, Bethel's, Walkers, Parker's—and then the head of
Long Pond. Tremendous flights of waterfowl had used those bays
and sloughs and pockets for centuries.

To reach the head of Long Pond we traversed Little Lake and
entered an arm of narrow water paralleling the Big Lake for three-
quarters of a mile. What magnificent large-mouth bass fishing that
stretch used to afford! Its union with Big Lake formed a shallow,

sweeping inlet lush with aquatic foods for wildfowl and fringed with "saw" grass and willows. Ashore, behind the blind, pecan and hickory trees mingled in profusion. And it was there we ate picnic lunch or held barbecues when Jenkins was along to make the sauce and baste. Out front, across more than a mile of open water, a ridge of giant hardwoods and primeval cypress, magnificent in their woodland virginity, met the horizon. And from the Mississippi, beyond, poured flights of swan, geese and ducks that at times seemed to obscure the heavens.

Be sure, however, that in nominating the head of Long Pond as my life-long choice of duck shooting stands, many another such sporting Utopia passed in review. The Woodbury Pool in Beaver Dam's north end; its Clover Leaf Hole, where mallards showered down through the lacy cypress tops like flaming plummets; or the hollow log in that pin oak flat of Clarences in the rice fields. Or what about the Cajun country of Louisiana, the Laramie plains, Grand Prairie's undulating surprises, or Colorado highlands where teal and sprig flights wove sarabands of blue and white above our meandering meadow cricks? So, now for the day when Horace and I are back at the head of Long Pond, along with Pat, noblest of sires in my long line of Chesapeake Bay dogs. There has come a lull in the flight, it is getting on toward snack time, and Horace is no hand to sit idly by.

"Horace," I asked, "what was the toughest day you've ever put in, out duck shooting?" Cogitating deeply, Horace gave lengthy pause before tackling that one.

"Well, suh, I kin think uv er whol' lot o' turrible times. F'instance, whin d' towboat all but runned ovah an' drown't yu an' me dat time. Agin, whin yu an' me kilt all dem geeses away up on d'haid o' Ship Islan' bar an' had t' lug 'em all d' way home.

"H'it mought bin d' night ol' Cunn'l Carrol an' me got los' in d' snow storm out yonder on d' Big Lake, an' spint d' night in d' woods by er fia'ah. An' dat wuz er turrible rookus whin d' cyclone swep' jes' pas' me an' Mist' Tim o'dare an' 'stroy'd d' Beaver Dam clubhouse. L-a-w-d-y—L-a-w-d-y—dat wuz night turned into er thousan' demons by d' fo'ces uv evil." Horace buried his face in his hands and shuddered. He had lost his old mother in that storm.

"But, suh," he looked up to say, "now ef yu wuz t' ast me what wuz d' mos' worrysom' day evah I put in whar dis duck shootin' bizness is c'ncerned, dat would be easy, Mist' Nash."

"Well, what was it?" Horace got up off the decoy coop and carefully scanned the horizon for prospective victims.

"H'it wuz d' day befo' shootin' season opened, sev'ul years ago—whin yu all had d' houseboat tied up jes' above Mist' Ed Williams landin'—'member? I means d' time dat fat funny-lookin' l'il ol' brief-talkin' man jined d' club—d' man whut owned d' gun an' cottige fact'ry an' got d' whol' place in er swivet. D' one yu all call't Mist' Chancy. He claim Mist' Homer Jones sold 'im d' mimbership th'u Mist' Hinry Davis. But Mist' Hinry he later on denied dat sech wuz d' fac's in d' case. Y' know, Mist' Nash, yu didn' git dar until atta' d' rookus wuz ovah wid, an' nevah prop'ly understood jes' whut I wint th'u wid." Horace peered right, left and center again, before resuming.

"I wuz wukkin' roun' d' houseboat long 'bout noon time, whin up on d' high bluff bank by d' Injin Mount driv' er l'il ol' possum-faced nigger f'm out at Clayton. He had dis Mist' Chancy wid 'm, an' say dad d' agent, Mist' Dobbins, had tol' him t' fetch d' gent'-man on ovah heah—dat he wuz d' new mimber o' d' goose club. Mist' Chancy wuz er funny-talkin' l'il man, sho'. Befo' long he had d' place in er uproh, an' me an' Bubbin lak er couple o' ol' wim-mens fightin' bees. He ast so minny ques'shuns t'well befo' I c'd answer d' firs' one he wuz fo' er five ahead o' me. I cooked him up som' fraish aiggs an' country ham an' hot biskits wid red gravy, but I c'd see fum d' way he looked at 'em he didn' think much o' sich prep'rations an' dem kin' o' vittles.

"Mist' Chancy say—'m' man,' he say—'how 'bout some brockly wid limmon juice?'

"I say—'som' limmon juice wid w-h-u-t—suh?'

"He say—'brockly—b-r-o-c-k-l-y—ain' yu nevah heer'd o' b-r-o-c-k-l-y?'

"I say—'Cap'n I'se sho' sorry, but us don' hav' no sech growin' roun' heah—' I say—'whut do d' stuff rizzimble—whut do h'it look lak, suh?'

"He say—'hit look sorter lak spinach afflicted wid d' warts—only h'its mo' wavy, an' don' tase much lak nothin' in p'ticler—less'n yu doctahs h'it wid er lot o' 'gredients an' den thinks mos'ly 'bout dem er sump'n' else differen', whilst yu's tryin' t' swaller d' brockly! But d' reason I eats h'it is b'case o' vittymins.'

"I say—'great—I—am'—I say—'whut is dem, Cap'n?'

"He say—'vittymins is d' invisible mates t' som' other sorter sump'ns whut is 'sposed t' be d' excuse f' sech plants esistin'. In other words, d' vittymins is good f' whut d' doctahs guesses is d' matter wid yu.'

"I say—'t'morrer, I gwi' bile yu up er bait o' dandelion mustard tops an' som' o' Mist' Ed Williams long shank red peppers.'

"He say—'is dey got plenny vittymins?'

"I say—'Cap'n, now as t' dat, I kain't swear, 'caus' I ain' nevah, pussonally, met up wid no vittymins, but, dem dandelions an' long shank red peppers is sho' got sump'n on d' ball an' will mek dey presence felt.'

"Mist' Chancy he look aroun' outa d' window an' say—'dis heah looks lak rich groun'—ef I laks dis place an' stays in d' club,' he say—'I gwi hav' yu plant er big patch o' brockly an' I'll hav' er plenny, nex' time I com'. 'I say—'I'll be proud t' plant d' brockly, suh.'

"But, jes' d' same, atta Mist' Chancy tase dem ham an aiggs, he sorter squinch his chair closer t' d' table an' say—'uuummm—uuummm—say—'dese heah eats right whar yu holds 'em don' dey?' Den, Mist' Nash, I mean he really drapped his appetite inta high gear.

"Atta lunch, he say—'who's is dem bird dawgs out yonder?' I say—'dey b'longs t' Mist' Nash Buckin'ham.' 'Well, den,' he tol' me, 'whut is us waitin' fer—le's go quail huntin' an' tackle d' geeses later dis afternoon.' I say—'Cap'n,' I say—'does yu know Mist' Nash well ernuff t' borry dem dawgs?' He laff an' say—'I knows him so well t'well he would be proud t' know I was condescendin' t' use 'em—he would tek h'it as er favor t' realize dat dem dawgs wuz in d' same fiel' wid me. Why, Ho'ace,' he say, 'I gives d' bigges' dawg show in d' worl'—fo' thousan' dawgs is in my yard at d' same time—why—why—dem dawgs yonder couldn' git in at d' same gate as d' dawgs whut com's t' my show.' I say—'Well, Cap'n,' I say—'yu sho' ain' fixin' t' run outa dawgs no time soon, is yu—an' yu mus' sho' hav' som' fine ones—but—' I say—'whin h'it com's t' findin' an' handlin' pottiges dem two slab-sided rascals yonder done wrote d' book on dat kinda bizness,' I say—'Mist' Nash he's pow'ful p'ticler 'bout ennybuddy 'cep' me handlin' dem dawgs.' He say—'t' hell wid dat'—he say—'com' on, yu do d' handlin' an' I'll do d' shootin'.'"

Two mallards came over the timber to our right and Horace used his duck call ineffectually for a few minutes.

"An' den I say—'Cap'n, yu know d' duck shootin' season don' open t'well'st t'morrer.' He say—'w-e-l-l—in sech case, I'll jes' pry d' lid off er trifle in advance.' He say—'by d' way I lef' my gun ovah at d' railroad wid d' res' o' my baggage—h'it won't be heah

till dis evenin'—is dey a gun roun' heah?' I say—'yaas, suh,' I say
—'Mist' Homer Jone's fine gun got heah yistiddy—does yu know
him well es yu knows Mist' Nash?' " Horace's mirth mounted at
the recollection.

"He say—'w-h-o m-e? *Does* I know Homer Jones? Why—say—
he's d' man got me t' jine dis club—I kin use ennything he's got—
w-h-u-t does yu know 'bout dat—d-o-e-s I know Homer Jones?' he
say—'le's me an' yu git goin'—'cause' I'se quail hongry an' longs
t' bust loose on 'em.' So I washed d' dishes an' den unleased Jim
an' Don, an' me an' Mist' Chancy walked on out cross d' fiel'. Us
hadn' bin gone hardly no time t'well Jim hit er gang o' pottiges
an' begin roadin' 'em. Mist' Chancy he kep' runnin' right 'longside
o' Jim an' sorter wavin' an' weavin' his gun roun' in d' air.
All at onct Jim stop an' frez tight. I looks whar he's lookin' an'
dar in er l'il patch o' sumach stalks I see's er big hover o' birds.
Mist' Chancy th'ow'd up his gun an'—ker-blouie—he cut loose into
'em right on d' groun'. I say t' m'sef, I say—*Jesus marster*—if Mist'
Nash an' Mist' Homer see'd dat'—I say—'whut kin' o' huntsman is
dis?' Whin I got t' whar d' quails wuz, Mist' Chancy he wuz stuffin'
d' slain ones in his pocket. He say—'by golly, dis is er bird hunt
right' he say—'dese things is easy t' hit—us'll hav' er sack full in
no time.' I say t' m'se'f, I say—'Aw—aw—I gotta git dis man away
f'um heah, er dey'll sho' be deep trubble.'

"I say—'Cap'n yu sho' is er darin' shot, but us got all d' quails
us'll need f' supper—le's us go on atta d' geeses.' But I done made
up my mind dat dis man didn't keer nuthin' bout no laws o' no
kind, an' dat I wuzzn' gwi' be roun' whilst he wuz bustin' em. Us
wint on t' d' houseboat, an' me an' him walked on up d' sandbar t'
whar I had done dug som' pits. I holped him down in one o' dem
an' sot out his m'coys. Den I say—'Cap'n,' I say—'yu stay heah
t'well late an' den jes' follah yo' own tracks on home th'u d' san'.'
I say—'geeses flys ve'y late in d' evenin'—dat is dey mos' jinrally
dooes.' " Horace's story was interrupted by the return of those two
mallards he had tried to call in. After Pat's retrieve, Horace took
up his recounting.

" 'Bout sundown heah com' Mist' Homer Jones an' Mist' Hal
Howard an' Mist' Sam Walker. I tell 'em 'bout Mist' Chancy bein'
dar. I tho't Mist' Homer looked kinda p'culiar. Dey say—'whar is
he now?' I say—'he made me put him up on d' bar—but I ain'
heer'd him shootin' none.' But 'bout dat ve'y moment—wid d'
moon fixin' t' com' up—Mist' Chancy he turned loose no less'n
fifteen or twenny shots. Mist' Homer say—'well—say—he's done

played hell now, boys.' So dey sot down t' supper an' I sont Bubbin on up d' sandbar t' fin' Mist' Chancy. Whin Bubbin gits back wid 'im, Mist' Chancy jump all ovah me. He say—'why didn' yu com' back an' show me d' way t' git home? D' geeses nevah come in t'well jes' befo' night an' I got t' chasin' one whut I crippled—an' got los' in d' bushes—say Bubbin yu had d' hell uv er time evah findin' me. Didn' yu all hear dem later shots?' Mist' Homer say—'yes, we heer'd 'em—whut wuz yu celebratin'—yo' own idea o' independence?' Mist' Chancy say—'why—didn' yu recognize dem distress signals?' Mist' Homer say—'distress signals?' say, 'dem ain' nuthin' c'mpared t' d' distress d' game warden gwi' occasion us ef yo' kinda bizness keeps up.'

"Du'in' all dat talk, Mist' Homer Jones wuz lookin' in his locker. He say—'Ho'ace,' he say, 'whar is my gun?' I say t' m'se'f—I say—'*Jesus marster!*' I say—'Mist' Chancy wuz usin' h'it. He say yu wouldn' min' his doin' so.' Mist' Homer say—'Chancy, whar is my gun?' Mist' Chancy say—'I lef' h'it in d' goose pit t'well mawnin'.' Mist' Homer shout—'YOU—LEF' HIT W-H-A-R?' Mist' Chancy say—'in d' goose pit.' Well, suh, Mist' Nash, Mist' Homer he jes' fall back an' cussed. He sint Bubbin back atta d' gun an' whin he got home wid h'it, h't wuz so full o' san' an' mud dat h'it tuk me an' Mist' Homer an hour t' clean h'it.

"Mist' Homer gits me an' Mist' Hal Howard out on deck an' say—'I gwi' fix dis fellah's clock'—say—how in d' hell he evah got in dis club is mo'n I kin see.' I say—'Mist' Homer,' I say, 'Mist' Chancy claim yu is d' one sol' him d' stifticket.' Mist' Homer he all but runned an' jumped in his hat. He say—'Com' on wid me— I'se gwi' down an' see Ed Williams.' So us wint on down an' Mist' Ed an' Mist' Homer day helt er long conversayshun, du'in' which dey wuz se'ul toasts. De deal wuz done fixed. On d' way back t' d' houseboat, Mist' Homer he jes' grunt t' hisse'f an' grunt.

"Mist' Homer say—'well, Chancy, I'se arranged er gran' hunt f' yu tomorrer. Yu's goin' across d' river wid Ed Williams, an' he'll put yu in er place whar yu kin' spread ruin untol' 'mongst d' ducks an' geeses. Le's git t' bed early, 'cause yu gotta git goin' ve'y early, so ez t' be in yo' pit befo' daylight.' He say—'but don' give dis man Williams no liquah—'caus' wid dat stuff in him, he's er demon!' So, me an' Mist' Homer got Mist' Chancy up 'bout three o'clock in d' mawnin' an' took 'im down t' Mist' Ed's landin'. Mist' Ed put him in d' gasboat an' on 'crosst d' river dey wint. Befo' daylight I heer'd Mist' Ed's boat comin' back. Mist' Homer say— 'yu didn' fix Mist' Chancy no lunch, did yu?' I say—'now, suh, yu

tol' me he'd be back in time f' lunch. 'Mist' Homer he jes' grinned.''
Again Horace's story was interrupted by the arrival of some sprigs.

"Mist' Homer an' Mist' Hal an' Mist' Sam went on up on d'
san'bar an' had er gran' day. I tuk 'em er big bait o' hot lunch an'
dey com' on home atta sundown luggin' all d' ducks an' geeses dey
could tote. Atta supper, Mist' Homer say—'com' on, Ho'ace, us
gotta go git Mist' Chancy.' Atta us gits t' Mist' Ed's him an' Mist'
Homer fixes up d' proceedin's. H'it seem lak Mist' Ed had don'
talked Mist' Chancy inta givin' him er drink early dat mawnin'—
jes' ez Mist' Ed wuz fixin' t' start back 'crosst d' river. So Mist'
Homer an' me got in Mist' Ed's gasboat, cross'd river, an' landed
inside er big reef point. Long befo' us got dar, us heer'd Mist'
Chancy hollerin'. An' wuz he mad? He say—'I bin heah all day
long, widout er bite t' eat an' I ain't had er shot—d' geese an' ducks
all flys away ovah yonder.' Mist' Homer say—'well, say—ef yu
didn' hav' sense ernuff t' carry no lunch, h'its yo' own fault. But
dat ain' nuthin' compared t' d' trouble we's in now. Yu disobeyed
my orders an' giv' dat man Ed Williams er drink an' now us got er
fiend on ou'h han's.'

"He say—'das how com' me an' Ho'ace done had t' com' atta yu.
Ed's don' gone plum ravin' crazy an' may hav' shot up d' houseboat by now. Me an' Ho'ace com' atta yu at d' risk uv ou'h lives.
He was raisin' so much hell, us jes' slipped d' boat loose an' come
on—he missed whin he shot at us.' He say—'now lissen, Chancy,
whin us lan's, us'll try t' slip pas' his house in d' dark, an' not git
in no row wid 'im. 'Cause whin he gits fired up wid dat stuff he
meks hisse'f, dey ain' nuthin' he laks better t' do den jes' fill d'
countryside an' hits citizens, black an' white, full o' buckshot er
whatever size he happens t' hav' in d' gun, ur his pis'sul.' I say, all
tremblin' lak—'Mist' Homer, I got jes' one las' reques'. He say—
'whuts dat, Ho'ace?' I say—'I heer'd tell dat Mist' Ed's got som'
Injin blood in 'im, an' scalps d' folks whut he slays—f' goodness
sake,' I say—'ef I falls, try t' save dis nigger f'um bein' scalped.'
Mist' Chancy he jes' sot dar shiverin' all d' way back. He jes' spoke
onct. He say—'I'se made er lot o' mistakes in dis life, but jinin' dis
Gawd-fersaken outfit is d' s'preme in vacc'ums!'

"Us landed on d' upslant bank an' made d' boat fas'. Den us stol'
on th'u d' big woods t'well us had t' pass Mist' Ed's houseboat. All
at onct his do'h wuz flang open an' out he com'—ro'ahin' wussn
d' town bull. He wuz wavin' er long pis'sul in one han' an' er
butcher knife in d' other. Mist' Chancy he th'ow'd down his gun
an' lit out cross d' cotton patch. Mist' Ed, he shot off d' pis'sul

three times an' yell'd t' beat enny Injin dat evah lived. Mist' Homer say—'Ho'ace,' say—'yu betta ketch up wid Mist' Chancy 'caus' he's liable t' run hisse'f wuss'n los' out in dem jungles.' He say—'Ed,' say—'yell agin, an' shoot'—say 'he might slow down!' So I lit out atta Mist' Chancy, an' co't up wid 'im all tangled up in rattans an' grapevines. I say—'Mist' Chancy, le's git outa dis, 'cause dat man don' shot Mist' Homer an' is pirootin' up todes ou'h houseboat.' He say—'dis is d' en'—I is leavin' dis damn country immediately ef not sooner. Lead me t' d' houseboat, an' hav' Bubbin hitch up d' mule—I jes' natcherly b'lieves I kin do bettah in d' broad road.'

"Us 'rived at d' houseboat all tuckered out. Mist' Homer had done instructed Mist' Hal an' Mist' Sam, an' dey wuz actin' dey parts. Mist' Ed, he wuz still shootin' an' hollerin'.

"Mist' Hal say—'yu ain't desertin' us, is yu Chancy?' he say—'yu gotta go wid us an' he'p rescue Homer, dat man don' shot 'im.'

"Mist' Chancy say—'well ef sech bees d' case das jes' too bad'— he say—'yu all tol' me dis wuz er shootin' club, an' yu don' mo'n named d' place rightly.' By dat time Bubbin don' got d' mule hitched t' d' buggy, an' th'ow'd his bag in d' back. Mist' Chancy had 'im er big hick'ry stick fer er whup, an' he say—'ef dis lasts, I'll reach d' United States in safety.'

"Bubbin clucked to d' mule, an' Mist' Hal say—'Chancy—whut yu want us t' do wid yo' mimbership in d' club?' " Horace folded his arms across his knees and rested his head on them. His shoulders heaved.

" 'Bout dat time, Mist' Ed shot off dat pis'sul agin, an' d' mule jumped fo' feet. Mist' Hal hollered—

" 'Whut yu want us to do wid yo mimbership?'

" 'Mist' Chancy holler—'th'ow h'it in d' river!'

"I holler—'Whar yu want me t' plant all dat brockly—Cap'n?'

"He shout back—'I knows er place yu kin put dat, too!' "

RAYMOND R.
CAMP

The Magic Rifle

Since no one was in a position to prevent it, I maliciously inserted
one of my own creations in this collection. I had an excuse, since it
involved a phase of shooting which is not widely treated. Muzzle
loader shooting and hunting is now enjoying a revival, so perhaps
it is not out of place. Among the letters received after the publi-
cation of the story was one which has the questionable distinction
of being the most insulting I ever received. "I read your story
with great interest," this rotter wrote, "but I was not surprised to
learn of your abilities in fiction-writing, since I am a daily reader
of your [factual] column." The beef shoots which formed the
basis of the story are still held each spring at Cataloochie, N.C.

Young Dan gave his trousers a final hitch and turned to rest a
big hand on his father's arm. "That was a right good supper,"
he admitted. "Don't know why ham an' greens eat better up here
than they do down to Asheville."

His father chuckled. "An uphill walk makes a tasty sauce," he
suggested. "Could be you was hungered after climbin' up from the
county road. Unless yo're wishful to spend the night, it's time you
moved off. Takes a mountain man to trace the path, come dark, an'
you've lived too long in the vales."

The old man's tone was bantering, but a sharp edge of candor
cut through his words.

"Might be yo're right," his son smiled, then frowned. "I still wish
you'd come down an' stay with us. Don't seem right, you livin' up
here so loney."

His father shook his head in a firm negative. "I'd be loney in the clearin's, boy. Loney an' lazy. An' now you'd best be movin'."

Young Dan shrugged in defeat. "Guess so." He shuffled his feet in the soft dirt of the trail. "See you, come mornin'. Now try an' be to the grove 'fore noon, else you'll miss the chance fer a sightin' shot. There'll be a mixin' of touristers to the shoot this year, an' the Asheville paper had it that the gov'nor hisself was comin'. Sleep soun' an' rest easy, fer I sure want a bite of that steer meat they give as a prize."

Old Dan shook his head in mock sorrow. "Lean pork is rich enough food fer a Shackleford who fergot how to shoot. Don't you fear, boy, I'll be there fer my sighters."

His son hesitated a moment, then raised an arm in farewell and trudged off down the dusty track.

Old Dan stood in the doorway of the old cabin and watched his son as he moved down the path, noting the stiff-hipped gait— certain mark of the city man. What was it old Hell's Brimstone Pruitt had roared out at the last camp meeting? "The fathers done et some sour grapes, an' the childern's teef is on aidge."

He chuckled in his beard at the memory. Miz Anders sure raised a fuss over that. Trudged clean down from the fringe of Hooper's Bald, she had, draggin' that snaggle-tooth boy of hern along. An' then to be mocked by a preacher. How she did screech ol' Pruitt down fer mockin' at her pore boy, an' him with his paw long dead.

The old man ran a hand through his beard, a gesture which even his hound would have recognized as a sign of profound meditation.

"Don't mind ever eatin' no sour grapes." Old Dan spoke aloud, after the custom of men much alone. "But my boys are sure on aidge. Head an' teef. Crowdin' in with all them people down to Asheville. Workin' fer wages, when they could live on their own in the free hills."

Old Dan paused to embrace his own riches with appreciative eyes. The small patch that had been in tobacco, its leafless stalks now rustling softly in the sunset breeze. A small money crop, true, but enough for his quiet need. Behind it the four acres of shocked corn. Enough feed to carry the mule through the winter. Even a few bushels over, might be, to carry down to Jim Cass' boy for transmutation into clear, heady liquid.

Beyond the corn patch, the ridges, moving upward and onward in irregular green and gold waves, then sweeping downward to the wooded valley. No crowds. No smoke other than the fragrant wisps that curled from his own fire.

His domain was settling for the night. From the sagging lean-to back of the cabin he could make out the drowsy "curr, clurrrk, currr" of the hens, and the contented grunt of the old sow with her hungry pigs.

A fox barked sharply from a distant ridge and something stirred at the old man's feet. Jess, the old hound, whose canine age was equal to his master's, was instantly alert. He raised a scarred muzzle and twitched the ragged ears, both glorious tributes to courage. The dog canted his head to listen, and when the barking ceased he looked up at his master.

Pulled from his reverie by the fox, old Dan listened, too, but shook his head at the hound's mute query.

"Not this evenin', Jess," he explained. "Ol' men an' ol' dogs need sleep an' rest. We're movin' down, come sunup. That fox'll keep. A tetch from the jug an' we'll rest our bones."

The dusk was intensified inside the cabin, but a few sticks of fatwood on the embers of the supper fire supplied all the light old Dan required. He hauled a gallon jug from its place under a splint chair and swung it to his shoulder with a practiced sweep. But the jug was never tilted.

Outlined by the last light, old Dan's eye caught the shape of a tall figure in the doorway. Mountain hospitality was automatic.

"Step in, man; step in."

Lowering the jug and its corncob stopper to the chair, he turned to greet his visitor. Another man bound for tomorrow's shoot, he decided. Probably from the far side of the mountain. He repeated his welcome when the other did not advance.

The visitor approached the fire, his moccasin-clad feet making no sound on the puncheon floor. His beardless face was browned by sun and weather, and lined with age. The coarse cloth of his shirt and trousers hung loosely from his tall, spare frame. Old Dan peered as sharply as courtesy permitted, but recognition did not come until his guest had spoken.

"Reckon you wouldn't remember me," the man drawled. "Been many a year since I touched these parts. I knew yore gran'pappy, an' I curled many a night 'fore this very fire." His glance swept to the long Lancaster rifle over the high mantel. "An' that of mine has rested here these many years."

The smile in old Dan's eyes now matched the one on his lips. "My pappy said you'd show here, in the fullness of time," he nodded. "He was a man fer strange words." He pointed to a chair. "I bid you welcome. It's a wearisome journey to this cabin fer ol' bones. Rest, an' I'll put yore mule in with mine an' give him a bait of corn."

His guest halted him with a gesture. "I come on shanks' mare," he explained. "Time an' distance is all she eats, an' she's had a bait of both this day. I'll sit, though, an' thank you."

When his guest had settled into the other chair, old Dan picked up the jug and proffered it silently.

His guest shook his head.

"Jest a tetch?" old Dan suggested.

The shake of the other's head was barely perceptible in the flickering light of the fire, which sent irregular lances of light dancing about the dark log walls.

"Smells right good, though," he admitted. "But it wouldn't do. Never was one fer likker, an' times I tilted the jug I couldn't put her down. Sure smells like rich likker."

Old Dan let the jug settle to the floor with a decisive thump.

"Oughta be." He emphasized his words by driving home the cob with the heel of his hand. "Some of the las' run Jim Cass ever made. Went to camp meetin' right after that run, Jess did. After hearin' ol' Pruitt rant on drink, he was pizened on likker from there out. More'n twenty year since he died. Come home from that meetin' an' took the ax to his still. Then took ever' jug from under the woodpile an' poured ever' lastin' drop in the branch. Even smashed the jugs. Nex' day he got snakebit. Some said it was a judgment on him."

He glanced at his guest and ran a tongue over his dry lips, then drew the cob from the neck of the jug.

"Sure you won't change?" At the other's silence he raised the jug to his shoulder. "All this talkin' makes a man dry." He took a deep pull and wiped his lips with the back of one hand. The mellow perfume of the corn whisky mingled with the fragrance of the smoke as he exhaled with a contented grunt.

The old hound, returned from a private hunt, paused at the cabin threshold, then advanced slowly into the cabin. He blinked several times at the fire before his heavy head swung toward the stranger. For a long moment his glance was steady. The dog then turned and moved to the side of Dan's chair, where he dropped heavily to the floor. Head between his paws, he gazed steadily at the visitor, a complaining growl rumbling in his chest.

Old Dan watched this performance with questioning eyes, then dropped a rough hand to the dog's head.

"Don't heed Jess none," he apologized. "Not many visitors get this far, an' he ain't sociable like he was when a pup."

Jess flinched nervously as the hand rubbed his ears.

"Good-lookin' houn'," the stranger complimented. "Who'd wish fer a dog that took up with ever'body? Good bear dog?"

There was a proud ring in his host's reply. "None better in these hills, nor any other. Traded fer him with the Plotts. He'll hold a bear whilst the Walkers an' Triggs are still workin' out a back track."

The stranger bent forward to peer carefully at the hound. He straightened up. "Always wanted a good bear dog," he confessed. "Save a man a span of time an' trackin'. I mind the las' bear I kilt. Some north of here, it was. Follered the track most of a day. Thick bresh an' weary trailin'. Come through that very place this journey, an' it was all cleared away. Scarcely a big tree standin', an' no game but rabbits. No country fer a man likes the big woods an' huntin'."

Old Dan bobbed his head in agreement. "Know jus' how you feel. My boys has moved down to the clearin's. One's clean down to Asheville. Keeps after me to move in with him. Always at me." His voice took a tone of mock anxiety. "Suppose you was to git snakebit? Suppose you was to bust a leg? Suppose this. Suppose that. A man's got to live out his time in his special place, an' this'n is mine."

The hound's whined interruption was choked off short by old Dan's sharp "Hesh!"

There was a long pause while the two old men gazed into the fire. Jess sighed deeply, then relaxed. It was old Dan who broke the silence.

"I'm pleased my foot don't itch like yourn, spite all the country you've seen. I wonder you found your way back here." He hesitated. "While I give you fair welcome, I ponder yore cuttin' a back track. An' I ponder on the feed you give shanks' mare. I'm down to follerin' Jess on a wide-steppin' mule, an' yo're seemin' spry as a ruttin' buck. Yore eye is clearer'n mine right now. Did you keep movin' ahead of time?"

The other shook his head and the leathery cheeks wrinkled in a half smile. "There's slight moss er gold in my pack," he confessed. "But I'm one must keep to the woods till they hew 'em down. I come back fer the shoot, but couldn't go it alone. Planned comin' some years back, but word got 'round the war 'cross the water had put them off. I know'd you'd keep the ol' gun in shape an' pondered did she still throw true."

The stranger paused to raise his eyes to the long rifle on its pegs over the mantel. Tall as a man, every inch wrought by the hand of a master craftsman, the rifle had a cobra gleam in the flickering light. Shadows as vague as the memories of the two old men shuttled and danced across the curly-maple stock. Clever hands had created it. Loving hands had kept it bright.

"True as the die," old Dan pronounced. "My oldest boy give me a light britch-loader fer the woods, but I take the ol' gun down ever' so often an' try it on a mark. My hand's not so steady as it was fer a standin' shot, but I can line it true from a rest. I hadn't figgered to shoot this year, but young Dan come up today to urge me. They're bringin' in some touristers to see the mountain men shoot the ol' guns, an' the boy says the gov'nor is comin' too." He paused. "My boys is somethin' of a sorrow, in a way, fer they've give up the ol' guns. Prob'ly young Dan would've passed up the shoot 'cept fer his hope of gettin' a piece of the beef."

Quiet once more rested in the cabin, finally broken by old Dan's audible yawn. "High time I found my bed," he announced. "Tired eyes never won no beef, an' I'll be shootin' agin young eyes, come tomorrow. The bed'll sleep two when yo're ready."

His guest shook his head. "I'll rest where I sit fer a time," he proposed. "But git yore sleep. An' have no fear fer cuttin' the mark at the shoot. I'll be sightin' back of yore shoulder. 'Tween us we'll cut out the cross."

Anticipation and slumber are poor bedfellows, but they ceased their ageless battle as old Dan stretched out on the chicken-feather tick. He was asleep before Jess could curl up at his feet, and did not stir until the rooster greeted first light.

The smells of the morning were still sharp when old Dan, the long rifle cradled in his arms, his guest riding pillion behind, thumped the mule's ribs with a heel and turned him down the track to the valley. The start had not been without incident, for the hound had growled deep in his chest when the guest mounted, and the mule had shied. Old Dan's sharp "Hesh" to the dog sent him trotting ahead, but it took several sharp blows of the reins to quiet down the mule.

Not a soul crossed their path until they splashed across the branch at the head of the valley. Here they came upon the two Satter boys, long rifles across their shoulders, who nodded a silent greeting as they stepped off the narrow trail to let the mule pass. Their skinny hound scurried to their heels at Jess' angry snarl.

"Good boys," old Dan announced. "Carryin' rifles their gran'ther made, lock, stock an' barr'l. Not a patch to the Lanc'ster guns, but better'n others that come from these hills."

Another mile found the trail merging with a wagon track. Another, and it opened abruptly on a wide, grassy meadow, its eastern margin fringed with huge oaks. A small cabin crowned a knoll almost in the shadow of the oaks, and about it was clustered a small group of men.

"We'd best hitch the mule off here, in the shade," old Dan advised. "You can rest whilst I get a board fer my sightin' shots."

He glanced at his companion, and nodded toward the group at the cabin. "It's early yet, an' they'll look real sharp at a stranger now. Could be you'd do well to rest here with the mule till the touristers show. Not all the corn in these hills goes fer stock, an' strangers have been knowed to blow stills."

The other nodded agreement and slipped from the mule with an ease that questioned his years.

Old Dan unsaddled and tethered his charger, then spread the blanket near a big oak. Leaving the rifle, powder horn and shot pouch with his guest, he moved across the clearing to the cabin.

An exchange of greetings and some good-natured banter signaled his approach. The early arrivals were sorting out targets and target boards. These boards, measuring eight by twelve, and one inch thick, were charred black on one side.

Selection was never made in haste. Each shooter sought a smoothly charred board. To this he tacked a rectangle of white cardboard, from the center of which a three-inch diamond had been cut. Then, with a keen blade, a line was cut on the charred wood from each point of the diamond, forming a thin cross in the center. The diamond served as the aiming point, but the cross was the scoring medium.

Each contestant was permitted three shots. Each bullet hole was pegged, and the distance from each peg to the center of the cross was carefully measured. The man who placed his shots closest to the cross would lead home the fat steer which constituted the prize.

Old Dan sorted through the boards until he found two with faces smoothly charred, their surface unmarred by a blister of resin to gleam in the sun. To these he tacked two cardboard cutouts, one for his sighting shots, another for score.

With a board for straightedge, he cut his crosses with care, then employed a stump of a pencil to print his name on the scoring target. This he stacked behind a dozen others, for the order of targets was the order of firing. Being early, he was assured of good light for shooting.

The morning quiet was shattered by an echoing "boom," as the first of the shooters began his sighting shots. Old Dan's nostrils flared as the faint breeze carried the acrid fumes of black-powder smoke past the cabin.

Returning to his guest, he offered the board for inspection.

"Black's the inside of a cow," was the comment. "But a big mark fer sixty yards."

"Not too big fer my ol' eyes," his host insisted. "But let's seek a stump an' set up the board. I'll pace it off an' get in my sighters 'fore the crowd arrives."

With the board wedged tight against the face of a stump, he carefully paced off the required distance and dragged a heel in the loam to mark the firing point.

He ignored the other's frown of disapproval when the saddle was placed on this line to serve as a rest. Old Dan now concentrated all his attention on the process of loading.

First he swabbed out the barrel. Then the powder was measured carefully in a hollowed boar's tooth and slowly poured down the barrel. His companion nodded approvingly as he slapped the stock to settle the grains. The carefully molded bullet was then shrouded in a square of oiled linen and seated in the muzzle with a sharp rap of the hickory starter. Trimming the patch with a razor-sharp knife, old Dan then thrust the bullet home with an even sweep of the ramrod. Then, with a thin priming wire he picked at the hole and channel, measured a pinch of fine priming powder into the pan and snapped the cover down.

Stretched prone behind the saddle, he squirmed for several seconds until he found a comfortable position, flushing beneath his beard at the derisive smile on the other's lips. With his cheek snuggled tight against the polished comb, he lined up the sights with fine precision before moving a finger inside the trigger guard.

"Ain't you a mite high fer a cold barr'l?" his companion inquired.

Grunting an affirmative, old Dan let the muzzle drop a hair, and held his breath for the shot. As the rifle roared he nodded in satisfaction. His companion, stretched prone behind him, peered at the target and produced one of his rare smiles.

"A mite low an' a tetch right. She'd never do so with a buckskin patch. A man can't hope fer much with a petticoat patch. Load her ag'in, an' hold dead on. Three like that might win you the beef."

Although the succeeding two shots made a one-inch group, the guest was not content. His host, however, stared at the target with awe. For an instant he seemed about to speak, then pressed his lips firmly together. He strode to a seat at the foot of the oak.

"We'll rest here till the match gets goin'," he said as the other dropped down beside him. "Once the crowd is gathered, none will pay heed to you."

The other nodded without opening his eyes, and old Dan let the warm languor of the spring morning lead him to sleep.

The crack of the opening shot aroused them, and although his guest leaped to his feet like a boy, old Dan came erect in stages, his bones creaking in protest. Young Dan had not stretched the truth, he decided, for fully a hundred touristers and an equal number of mountain folk were strung out from the cabin to the firing line.

From his vantage point he could make out a cluster of bright beach umbrellas behind the firing line, shading a small group seated on camp chairs. His quizzical frown faded when he remembered the "gov'nor hisself" was to be present.

"We'll move down to the aidge," he suggested. "My boy'll be roustin' all over the place, huntin' me out, an' he'll make certain the mule carried me over a cliff if I ain't in plain sight."

The two old men halted on the edge of the crowd, near the firing line, and watched the first contestant, a lanky mountain farmer, prepare to touch off his third and last shot.

A large hand grasped old Dan's arm just as the rifle belched smoke, causing him to jump in surprise. He turned to look on the worried face of his son.

"Stop yore frettin' now, boy," he commanded. "I got in my sighters 'fore you et your grits, an' we—that is, I—been restin' back in the shade. That was Rob Daniels just shot. Go an' see did he tetch the board."

As his son moved away toward the group surrounding the governor's chair he brought his guest up to date on local history.

"Rob Daniels is a good shot, but he's excitable. Last shoot we had he fell down whilst comin' up to the rest log. His ball took two toes off'n the youngest Turner boy. The Turners argied that the shot was one of Rob's three, an' the jedges upheld 'em. We shot fer a quarter of a beef that time, four high scores dividin' the steer. One of the Turners won a quarter, so them an' the Danielses ain't spoke since." Old Dan paused and his eyes gleamed with a sudden decision. "Do I win the steer today, I'll give the whole critter to young Dan. That'll keep him so busy he'll fergit to bother me 'bout livin' up in the hills."

He paused to meet the puzzled glance of a nearby tourister. As their eyes met, the tourister cleared his throat nervously, and moved quickly off to a place nearer the firing line.

Young Dan returned with a grin that spoke clearly of a poor showing by Daniels. "Rob's group was that wide you couldn't cover it with a fingerspread," he reported. "I'm off to find Brud an' his jug, but you'd best leave the cob alone till after you shoot. I'll be on the side when yore turn comes. An' remember, my mouth's set for red meat."

Old Dan turned his attention to the next shooter, already stretched prone behind the rest log. This man was one of the few who still shot a flintlock, most of the rifles having been converted to percussion. He shook his head in sympathy as he watched the hammer fall, drawing sparks from the flint, but no ignition to the powder. The shooter reprimed, and although there was another flash in the pan when the hammer fell, the rifle again misfired.

"Over the hill," came a chant from the spectators. "Take it over the hill."

The disconsolate shooter rose to his feet and moved slowly over the crest of the knoll. Here he would pick and prime until the fouling was removed. A misfire cost a shooter his turn, but not his place, and he could return to the head of the line when his rifle was in firing condition.

After watching a half dozen other shooters make their bids for the beef, old Dan nodded to his quiet companion and led the way back to the mule.

Once more the rifle was carefully loaded, and the hammer lowered to half cock. Upon his return to the knoll, old Dan found his target was next in line. He led the way to the firing point and handed his board to a boy, whose task was to retrieve each target and place the next one against the butt.

The preceding shooter had done quite well. The three holes, when pegged, formed a triangle around the cross, and all could have been hidden by a half dollar. This drew but a disdainful sniff from his companion, however, and old Dan could not suppress a shiver.

A crowd such as this, full of touristers, made a man jumpy; to say nothing of having a man at your elbow, ready to criticize your hold and squeeze.

He did not remember getting into position behind the rest log, and was startled by the click of the hammer as his thumb drew it back to full cock. The long barrel swept slowly to a level across the log, steadying when the sharp picket of the front sight rested squarely in the notch of the rear sight. He let the muzzle drop slightly as he took his breath.

"Dead on, but a mite low," whispered a voice at his ear. "Raise her a mite. Thar. Thar. Thar."

The old rifle thrust solidly at his shoulder, and the dense smoke of the black powder obscured the target. His eyes strained to pierce the screen.

"Fair on the cross," came the whisper. "Fair on, but hold a tetch higher on the next one."

Old Dan's fingers trembled with excitement as he went through the loading ritual, and he feared lest a few grains of the charge might be spilled at the muzzle. Again he took his position behind the rest log. This time he held a hair higher than before, and when the long barrel steadied it brought only a faint "Aaah" from his companion.

He needed no report on that shot. The inexplicable sixth sense of the shooter told him it had been true.

As he reloaded, old Dan was conscious of a trickle of moisture that the tension sent down his back and chest. One more shot and he could escape to the shelter of the trees, free of the oppression of the crowd.

When he held his breath for the final shot his sights again dropped below the center of the diamond, but he made the correction before his mentor could hiss a warning. His finger tightened almost imperceptibly as the sights edged upward to the center, and the hammer fell as they reached it, almost as though another finger pressed his own.

There was a murmur that swelled to a roar as the target boy raced back with the board, forgetting to place the new target in his excitement. When the judge had pegged the holes he held the board aloft for the crowd to see. The three white pegs formed a tight clover leaf that completely obliterated the center of the cross.

Old Dan acknowledged his introduction to the governor with a nod and a handclasp that caused the executive to wince through his smile. Out of the corner of one eye he saw young Dan leaping high into the air, his big feet smashing his best hat to a pancake in the dirt.

"He did it!" young Dan almost screamed, to the delight of the spectators. "He did it! The old man showed 'em, he did. He did."

Cradling the rifle in his arms in a manner that was as old as the American hunter, old Dan pushed through the excited crowd and dodged the heavy hands that smote his back and shoulders in passing. His companion awaited him near the tethered mule. Old Dan shot him a guarded glance.

The other shook his head.

"A firm log fer a rest, a true barr'l, an' they needed three pegs to plug the holes. The first Dan'l in the Good Book was better'n that, an' with only a rock an' a sling."

Old Dan's brow wrinkled in a frown. He had taken enough this day, guest or no guest.

"Reckon you ain't read the Book in some time," he snapped. "Dan'l was the man had a time with the lions. Never heard he was anythin' special with a sling. Reckon you mean David."

His companion was not to be defeated so easily.

"Ever meet Dan'l?" he asked.

Old Dan shook his head, then smiled. "My chance ain't far off, I reckon. But a sinner of my name'll never pass Peter's gate. You're my guest, an' I shame to have spoke so. It cut me hard, yore belittlin' the best score I ever shot. I ask yore pardon."

The other grinned. "I aimed to stir you," he admitted. "Might be I was some greeny-eyed, truth be told. I never done better when my eyes was young."

The two old men smiled at each other in understanding, and took comfortable seats, with the great oak for a rest. They watched the contestants, one by one, approach the firing line, touch off their ancient rifles and give place to another. As the blossom of smoke heralded each shot, some of the tension of each shooter was reflected in the two old men, for real riflemen are like that.

Shadows were lengthening when the last man fired and his target was pegged. Touristers and mountain folk crowded close to the governor's chair now, but hardly a moment elapsed before the burst of cheering reached the watchers' ears. A wild figure, his battered hat jammed down over his ears, raced to their vantage point.

"I'll jest move down an' look over yore beef," the guest announced, and faded into the dense cover as smoothly as shadows merge when a cloud passes under the sun.

Young Dan gasped out his message between labored gulps for breath. "You done it!" he cried. "The gov-nor wants you down yonder, right now. Come on. He wants to shake yore hand ag'in."

The crowd parted as young Dan led his father to the governor's chair. His excellency, unaware of their proximity, was shaking the hand of one of his aides.

"Bill," the governor whispered, "you've kept me moving from the Outer Banks to the Tennessee line. I've danced with Cherokees, drunk with bear hunters, commiserated with farmers, and hobnobbed with fishermen. You've set me a tiresome pace, and written me some of the worst speeches ever delivered by a governor of this great state. But you've paid off for it all. It's a poor dog hasn't got one buried bone, and you dug yours up today. There's been no shooting like this since Dan'l Boone ranged these hills."

The governor broke off at his aide's imperious signal, then rose to his feet and took old Dan's hand in a grasp as strong as his own.

"Mr. Shackleford," he roared, "my aide wrote out a speech for me to make to the winner of this shoot, but I can't remember a single word of it. At this moment I can only think of your shooting." He whirled to grab the target board from the hand of his aide. "I know you want to take this target home with you. I would if it was mine. But I'm going to ask a favor of you. I want to take this target back to the Statehouse, where it will hang on the wall of my office. Hang where other governors will see it, and be reminded that our people can still hold true and shoot straight."

When the roar of the crowd had subsided, old Dan, his fear departed, nodded at the governor.

"I'd be right proud to let you take it," he smiled. "Can't tell, one of my kin might warm your chair one day. Strange things happen, in the fullness of time."

It was an hour before old Dan, anxious for the well-being of his guest, could escape from the crowd. He found young Dan with a fast-drying jug, and tilted it once in a parting drink.

"I want you to take the steer, Dan'l. Take it, an' divide with Brud an' the others. But remember to bring me some stew meat when next you climb to the cabin. I'm growing wearied, an' it's a far climb fer the mule."

Young Dan stood speechless and slack of jaw. He raised one hand as his father reached the fringe of the oaks.

The guest was waiting when old Dan reached the mule, and no word was spoken while he saddled up. He was about to mount when the other touched his shoulder.

"Tarry a bit," he requested. "There's a thing I clean fergot to do."

Old Dan watched with a puzzled frown while the other trotted to the rim of the oaks and approached the tethered steer. He peered sharply while his guest stood for a moment contemplating the prize, patting the animal several times on the flank, then turning to trot back.

"Man's vanity," was the only explanation the other offered.

Jess, the old hound, growled deep in his throat once more as old Dan mounted the mule and gave a hand to his guest. The mule, still half dozing, snorted as the guest mounted, perhaps in complaint at the added load.

Old Dan jerked the reins in sharp rebuke and dug a heel into the mule's tough hide. Led by the stiff-legged hound, the little group disappeared around a bend in the track.

Dusk was settling when young Dan dropped the empty jug on the floor of his truck and backed the battered vehicle to a cutbank, which would provide a natural ramp for the loading of his father's prize. He led the fat steer to the bank and into the truck, knotting the rope securely to a ring at the rear of the cab.

It was then his eye noted the rough spot on the steer's flank. He smoothed down the hair with a tentative hand, and paused as if frozen. What at first glance he had thought a brand was more than the mark of a hot running iron. With a shaking finger he traced the crude letters, pushing off the effects of the jug as a man shrugs a cloak from his shoulders.

Young Dan turned his glance westward, his eyes straining to pierce the deep dusk now shadowing the hills. What had the old man said to the governor? His head bobbed in recollection. "Strange things happen—in the fullness of time."

He bent once more to trace the letters on the smooth flank of the steer.

"D Boone shot hir this day."

ALMET JENKS

The Huntsman at the Gate

Although few persons other than those personally involved in the activity are interested in the pink-coated form of hunting, I am ready to argue interminably on the justification for this story. You do not need interest in any form of hunting to accept this as a great piece of writing. When I was younger, had the time, and could afford it, I held an unofficial record for broken fences and bones in a pack that no longer exists. While bones were knitting I devoured fox hunting literature. This is, to my mind, one of the classics of that form.

"Go sink the wind!" said the huntsman, who had been reading some old books on fox hunting. He spoke to his second whipper-in and—for his own enjoyment—in a tone of voice one might use in saying, "Go climb a tree!" He went on quickly, "Try and get a view. Be ready to stop 'em if it's—if it's a racing leopard or something. It's like no fox I ever knew."

That had been three hours ago, at a short check. The field—the few that were left—were in earshot at the time, and it amused the huntsman a little to think that none of them, probably, would have any idea what the order to the whip meant. Nor would the whip, at first—the expression was long out of date—but would figure it out at the second command. "Try and get a view." As expected, the whip looked blank, then nodded quickly, but did not make off. The huntsman ran the show; as little discretion as possible was committed to the staff, in the field, in the kennels and stables. So the whip waited for further directions.

"Gallows Corner," the huntsman said without hesitation. This might be quite wrong, of course, but it seemed the best bet—considering the way the quarry had been running. A decision had to be made at once, and he was the one to make it. He said, "That'll give you a view of the road for half a mile."

The whip touched his thonged hunting whip to the visor of his velvet cap, turned his horse, trotted a few steps, put the horse into a gallop and made straight for the highway. The few followers left in the field watched him go thudding by, the hound couples dancing up and down against his horse's flank. What this maneuver meant, they had no idea, but they were careful to show no sign of ignorance. They kept quiet and looked wise and stayed carefully away from the hounds at all times, a well-disciplined field, knowing little of the art, the science, or the sport but wonderfully conversant with its proper dress and peculiar language.

The whip's way was straight down wind, well out on the flank of the nearly straight line that the fox—or whatever the hunted animal might be—was taking, and fast, but at the same time saving his horse as much as possible, along the grassy shoulder of the highway, which fortunately ran that way, to the high crest on the turnpike, known as Gallows Corner. Here, far down wind and far ahead of the hunting hounds, and in great loneliness, for this was a strange and sparsely settled part of the country, he would sit his horse and keep his eyes glued to the half-mile of dirt road that crossed a roughly straight prolongation of the line that hounds were now hunting. Posted there, sometimes standing in his stirrup-irons, leaning forward, he would stare so hard he would be seeing things—all kinds of wild creatures; he would, if the huntsman had guessed right, first hear in the distance the faint, wonderful music of the pack. Nearer and nearer, swelling, rising to a great crashing chorus, it would come, and the whipper-in, half blind now from gazing, would suddenly see—and his heart would be in his throat—the tired red fox slowly, deliberately pick his way across the road . . . or, if not a fox, then a racing leopard or water-buffalo or some strange beast that had escaped from the circus when it left town last summer.

But the second whip got a view of nothing that day. He heard hounds once, far, far off, and then not again. He saw no one, no living creature. Darkness came soon in these short winter days, and night followed fast—no moon that night, no stars—and he could not have seen an elephant cross the road. He stayed till dark, and now the hunt must be far away or blown off, and there was nothing more he could do out there, so he walked his horse down to the highway and began the ten-mile-or-so ride home.

After the whip had galloped off, the huntsman sat motionless on his big bay horse, never touching his horn, watching hounds make their cast. There was no question, no doubt in his mind: one of the old, trusted hounds—Artful, say, or Mermaid or Mournful— would pick up the line in a moment—no check that day had lasted more than a minute or two—and they would be off again, to where, God alone knew! They had been running from quarter past eleven that morning, and it was now going on to four, but it was not so much the elapsed time as the terrible pace the quarry had imposed. The sun would set shortly after four and they could go on for a little while after that, and then they would be benighted. Yet the huntsman could not bear to whip hounds off the line or blow them off during one of the infrequent checks. They had had little luck so far, that season, and their season of hunting was, at best, a short one. The young entry—four and a half couples of them were out that day—needed blooding. At the same time, he knew that, mounted—he was thinking now of himself and the whipper-in that remained to him, not of the field—they could not follow hounds across country, over fence and ditch and brook, in the dark. But if this were a *gray* fox they were hunting, a quarry that usually ran in circles, he and the first whip could turn their horses over to someone in the field who would take their horses home, and then huntsman and whip could go on, on foot, all night if necessary. If it had been a gray fox.

But of course it wasn't, but was certainly the red fox of the world—or maybe a racing leopard, springbok, hartebeest. . . . Deer, the huntsman didn't like even to think of. There were deer in the country, all right. Where were they not? The gentle, soft-eyed . . . he had several names for them, none printable. They had deer— tame ones—in the kennel run, to break hounds to them, and hounds paid little attention to these four-footed friends in kennels, and the huntsman knew he could have lifted his pack intact through a deer-park, but let hounds be running a fox, with their blood really up, and let a deer cross that line, and good-bye, boys! The scent of deer was, apparently, far more ravishing, for deer, after all, was their more natural quarry.

But, despite the day's burning pace and the straight line and this strange country they were coming to, where foxes did not usually dwell, the huntsman was almost sure it was not deer. He could have given you several reasons for this belief: the way the old trusted hounds were hunting, the voices of certain hounds and the cry of the pack, the way they cast and, once the line was owned, the way they ran. It was his business to know all these things, and these things were, now, his whole life. But, like a truly great commander, he tried to button everything up. This was a grass country and the few dirt roads they had crossed were iron hard and took no impression of pad or hoof or foot, so neither he nor his two whips— no one in the field, he suspected, (any possible Boy Scouts being in school) knew enough to tell the print of a rabbit from a skunk— had been able to prick the hunted animal. Therefore, in the hope of making absolutely sure, the huntsman had sent his second whip far down wind to an observation post on a road the quarry would cross. If it turned out to be *not* a fox, then the whipper-in would instantly gallop to the point on the road where the hunted animal, whatever it was, had crossed, and there take his stand, whip ready, and when the lead hounds appeared, would, riding in among them, very much as would a mounted policeman among a crowd of rioters, smack his whip and rate them in shrill, angry screams and so try to stop them and hold them there while the huntsman and the other whip came on to him.

As the huntsman watched the cast, a member of the field, sometimes referred to, when not present, as the Rubber Baron or "that shad-bellied (meaning the style of his scarlet field-coat) so-and-so," walked his almost beaten horse over to him. The huntsman, who was never mysterious or oracular about his tactical moves, explained briefly the mission of the second whip.

"Why, a fox, I'm sure," the Baron said confidently. "And a straight-necked one, what?" This was straight out of Surtees, the expensive, scarlet-and-gold edition; the Baron, an Anglomaniac, had not quite dared "straight-necked 'un." The huntsman, keeping his eye on hounds, said: "I'd take that horse in, if I were you, sir." There was no trace of servility in the huntsman's use of "sir." He was, in a sense, in the other's employ, for the Baron was a very large contributor to the support of the hunt and the "keeping up" of the country. And the huntsman—he was only human, after all —preferred to maintain the barrier between them, happy, in this case, to be on a separate, if lower level. For the huntsman was a gentleman—if the term be allowed—that had come down in the world, while the master was another kind of man that had come up.

"Oh, he's just blown a bit," the Baron said now, referring to the condition of his horse.

"He's lame, sir," the huntsman said shortly.

As he spoke, Mourner spoke too, in her high, thin voice, and then Dawdle and Gamin, and the rest closed on these three, and now the fourth and last movement of the symphony swelled to one tremendous chorus. The huntsman took up on his reins and closed his legs on the tired horse. He stuck the gleaming copper horn between the breast-buttons of his scarlet coat and rode for what looked like a gap at the end of a low broken-down stone wall. He thanked God in his heart that they were in a far outlying country where the hunt did not keep up the fences and build up the stone walls. To stay with hounds and still save the aged hunter he rode. . . . A worn grass wagon-track led into the next field, across which hounds were streaming in full cry. The huntsman, hating it, closed his legs sharply, just touching his blind spurs to the lathered flanks. The old horse broke into a gallop. The rider, getting himself out of the saddle, leaned far forward to free the tired quarters. Behind him came the four that were left of the field. The Baron was no longer among them, the master was not there—he had had a fall earlier in the day, nothing serious, but the delay, in view of the pace, was fatal—but—the huntsman did not have to look back to see—the master's daughter would, somehow, follow to the end.

All that day, and especially during the last few hours, the huntsman wished he could lose the field. Then, good and lost, they would go safely home. He had wished this, as he wished it now, because of the master's daughter. She was not good with a horse— she was a beginner, really—and here she was today, up on a flashy-looking chestnut that went boiling into his fences. . . . The huntsman had a way of seeing these things—when it came to her, anyway. The girl rode sidesaddle, and the chestnut, obviously, didn't like it, didn't like the strange skirt, streamlined though it was, and resented the uneven weight, for she did not ride well. What could the huntsman do? He scarcely knew her, it was his first season with this pack, but once he had spoken to her about a beautiful worthless brown horse that some coper had unloaded on her father to the tune of three or four thousand dollars, probably. One morning in the early cubbing season she had been having a hellish time with the horse, and when the huntsman told her she should get rid of the animal, the tears of defeat came into her eyes, and he was sorry then that he had spoken. The huntsman liked the girl— what he saw of her—and he wondered at her courage in keeping on with something that she did not really care for and that she probably feared. For he suspected, although she put on a good show of being calm and cool, that most of the time out hunting she was afraid. You might think that this would have lowered her in his eyes, but the huntsman had reason to know that one could face a withering enemy fire coolly enough and yet shudder at the thought of a steep rock climb.

Perhaps she had, inadvertently, betrayed this fear to him. The facts of the case were simple, but the resulting situation was terribly complicated. The master's daughter, his only child, heiress to one of the great fortunes—her mother had died when the girl was very young—had fallen in love with the huntsman. He would never have imagined such a thing, had it not been for a young man, a member of the hunt, who, coming to the kennels one night about a hunt matter—walking hound puppies, or something—and having had plenty to drink, had told the huntsman what a good part of the countryside was talking about. The huntsman was dreadfully embarrassed and troubled to hear this. He was a poor man—he had nothing put away, really nothing; his sole means of living was the salary paid him as a professional huntsman. . . .

All his friends would tell you that he had simply had bad luck; the small business he had put his small capital into had failed, and the hunt he then hunted with, having suddenly lost its professional huntsman, offered him the job, to tide things over. Hunting hounds was an art and a science that he took to, so he stayed on the job another year, and another year after that. Then *that* hunt folded up when a few rich people abruptly withdrew their support for reasons having to do with the social hierarchy—reasons that the huntsman never did fathom—and he counted himself lucky indeed, though he was duly sorry, when the huntsman of a neighboring pack had a fall—not over a fence, not even in the field, but at a walk on a hard greasy road—had both legs crushed, no chance of ever riding again, was pensioned off, and the job offered *him*.

And now the waters were all muddied again, by a foolish, pretty girl. Yes, he would have to admit her prettiness . . . her beauty—to him, anyway—when dressed up in the dark blue sidesaddle habit, little hard hat, veil, and the rest—a costume that would not appeal to everyone, in a role for which she was totally unfitted.

What could the huntsman do about it? He could, their small world said, run off with the girl and marry her; she would ride at a five-foot stone wall (with her eyes shut) if he told her to. So it was generally believed that a wedding over the border would be the upshot—the huntsman could count on being taken care of some way. But to be fair to him, this never entered his mind. He liked the girl and he was angry to see her torturing herself over a mere sport. Even if he had fallen in love with her—and he would have thought that foolish to suppose, she being for one thing so much younger than he, about twenty, a mere child really—even in that case, a marriage, with the heiress aspect and all the complications, was out of the question. It would be too embarrassing.

Two fields further on, hounds turned right-handed in a wide arc, taking the curve at top speed. The huntsman pulled up, expecting them to swing down wind again, but they kept straight on, and with louder cry, across the light wind, which was blowing from the north. As the afternoon waned and the air grew colder than the sun-warmed earth, scent had improved—that was one theory, and it seemed to be working out today. Now the sun was already behind the foothills to the southwest, and scent was burning. Suddenly they burst into a strange country—strange to the huntsman, anyway. But he could not be expected to know all that vast country in his first season, and, as he galloped, he glanced back at the field with the idea, first chance he got, to ask where they were: what about this country? any precipices? any bottomless chasms? Any—and he saw that there was no one left but that damned girl—no, he didn't mean that. She was all right, a trouble, a worry, that was all. His first whip was on the left flank somewhere. The whip—and the huntsman didn't think much of his judgment—might know this country and know what he was doing; the best place for him to ride with only one whip remaining. As for the second whip and his lonely vigil at Gallows Corner, he was lost for good this day, and no great loss, either.

The huntsman decided he would not question the girl as to where they were. In any case, there was no stopping hounds at this point. He would not stop them if he could, even though the quarry was heading straight for the fiery furnace. For any instant now—so you would have thought—they might break from scent to view, and the day would be saved. There was every chance. If they could bowl him over here in this open country before he reached . . . What was that ahead? In the quickening dusk it looked like the great wall of China.

That was the trouble, the dark. If they could beat the darkness, if they could kill before night . . . The huntsman felt his heart lift. This might be his lucky day. In a way, he had it coming; so far, this year, he had had so little luck.

And then—such was their fierce, burning pace—Gamin and Warrior, the lead hounds now—he could still recognize them in the fast-fading light—were closing the wall; the rest of the pack on their very heels. The wall, the huntsman saw as he came on, was a high board fence, boards so close together as to show little or no daylight between and to appear, in the dusk and at a distance, a solid gray wall. He saw Gamin leap at the fence and be instantly thrown back, as if by some unseen barrier. Warrior, Sambo, Mourner followed, and the two of them went over, sprawling, and the huntsman saw then the strand of wire stretched from post to post, a foot above the top board. Hounds were charging the fence, scrambling up, falling backwards, leaping again with fierce, angry cry. Most of them managed to get under the wire—some actually clawed their way over it.

The huntsman rode up—it was new barbed wire, he saw now— and he was about to dismount to cut the wire when he realized by the time he had done so, hounds would be over, even the new entry, who were having the worst of it. But he would have to cut the wire anyway, to jump the fence, and he freed his right foot from the iron. . . .

Suddenly he thought of the lone girl behind him; she was just waiting to follow him over, on the fool horse. How had she lasted this long? Even without the wire, the fence was terribly high. He judged it was a shade under five feet, and he was a good judge; men that hunted and rode races over timber had a marvelous eye for picking that part of a fence a fraction of an inch lower. . . . Almost all the hounds were over the fence now. It was not the kind of fence you met with in a fair hunting country, no matter the loose talk that goes around about five foot fences.

He looked right and left; the wire ran in both directions—and then he saw, some distance off to the left, but not clear in the half-light, what he had not noticed at first; a break of some kind in the uniform height of the fence. He turned and galloped down the fence line.

It was a gate, not quite so high as the fence, and chained and padlocked. For some reason—he did not stay 'o wonder why— extending upwards a few feet from each gatepost was a dead tree limb that looked as if it had been nailed to the post. It was a five-barred gate, showing plenty of daylight—what little was left. A nasty thing to get tangled up in. He turned the big bay horse and rode him back a little from the gate to place him for the jump. He thought of the girl again, who had followed him down the fence line. Hounds had gone on, on the other side. Cry was fading,

fading. He must get on, too. He owed her nothing. It was her choice. It was her own—

"Will you help me, please?' he said, turning to her and speaking fast. "The fox is sure to turn left-handed—down wind again. Ride down this fence"—he pointed with his whip—"to the corner." If there is a corner, he thought; there must be a corner. "Then turn right and ride along the fence—*stay outside the fence*. If you try to get inside, you may head him. See if you can get a view."

"What are you going to do?" she asked him. Behind the veil her eyes looked enormous in the dusk.

"I'll be with hounds."

"Please, I'd like to stay with hounds," she said, staring at him. "You have a whip out there on the left."

"I don't know where *he* is," the huntsman said, raging. She was not so dumb, for a pretty girl all dressed up in dark blue, white stock. . . . He was trying to keep her from getting hurt. Time was running out.

"*Will* you go?" he said in cold anger. He put everything he had into these words. "If it's the last thing I ask you, will you go *now*?"

She gave him one look, turned her horse, touched him on the flank with her coiled whip and rode off into the darkness. Not quite straight and easy in the saddle, she would never be really good. Well, there were other fields, other diversions, such as love, marriage. . . .

The huntsman gathered his tired horse to put him at the gate, and suddenly, for no reason that he could name, in that moment of time, everything seemed to go to pieces inside him. There is the old tale of the drowning man who sees his whole life unwind before him in the little while he takes to drown, and it was like this now with the huntsman. The thoughts crowded in. It would be dark in ten minutes and he would have to whip hounds off, if he could—alone, probably—the best line they'd had all year. He should have done it earlier, when it was still light; a bad mistake. All his life he had made mistakes; one after another, and he had got nowhere. What was he, who was to have done such wonderful fine things? A huntsman of hounds! Paid servant of a . . . what did they say about it? "Cruel, artificial, rich man's sport." How often he had defended it against these charges! And that girl's face when she had looked at him a moment ago—he was not a complete damned fool, and he could see her whole soul staring out of her eyes, and he knew the trouble she would make for him. A great, vast, terrible despair closed down. . . .

"Over we go, old man," he said to the tired horse and rode at the gate. He thought she was a pretty girl, and if things had been different, he rich, and she poor . . .

He felt the big bay hunter put in one tremendous thrust and then, too late, the huntsman saw the wire—a strand of wire between the two tree-limbs that ran upwards from the gateposts. He ducked, but the wire caught him anyway, across the eyes, and jerked him back. He let the reins go, but not quick enough, for the old horse hit hard, a terrible splintering crash, an instant of blinding, searing pain, and the sudden dark.

He was alone, on foot, in the dark. At first he thought it was his eyes—that he had been blinded, and he pulled off his right glove and put his right hand gingerly up to his eyes, to see if he could tell, by feel, how bad the wound was. He felt his eyes and face, and his eyes seemed to be all right—he could see his hand, now that his eyes were getting used to the dark—and there was no wetness from blood or any wound at all, so far as he could tell. He thought that strange, for he had taken the wire right across the eyes, and then he thought that this was a dream, that he was not, could not be, really whole and unhurt, and that in a moment he would wake to the reality of blindness and pain; he must face the consequences of that terrible fall. Or was the fall—was all that, the gate and the wire and, before that, that tremendous run, and all the rest, but a dream? He shook his head to clear it, to get things straight. And who but a fiend would string a single strand of wire between those two sticks running up from the gateports? What could be the purpose? In broad daylight anyone could see the wire. Only because of the failing light had he failed to see it. Had the wire been strung there for just this one contingency—that someone would try to jump the gate in the semi-darkness? As he had tried.

He stood there, listening, straining his ears. He could have heard one of his hounds speak if it was half a world away. Now he heard not the faintest sound of hounds hunting. He had lost them completely.

The huntsman could see better in the dark now, and he saw that he must have wandered away from the broken gate and the board fence for there was no sign of either. Nor was there sign or sound of his horse. The old fool had probably gone trotting off, reins dangling, the way horses do in their dumb way after a fall, after you've pulled their legs out from under a fence rail, off they go, not waiting for you, without so much as a thank you. His hunting whip had gone. This was a stag-handled, silver-ringed affair, a gift from the other hunt, and he thought of trying to look for it, but then he knew it would be hopeless, in the dark. The copper horn was still stuck fast between the breast-button of his coat.

What to do? Which way to go in a strange country? He looked up, but no stars were out. The wind, which had been blowing from the north, had died: now there was not a breath of wind. The line they had been hunting had run, before hounds turned right-handed, roughly in a southerly direction. So he would have walked north, towards the pole-star, the general direction of kennels and his three-roomed house in the stable-yard, his home. IF the pole-star had been out.

He took a few steps, rather aimlessly; and saw to his glad surprise, a country road. A road, like a river, is likely to lead to some habitation, so he began to walk along the road in the direction he had been facing. He did not limp, he felt no pain or hurt of any kind. Still not believing, fearing that somehow he must have been mistaken, he put his right hand up to his eyes, to his face again. No blood, no cut or wound that he could feel; he had not been mistaken.

He walked on. He walked on, not thinking much of anything, just kept on walking. He must have walked a good two miles, but no car came by, nothing came, from either direction. He did not know what to do but keep on the way he was going, though it might be north, south, east or west, for all he knew. It was not something he would choose to do, walk a rough, rutty dirt road in top-boots that fitted him now, too well—for it must be admitted that the huntsman was somewhat vain when he could afford it, in the matter of such things as hunting livery, military uniforms, formal dress. Suddenly he thought of something.

He stopped, pulled the hunting horn from between the buttons of his coat and, pressing the horn to his lips, blew. He blew the long, rising, falling call he used for calling a lost hound. As the last note died, he felt rather foolish—standing there in the road, childlike, blowing a horn. Still, it could do no harm; there seemed to be no one to rouse. It was like shooting off a gun when you were lost in the woods. Someone might hear; someone might answer. Recklessly, he blew again.

As he took the horn from his lips, he thought, for an instant, that he was hearing an echo; who else in the country would be blowing a hunting horn? The master carried a horn in a case on his saddle, having arranged a set of signals with the huntsman in case they should be some distance apart; one was "Let's call it a day." But the master blew his horn on only one occasion; the horn was not an honest hunting horn but had a reed, and it gave out a thin, emasculated note, highly ludicrous, which, on this one and only occasion, the huntsman did not happen to hear—only heard about it afterwards.

Oh, nothing like the horn the huntsman heard now! For this was not an echo. Someone else was blowing—someone that really knew how to blow. The huntsman listened with delight. A high, clear, flawlessly clear note—far beyond the huntsman's capacity. But, he would swear, not on any short copper hunting horn. Not *that* music. Ah, someone was mocking him, showing him up!— and ashamed, he tucked his horn away. . . . But, as he stood listening to the other horn, he knew, somehow, that it was not mockery although the call was indeed something like the one he himself had just blown, only more beautiful, more insistent, more compelling. "Come away-ee . . . away-ee . . . away-ee" it seemed to say, and that was what it meant. Come along in, come along home, the day is done—come away! What poor lost hound would not leave a line that must be hunted no longer and come along home, when he heard that call? The music died away. But it had come from the general direction in which the huntsman had been walking, and so, much puzzled, he continued on his way.

He walked on and on, and it seemed to him that he had walked many miles, and still no car passed, though the evening was still young; and no house or barn or building of any kind appeared along the road. The road, so far as he could judge in the dark, still ran fairly straight in the direction of the horn-blowing, and since *someone* must have blown the horn, it seemed best to keep on going the way he was. But he was terribly tired from the long, hard day in the saddle and the long trek on the country road, and his feet, in boots meant for riding only, were fast becoming an agony. This road, of course, might run on for twenty or thirty miles in a back country—and this was probably that type of country—and not lead past any habitation and finally end up—as it must, sometime—in a strange town or village; but whether he could last that long, he wasn't at all sure. He plodded on along the hard, rutted road and presently he became really discouraged, he was losing hope, when all of a sudden he saw, some distance ahead and close to the side of the road, a light. He thanked Heaven—he felt like kneeling down there in the road and offering thanks to God, the way pious people do when thrown up on a safe beach after a shipwreck. And now, seeing the light, seeing that it was a lighted house

by the side of the road, and knowing that he could get help and
that somehow they would find the hounds and get them back to
the kennels—though that might not be easy, might even take days
—he was ashamed that a few minutes before he had been so close
to damning everything, and railing at the hellish time, as he had
begun to regard it, he was going through; the utter weariness, the
torture of putting foot to ground, the despair of finding anybody,
any human creature, that night. For—when he remembered the
mantrap he had run into—he was really lucky. It might have been
so much worse. Suppose in the crashing fall—but had there been a
fall? and he put his hand up to his eyes and face again—suppose he
had broken his back or his pelvis, or even a leg, and so had been
unable to move? He might have lain there all that night—but no,
the girl would have come back and found him—and that would
have further complicated things. He was lucky that he had not
been badly hurt—he had not been hurt at all, which was a miracle
—and that he had been able to get up and walk and, in the end,
find a house, a lighted house.

There were several lights, he saw, as he turned in at the drive-
way. Curtains were drawn across the windows of lighted rooms,
all was quiet, no car stood in the cobblestone drive, and yet there
was the air of a party going on. And the huntsman saw at once,
even in the dark, that this was no bare, stark farmhouse, such as
one might expect to find in a back country. From what he could
make out, it was a small house of two stories, somewhat spread out
for its size—the kind of house he would like to have had. In a
country he once knew when he was a boy, where he had grown up
on hunting and where, perhaps, he had been happiest, there had
been many houses such as this: little houses that could honestly be
called hunting-boxes, since they had been built in a hunting country, so called, and were actually quite small. But in many hunting
countries hunting-boxes were, more often than not, imposing
mansions.

Finding no bell, but there being a brass knocker on the door,
the huntsman let the striking part fall gently so as not to make too
loud a knock. Almost at once the door opened—someone must
have been standing on the other side.

"Come in, Mr. Huntsman," a courteous voice said. "We have
been expecting you."

Now, if we put ourselves in the huntsman's place, we must
remember that he was, at the moment, close to the point of exhaustion, that he had been riding hard since not long after eleven that

morning to four in the afternoon, that he had had a bad fall—if the fall had been a dream, then all was but a dream—and that he had walked . . . well, some six or seven miles on a rough dirt road, and that he had had no food or drink since an early breakfast, except for the usual bacon sandwich, which he carried done up in wax paper in a pocket, and a quick swallow of sherry from a member of the field during a check. So, when the door opened and a voice at once called him by name, or anyway, by his professional title, and especially when he saw the strange, fantastic figure that faced him in the rather dim light of the vestibule, no wonder he felt that he was entering another dream world, less real, even, than the one he had just left, where he had found himself unmarked, apparently, by the wire, unhurt after that shattering fall. . . .

But this is my old hunt, was the huntsman's first thought, for the short, lean, bearded figure at the open door was dressed in a scarlet full-dress evening coat with the yellow lapels and black velvet collar the huntsman knew so well. But before my time, thought the huntsman, for he had never seen this little ginger-colored gentleman before—and then, struck dumb, the huntsman saw the black silk knee-breeches, the black silk stockings, and pumps with silver buckles. This chap had really done the thing in a big way; no one, in the huntsman's day, had ever dared go quite so far.

"Thank you," the huntsman said, stepping over the threshold.

"You are a little late," the other said. He shut the door, looking up at the huntsman, smiling, showing very white, rather fierce-looking teeth. His reddish beard was carefully trimmed to a fine point; his mustache had an upward sweep. "We waited and waited," he said, in his polite way, "and then we went ahead. But we saved something for you."

"Thank you," said the huntsman again, wondering what it was all about, trying to recall if he had accepted a dinner invitation, and then knowing of course he had not. He said, "Now, if I could use your phone—I must telephone kennels. My hounds got away—"

"Everything is taken care of," the figure in scarlet interrupted him. "Your first whip stopped them, just before dark. Aided by your young lady, I might add. They're safe in kennels now."

The huntsman stared at him. "But—but—how—how d'you—"

"How do we know?" the other finished it for him. "Oh," he said gaily, "we have many little birds here."

Very facetious, the huntsman thought. He did not feel at all that way. "There's also a loose horse," he began stiffly.

"Your aged friend?" the other asked, smiling. "We have him in our stable. You see? There's nothing in the world to worry about."

"Is he . . ." the huntsman hesitated. "Is he all right?"

"He's perfectly all right," the other said, suddenly serious: "now." He took the huntsman's arm and steered him towards a flight of stairs leading to the floor above. "Fed and watered—or, I should say, beered; he drank half a bucket of beer," he explained. "Your room's the second—"

"And by the way," the huntsman said, to put things straight, "the young lady you speak of is not 'my young lady.' If any—"

"Is it even so?" The little chap in scarlet looked up at him in a mocking way.

"If any little bird told you *that*," the huntsman said, smiling, "you can—"

"They're great gossips, of course," the other said; "especially the sparrows. The story was you might bring her along with you this evening. We'd have managed a—" he paused—"a hen party for *her;* this, of course, is a strictly stag affair." He stopped and looked up at the huntsman. "For a very good reason, which you will soon understand."

But the huntsman was thinking of something else. "She helped to stop the hounds, did she? Well, good for her! I sent her to the right place, then, after all."

"The right place?" the other repeated, giving the huntsman a strange look. "Well . . ." Then, abruptly he left this, and said, "Your room's the second on the right. You'll want a bath and a change. D'you mind a white tie? It's rather an occasion, you see."

"But I have no evening clothes—"

"But they were *made* for you," the other said gaily. "Come down as soon as you can. The dining room's in there." He nodded at a closed door beyond the stairs. "We'll be still at table—these chaps sit forever over their port."

"A bootjack?" the huntsman said, hesitantly. "Could I borrow—"

"This is a hunting country, Mr. Huntsman. There's a bootjack in every room."

The huntsman smiled. As he turned to mount the stairs he said, "I recognize your colors. You must have been a member before I came. I used to hunt hounds in that country."

Smiling, the little gingery chap looked up at him. "I am

tempted," he said, "to a slang expression I never liked. 'Are you telling me?' " He threw back his head and laughed, so infectiously that the huntsman began to laugh too, though why he could not say. "Do you remember," the other asked, "the great January run, over Mount Mercy, beyond the Fishing Dam?"

"Do I?" the huntsman broke in. "Why, there never was such a run, except today."

"Oh, come now!" The other's face fell.

"Of course," the huntsman hastened to add, "that Mount Mercy run we accounted for our fox."

"You did indeed."

"You were along that day?" the huntsman asked, politely, but he thought perhaps this little chap was one of those cheerful liars that jump those five-foot fences and have all those tremendous adventures when no one else is there. For the huntsman knew the Mount Mercy run by heart. It was during his huntsmanship—and he could name everyone there, not many, in the field that day. "The kill was made just beyond Crabtree Run. You were there?" He made it scarcely a question, said it in a perfunctory way, still very polite, as one stating an obvious fact.

"Yes." Still smiling his rather fixed smile, the chap in scarlet gazed straight at the huntsman, and such was the look in his eyes, so open, fearless, and, at the same time gentle, that the huntsman must believe, even though he could swear that the truth was the other way. "Yes," the little chap said again; "I was there." He gave the huntsman a kindly pat in the small of the back. "Now run along."

The huntsman went up the stairs and into the second room on the right. Lights were turned on in the room and a little fire was burning in the fireplace, but what caught his eye first was a scarlet full-dress evening coat with the facings and collar of his present hunt; this was hung over the back of a chair, and across the chair's seat were the braided evening trousers—not knee-breeches, to his relief, for he was a conservative man, and, on the rug beside the chair, a pair of patent leather evening shoes with trees. Laid out on the bed were a white starched shirt, studded and cuff-linked; a white waistcoat with the hunt's brass—or gold, perhaps—buttons; collar, white tie, folded white handkerchief—the full equipment. A mahogany bootjack with handle bar stood up on its own feet near the fireplace.

The huntsman stood motionless for a moment, gazing at the scarlet evening coat, and suddenly—perhaps because he was so weary and so confused as to what had happened to him, and what was now happening—suddenly he felt the tears smarting in his eyes and he had to swallow hard. Such a small, unimportant thing, but he had never in his life owned a scarlet evening coat. Now, in a hunting country the first thing, generally, the gentlemen that are entitled to wear pink, or scarlet, in the field do is buy—since all is vanity—a pink or scarlet evening coat, and this is generally worn at all formal evening parties during the hunting season. Such a coat, with its brass, or gold buttons, engraved with the hunt's initials or device, even of more elaborate design, with its dyed silk facings and velvet collar of the hunt's colors, is fearfully expensive, and the huntsman, before he was a professional huntsman, never felt he could rightly spend all that money on, after all, a kind of fancy dress. Even in the hunting field, when he was simply a member of the field, he did not wear scarlet, though urged to, but an old-fashioned, long black coat that had belonged to his father, a coat so stiff and weathered that, like a suit of armor, it could almost stand up of itself. Now—and when he had served as whipper-in— his livery for the field—scarlet coat, white breeches, velvet cap, and the rest—was provided by the hunt. But, of course, no evening dress, and anyway the huntsman held that a professional, a hunt servant—which was what he was—should not wear the scarlet evening coat—though people would have told him his case was different—and so he had never owned one. And now . . . he stood gazing at the beautiful garment—"made for you," his host downstairs had said. Well, anything was possible, *this* evening. . . . And he felt, even with the childish tears in his eyes, suddenly quite happy. . . .

Now bathed and groomed, and dressed to the eyes in the perfectly fitting scarlet swallowtail, the huntsman opened the door to the dining room and saw, in the light of many candelabra, what he might already have guessed—that he had chanced—*chanced?*— upon a hunt dinner. The room was ablaze with scarlet. Some twenty figures in scarlet coats—about ten couple, he would say at a glance, as he would say in counting hounds—sat at a long mahogany table from which the cloth had been drawn. And then he saw —and in that instant his heart seemed to contract and he felt a numbing fear as in beholding some supernatural thing—he saw— his eyes swept around the table again—yes, each figure wore a pointed, reddish beard, like that worn by the one who had opened the front door. *They all looked alike.* That was the strange, terrifying thing. . . .

All talk died as the huntsman entered, and now a chair was pushed back at the other end of the table from the door, and one of the scarlet-clad figures came to meet him, and when the courteous voice said again, "Come in, Mr. Huntsman," he recognized him whom he thought of as his host, the one that had opened the front door. For there was, indeed, scarcely any way to tell one from another, except perhaps by their manner of speaking, by one's having a beard a little grayer, more grizzled than the figure on his right or left. And then the huntsman saw, too, that besides the uniformity of the scarlet, each coat had the yellow facings and black collar of the huntsman's old hunt. And it broke upon him then—dazed and confused as he was, taking part in some crazy dream—that the whole thing was a joke, an elaborate, practical joke, with false beards, or masks, perhaps, and that these were all men he knew, members of his old hunt, and that in a moment or two the beards, or the masks, would be taken off. . . .

"This way, Mr. Huntsman," his host said, and led the huntsman, behind the backs of the chairs, along one side to the head of the table. Talk had been quickly resumed and, politely, everyone avoided looking at the huntsman who had arrived so late and was, at the moment, so conspicuous.

"This is your place, Mr. Huntsman." His host indicated an empty chair, the seat of the most honored guest, at the right of the head of the table. Another scarlet-coated figure, wearing silk knee-breeches—exactly like all the rest, the huntsman presumed—pulled back the chair.

"Thank you," said the huntsman to him, for the latter, dressed as he was, was obviously not a butler or footman—not even a hunt servant, the huntsman thought, smiling to himself. He was somewhat taken aback at this extreme courtesy. His host, standing behind the chair at the head of the table, waited for the huntsman to take his seat; his host, then, was the owner of the house, or the toastmaster of the dinner, or the master of the hunt—another hunt, though the colors were the same. . . . For the huntsman saw now that the face was not a mask and that the beard was not false and that this was no one he had ever known.

A place had been set for him on the dark, gleaming board. He unfolded his napkin and sat staring down at the empty plate with intense concentration as the voices rose about him. A plate of clear soup was set before him and then at once his sherry glass—one of four wine glasses, he counted—was filled. Both arms that served him had scarlet sleeves, and turning slightly in his chair, he saw that he was being waited on by two of the scarlet-clad figures. Embarrassed, he looked at his host.

"Am I so awfully late?" he apologized, meaning so late that the servants had been let go and that now two of the guests were taking their places.

"Not at all," his host said. "It is one of our customs. We call them 'Apprentices,' " he explained. "They *serve* a certain term," he smiled at the mild joke, "before being admitted to full privileges and obligations."

"What a good idea!" said the huntsman politely. "Solves the servant problem . . . I hear so much about," he added, to dispel any thought that he might have such a problem.

"The servant problem," his host said, not in surprise, not making it a question. He might have been recalling something out of the past. He looked at the huntsman and said in his gentle, courteous voice, "We are all servants here."

The huntsman was not embarrassed; he believed him. Now this was a strange thing, for it was the kind of remark one doesn't generally hear at a dinner party, much less at a stag affair such as this, held, you might say, in celebration of one of the cruelest of blood sports. Any other time, the huntsman would have put it down as sententious and smug and stuffy in the extreme, and, with a polite murmur of agreement, gone on to something less ponderous. But he did not have that feeling. No, it seemed to him that the little bearded chap, dressed as he was and, evidently, a killer along with the rest of them, had spoken in all sincerity; that he was sustained by an inner spirit, a belief, a conviction—the huntsman was not sure of the right word—something, anyway, that he himself had never known.

"Well, Mr. Huntsman," his host said in a different tone of voice and with a slight note of raillery, "you came to the horn, didn't you?"

The huntsman nodded, smiling at the other's use of hunting parlance. "Actually," he replied, "I was on my way here—I mean, I was headed in the right direction."

His host smiled too, showing his fine teeth, of which he may have been justly proud. "Yes," he said gravely, "I think you may say that, Mr. Huntsman."

"I beg your pardon?"

"That you were always headed in the right direction."

The huntsman, not quite sure what the other meant, picked up his sherry glass and drank. He knew little about wine, he was not much of a wine drinker, or a drinker of any kind—his job was too demanding and strenuous—but he knew when he sipped the sherry that this was something special—just as the clear soup he was now drinking was the best he had ever tasted. Yes, these chaps really did themselves well. They were busy with the port now, and he saw, to his surprise, that the decanters were being sent around the table against the course of the sun—as the phrase was, counterclockwise, and, in a way, this seemed the strangest thing of all. To the huntsman, it was like finding himself suddenly transported, without sea trip or flight, to a country where the rule of the road was different.

He said now, as an Apprentice removed the empty soup plate and put in its stead what the huntsman saw was the fish course, "I meant to say—I meant to ask you about that horn. I've heard some of the best"—he forebore from putting in that he himself had won first prize for horn-blowing in a not very large horse show—"but the chap who blew me home"—he corrected himself—"blew me here tonight—"

"Blew you *home*," his host interrupted him in a firm voice. "That is quite right, Mr. Huntsman. You must learn to think of it" —he made a sweeping gesture to include the room, the house, perhaps this far country itself—"as home."

"You are very kind," murmured the huntsman, accepting it as a kind of excessively hospitable remark one makes when the wine flows freely.

"Yes," his host went on, after a moment's silence. "He's one of our best horn-blowers . . . but I think it is only fair to tell you that he uses a trumpet rather than one of your little hunting horns."

"I thought so," said the huntsman.

"Yes," the other said, "we think that some day he'll . . . how shall I put it? . . . well, receive almost universal recognition."

"I should certainly think so," said the huntsman politely. An Apprentice filled one of the huntsman's glasses with a pale, still, yellow wine. The huntsman had emptied the sherry glass. Now he sipped the chilled, dry white wine and he wondered from what famed vineyard, of what great year? Already he was feeling a little lightheaded from the long hunt, the long, long walk on the road. . . . "I was wondering," he said, turning to his host, "where the road led to. I was quite lost in a strange country. To some village or town, I suppose."

"Eventually, of course, to the city," his host replied. The huntsman waited, but the other did not name the city, and the huntsman was ashamed to ask, ashamed of his ignorance.

"I'm glad I landed here," the huntsman said. "What would they have thought—my turning up in the city, in a red coat, on foot—"

"The Marines would have stopped you," said the other, laughing. "Along one of the purple streets." Confused, the huntsman stared at him. The other went on. "Some PFC from a green mountain who never heard of your kind of hunting would think one of Cornwallis' lobsters was on the loose."

His host was choosing to be obscure. One thing the huntsman did understand. "The Marines?" he repeated. "Troops, you mean. Sounds like martial law—"

"Oh, there's nothing to worry about," the other broke in. "Here, the situation has always been well in hand. But it's a duty those soldiers of the sea always wanted, and—I might add—one they were pretty sure they'd get. Perhaps that was one reason why they were always being pushed around. But who could refuse them? Surely, they were about due for a soft job after all the hard ones they had."

The huntsman tried to stop an Apprentice from filling another glass with red wine. The white wine had not kept pace with the fish course, which was gone, and now the meat was before him. The huntsman's gesture was insincere and feeble; he managed to stop the Apprentice just as the red wine reached a proper height in the glass. The huntsman was now feeling in top form, but he remembered the cost (for he never could stand much to drink) and as he tasted the dark, rich, heady draught, he turned to his host and said:

"I shall pay for this in the morning, I know, but one doesn't often meet with such wines; at least, I don't—"

"That has been corrected," his host interrupted him again. "You may proceed with impunity—up to a certain point, which you will soon learn to recognize. Me, when I find myself telling how I beat Eliza, one of the best of the bitch pack—before your time— over the ice, then I know I've reached what we may call the saturation point."

"I know," the huntsman said, somewhat puzzled by the last statement, but anxious, for his part, to confide in this delightful chap. "On occasions I have the most tremendous desire to sing close harmony. Then I know; for I'm really very bad with music. But I should have to be fairly tight for that. As a matter of fact, I do feel at this moment that I'm not so far off from wanting to join in in . . . oh, 'Drink puppy, drink' or 'D'ye ken John Peel' or—"

The other threw back his head and burst out laughing. "What contempt we used to have for those lays!" he exclaimed. "I remem-

ber standing on the hill one night in the moonlight, and I remember the house below—with a dinner much like this going
on—the house all lit up, and the guests the same, and those awful
songs, all off key. . . ." He paused, and then, smiling, looked at the
huntsman and said, in his kindly way, "They're very fine songs,
really. Now, of course, we understand."

But the huntsman was all confusion again: What was his host
doing up on a hill in the moonlight? One of those Southern night-
hunters? Was that it? A farmer—or a moonshiner, perhaps . . .
and what about this question of drink? "You mean," the huntsman
asked, and he touched his glass of red wine, "that this is . . . well,
that this and all the rest, won't—er—won't give one a head in the
morning?"

"The unduly heavy penalty," his host began, taking a sip of
port and giving his moustaches a brush upwards, "prescribed for
. . . well, for merely a modest binge if I may put it, was conceded
to be a mistake. Unfortunately, once the rules had been formu-
lated involving, as they did, certain chemical actions and reactions,
nothing could be done about it at the lower level, as we say in
government circles. It was, as you may imagine, engineered by a
strong and aggressive minority. Of course, once you get beyond the
finite order," he made a wide gesture with his right arm, "all that
can be changed. You will understand that, I'm sure."

The huntsman was not sure he did. Certainly it was against all
the rules *he* knew. He tried to put his thought in words. "Somehow, it doesn't seem quite fair. What I mean is, that I should go
through all these," he indicated the array of wine glasses, "and
wake up feeling like a, like a . . ."

"Lark," the other supplied, "the bird, I mean. One of our
favorites. There's one always around. Yes," he went on after a
moment, "it was agreed among the higher-ups—if you understand me—that a constant and cordial relationship with certain
products of the grape *and* the grain should not entail the morning-
after malaise, lassitude, distaste for all nourishment . . . that is to
say, the usual punishment was conceded to be unduly cruel, and
the whole thing was, so to speak, declared unconstitutional—as
affecting the higher level, that is."

"The higher level?" the huntsman repeated, confused at what
he considered to be annoying double-talk.

"In other words," said the other, laughing, "there is pie in the
sky. Yes, Mr. Huntsman, I guarantee that you will be joining the
lark in a duet in the morning; however" and he pointed to the

huntsman's fourth glass, which had not yet been filled, "it might be well for you to take the bubbles out of the champagne."

The huntsman thought that when it came to the champagne he would forego *that,* and he glanced round the table to see how the others were doing with their port, and suddenly he saw something, or rather, someone he had not noticed before; this was a figure sitting back a little from the table and partly hidden by the companions on his left and right, and he wore, instead of the scarlet coat of all the rest, a coat of light gray—with orange facings, the huntsman saw, not yellow, and a dark brown, instead of a black collar. A visitor, evidently, from another hunt, he looked leaner, yes, actually less well-nourished than the others. He had not their bold, assertive look, and perhaps that was the reason the huntsman had not noticed him earlier.

Curious, he turned to his host. "I don't want to appear inquisitive," he said, diffidently, "but your friend in the gray coat . . . I've never seen that before. Is he . . . ?" the huntsman hesitated.

"Not one of ours, as you see," his host replied—rather shortly, the huntsman thought. "He comes from another county, a county, by the way, that we finally gave up. Sour grapes, of course," he said, giving the huntsman a meaning look. "But . . ." and here he paused in the manner of one about to get off something good, "we never did move in his circles."

The huntsman laughed dutifully, hollowly—the way one laughs when he knows a joke has been made but does not see it. He thought he was getting a little dense from all the wine he had drunk—despite what his host had said about impunity—and he was casting about in his mind for a new subject, when the other leaned towards him and, fixing him with his tawny, yellowish eyes, said slowly, significantly:

"Actually, he asked himself when he heard you were coming."

"Oh, no thanks," said the huntsman, putting his hand out and preventing the Apprentice from filling the champagne glass quite up to the brim. "What was that?" he said, but he had heard every word. "I never saw him before," he said, glancing down the table at the figure in gray.

"That will come later," his host said in a calm, level voice.

When one of the decanters of port came round to him—the wrong way, of course, but that seemed to be their rule here, like driving on the left of the road—the huntsman did not take the stopper out but slid the heavy decanter along the mahogany to his right.

"Aha!" said the latter, giving the huntsman a look. "Close to close harmony, what?"

"Oh, very good!" the huntsman said, laughing loudly, knowing, of course, underneath the layers of sherry, Chablis, Burgundy, champagne and, now, port, that it was nothing to roar with laughter at. But he had a feeling, closer to unmanning fear than he had ever known, that he must be terribly agreeable now; that these people were against him, for some reason, and that he must do everything he could to placate them. And yet the little chap on his other side, his right, seemed friendly enough. He had been rather silent, at first, but that of course was to let the huntsman finish his dinner undisturbed. Now he began to talk.

"New Year's Day at Greenhill?" repeated the huntsman in answer to a question from him. "Yes, I remember; we only hunted that country once, in my time. Very short run, that day."

"Fortunately! You had all been up till dawn—"

"Not I—"

"Well, most of the field had. I always say, you can't mix alcohol and—"

"Gasoline?"

"Not our dish, of course. No, I meant hunting. On the lower level, that is." (Damn all this lower and higher level stuff! thought the huntsman.) "Too much bubbly water," the other went on, "the night before. Why, I saw five refusals at a three-foot chicken coop; my good friends the horses knew what was wrong."

"I suppose," he said, after a moment, "you might expect an apology from the enemy for putting up such a poor show—forty-three minutes, to be exact."

"You've a good memory," the huntsman said. He couldn't remember the time of that run, but he was sure the other was right.

"It's the sort of thing one doesn't forget," said the other with a peculiar smile. "Well, to be fair, the enemy was not up to snuff. He'd been having a bit of a moonlight celebration himself the night before, big chicken dinner and—"

"And moonshine whiskey, I suppose," the huntsman put in, smiling, trying to please. Who were these people, anyway? His neighbor said, "The enemy rather counted on New Year's Day being like Christmas, or Easter—holy days, days of peace."

"I'm afraid war doesn't wait on holy days," the huntsman said soberly.

"That's true. Not any more, anyway. Damn little of that thing left."

This was the sort of talk that went on round the table, the kind you'd hear at any hunt dinner, about this tremendous run and that —all a deadly bore unless you yourself had been along. These dinners—so the huntsman had observed in his time—could be quite a different thing from dinners held in celebration of other sports, such as yachting, or football, for example. Fox hunting was a blood sport, and the huntsman used to wonder sometimes if the presence of that element and the ever present chance of injury or death to its followers could account for the peculiar behavior of its celebrants. The men that devoted a large part of their lives to hunting—and by hunting he meant riding to hounds for the purpose of killing the fox, the stag, or the hare or of simply following a bag of anise or other artificial quarry across country—hunting men, as they were sometimes called, and a few women he had known, were more rapt, more fanatical, than other sportsmen, and their lives were, sometimes, terribly limited. The huntsman, who found time, though not much, for other interests, other pursuits, thought of these men as belonging to a peculiar order, devoted to one certain purpose—to kill. And now, this night, going back in his mind over the years he had spent with people of this kind, this dinner tonight and those scarlet-clad, fierce-eyed little chaps reminded him, in a way, of the mess of a fighter pilot squadron on active duty. Death was not here so wholesale, but, as had been remarked, the grave was always open.

Well, wars would go on, he supposed, but the sport of fox hunting was, perhaps, on the skids. And suddenly it struck him that he was thinking of his hunting days—his very life, then—as being over and done with, and this was a strange thing to be thinking, for hunting would probably last as long as he did, and he put the thought out of his mind. For, he told himself, the pack was safely kenneled—thanks partly to that girl—and they would all go a-hunting the day after tomorrow.

"You spoke of that young lady," he heard himself say to his host, and he knew he should not have gone in for the strong, full-bodied port after all the rest.

"I'm sorry . . ." the host bent his head towards the huntsman; the table was getting noisier.

"The girl who helped the whip stop hounds."

"Oh, yes. Certainly. What about her?"

"Nothing," said the huntsman, thinking better of it. Except . . ."

"Except what?"

"She ought to get rid of that horse," the huntsman said, and felt the anger rising in him.

"Why, Mr. Huntsman," his host began, teasingly.

"I'm thinking of hounds," the huntsman said. "I don't want my hounds overridden."

"Aren't you thinking of her, too?" the other asked, and he was deadly serious now.

"I'm thinking of the rest of the field," the huntsman said, like a small boy, persisting. "The horse is a menace—crossing people at fences. She can't hold him—"

"But aren't you thinking of *her*—first of all?"

"Naturally I don't want to see her hurt," the huntsman said gruffly. "You see," he said, deciding suddenly to confide in his host, "she's really not very good with a horse. She never will be, I'm afraid."

"She never will be," the other repeated; "but I'm not afraid."

The huntsman looked at him. But his host went on quickly, now in a teasing way again. "Of course, that would hold no appeal for you."

"What did you say?" Everybody seemed to be talking at once.

"Wouldn't you find it strange, Mr. Huntsman," the other asked, smiling at him, "to find yourself falling for a girl who couldn't tell one bay horse from another?"

"Falling?" repeated the huntsman in astonishment. "Me? I'm afraid one of your little birds gave you the wrong steer there."

"I think not."

"You're imagining things—"

"You never would, Mr. Huntsman."

"Not that, certainly," said the huntsman firmly. "In the first place, the thing would be impossible—"

"In the first place, yes," said the other, looking full at the huntsman; "but in *last* place?"

The huntsman did not attempt to answer. He put the remark down as one of those too profound to inquire into or as a bogus epigram made more for the sound, the contrast, of the words, rather than for any real meaning. He fell silent and, turning the empty wine glass in his fingers, listened to the high-pitched voices around him. They spoke a strange language, but the huntsman understood most of it, and he sat there, and now the thing began swiftly to unfold, to assume a dreadful clarity.

"Foil—foil. . . . Ranger's Brook—yes, but damned cold on the feet—" "Better than burnt-over fields, still smoking—" "The hotfoot, you might say." "Tied up in a bag—your uncle, really?" "Damned humiliating—" "A bagman, they call 'em in the old country; sounds so underprivileged—" "Rioted on a duck, I give you my word—" "Oh, a point of ten kilometers—"

The huntsman turned his head sharply. He did not hear the rest. He said in a low voice to his host, "Someone said 'kilometers'? I heard the word distinctly." He felt the fear coming back on him. "Where . . ." he began and was about to say, "Where *are* we?" but he could not bring himself to ask; he was afraid.

"Oh, yes," his host said carelessly. "We use the metric system. We think it better." He smiled. "We believe in retaining the best features of each."

"I notice," the huntsman said, and, so help him, he could not keep his voice steady, "that you send the port round the table the opposite way—that is, counterclockwise—against the sun, as some would say. . . ."

The other was looking at him, smiling, showing his white, beautiful teeth through the red beard. "Against the sun?" he repeated. "But Mr. Huntsman," he said in a high, triumphant voice, "doesn't that depend on where you are?"

"Of course," the huntsman said; "yes, of course."

He tore his eyes away from the other's steady gaze. Round him the voices went on.

"So they started digging—"

"Sent back to kennels for the terrier, I understand?"

"Yes, I gave little Jonesy one he didn't soon forget. . . ."

The huntsman found himself staring across the table at the figure that had just spoken—one of the older, more grizzled sportsmen. The latter may have sensed the huntsman's intense gaze, for he turned from the companion on his left and looked at the huntsman.

"Yes," he said, and it seemed to be for the huntsman he was speaking, "I had nothing against young Mr. Jones, but I was naturally annoyed when they brought *him* into the picture. This was something new; they'd never gone in for *that* refinement before." Here he leaned across the table and spoke directly to the huntsman. "You can confirm me in that, sir."

So it *is* a dream, the huntsman thought, and tried to wrench himself awake, out of the fear, the horror—the way one does sometimes when a dream can no longer be borne. But he did not come awake.

And now he realized that all the others at the long table were quiet, were hanging on the words of the figure that had just spoken.

"Young Mr. Jones," the speaker went on, "came fast and straight down the corridor. Of course that's what the terrier breeds are so proud of: take on anything. Stupid, we used to think. But each must have his pride. . . . As I say, I had nothing against Jonesy. I'd seen him and his brothers and sisters, from quite close too, for there was no danger of gunpowder in *your* country, sir"— and he gave the huntsman a little formal bow. "Playing around the kennels, they were, and they were such a gay, lively lot. I took quite a fancy to them. But this little Jones was asking for trouble and for a moment or two I thought seriously of sending him along ahead of me. For, of course, I saw then," he added in a matter-of-fact way, "that the game was up, as we used to say."

He paused to refill his glass from one of the decanters of port, which had reached him some moments before. The huntsman sat there in stricken silence. And then the other did an unexpected thing: he leaned across the table, seized the huntsman's glass, which had stood empty for some time, drew it towards him and filled it from the decanter.

"Oh, no thanks," the huntsman said in a strange, cracked voice. He made a long arm in vain protest. The other slid the filled glass across the table to him.

"You'd better have a drop," he said, kindly, "you've had a long day of it."

The huntsman, blindly obeying, started to raise his glass, but he saw that his hand was actually trembling, so he left the glass there on the table. No one noticed—or if they did, they showed no sign.

"You see," the storyteller went on cheerfully, "I was no longer young, and what with the shovels and spades and picks and mattocks, *and* Mr. Jones, they meant to have an end of it, one way or another. Yes, I could have sent young Jonesy on ahead of me, down there in the darkness, but, instead, I let him have one or two to teach him not to be so cocky, but nothing really serious, for he was a young chap with a brilliant future—as it turned out—and he came of such a nice little family."

At this a great roar of laughter went up, and while the table rocked, the huntsman picked up his glass, with steadier hand now, and swallowed some of the strong wine.

"So," the storyteller said when the laughter subsided, "I simply bolted—which, as you know," and he looked at the huntsman, "is a way we have. You were kind enough," he added, speaking directly to the huntsman, "to allow five minutes law. However, it was not enough—that day—as you may remember."

Yes, the huntsman remembered. He remembered this chap . . . and he would remember the others, all of the others there, should they care to identify themselves to him. He knew who they were now, and as he glanced around the table in a kind of horror, the scarlet ones, the bearded faces, these dread figures, seemed to press closer and closer, and he tried, he tried, with awful desperation, to blot out the room, the faces, the masks, all this thing, and to burst into the real world. . . .

"There is nothing to fear, Mr. Huntsman," he heard his host say. "And there is nothing to regret." He spoke in the cool, measured voice of authority, and all the table listened. The huntsman sat with lowered head, endlessly twisting the stem of his wineglass round and round in his fingers. He heard one of the heavy decanters being slid along the gleaming board; for a moment there was no other sound. Then his host began to speak, and it was a little like an after-dinner speech—though he did not rise—in that it had a certain formal ring and seemed to be addressed to the whole room.

"Once, without ever being sought, life was thrust upon us all, and to live, one must eat, and to eat, one must kill and, yes, one must sometimes steal. And once, in the old, old days it was a kind of game—rough, to be sure; no quarter asked or given—but fair enough, fair enough. . . . And then later"—here he turned his head and spoke to the huntsman—"later you asked yourselves, Why should we be fair to the thief of the world? And so instead of depending on the nose and speed and power of one, you packed together hundreds of villainous dogs—"

"Hounds," someone said, laughing at the speaker's vehemence.

"I'm sorry, hounds." The speaker smiled and went on, more mildly: "And they sent to the ends of the earth for the blood of swifter horses, and they sent men out at night when all decent folk were *not* home and *out* of bed" (laughter) "to barricade those same homes against the decent folk's finding sanctuary—"

The huntsman looked up—turned to him. "We never stopped earths in our country," he said quietly.

"You alone are not on trial, Mr. Huntsman," the speaker said. "It is so-called civilization."

"Hear, hear!" several cried out, laughing.

"They used spades and shovels and pickaxes and crowbars to tear up these homes and so to evict these decent folk. They imported specialists in the underground—otherwise known as terriers" (more laughter). . . . "Maneuvers," he went on, when they were quiet again, "maneuvers, tricks, gadgets—all to catch this poor thief of the world." He gave a little scornful laugh, and then in a voice several notes lower and in an organ-like tone, said, "All to destroy these same decent folk."

"Hear! Hear!"

"Splendid form he's in tonight, isn't he?" the huntsman's neighbor on his right whispered. The huntsman, who was not impervious to the orator's art, gulped down the last of his wine.

"Once," the speaker went on, slowly, spacing his words, "regarded by these same decent folk as mean, dastardly, but now"— here he returned to his earlier, lighter manner—"well, fair enough, not too unfair . . ."

"Not too unfair," he repeated, and now he was playing another movement, gayer, almost dancelike, "to be bundled into a sack, like the uncle of our friend here, and dropped in some dark cover. . . ."

"Who was it," one of them interrupted, "who was tied up in a sack and thrown into the Seine, or was it the sea?"

"Better a cover than the river," someone sang out, as if in answer to a cue.

It was a song familiar to all there evidently, for now all joined in, in tremendous voice:

> "Better a cover than the river,
> Better a brief hour, clear and free—
> Even the heartbreak over the stubble—
> Better a spinney than the sea."

The host held up his hand. "So we all thought," he said, smiling, "once."

"Not too unfair," he went on, spinning out the theme, "to send a whip to sink the wind"—he gave the huntsman a sly glance—"or even to send a pretty girl to get a view." But the huntsman did not rise to it, he sat there with bowed head, twisting the stem of his empty glass. There was a short silence. Then the speaker, in a different voice and speaking directly to the huntsman, said with great seriousness:

"Mr. Huntsman. So far as our members are concerned, you have played the game fair and square. We have not one single charge to make, not one fault to find. A just man, a loyal friend, a fair foe, you are our dear guest tonight. What more can I say—for us?"

"But"—and now he looked away from the huntsman and, gazing straight ahead, spoke in solemn, sorrowful tones—"there is one among us here tonight who . . . how shall I put it? how *can* I put it? . . . well, who would close the gates to you, Mr. Huntsman." And, like the brave, honest chap he was, he turned and looked the huntsman full in the face.

The huntsman returned the gaze steadily, but he felt his heart turn over, and despair seized him—he thought he had never heard such terrible, final words said to anyone. And now they had been said to him, to him. There wasn't a sound in the room.

"Yes?" said the huntsman at last. For clearly they were waiting for him to speak.

His host leaned forward and looked at someone far down the table. "All right, my Alpine friend," he said. "It is your turn now."

The huntsman saw the figure in the gray coat stand up. Ah! things were getting clearer. "My Alpine friend"—suddenly the huntsman understood; the gray fox could climb like a cat, something the red fox could never do. Often, when hunted, when pressed, the gray fox would take to a tree. . . . The red and the gray did not get along well together. The huntsman knew of a case where the red fox, being introduced for hunting purposes into a country where the gray predominated, was soon run out. And he recalled his host's remark a little while back: "He comes from another country—a country that we gave up. Sour grapes"— and how apt that was! And—now he saw the joke—"We never moved in his circles." And, despite the fear in his heart, the huntsman had to smile: for it was true that the red fox, as a rule, traveled fairly straight before hounds—witness this day!—while the gray was wont to circle, like some of the lesser breeds.

"—not exactly in training." The figure in the gray coat was speaking now, and it behooved the huntsman to listen to every word, for this one, for some unknown reason—unknown to the huntsman—was his mortal enemy.

"We had, of course, rather gorged ourselves," the little chap went on in a thin piping voice, "been up very late and all that sort of thing." The huntsman, hands clasped on the table in front of him, leaned forward, the better to hear. "We were prepared to sleep it off, as usual, when at an unconscionable hour, without drums or bugles, so to speak, the attack jumped off."

He paused, and the host took the opportunity to whisper in an aside to the huntsman, "He likes to put things in military jargon. You understand, of course."

"I understand," the huntsman said in a low voice. "I remember. Hounds were thrown in, about six in the morning."

"Exactly."

The figure in the gray coat suddenly burst out in a much louder voice, "And I should like to seize this occasion to enter my strong protest against the modern so-called sneak attack. In former times no one would have considered beginning hostilities without a formal declaration of war, properly signed, sealed, and delivered. One marched against the enemy with banners flying, bands playing—fife and drum, anyway. . . . Even on the very field of battle— you remember the classic example of Fontenoy—there was a certain ceremony, a show of *politesse*. I would inveigh—"

"He's off," someone said in not-too-hushed a voice, and at this point the host broke in:

"Yes, yes, my dear sir, we all know how he—er—the High Command"—he smiled at the concession he was making in adopting, for the moment, the other's language—"feels about beginning wars—not to mention war itself—without ultimatums, orders of mobilization, executive or legislative declarations, and other manifestations of an earlier and better civilization, so called. Just as we knew the general concensus on the highest level with respect to the employment, *imprimus,* of unconventional—a rather mild term, be it said—weapons."

The figure in gray, arrested in full flight by this ponderous stuff, bowed. "I feel very strongly in the matter," he explained.

"Naturally," said the host; "so did we all. But much is forgiven, as we know."

"Very well," the little chap in gray said. "I make no issue of the dawn, sneak attack, though in former times it was the custom to give the enemy a little time for the normal digestive processes—"

"Please proceed," the host said shortly.

The figure in gray stood in silence for a moment, gazing down at the table. Then he looked up and began to speak quite simply and clearly and in a voice that seemed to come straight from his heart.

"I do not wish to bring the children into court, as the saying is. And if I say 'I, I, I,' as my story might require, it might seem that I were crying out in pain, 'Aie! Aie! Aie!' and that, as I see it, would be unfair to him whom all of you have found to be so scrupulously fair.

"So, with your permission, it shall be a story told in the third person, of . . . shall we call him Sergeant Gray? Indeed, I sometimes think of him as a lone trooper of the old Confederacy. . . ."

"You see," the host murmured for the huntsman's ear; "still the professional Southerner. We're all dam-yankees to him. They've forgiven, of course, by this time. But will they ever forget?"

"—recognized at once," the speaker was saying, "that he was, as usual, outnumbered: this time, some fifty to one. Outnumbered!" his voice rang out. "Who but we knew the dreadful import of that word? You hear the expression 'The odds were against him.' Who but we knew what those odds could be? We alone—"

"Oh, come now!" a voice interrupted.

"What about the stag at eve?"

"Brer Rabbit," said another.

"Ferdinand."

"And poor sister Anise." This was apparently an old, outworn joke; no one laughed.

"Yes, yes," interrupted the host. To the speaker he said sternly, "That's all over the dam, sir."

"You'll have to pardon me, Mr. Chairman," the speaker said. "You see, Sergeant Gray was a very young recruit indeed and quite unaccustomed to the wrongs and snares of the world.

"Yes," he continued, "he'd rather gorged himself, as I've said, made rather a night of it like any other foolish, reckless young fellow, and so was in no condition to take the field of honor. A retrograde movement was definitely indicated.

"The order of battle, then—"

"We've had that," the host, or chairman as the speaker had called him, interrupted.

"Oh, yes. Well, the assault troops hit the cover at 0601. . . ."

"Dull as an Action Report," murmured the chairman.

"The line of retreat," the speaker was saying, "ran in a wide arc from Ten-Acre Meadow—" when the chairman again interrupted:

"If you don't mind, sir, do spare us the details of the withdrawal. We all know the tune. 'Found at the Dingle Dell cover, ran to the Locust Ridge, doubled back to Pine-Tree Ford. . . .' That's one form of torture we've usually been spared: the loser in our game is in no mood to go in for post-mortems. Perhaps we should count ourselves lucky. I am reliably informed that those who have had to listen to this sort of thing consider it a fate worse than television."

The figure in gray bowed again—he might have been a rather flustered counsel dressed down by a biased judge.

"I understand, Mr. Chairman," he said humbly. "Only those who were there are really interested."

"Exactly."

The speaker was silent for a moment. Then he seemed to collect himself, as if for a great effort—as if indeed he were arguing a case and had not done very well and now must put everything he had into it.

"I wish I could say," he said in a stronger, clearer voice, "that Sergeant Gray ran rings around them, the way his daddy, the colonel, used to do."

"Colonel!" said the chairman under his breath. "I'd like to see his commission!"

"But the sergeant was young and inexperienced," the speaker continued, "while the enemy was in great force and pressing hard. Well, gentlemen, I'm no General Francis Marion—"

"His favorite campaigner," said the chairman aside to the huntsman; "naturally."

"—nor do I pretend to compare the retrograde maneuver to a Mons or Coruna or—"

The chairman gave a rude and audible chuckle.

"Oh, I know, I know," the speaker said with a mournful smile. "We flatter ourselves, we like to think we have done well, even when we have run away. But if I could tell you something of the terrain, of the overwhelming advantage held by the enemy in the matter of atmospheric conditions, comparative temperatures of earth and air, barometric pressure, percentage of precipitation—"

"You mean 'scent'," a brutal voice interrupted. "Why so Nice Nelly?"

"—you would understand," the speaker went on, looking slightly reddish, "that at the end of an hour and twenty minutes—"

"One hour and forty-seven minutes," someone put in. "That's the figure on the plaque."

"Very flattering," the chairman said. "And just about as accurate as history ever is."

"One hour and twenty minutes," the figure in gray repeated firmly. "He claims no more than that. . . . Gentlemen, if I told you of these things—not forgetting the aid given the enemy by non-combatants, spectator sportsmen, filthy agriculturalists—"

" 'Dirt farmers' would be more polite," the chairman objected.

"I'm sorry," the speaker said quickly. "Anyway, many things seemed to conspire against Sergeant Gray that morning. The odds, the heavy odds we all have to face, were, so the sergeant thought, more weighted than ever. I like to think he put up a good show, though perhaps not a very long one. No, it did not take long for him to realize that he was utterly spent, in the last desperate stage of exhaustion. He had circled back to the Singing Brook"—the speaker broke off and threw a scared look towards the head of the table. "I'm sorry Mr. Chairman; I mentioned the locale only because it's very close to the end—"

"Quite all right," the chairman said gruffly, in a kindlier voice.

"Sergeant Gray had his back to the wall," the speaker said earnestly, "and the swordsmen were coming at him from all sides—"

"I wish he'd stick to one era," the chairman murmured.

"—of course, the sergeant had his crampons along," the speaker said, slurring over the sentence in an apologetic tone. Defensively, he glanced around the table. "I realize that you gentlemen do not approve of certain articles of equipment that Sergeant Gray would naturally regard as indispensable—"

"*Naturally,* is good," the chairman interrupted, smiling at the speaker. "It's not so much that we do not approve. Isn't it, rather, a question of—shall we say—Government Issue?"

At this, a great laugh went up, but the speaker did not laugh or even smile. No, he was in Sergeant Gray's boots—with the climbing irons ready—his back against the wall, his breath gone, his little heart bursting, and the hosts of the enemy were closing in.

"Ash or oak, he never knew," the speaker went on, and his voice shook a little, "and that was strange because the sergeant was a great one for knowing all the trees by name. But he never saw; up he went like a sailor up the shrouds in a sudden squall, and scarcely a moment later, there was the enemy below.

"There were the hounds, at the foot of the tree. . . ."

Thus, abruptly, the speaker abandoned the fiction, the thin disguise, the military jargon. The room was deathly still. Before, all during his speech, there had been whispers and low voices, the asides of the chairman, the sounds of matches being struck, of decanters sliding along the mahogany, but now there was not a sound, not a breath, and the silence was like a living thing in the room.

"There were the hounds, baying," he said again, and the look in his eyes, the mounting pitch of his voice put you right there, in the ash or the oak, but not the bonny willow tree this time, with the tired gray fox gazing down on the death below. "Flinging and hurling themselves against the tree, they were," he went on, "and running up the tree a few steps, and falling back. And the cry, of course, all the time, the terrible cry. And the master and the huntsman and the two whippers-in, and all the field on their horses, all

panting and laughing and congratulating the huntsman and marveling at the wonderful, wonderful hounds—all, all, were there
for, though the young fellow had done his best, he had not, as I
have said, given them a very long run.

"This was the end—he knew enough for that, though this was
his first brush with the enemy—"

He broke off. No one laughed at the terrible inadvertence; all
knew that he had never intended a joke at such a time.

"Who could help knowing," he said quickly; "seeing what was
there below? His heart was in his throat and the little wings were
beating below his diaphragm, but he tried not to show a sign. He
was swaying a little with the tree in the wind that had sprung up
with the new day, and he felt a little tree-sick and also a little sorry
for himself because he was so young and because he loved the
wild, free life he led, and—well, somehow it didn't seem altogether
fair. The young *do* feel that way. And he wondered how the end
would come. He had heard stories: once a tree had been cut down,
once a lucky shot with a stone had found its mark. . . . And then,
suddenly, he remembered that in all observed cases, the hounds,
after marking the tree, had been taken some distance off . . . and
what would happen then was that the sergeant, once somehow
brought to the ground, would be given a few minutes law, and the
battle would be on again. And he wondered if he would have
breath and heart enough for another go. And so, while clinging
fast to the branch, he tried to relax and rest and restore his
strength, the way a boxer does between rounds.

"But the minutes went on, and hounds were not taken away.
And the fierce, yelping cry went on, although now some hounds
stood silent, staring upwards, and some lay panting, and a few still
kept charging the tree and climbing a few feet up and falling back
again. Of the riders, almost everyone had dismounted, and three
or four, having turned their horses over to the others to be held,
went about looking—the sergeant soon realized—for missiles to
throw at him. For now stones and heavy pieces of dead wood began to hurtle through the air. He clung tight to the tree's branch,
then, ready to duck and dodge, and all the while he looked quietly
down at them. The two whippers-in were the most persistent—
eager beavers always showing off, keeping up a continuous, wild
bombardment, they were both poor shots—and the sergeant hated
them the most, and the huntsman next.

"It seemed unfair, too," he said after a slight pause, "that they
should be able to use the same ammunition over and over again.

However, I don't think there was even a marksman among them, for the sergeant never had to move. He just lay along the branch and, with both eyes open, keeping constantly on the alert, watched them. And presently they tired of the game and left it and stood about in groups talking the situation over—the issue now, apparently, being in some doubt. And far up, near the top of the tree, the sergeant wondered what deviltry they would be up to next.

"And then he saw that the huntsman had taken off his scarlet coat and yellow waistcoat and had come to the foot of the tree. Then the two whips were giving him a leg up to the lower branches. And now he began to climb—the huntsman himself!—and the sergeant looked down, very quiet and still, and, so far as he could see, the huntsman was unarmed—that is, he didn't have his hunting whip tied to him by the thong, or anything like that.

"The sergeant waited there, never moving, and his heart began to pound again and fear came back on him. The man below had climbed steadily, pulling himself up from branch to branch; at the foot of the tree the hounds were milling once more, and their cry swelled to a new pitch of excitement. The little crowd of people stood like stones, silent now, staring up at the sergeant. Only the quiet horses seemed not to know or care what was going on.

"Through the bare branches the sergeant could see, coming closer and closer, the dark blue velvet cap of the huntsman, the long, shirt-sleeved arms and gloved hands, pulling himself up and up. . . ."

The speaker stopped, and it seemed for a moment or two that the telling had become so unbearable to him that he could not go on. Someone near the head of the table cleared his throat, and the sound was like an explosion in the still room.

"And now"—the speaker seemed to be forcing the words out—"the huntsman came to the last branch, and his velvet cap was only a few feet below the branch where the sergeant lay—so close that the sergeant could hear the young man breathing, panting a little from the hard climb. And the sergeant wondered what the next move would be . . . and then the huntsman looked up, and I swear he was smiling and he said: 'All right, old man' and he reached one arm up.

"That's what he said to me," the speaker cried out, and his voice was a terrible thing to hear. "And what did I think? Why, I thought he had come to save me! For he knew I would never jump down, and so he had come up. For some reason—I had no time to think about it all—he had changed, he was my friend, and so I jumped

into his arms and put my head against his cheek, the way a dog
does, in love, to his master, and he tore me from him and flung me
to the hounds."

No one spoke or moved. The huntsman sat with bowed head,
hands clasped in front of him. Then, at last, he heard his host, the
chairman, say in a calm, detached voice:

"Well, Mr. Huntsman?"

The huntsman raised his head and looked straight at the figure
in gray, who was still standing at his place.

"I had to blood my hounds," he said simply.

He would ask for nothing, say nothing more. That was the
truth. How could he say here, among these, that it had been his
first season as huntsman, that for the first three months they'd had
no halfway good hunting, that the hounds were getting lax, losing
interest, skirting, babbling, rioting on rabbit or whatever jumped
up in front of them? How could he say, here, that his livelihood,
that life itself, depended upon "showing sport" to the hunt members, to the field? And how could he tell the little chap in gray that
the gray fox, in that country, was a nuisance rather than a hunt-
able quarry? And say, outright, that this little chap hadn't really
stood up to them, hadn't really put up a hunt, but had run round
in a few panicky circles and then run up a tree? Gorged with food,
so early in the morning—that was true. Well, that was the way
wars were fought these days. Any one of these chaps in scarlet
would have done better. . . ."

These were the reasons for what he had done, and, though the
huntsman remembered that morning so well—somehow it
wouldn't go out of his mind—these reasons were sufficient for him.
But he could not say so here, so he said again, qualifying the statement slightly out of deference to his host and the others there:

"I felt I had to blood my hounds."

Then, silence. Perhaps they were waiting for the figure in gray
to reply, or for the chairman to say something, but neither said a
word, and the silence went on and on.

And now the huntsman was sure that it was the end, for him—
that the whole business, whatever it was, was over and finished and
he had lost out. He had been tried and found wanting, he had
done a thing he could never undo, and there was no hope for him,
ever any more. But how else, he asked himself bitterly, could he
have fared in such a tribunal? If ever a court were rigged against
a man! . . . There were those who thought it unfair that the

victors should sit in judgment on the vanquished. What would they say to the other way round? Well . . . he turned and looked at his host—host, chairman, judge, all in one—and waited for the verdict.

Someone pushed back a chair, there was a slight disturbance— but the huntsman did not glance round. He heard, then, the tread of feet behind him, and a strange look—of joy? of triumph?— came into his host's face, and the next moment the huntsman felt an arm, thin and sinewy through the gray cloth, across his shoulders.

"It's all right, Mr. Huntsman," a voice said close to his ear. "I understand. I should have remembered. You had your hounds to think of. Everything is all right." And the little chap in gray gave the huntsman a fierce squeeze—to hurt him with love—and went pattering back to his place at the table.

The chairman was getting to his feet. He held a brimming glass. Someone began to clap, and then the whole table burst into applause.

"To *Lieutenant* Gray!" the chairman cried. Cheers and more applause. Through the din the huntsman heard: "—happy to announce . . . promotion . . . in the field, so to speak. . . ." The chairman leaned down and whispered to the huntsman, "Nothing could please him more."

Now all were getting up, calling for the decanters, filling glasses. The huntsman's neighbor on his right splashed some wine into the huntsman's glass. The huntsman rose, trying to hold his hand steady. All stood, facing the figure in gray, who was leaning back in his chair, his features fixed in a broad, foolish smile.

"Lieutenant Gray! Lieutenant Gray! Lieutenant . . ." It was like a salute with all pieces not going off at once, quite unrehearsed.

"For he's a jolly good fellow," etc., etc.

Now they were all seated again except the chairman. The decanters were shoved round, glasses recharged. The chairman held out his empty one to the huntsman who filled it. The chairman raised his glass on high again, and the huntsman wondered what was coming—

"To the huntsman!"

All up on their feet again.

"The huntsman! The huntsman!" they all yelled. It was just as loud, just as enthusiastic. Oh, dear God, thought the huntsman, how shall I begin? For he was never any good, he hated to make a speech. The chairman leaned over to him.

"You may say 'Thank you,' " he said. "But no more. That is the rule."

"No speech?" the huntsman asked, and a great wave of relief went over him.

"No speech," the chairman said firmly, as he resumed his seat. "You might have guessed—if you had thought about it—that we would have no after-dinner speeches here."

Now all were seated again, and the huntsman rose. "Thank you," he said, looking all round the table till his eyes came to the little chap in gray. "Thank you," he said to him. That was all they expected. He sat down. He had never been so happy. . . .

But when talk was resumed and the decanters began to circulate again and they all looked like settling down for a night of it, the huntsman remembered how far he had to go and that he would have to get a car from kennels to come for him, and so he turned to his host and said:

"You've been awfully kind, and I can't tell you how much I've enjoyed this evening. But I shouldn't be sitting here, having such a good time, drinking your fine port." He smiled. "Why, pretty soon, I'll be looking for some close harmony—"

"We'll get around to that," his host assured him.

"Another evening, perhaps," the huntsman said, being most polite. "But now I'm afraid—if you'll excuse me—I'll have to see about getting home."

The chairman looked at him a long moment without speaking, and the huntsman could see now that the other was his friend, would always be—why, he could almost feel the kindness, yes, the love, the true loving kindness, that was in the other's heart. And, for an instant, for a split second of time, the huntsman had the strange feeling that comes to almost all of us occasionally, which, for himself, he could never define or explain, that all this had happened before, long, long ago, in another world, another life: that his host and he had once sat thus together and that the other had spoken the very same words he spoke now:

"Home?" his host said in a low voice for the huntsman's ear alone. "Surely when *he*"—with a nod he indicated the chap in gray down the other side of the table—"when he did what he did and said what he said, surely you realized, Mr. Huntsman . . ." He looked at the huntsman hopefully. "We try to break it gradually," he murmured: "tonight is only the beginning . . . the tidings of great joy . . ."

And then the huntsman knew.

H AVILAH B ABCOCK

'Possum Up de 'Simmon Tree

Running hounds at night in pursuit of the 'possum and 'coon is
not a sport that is widely followed, although the growing numbers of both animals is increasing the ranks. The recipe for preparing roast 'possum is somewhat similar in its introduction to
that of rabbit stew—first you get a 'possum. This, as Havilah
Babcock points out, can prove an interesting and even exciting
task. The woods at night are not the same woods the hunter walks
by day, and Babcock has the faculty of taking you into the night
woods.

I s that hound any good, Uncle Spiller?" I asked, pointing toward
a malevolent-looking brute sniffling at the old darkey's heels.
"Lawdy, Cap'n, if dat dawg had a-been much better de good
Marster would a-kept him for to hunt 'possums wid hisself! Dat
Ole Blue, de high cunstable ob de swamp."

"And what about these others?" I asked, as three churlish-look-
ing varmints emerged from under the cabin.

"Dis here Squaller, and dem two Big Mouf and Snake," he
pridefully informed me. "And dar ain't no passel o' dawgs in de
country dat's a sarcumstance to 'em, sah. Course I don't mind you
speakin' discontemptuous-like about 'em, kase you ain't hunted
wid 'em yet."

The dogs were as scurvy and unprepossessing a bunch as I had
ever seen. Their ancestry, I felt sure, would have defied a genealo-
gist, but if their family tree had a 'possum up it there would be
no complaints from me. Uncle Spiller had such an immoderate
pride in his mangy pack that I forbore comment. Besides, we were

depending upon the old darkey to "chaperon" us on an all-night hunt through the mazes of Inktoe swamp and I was too prudent to incur his displeasure at the outset.

Uncle Spiller is of uncertain antiquity. I have no idea whatever as to his age, but I have nothing on Uncle Spiller: neither has he. He has dried up until he looks like an African mummy. Malaria, rheumatism, and the other "complaints" of the low country have long ago worn themselves out on his leathery carcass and given him up as a bad job.

The old codger looks as if he were about ready for Pilgrim's Progress, but before that night's hunt was over I conceived a profound respect for the stamina that lay wrapped up in that scrawny and ageless body. And he has about him an infectious good nature.

"Old Spiller ain't got but two teefths," he chirruped, "but tank Gawd dey hits."

We also took with us one July, a weazened counterpart of Uncle Spiller, his grandson and the apple of his eye. "Dat pickaninny got monkey blood in de vein!" the old darkey proudly told us. "He is de tree-climbin'est varmint in de swamp. Ain't yer, July?" The little Negro accepted the compliment with gleaming teeth.

I had invited Bill, a "regular" guy who had been *particeps criminis* with me on more than one doubtful venture, and Professor Smathers, a biology instructor in the state university who, I thought, might enjoy the novel experience of a night in the swamps. That half-witted professor! But it was my fault, as Bill reminded me later; I ought to have known better in the first place.

Anyway, our 'possum "safari" was made up, and nightfall found us threading the devious recesses of Inktoe swamp. Within an hour I was hopelessly befuddled as to any sort of direction, but it didn't matter, Uncle Spiller trudged serenely on, leading us over harricanes, windfalls, across glistening streams of black water, and through apparently impassable canebrakes with the unfaltering sureness of a child of the swamps.

As we penetrated the depths of the swamp, the black void about us became animate. Night is the true democracy. Innumerable birds flitted uneasily in the inky ceiling overhead. Small animals, disquieted by our passage, scampered noisily away through the underbrush. Once a wild hog, surprised in its lair, emitted an explosive snort and bounded away. Now and then an enormous owl let out a spine-tingling WHOOOOOOOOOP! that reverberated through the swamp.

Cypress knees loomed grotesquely in the spasmodic flicker of the lanterns, like the snouts of reptilian fossils peering at us from the black muck. Shadows danced eerily. Now and then came the phosphorescent sheen of a decaying stump, whereupon July would mumble, "Dat ole Plat-Eye!" and sidle closer to his grandfather. Finally Uncle Spiller stopped.

"Dis here ole Tom's stompin' ground. Us mout strike 'im and again us moutn't. Luck a funny t'ing," he offered.

"Who is old Tom?" Bill asked.

"Ole Tom de king 'possum uh Inktoe swamp. I been atter him five years, I speck. I done cotch him oncet."

"You caught him once? Why did you turn him loose?" I pursued.

"Didn't tuhn 'm a-loose. Ole Tom, he tuhn me a'loose," he said, crytically. Extending a gorilla-like arm into the region of light he pointed to a jagged scar at the base of the thumb. "Yassah!" he clucked. "I was a-possumin' dat night, but ole Tom he was a-niggerin'. 'Twas nip an' tuck, sah, and we parted de bes' uh friends.

"Hish," he interrupted himself. "Hear dat? Ole Blue done struck."

A tremendous wail resounded through the night, followed by a series of heavy-throated bellows: "Woo-woo-woo-woo-woo-woo-woo! Woo! Woo! Woo!" Again the tremulous deep-chested wail, and again the staccato sequence of "Woo! Woo! Woo!" from the cavernous throat of Old Blue. Each time the rhythm was repeated, the cadences rising and falling on the mellow night air. In a few minutes, another dog chorused in, then another and still another, their voices merging into the volume of an orchestra. They were presumably following a devious trail, the baying alternately waxing and waning away in the distance.

As if reacting to a galvanic shock, Uncle Spiller suddenly jumped atop a stump, cupped his hands to his mouth, and emitted a penetrating cry that echoed and re-echoed until it died dolefully away in the dismal depths of the swamp:

"YeeeeeeeeeeeEEEho! YeeeeeeeeeeeeEEEho!"

As if in response to his encouragement, the tempo of the baying increased.

"Dey's a-trailin', and a-comin' dis way. Dat Snake dar. And dat ole Squaller done open up. Hey, dat ole Big Mouf done chime in! Dat 'possum mos' ready for de kurriner and dat's a fack!"

"What do you mean by *kurriner?*" I asked mystified.

"You know, Cap'n, kurriner. De man whar say you daid afore dey buries you."

The trail was obviously getting warmer and coming toward us. The dogs were now within two hundred yards, their voices rising in a clamorous crescendo. Suddenly from the underbrush behind us emerged the pack, with heads down and throats swelling. But why were they coming straight toward us? That was a mystery soon resolved as Old Blue trotted importantly forward, thrust his battle-scarred muzzle up the very tree against which Uncle Spiller had been leaning, and wailed disconsolately. The other dogs lunged forward and pandemonium broke loose. The younger dogs set up a clamorous bawling, gnawing at the base of the tree, leaping up the trunk and trying madly for a footing in their frantic efforts to get at the quarry. The old darkey stood with a look of chagrin on his wrinkled face.

"Dar now! Whoever heard o'sich doin's. Leanin' 'ginst a tree wid a 'possum up it. In my younger days, old Spiller would ha smelt dat 'possum hisself." He looked around with a comic seriousness, begging for a spark of credence. "If dem smart-aleck niggers on de oder side de swamp hears 'bout dis, ma hash am settled."

"Come here, July," he ordered. "Shinny up dat tree and shake dat 'possum out."

The little Negro emerged from the shadows and prepared for the ascent. I cast a flashlight beam up the towering sweet gum. The trunk was two feet in diameter, and it was perhaps twenty-five feet to the first limb. At once I became concerned for July's safety, and felt it my duty to protest.

"Uncle Spiller, July can't climb that tree. Nobody but a lumberjack or a . . ."

But the old Negro disdained to hear me, busying himself with his operations. Taking a piece of stout rope from a pocket he tied one end securely to the wrist of July, who promptly embraced the trunk of the tree with his arms. Uncle Spiller then carried the unattached end of the rope around the tree and looped it over the other wrist of July, leaving sufficient play in the cord to permit its being flipped upward or downward at will. The boy was visibly pleased to hold the center of the stage.

"Stand back, gents!" the old darkey ordered in his best showman's voice.

Then, as we stood agape, July extended his feet partly around the tree, thrust his naked toes into the rough bark, and gave a light upward flip to the cord encircling the trunk and attached to his wrists. As the cord caught and tightened his body swung upward perhaps two feet. Quickly repeating the maneuver, he scrambled up another two feet. And in less time than I have taken to describe the performance, he gained the first limb. Crooking an elbow over the limb, he quickly disengaged the looped end of the cord and scrambled up, disappearing in the thick top.

Meanwhile the varying behavior of the dogs was diverting. The three younger hounds were fairly beside themselves with excitement. While July was scaling the tree, they kept up a frenzied barking which ran the whole gamut from eager whimperings to bellows. They pawed, gnawed the bark, and cut all sorts of didoes. But not so with Old Blue. That veteran had lost some of the effusiveness of youth, and he looked with mild tolerance on the antics of his juniors. Indeed, when July prepared to climb, Old Blue nonchalantly stalked off and sat quietly on his haunches, like an elderly gentleman watching his frolicsome children at play. Kindergarten stuff to him! But the second July's voice drifted down, his ears pricked up and he was all 'possum dog again.

"Done found 'im!" The voice of July seemed to float down from nowhere.

"Shake 'im out den," Uncle Spiller called back.

"Done cotch 'im by de tail. Gwyn fling 'im down."

A branch cracked sharply, a heavy body thumped against a limb and came hurtling downward. One of the younger dogs, jealous of his prowess and over-eager to be in on the kill, leaped up and attempted to close in on the body in midair—and was knocked flat on his back by the impact. He would remember that lesson. Old Blue had learned it in his youth, but he was nothing reluctant now. Timing his spring to the split-second, he was the first to close in. Then a mad scramble followed, with Uncle Spiller and the dogs in an indiscriminate pile. In a few seconds, the old man emerged holding a big, fiercely grinning 'possum by the tail. I guessed its weight at twelve pounds.

"One fer de bag, an' a nice un, too!"

Before we had finished inspecting the first catch July was down again, descending as he had ascended, and grinning broadly, having verified his grandfather's boast that he had monkey blood in his veins.

The hunt was resumed, and by midnight we had bagged three other sizable 'possums, having had the good fortune to find two feeding up a persimmon tree. It was a fair start, and we were all in high spirits. Uncle Spiller, walking ahead and carrying the bag of 'possums on his back, broke into song. His voice was falsetto, but his heart was in the right place, and his chantey rang with the melodious and weird cadences peculiar to his race:

> "Got ma 'taters,
> Got ma rice,
> Ain't gwyn worry
> 'Bout de white man's price,
> Got a fat 'possum at home!
>
> Meat outer sight,
> Times gittin' tight,
> But I ain't gwyn roam
> Cause 'simmons gittin' ripe,
> An' I got a fat 'possum at home."

And in the hunter's triumphant chant was more than the natural ebullience of the race, for the 'possum, especially in times of depression, is of no little economic importance to the Negroes of the lower South. As a source of food the *Didelphis virginiana,* as the encyclopedias call him, is not to be overlooked, and he abounds in the wideflung lowlands as well as in the hardwood uplands of the South. The darkey may be content with sweet potatoes, rice and corn meal as weekday rations, but on festive occasions he has got to have a 'possum. It is the pork of the destitute lowlander. In fact, 'possums are sometimes kept in captivity and fattened like pigs.

Along toward two o'clock it commenced to get chilly, and Bill began to bemoan his lack of foresight in not bringing along a little something to fortify his courage, the *sine qua non* of an all-night hunting trip. *Sine qua non* is Latin for "not without which," without which Bill usually was not. But the patron saint of 'possum hunters is a regular fellow.

Presently, Uncle Spiller appeared to stumble heavily, falling forward with a vociferous grunt. Regaining his feet, he brushed aside a pile of leaves, exposing, of all things, the protruding top of a wooden keg! The old darkey seemed puzzled. Bill's interest picked up instantly. Kneeling down, he popped the wooden stopper from the bung hole, thrust his nose in like an anteater, and inhaled deeply and feelingly. Then he sat down beside the keg, sighed heavily, and drawled:

"I'm awful sorry, but I'm plumb tuckered out. I just got to stop here and rest a spell. You all can go on huntin' and maybe I'll overtake you some time or another. If I just had a straw or somethin'," he sighed. It was very touching.

Uncle Spiller's ancient features broke into an expansive grin. Shuffling over to a hollow log, he fumbled around a minute and came up with a long hollow reed. The pious old fraud! It was his own keg, and he had deliberately led us to it. Bill stuck the reed in the keg and commenced drenching himself.

"What is it?" I demanded. But Bill had a one-track mind. After about five minutes he settled back on his haunches and wiped his mouth with the back of his hand.

"Persimmon beer, old son, and of all the persimmon beer I ever sampled . . . well, take a swig and decide for yourself."

Uncle Spiller was immediately bombarded with questions, and his explanations cleared up the mystery of the keg.

"I brung de kaig to de 'simmons stead o' haulin' de 'simmons to de kaig. John Hennery's boy brung me de honeylocusts, and I got de extrys here an' dar. Ole nigger haffa hide kaig in de swamp to keep dem scallions at de house from gittin' it all."

Well, we squatted around the keg and held a caucus, passing the reed from one to another. Bill's judgment stood unimpeached. Cold, sparkling, and mellow, it stole the chill from the frosty air and filled us with a persuasive benevolence and brotherhood. With Professor Smathers, to whom the concoction was new, it was a case of love at first sight. First he knelt down and sucked, then he sat down and sucked, and finally he lay flat on the keg and sucked. Then he took time out to catch his breath and sucked some more, as if he thought it a breach of etiquette to quit before he emptied the barrel,

"Dat gentleman better not drink too much," Uncle Spiller cautioned. "Dat stuff got purgitude in it!"

The professor finally straightened up, his eyes snapping. He was getting "fou and unco happy," as Robert Burns says. Normally of a quiet, retiring nature, he now became highly garrulous, proceeding to deliver to us a grandiloquent lecture on the 'possum, and in his best classroom manner. He descanted at length on its idiosyncrasies, its love life, its intimate family affairs, with numerous references to "nocturnal and arboreal habits," "prehensile tail," and what not. He wound up, or rather unwound with: "It is the only native marsupial in this country. Ain't it a fine marsupial, Uncle Spiller?" he demanded.

The old darkey, who had been visibly impressed, blinked owlishly and apologetically replied: "Possum hash am fust-rate, sah, fer a fact, but I can't say how de *soup* would be, sah."

A distant baying recalled us to the hunt, and we soon came upon the dogs treeing in an uprooted tupelo. The professor, who had a lively interest in affairs now, immediately scrambled up the fallen trunk to find the quarry, protesting that he could outclimb July any day in the week. In a few minutes his flashlight began to play over the thick branches around him. Presently the roving beam stopped on a clump of leaves.

"Ah, I perceive the object of our search, gentlemen. 'Tis an elegant creature. Tail extended and bushy; head tapering and graceful; evidently carnivorous in habit; white longitudinal streaks down its body. Ah, I have it! 'Tis a very, very fine specimen of *Putorius putorius*," mooned the professor.

We brought up together two hundred feet away, panting and brushing the cobwebs from our faces. The light still glowed in the tree, and we could hear the indistinct maunderings of the professor.

"Run, you damn fool. That's a polecat!" Bill yelled.

"Run and miss this specimen? Ah, my good man, that is not the way of science. Your fears are unwarranted. It is true that the *Putorius putorius* may emit a somewhat unpleasant odor from its anal glands, but it is inoffensive unless irritated, and I do not propose to irritate it. Besides it cannot emit the odor as long as its tail is down, and I shall observe the caudal appendage closely. A beautiful specimen!" he murmured rapturously.

Well, he could stay in the interest of science, but in the interest of humanity we couldn't see it that way. We shouted; we coaxed; we cursed; we threatened him with mayhem and manslaughter, and still the professor sat rhapsodizing to that polecat.

"He's drunk as a boiled owl off Uncle Spiller's beer. Why did you bring such an idiot with you anyway? Now what'll we do?" demanded Bill sourly.

In disgust we decided to continue the hunt, hoping the fool would return to his senses and follow. Uncle Spiller had in the meanwhile held the dogs on a leash, explaining that contact with a skunk would so demoralize their sense of smell that they would be worthless the rest of the night.

An hour or so later, during which time we had bagged our fourth and fifth 'possums, we heard someone shuffling through the underbrush. A light flashed on and off. It was the professor and he was carrying a sack and mumbling contentedly. He had evidently caught and sacked a small 'possum without the aid of the dogs, as sometimes happens. Weaving his way into the circle with a fatuous smile on his face, he announced:

"I've got a nice one. Look."

Bill opened the bag and nearly had a stroke. It was that same confounded polecat! Now don't ask me how the professor caught him, or why the polecat did not resent, in his customary manner, the overtures of his captor. I don't know, and, furthermore, I don't give a damn. And the professor doesn't remember. As a matter of fact, the next day, after Uncle Spiller's beer had died out, he indignantly denied the whole business. Anyway Bill picked up the sack, counted one, two, three for our benefit, and hurled it as far into the swamp as he could.

That odoriferous episode over, Uncle Spiller released his dogs again and we straggled on. We had already had a good hunt, but as it turned out, the climax of the night was yet to come.

"De big boys don't move 'round much twell jes befor' day, an' dey don't climb trees much. Dey's too heavy," Uncle Spiller told us, and his statement was soon verified.

It was in the intense blackness just preceding daybreak that Old Blue struck again. The trail was hot, and within fifteen minutes the dogs were treeing in a thick windfall. We promptly surrounded the fall to cut off all avenues of escape. The dogs were held back to prevent their closing in too fiercely and mutilating the catch. Snapping on my flashlight I started crawling under the entanglement, worming and bellying my way along until I got to the center. Then I began to play the light around me. All at once the rays caught and held two gleaming pools of fire. Then the beam fell full on an enormous 'possum. He was at bay and in a belligerent mood, his jaws glistening and extended, his breath hissing.

In a voice as casual as I could make it I called the old darkey to me. Scrambling through the windfall he soon squatted by my side. When I flashed the light on again his eyes popped incredulously, and I felt his body grow tense against mine. Old Tom at last!

I continued to hold the light while Uncle Spiller advanced to the attack. Then began the hand-to-hand encounter. It was check and countercheck; maneuver against maneuver; finesse against finesse. It was blackjack against thunder. They were old adversaries, these two, and they respected each other. The Negro found himself repeatedly outsmarted in his efforts to get at the tail. Finally he poked a stick at the hissing jaws and goaded the 'possum into snapping it. Its teeth sank deep and froze on the stick. Then

Uncle Spiller made a lightning swoop downward—and came up with both of his huge hands locked about his enemy's throat in such a way that he could not budge his head.

Old Tom was indeed the great panjandrum of the swamp. From tip to tip he was nearly three feet long and must have weighed twenty-five pounds. The long feud between Negro and brer 'possum was ended, and Uncle Spiller's cup was running over. Cocking his shaggy head, he sent an ancient ditty lilting through the mellow night:

> " 'Possum up de 'simmon tree,
> Raccoon on de ground,
> Raccoon said to de 'possum,
> Throw me some 'simmons down!
> Throw me some 'simmons down, Lawdy,
> Throw me some 'simmons down."

His excitement finally subsided, and he brought out a fresh bag to put the prize catch in. The big 'possum had desisted in his efforts to escape, now appearing to be altogether lifeless. Indeed, when Uncle Spiller, as a demonstration, placed him on the ground and released his hold, no signs of life were evident. "No use o' playin' 'possum! You ain't fool nobody," the old Negro shouted at his enemy.

Playing 'possum! At least, I smilingly reflected, this amusing little animal has done what few others have done—he has added a picturesque phrase to the English language and got himself into all the dictionaries. How much more vivid and effective is the idiom, "playing 'possum," than the round-about equivalent, "to dissemble or counterfeit death when endangered or about to be captured."

Day was beginning to break. We had seven 'possums, more than anybody wanted to tote, so we turned our steps homeward. We soon discovered that we had traversed a wide circle, and were agreeably surprised when we emerged into a frost-covered cotton patch within a short distance from Uncle Spiller's cabin, where we had left our car the preceding evening.

Arriving at the cabin, we found that we were expected. Uncle Spiller's granddaughter met us with a gallon of steaming black coffee, the finishing touch to any hunt. We had gotten in our car and started down the lane to the big road when I happened to think that I was taking one 'possum home with me, and that the missus might not know how to cook it. Backing up, I called the old Negro to the car.

"Uncle Spiller, what is the best way to cook a 'possum?"

"Dat very praper question, sah. Hit make a big diffunce. Fust, you hang de 'possum up by de hind feet, lak a hog; den you pull de hide off and entrail 'im; den you wash 'im good and clean; den you builds a good hot fyar in de stove and gits de pan ready; den. . . ."

"Then what?" I prompted.

"Den you sends fer me!"

I did.

G. E. BULGER

Moose in the Snow

This is another of the "Leaves from the Records of St. Hubert's Club" that formed the literary bough of Bulger, who wrote for amusement rather than recompense. An active sportsman of the past century, his reports on the many forms of hunting were detailed and descriptive. His interest was not only in hunting, but in the life and background of the animals and birds he hunted as well as the trees, shrubs and flowers of their habitat. In some of his work the footnotes were as voluminous as the text, but perhaps in removing the extraneous matter from the text he added to its character. With the footnotes removed, I think you will find this an interesting report on the sport of 150 years ago.

The morning broke clear and without a cloud, but intensely cold; a fine, joyous, bracing cold, however, that only seemed to elevate the spirits, in proportion as it pinched the ears and nose; and the crisp, spotless snow glittered under the brilliancy of the bright sun as few things else on earth can glitter; and seemed to invite us forth to enjoy a walk upon its frozen surface. Charley's sleigh was at the tavern-door half-an-hour before the time; and John was busily employed in stowing away in its various receptacles his master's and my luggage.

The sleigh, or drag, as Charley called it, was a fine, roomy, comfortable-looking concern, with deep seats, covered by a profusion of black bear-skin robes, that is, the dressed skins of the black bear gaily lined and trimmed with scarlet. The vehicle had seats for four passengers, and on an emergency six could have been accommodated without inconvenience. The horses were powerful, yet graceful animals, and full of life, as their impatient attempts to start showed full plainly.

We were soon comfortably seated, and the handsome nags, obeying a low whistle from Charley, started off at a rapid trot. There was just enough snow upon the roads to enable the sleigh to glide along with ease and rapidity; and in less than a couple of hours, we had arrived at Johnson's snug little farm-house, on the edge of the great woods, and rather more than fourteen miles from Derrington.

Having handed our sleigh and horses over to the care of one of Johnson's sons we entered the dwelling, where Charley was warmly greeted by the farmer and his good dame; both of whom seemed very happy at seeing him again.

Charley's father had served, during the revolutionary war, as a captain in one of the British regiments; and, some twelve or fourteen years subsequently, he had purchased a quantity of land adjoining his Government grant; where he finally settled down as a colonist for the remainder of his days. At his decease this particular portion of his property descended to my friend; and Johnson, who had been a tenant of his father's, still retained the farm under Charley. The terms on which Johnson held his land were exceedingly easy. Charley would not sell the property, which had been granted to his father for gallant services; but he was no exacting landlord and the honest farmer paid but a nominal rent for seven hundred acres of the finest land in Ryeburn. This generous liberality on the part of my friend, together with the fact of his having been born on the estate, and his own amiability of character, had won the gratitude and love of the farmer and his good dame; and few faces shed a more brilliant glow of gladness round their homely fireside than that of Charley Rivers.

For his sake I, too, was warmly welcomed to "The Hemlock Grove," as the farm was called, and we were speedily enjoying what Charley, in his favourite seat in the corner, termed the *dolce far niente* of existence.

"And now, Johnson," said my friend, "tell us all about the Moose."

"Well, sir," replied Johnson, "I have not seen him myself, but my son has fallen in with him twice; and I have crossed his tracks more than a dozen times; we had not heard of one in this part of the country for many years before."

"And," said Charley, "what course of operations would you recommend?"

"I think, sir," answered the farmer, "that if you were to make Raymond's shanty your head-quarters, you would be nearer your work than if you went down to the shooting-box by the river. It is not perhaps quite so comfortable, but I will send some of my men over this afternoon to set it to rights and cut you some wood."

"Just my idea, Johnson," said Charley; "but we must not have more men about the place than necessary. Frank and I have too much of the sportsman about us, I hope, to trouble ourselves with trifles; and John will cut us all the fuel we require; so if you will tell them to get your ox-sleigh ready to carry our traps, we will start hence in an hour."

At this moment Mrs. Johnson said, "Now, gentlemen, come and eat something before you go": and down we sat to discuss the merits of a smoking "venison-pasty," that had been cooked in a manner to excite the envy of a Soyer had he been there to see. I suppose I must have been unusually hungry after my drive in the frosty air, but I never recollect having enjoyed any meal so thoroughly as I did that impromptu luncheon, which we washed down with a draught of most exquisite cider.

Having seen our belongings safely on their way to Raymond's shanty under the guardianship of the faithful John, Charley and I donned our snow-shoes, and struck into the woods which still covered a large portion of the farm.

In about two hours we arrived at our destination, and found that John had been there some time; and that the shanty was in much better preservation than we expected. A few words descriptive of the edifice itself may not be out of place, while John is kindling up the fire on the hearth. The shanty, it seemed, had been originally built by a man called Raymond, who had rented the "sugar-bush," that is, a portion of the forest wooded with the sugar-maple, from Charley's father: subsequently, it had been increased in size, and had been fitted up with a chimney, and sleeping-places for the very purpose to which we now proposed to put it. It was built of round hemlock logs, and roofed with troughs of the rough bark of the same tree, while all the spaces and interstices were filled with dried moss. There was no window, but in summer the door always stood open, and admitted plenty of light; and in winter a huge fire built upon the hearth lit up the interior as brilliantly as a dozen candles. The shanty covered about fourteen feet square of ground, and, on the whole, it was by no means a disagreeable shelter for a temporary residence in the backwoods.

We were now in the heart of the forest. Johnson's house, which was eight miles distant, being the nearest settlement, and for nearly six leagues in the opposite direction there was not even a clearing to break the uniformity of the primeval woods.

The solitude of these silent forests is very remarkable, and it almost seems as if they were entirely deserted by living beings, especially in the winter; but this dearth of animal life is more apparent than real, for bears, wolves, and deer are not unfrequently met with, and raccoons, squirrels, and other small quadrupeds are numerous enough. In addition to these, are various species of grouse, owls, hawks, and many smaller kinds of birds, who make their home here, amidst the pleasant gloom of these majestic woods, where they are rarely disturbed by the intruding foot of man.

Shortly after we reached the shanty, the lengthening shadows told us that the short winter day was fast drawing to a close; and as we were to be up betimes the next morning, we at once set to work with our preparations. Bullets had to be cast; and pork packed away in sufficient quantity to enable us to carry with us two days' provisions at the least, so that, in case of necessity, we might follow the chase without returning to the shanty. Our axes and hunting-knives had to be sharpened; and last, not least, we had to arrange our plan of pursuit for the morrow.

Our preparations were speedily but carefully made; and excepting that we had not yet determined upon the plan of operations, everything was ready for a start; so about eight o'clock, we piled more wood upon our already huge fire, and rolling ourselves in our blankets, were soon lost in forgetfulness of all around.

All was still and silent, and a few red embers were the sole remains of the huge logs that we had left burning on the hearth the night before, when I awoke the next morning about six o'clock. The intense frost of the night had so chilled the atmosphere of the shanty, that I fairly shivered when I unrolled myself from my covering of furs and blankets, and jumped up to replenish the almost expiring fire. I threw some dry logs upon the embers, and resisting a strong inclination to creep back to my nest again, I called up John and my friend Charley, and then proceeded to make my toilet with as little delay as possible.

Having treated myself to a delicious wash in melted snow—the pleasantest of all water for ablutions from its softness—I donned my clothes, and sallied out to take a survey of the morning. The air was frosty and very cold, and the sky was studded with innumerable stars, which were glittering in the dark moonless heavens, with the pale brilliancy usual to them during the winter in North America. Morning had not begun to break, and everything was quiet and at rest; not a sound disturbed the stillness of the scene, save an occasional and gentle gust of wind, which, sighing through the branches of the trees, seemed like the flitting of some rambling spirits through the murky air.

I was charmed with the beauty of the morning; and my heart bounded with delight at the prospect of our hunt through these glorious woods in such magnificent weather, and beneath the splendour of such cloudless skies. I cannot explain the buoyancy of spirit which seems to take possession of the wanderer in these vast forests; but it is an undoubted fact, proved by the testimony of hundreds of witnesses, that no other scenes can rouse the spirit of the hunter to that pitch of joyousness which the primeval woods of North America in winter never fail to excite.

A hail from Charley disturbed my reveries, and summoned me to breakfast; and just as the first glimmer of dawn was lighting up the eastern heavens, we sat down to discuss our morning meal.

"Frank," said Charley, after a short pause, "if the wind would only rise we should have everything in our favour; but even as it is, I think the chances are ten to one against the Moose, for there seems to be a very tolerable crust upon the snow, which will lessen his prospect of escape very materially; while the light covering which fell the other day is still so soft and powdery that we shall have splendid snow-shoeing."

"Yes," replied I, "but may not that light covering have obliterated the tracks of the Moose entirely, and thus have done us more harm than good?"

"That I am quite prepared for," answered my friend. "I know these woods well, and I will bet long odds, that if you follow my instructions, you will see the foot-prints, at least, of the great deer, before the sun attains the zenith: that is, provided always he has not left this part of the country entirely—a contingency which I regard as by no means improbable."

"Well," said I, "if obedience to your mandates will ensure success, consider me the possessor of a fine bull-moose, for I shall attend most particularly to all your instructions; but now what are your plans?"

Charley answered not for a moment, but drew his compass from his pocket, and placed it on the table. When the needle had ceased trembling, he said, "Now, Frank, look here: Johnson's farm-house lies eight miles to the southward of this place; and Diamond Creek, running west and east, passes the shanty just seven miles away in the opposite direction; ten miles further, the Meenahga River, running in the same direction as the Diamond, forms the boundary of the township. Westward from here, eleven miles and a half, is the dividing line between the townships of Ryeburn and Malormis; and eastward, at the distance of about two hundred and fifty yards, is the division between Ryeburn and Sunnettring; and fifteen miles further, the boundary between Sunnettring and Glaston. Now if you will make a hasty sketch of the relative bearings of the shanty and these different lines, it will, most likely, prevent your being lost, and aid you very much in carrying out your plan of operations."

This was speedily done, and Charley continued; "About four miles from this, in a north-westerly direction, there is a large cedar swamp, through which you will find a blazed path; follow this path through the swamp until you come to a narrow ridge thickly covered with the canoe birch. Just thereabouts, under the shadow of the forest a quantity of moose-wood grows, and beyond the ridge, which is only twenty yards across, you will find Diamond Creek. It is said that close to this grove of birch-trees there is a spring, which never freezes even in the coldest winter; and although I have not seen it, and am sceptical regarding its existence, yet it is true that I have invariably found the common deer in that neighbourhood when I could get none elsewhere, and I have never yet failed in disturbing several Ruffed Grouse from amongst the moose-wood that I speak of. Go warily through the swamp, and when you reach the grove, walk as if you were treading upon eggs, and my life on it, if the old Moose is amongst the woods of Ryeburn, you will find him there. I need not warn you, Frank," he added, "against shooting at any lesser game, for a single shot might deprive us of our chance of the Moose; it is a most timid, wary animal, and the cracking of a rotten stick under foot has often spoilt a whole day's sport, and lost the hunter a mighty pair of antlers."

"And if I should not find the Moose where you have described?"

"Then," replied he, "you had better follow the course of Diamond Creek, beating the woods thoroughly as you go along, and I will take an opposite direction, and walk round to meet you."

"Agreed," said I; and I at once fastened on my snow-shoes, and prepared to start.

Charley was off by this time, but he turned and said, "Frank, a double shot will answer for the signal of success or a call for assistance."

I nodded, and we separated, leaving John to take care of the shanty until we should return.

Before proceeding with my story, I may as well say a word or two about our dresses and equipments. Charley and I had shot very much together, and our ideas on points connected with our favourite amusement were very nearly similar, as indeed they were in most cases.

We were robed in suits of the grey cloth of the country, which, from its warmth and resemblance to the trunks of the trees in colour, is by far the best material for autumn or winter shooting in the American woods. Our trousers were rather tight near the feet, but otherwise very loosely made, and we wore long double-breasted waistcoats, which buttoned up close to the throat. The coats were short and roomy, made something in the shape of a pea-jacket, but with a profusion of pockets.

On our feet, we had two pairs of thick grey woollen socks, the outer pair coming over the lower part of the trousers, and then outside of all, a pair of plain Indian mocassins. These mocassins are generally made of the skin of the caribou, and some of them are highly ornamented with dyed porcupine quills. They are so soft and pliable that the foot can work in them with perfect ease and freedom. Without them, it would be almost impossible to penetrate the woods in the depth of winter, for boots made in the ordinary way are miserably cold, easily penetrated by the snow, hard, unyielding, and totally unfit to be worn with snow-shoes.

Our caps were fitted to the skull, with stout folding-peaks and ear-covers, which could be used or not at pleasure. Charley's was made of the skin of the great northern diver, and was exceedingly light, but mine was constructed of heavier materials being formed of the beautiful fur of the pine-marten. Eschewing the rifles of the country, which, though of marvellous accuracy, were in our opinion too heavy for the woods, and only suited for target-shooting, we both were armed with English, double-barrelled, two-grooved weapons, made after the fashion of the Brunswick rifle, with which the rifle regiments of the army were then supplied. Charley gloried in his heavy, massive Purday, completely destitute of ornament, and carrying a belted ball of an ounce in weight. I was provided with a lighter weapon, from the good old house of Moore and Gray, which threw a bullet of three-quarters of an ounce, with deadly accuracy, when held straight and steadily. We each wore waist-belts of untanned leather, to which hung at the right side pouches of the same material, containing bullets, patches, and percussion-caps. On the left side were our *couteaux de chasse*, and behind us, with the handles downward, hung short hunting-axes.

Each wore a large blanket strapped across his shoulders, and —last not least—a fur bag, with two compartments, one of which contained spare nipples, a wrench, flint and steel, and an oil-bottle; while the other held our rations of pork and biscuit. A spirit-flask completed our rig-out, and with our snow-shoes on our feet we were quite ready for a start.

I went on steadily in the direction which Charley had pointed out for nearly a mile, and then I stopped and listened for some sound; but the forest was silent as the grave, and as deserted as if I was its sole occupant. The wind had died away entirely, and not even a dropping leaf broke the solemn stillness of the sleeping woods. I drew out my watch, and saw that it was only nine o'clock, so, seating myself on a prostrate tree, I lit a cigar, and began thinking about the Moose, and our chances of securing him. Close to where I was sitting, there was a patch of ground so screened and sheltered by a dense mass of white cedar branches from the wind and drifting snow as to have been at the time I speak of completely naked in spots.

Whilst I was puffing my fragrant Havannah, a brownish-grey bird, something like a young turkey in appearance, ran out of the under-brush, and began scratching away at these uncovered places, but the ground was frozen very hard, and the poor bird did not make much of the scratching, so it presently flew away. I recognised it at once as the Ruffed Grouse, a beautiful species, which is indigenous, and I believe peculiar, to the forests of North America. I could easily have shot it, as it seemed quite unconscious of my presence, and came within four or five yards of where I was sitting; but even if I had not been in search of the Moose, and necessarily very silent and careful in my movements, its exceeding grace and beauty would have saved its life.

It was nearly ten o'clock when I reached the margin of the swamp which Charley had described, and hitherto, with the exception of the grouse I have mentioned, and a few little tomtits, I had seen no living creature.

The portion of forest I had passed through was not very densely clothed with trees, and the underwood was remarkably thin, so that my progress had not been impeded in the least; but now I saw a tangled wilderness of cedar-trees before me, through which it seemed as if it would be impossible to pass. I skirted the edge of this swamp for nearly half-an-hour before I found the blazed road that Charley had mentioned, but at last, to my great delight, I stumbled upon it, and at once struck onward towards the higher land, which I saw looming up on the further side of this maze of tree-trunks. There was hardly any path, for although the under-brush had been formerly cleared away, it had grown over the place again almost as thickly as ever, and the only guide I had towards direction was the line of blazed notches on the trees. The ground was firmer and afforded better walking than I had expected, for, in spite of the intense frost, I have not unfrequently sunk up to my knees in icy-cold water, when passing through these swamps in winter.

I saw numerous tracks of deer in the snow as I passed along, but the animals themselves did not gratify me with a peep at them; I, however, caught sight of several hares and squirrels, and twice was startled by the loud whirr of Ruffed Grouse as they rose at my feet, and flew away to some neighbouring trees.

That swamp was one of the thickest I ever saw:—mighty cedars were lying prostrate across one another in piles; rotting away in the place where they had been cast by old age or some winter storm, and, amidst their ruins, living giants still sought the upper air, and raised their ever-green branches to the sun, high above the dead and dying mass around them. Parts of it, I should say, were well-nigh impenetrable, for even along the track I was compelled to climb up one side, and down the other, of piles of trees that had fallen to rise no more.

At the further edge of the swamp the ground began to rise suddenly, and I clambered up the steep side of the ridge which Charley had told me of. It was densely wooded with birch-trees, the tall white stems of which were very striking objects. The under-brush was exceedingly thick, and, as the wind had swept the greater portion of the snow off the summit and sides of the ridge, I found the bushes troublesome obstacles to my progress. The ridge was, as Charley said, quite narrow, and on its opposite side lay Diamond Creek, now frozen into a solid mass of ice, and nearly hidden by the depth of the snow-drifts. As I entered the grove of birch-trees a couple of deer bounded past me, and were soon lost to view in the swamp which I had just left. There were innumerable tracks along the ridge and on the banks of the creek, but nowhere could

I see what I so earnestly desired—the foot-prints of the Moose. I searched for nearly an hour, but in vain, and at last, started off towards the east without much hope, I confess, of succeeding in my search. The woods on the north-east of the Diamond Creek, to which I had now attained, were of a mixed character and tolerably open, though the surface of the ground was undulating and distinguished by rapidly succeeding ridges and valleys of inconsiderable height and depth. Animal life was seemingly very scarce, for, excepting the hollow tapping of the wood-pecker, or the dismal croak of a passing raven, my wanderings were uninterrupted by anything bearing life. I followed the stream for fully four miles, when I suddenly came upon a little frozen marsh, through the centre of which the course of the creek was strongly marked.

There were dense clumps of alders covering the ground for the space of an acre or two; and I had some trouble in forcing my way through their thick branches, which impeded my snow-shoes very much. As I entered the little marsh, I observed a fox stealing away quietly over the top of a neighbouring ridge, but I let him go his way in peace, wondering whether there really was anything bigger, or more worthy of pursuit, in the woods through which I had been wandering all day. In the thickest part of the alder copse I had to stoop my head to pass beneath the branches, when a white owl suddenly flew out and almost hit me in the face. He was a pretty bird, but I had neither time nor inclination for studying ornithology at the moment, so I forced my way through the thicket, and then sat down to have a smoke. It was at that time about two o'clock in the afternoon, and, having held council with my thoughts, I resolved upon returning to the shanty at once, lest I should be overtaken by the darkness. With this intention I sprang up, and drawing out my compass, I started for the hut.

Having crossed the river, I entered a thick spruce-wood of some extent, with here and there a gigantic white pine towering up above the surrounding forest. I passed as rapidly through this wood as possible, getting many a cold shower of snow from the massive branches of the spruce-trees as I passed along; and then I beheld before me a flat of some hundreds of acres in extent, covered with dwarf specimens of the hackmatack or tamarac, a species of larch. This place was thickly marked with deer-tracks, and once or twice I started the animals themselves within easy shot. One huge stag, or buck as the colonists call it, stood looking at me for fully a couple of minutes, and almost tempted me to fire; however, I did not do so, and next moment the beautiful creature bounded away, his tail showing like a white star through the trees. Once I stopped for a moment to tighten the fastening of my snow-shoe, and on the instant a sight met my gaze that sent the blood bounding madly through my veins; there—before me—not two feet away—was the broad, unmistakable foot-print of the noble deer—the *slot* of the great Moose!

To describe my feelings at that moment would be impossible, and even should I succeed in doing so, they would hardly be understood, for it requires all the accessories of solitude, a mighty forest, and an imagination warmed to the pitch of excitement which mine had attained, to appreciate the delight which came over me at the discovery of the moose-track.

One moment I resigned to rapture, and the next the spirit of the wary hunter settled down upon me, and I prepared cautiously for the chase.

I knelt down and examined the trail. It was not fresh, but, at the same time, I felt assured that it had been made since morning. I inspected the cones of my rifle, put on fresh caps, and started in pursuit.

The trail led me through the centre of the hackmatacks, and once more into the spruce forests, where the ground was a rapid succession of rather steep undulations. After the first hour I could see that the Moose was aware that I was pursuing him, from the huge bounds which he made in his course, but as yet I had not got a glimpse of him. I pressed on steadily and carefully, but without any unnecessary haste, for it was so nearly night, I easily foresaw I should have to "camp upon the trail." Another hour, and the darkness was almost complete, so that I slackened my pace, and looked about me for some sort of a nook where I could rest until morning should give me light enough to pursue the chase.

I cleared away the underwood from a sheltered spot amongst some gigantic hemlocks, and, gathering a lot of the driest sticks I could find, I drew out my flint and steel, and made a fire. Next, I collected a quantity of fragrant spruce-branches for my bed, and then set to work to erect a sort of wigwam. Two forked sticks, with a cross-piece resting on them, formed the skeleton of the edifice, and then I enclosed it on the side farthest from the fire, by sloping pieces of hemlock-bark, one end of which I rested against the cross-stick, and the other on the ground. I then lined the wigwam with birch-bark, which I found in great plenty close by, and thus I had a famous cabin for my night's lodging. The small branches of the

trees of the pine tribe make a particularly agreeable bed from their
delicious fragrance, and they are totally proof against damp, and
free from all kinds of insects. The white bark of the birch acts as
a reflector to the heat of the fire, and hence the reason why I used
it so plentifully in the construction of my wigwam.

Having completed the erection of my domicile, I drew out my
provisions, and proceeded to cook some pork before the fire, for
the long fast, the cold, and the exertion, had whetted my appetite
amazingly. Supper over, and my cigar finished, I pulled the ear-
covers of my cap down—placed my rifle securely in the inside of
the wigwam, piled up an immense fire, and, rolling myself in my
blanket, I took possession of my nest, and went to sleep in spite of
the howling of the wolves, which had already begun to make the
woods ring with their horrid cries.

I was awakened the next morning by the cold, for my fire had
burned very low, and, although I speedily caused a merry blaze
from some birch-logs, I did not get warm again until exercise
restored the circulation of my blood.

A hasty but substantial breakfast of pork and biscuit, washed
down by snow-water, tempered with some spirits, was soon disposed of, and, with the first streak of daylight, I was on the trail
again.

The snow was of very irregular depth. In the swamps and
valleys it lay in drifts, sometimes four feet in height, while on the
sides and summits of the higher land it was comparatively thin.
There was no crust, such as we had expected to have found; and,
although the depth of the snow must have proved a great obstacle
to the flight of the Moose, yet he was much more happily situated
than if there had been a heavy crust upon the surface, as we at
first thought there was.

For several long hours I followed him through woods of almost
every description; seemingly close upon his footsteps, yet still
without ever getting even a distant view of him. It may seem odd
that I should have been able to keep pace with so fleet a creature
as a deer for such a long period, but I believe none of these animals
continue their flight steadily, or at the top of their speed, when no
enemy is in view. They generally run for a hundred yards or so,
and then stop and listen, repeating the process as the person approaches them. I am not sufficiently acquainted with the habits of
the Moose to be sure that this is his custom, though it certainly
was the case in the chase I am describing, but, in all my experience

with the common deer of the American forests, I found this was invariably its plan.

About half-past two I attained the summit of a low ridge, which was densely clothed with hemlock spruce, and paused to look around me. At my feet lay a long narrow tamarac swamp, beyond which, at the distance of about two hundred yards, was another ridge higher than that on which I was standing, but running almost in a parallel direction. It, too, was thickly wooded, excepting on the slope next to me, where the forest was comparatively thin. As I scanned the scene before me with a careful eye, I suddenly observed something move at the edge of the wood on the top of the opposite hill, and, the next instant, a splendid head and antlers revealed themselves to my delighted gaze! My first impulse was to raise my rifle and fire—though even my practised nerves were shaking like the leaves of an aspen at the sight of the noble game; but a moment's consideration pointed out the folly of such a proceeding, and I restrained my eagerness for the time at least. I looked carefully around me, and saw that the ridge on which the Moose was browsing sloped suddenly down to the level of the swamp about eighty or ninety yards to the right; and that the one on which I was ended abruptly in the same manner amongst the tamarac-trees of the low land at its foot. The wind had risen slightly since morning, and it was then blowing almost directly from me towards the Moose, though, as yet, he displayed no knowledge or suspicion of my presence; but continued to graze quietly on the brushwood around him.

I saw that, although within range of my rifle, the chances were fifty to one against my hitting him in a vital part, if I fired from where I stood; and an attempt to approach him in a direct line, when he was dead to leeward, would have been an act which the veriest tyro in woodcraft might blush to acknowledge. Two minutes' observation made me master of my position; and, next moment, my plan of attack was decided on. I crept back on my own tracks as silently and as quietly as possible—with an innate dread, however, that some taint of my presence might be borne by the now freshening breeze to the susceptible nostrils of the Moose, and send him once more beyond my reach. In a very few minutes I had placed the ridge on which I had first stood between the quarry and myself, and, for a time at least, I was beyond his scent and hearing. In deerstalking, as in everything else, the simpler the arrangements the more likely they are to be consummated with correctness, and I bore in mind this great fact when I arranged my plan of operations. Having retraced my steps, as I have already mentioned, to the bottom of the hill, I turned towards the swamp, and followed the base of the ridge until it lost itself in the moist tamarac forest that enclosed it. Then I cautiously crossed over to the end of the other ridge, upon which I had left the Moose in happy unconsciousness, as I hoped, of my proximity; and, circling round my quarry at a respectful distance, until I satisfied myself that I had got well to leeward of his probable position, I began my approach.

It was nervous work, that half-hour's stalking which followed; and it required the exertion of my utmost care to thread my way silently amongst the dead and withered branches that were scattered everywhere around. I knew not the moment when some rotten stick would yield to the pressure of my snow-shoe, and ruin all my hopes of success. I proceeded, however, gingerly and cautiously, carefully feeling my way, as it were, at every step, and, at last, when my patience was becoming well-nigh exhausted, the light through the trees assured me that I was near the edge of the woods, and, consequently, within a short distance of the spot where I had last seen the Moose. I paused for a moment and looked anxiously round me, but there was no trace of the game, or any other living thing! The whole place was still as death, and, after listening in vain for more than five minutes, I began to think that something must have alarmed the Moose and driven him off. I continued my advance, however, with the same caution as before, occasionally stopping and examining the forest around me most carefully, and I soon reached the edge of the ridge, and stood within twenty feet of the spot which I had marked from the opposite hill. I gazed anxiously around, but my utmost scrutiny availed nothing. The Moose was gone!

To say that I suffered keen disappointment when I discovered that my long-sought quarry was missing, would scarcely describe my annoyance, and I felt most thoroughly angry and disgusted at my unsuccessful chase. I sat down on a prostrate tree, and began looking about me for a branch, against which I might rest my rifle, when the snapping of a twig caught my ear to the right, and mechanically, but noiselessly, cocking both barrels of my trusty Moore-and-Gray, I turned quietly in the direction of the sound. Can you fancy my joy and astonishment when I saw the Moose broadside towards me, feeding upon the mosses that adorned the trunk of a large tree not twenty paces distant? He had evidently neither seen nor heard me, and I gave him no time to make discoveries, but raised my rifle steadily and fired. For a single instant the smoke obscured my vision, but eyesight was not required to assure me that my bullet had done its duty. I heard the dull, heavy *thud* of the lead, as it struck the huge animal before me, and then came an appalling roar that woke the deepest echoes of the forest, as the gigantic brute crashed through the bushes and disappeared. I dropped the butt of my rifle upon my snow-shoe, and began to re-load rapidly and carefully, though my hand shook with excitement, and the blood was dancing through my veins at a startling pace.

The Moose fled with such rapidity that I greatly feared he would give me a long chase; however, I was ready for anything at the moment, and, having completed the loading of my rifle, I started in pursuit, mentally resolving that I would follow him to the death.

It was my intention to pursue him leisurely and steadily, but the excitement proved too much for me, and I soon found myself at running speed. How I clambered over prostrate trees, and penetrated through thick clumps of bushes, I know not, but, some way or other, I dashed onward, slipping frequently, tripping con-stantly, and falling more than once in my headlong hunt.

When the chase first commenced, the noise which the huge brute made in his progress through the woods, and his dreadful bellowing, were sufficient guides as to direction, independently of the well-marked trail, which was deeply stained with blood for a long way; but, as the distance between us increased, the sounds died away, and gradually ceased entirely. I continued my rapid pace, however, until want of breath reminded me that there was neither necessity nor object in such violent haste, and I at once slackened my speed and grew more cautious in my movements. I was pretty certain by this time, that I must soon come up with the game, for the quantity of blood which he had lost showed me that he was severely wounded; and I carefully scanned the forest in front of me as I moved steadily on, still following the deep trail that he left behind him. With all my caution, however, I had a narrow escape from the horns of the infuriated animal soon after-wards, for I came upon him suddenly; and, almost before I was aware of his presence, he uttered a tremendous roar and dashed straight at me. I never could understand how it was that I grew suddenly cool and collected after such a nervous and exciting chase, but such was the fact, or I should not be living to tell the tale. The brute was within twenty yards of me before I saw or heard him, and it so happened that I was on the slope of a small ravine where there were no trees at the moment of his charge. The instinct of self-preservation, I suppose, had something to do with it, but I calmly raised my trusty rifle to my shoulder and sent both bullets, one after the other, into his mighty chest. One convulsive roar, an awful plunge, and all was over!

I rushed to the spot and gazed with the most exquisite feelings of delight upon my victim, which had fallen on its right side with two bullets through his lungs. His gigantic limbs were fixed in death; and his beautiful eyes, glassy and cold as the ice which covered the frozen brook, seemed to reproach me for the wanton destruction of an unoffending life; but my heart at that moment was dead to compassion; I thought of nothing save my triumph, and I stood and gloated over the noble form of my slaughtered prey.

For some moments my feelings were so intense, that I stood wrapped in admiration of the splendid animal before me, and lost in forgetfulness of all around; but the distant howl of a wolf recalled me to my situation, and, drawing my watch from my pocket, I fairly started with surprise at finding that it was past three o'clock. I hastily drew out my hunting-knife to bleed the deer, and, having performed that operation, I stood for an instant to consider what was next to be done.

The sun was, by this time, obscured by heavy masses of dismal-looking clouds, the wind was howling through the forest, and snow was beginning to fall rapidly. The temperature had sunk as the wind rose, and it was most bitterly cold. My hands were so benumbed that I could scarcely cock my rifle to give the signal which Charley and I had agreed upon. I fired, and listened attentively for some minutes, hoping for a reply to my summons for assistance; but all was still, except the shaking of the trees by the blast, and the whistling of the wind through their branches. It was evident that I had wandered beyond the hearing of my friend, and, as the reality of my situation forced itself upon me, I was dreadfully perplexed and annoyed.

Darkness was fast closing round me, while the fierce gale shrieked and moaned through the woods, and dashed showers of snow and sleet into my face. I knew not where I was, and I felt assured that it would be impossible to make a fire while the storm lasted, so that I must either remain and guard the Moose—cold and half frozen as I was—until the gale abated, or leave it to the merciless fangs of the wolves—which I doubted not would soon make their appearance—and start off to find the shanty. Neither of these alternatives was pleasing, but the former seemed the more hopeless of the two, as, should the wolves come in numbers, even my presence would be no protection for my trophy, and, moreover, my own life would be in danger, both from them and from the cold. On the other hand, to quit the spot was to say farewell to my splendid Moose, as I could never expect to see a fragment of it again.

I hesitated a moment or two, and at last, sadly enough, I decided on a move. Drawing out my compass, I directed my course so as to strike the division line between the townships of Sunnettring and Ryeburn, to the eastward of which the chase had taken me throughout the day, and, with one last look at my trophy, I started. I had not gone fifty yards, when a rustling amongst the trees to the left drew my attention, and I carefully looked in the direction of the sound. Could I believe my eyes? In the indistinct light of the evening, I perceived, rapidly advancing towards me, the well-known forms of my friend and his servant! I rushed forward, uttering an exclamation of delight, and hailed Charley with the question:

"How far off is the shanty?"

"Scarcely a quarter of a mile behind us," was the answer that fell on my astounded ears. "I was standing at the door when I heard your signal, and I would have replied to it, but my rifle had just been cleaned, and I felt loth to soil it, as I knew I could find you without its aid; but what of the Moose?"

"He lies dead in his tracks scarcely a hundred yards from where we stand," I answered triumphantly; and Charley, as I spoke, awakened the old echoes of the woods, by a "who-whoop" at the top of his lungs, that must have startled the tenants of the wilderness for some miles around. His admiration of the Moose was almost as enthusiastic as my own, while he surveyed its noble proportions. It measured seven feet from the hoofs to the shoulder, and must have weighed more than a thousand pounds. The horns were twenty-seven inches from root to tip, and weighed forty pounds.

Our spirits were light, and, although the storm was now raging with terrific violence, and the shadows of night fast darkening around us, we heeded not, but lit the lantern which Charley and John had brought with them, and, having hidden the Moose out of reach of the wolves, we started for the shanty, which we reached in ten minutes; Charley's superior knowledge as a woodsman assisting us in no small degree to make our way at that late hour, whilst the wind and snow were driving in our faces, and causing everything to present the same desolate and cheerless appearance.

STANLEY
WATERLOO

An Old-Time Michigan Squirrel Shoot

Some of the selections included in this volume were made for the interest of the material rather than the craft of the writer, and this short example, by Stanley Waterloo, must fall in that category. Competition in hunting is not a new thing. Skill, however, was given greater emphasis in the good old days than it is today, as evidenced by the fact that in Waterloo's hunt a "barked" squirrel counted for three times the point score of a "shot" squirrel. It would be interesting to see what the score would be if one of these group shoots were held today.

The man who was in his prime forty-five years ago, who had the sporting instinct in him, and who lived in the eastern tier of counties of southern Michigan, had annually a quality of enjoyment of one adorable autumn day denied to the sportsman of the present time. He could participate in a squirrel shoot, and a squirrel shoot was a thing to be remembered. It brought out an illustration of perfect knowledge of the wood and all its creatures. It brought out an exhibition of exquisite marksmanship with the old muzzle-loading rifle, carrying say ninety to the pound, or else of blazing murderous skill with an old shotgun having any kind of a bore, loaded first with any quantity of powder topped by any fragment of a newspaper rammed down hard, burdened then by any part of a handful of shot, topped again by more newspaper, and backed by a "G" cap which generally worked well when smashed by a hammer which came down with vigor when the lockspring was in form.

Nowhere upon the face of the globe outside of the Eastern and Middle States has ever been afforded such area for the form of recreation known as a squirrel shoot. Sometimes it was a contest between picked hunters from adjacent townships, sometimes merely an offhand test between two groups of hunters—almost always farmers—living with their clearings close together throughout the township and pining for a day of recreation. Squirrel shoot was not an exact or proper name for the contest of woodcraft and good marksmanship, because other creatures than squirrels counted. A shoot being agreed upon, captains were sometimes selected before the event, that they might see to the success of the gathering in point of numbers, and then on a certain day the farmers met, the captains chose sides, and each party went out wherever it liked, returning at six o'clock in the evening to display its game and win or lose. The party making the lowest count paid for the big tavern dinner for both sides. This is about the manner in which the quarry counted:

Bear	100
Wolverine	75
Deer	50
Fox	20
Coon	15
Turkey	15
Ruffed Grouse—"Partridge"	10
Woodchuck	7
Quail	5
Barked Squirrel	3
Squirrel—black or gray	1

Each bird or beast named, little or big, was abundant in the forests of St. Clair County in the boyhood of men still in their prime, and on the occasion of one of these famous squirrel shoots, bear, deer, and turkey frequently added heavily to the scores. Ruffed grouse or "partridges," as they were called, were especially numerous and made a factor of importance in the count. It was the squirrels, though, upon whom each band of farmer-hunters chiefly relied for triumph. They existed in myriads, the gray and black, in that nut-blessed land of oak and beech and hickory, and the brush fences about the cornfields hewed into the forest were alive with the marauders. In numbers the black squirrel exceeded the gray, though now the black is practically extinct, his place being taken by the fox squirrel, which more readily adapts itself to forests less dense and to new sources of food supply. Each squirrel, however rudely killed, counted one; but a "barked" squirrel—that is, one thrown from the tree by a bullet placed between it and limb or bole, and so killed by the shock and fall, and showing no wound— counted always treble as a tribute to good marksmanship.

And a squirrel shoot was on which promised to be a record breaker. Was not one side to be captained by Lon Jones, popular farmer, great wrestler and excellent shot, and the other by Jim Granger of equally wide and excellent repute in the community? The shoot was to take place on Saturday, the place of assemblage was to be at Smith's Creek, a little woodland railroad station; the hunt was to begin at eight o'clock in the morning; and the count, as was the custom, to be made at six o'clock in the evening. Friday afternoon was one of the most glorious of all that rich October.

Both Jones and Granger were honest and honorable men. The word of either was as good as his bond, and either would scorn trickiness in any of the ordinary affairs of the droning life of every day. But, according to the ethics of the time and place, all was fair in love or war or a squirrel shoot.

So it came that on that yellow Friday afternoon neither Jones nor Granger could be seen at work in any of his fields, and inquiry at their houses would have resulted in the information that Jones had gone with a plow-point to the blacksmith's, and that Granger had taken a load of staves to town.

At about three o'clock of that same afternoon a tall, fair-haired, bronzed man might have been seen sitting, immovable, upon a log in the midst of a thick beechwood and, at the same hour, a couple of miles away, a slight, dark-haired individual might have been noted, slipping along silently as an Indian and with upward gaze, through a flat in the forest where the hickory trees were so numerous as to form almost a grove. And each of these two men carried a rifle and a powderhorn and a coat-pocket full of bullets and a box of "G" caps; and another peculiarity about these gentlemen of the woods was that the first bore a striking resemblance to Lon Jones and the other to Jim Granger.

The afternoon waned, the shadows of the dead trees in the clearings became longer and the mid-day quietude was past. The creatures of the wood returned to active life again. There was rustling among the leaves and the patter of many feet; nutshells came dropping from the tree tops, and then from the beechwood and the hickory grove came faintly to the distant roadway what sounded like the repeated cracking of an ox-driver's whip. The rifles were at work. As evening fell the cracking ceased, and two men took their way from different points toward the hamlet of Smith's Creek. They were not a hundred yards apart when they paused and each made a cache, concealing his game under dead branches and a heap of leaves. Jones had twenty-one squirrels, seven of them barked; score, 35. Granger had only sixteen squirrels, two barked, but he had a grouse; score, 30. Honors were nearly even.

"I wish there was more," said Jones to himself, "but they'll help out."

"Thirty's better than nothing," chuckled Granger.

The game concealed, ready to be added surreptitiously to the morrow's bag, the two men, each unconscious of the other's presence, started for home in different directions.

And old man Hank Goodsell, out looking for his hogs, which were running wild in the woods that autumn and fattening on "mast," saw the performance of both from a huge log upon which he had climbed to get a better view in the woods, and ten minutes later was making his way home with a decent load upon his back. Next morning they had fried partridge at old man Goodsell's house and at the end of the week his hired man swore that he wouldn't stand squirrel for breakfast, squirrel for dinner, and squirrel for supper any longer!

It was a fine and flashing Saturday morning which dawned upon Smith's Creek. There could be no doubt of that. There was hoar frost upon the trees and fences, a land of silver, rapidly changing in appearance beneath the beams of the sun arisen in a cloudless eastern sky, while the temperature was just crisp enough to make activity a pleasure. The farmers assembled for the shoot were in a riotously good-natured mood; there was chaffing over crops, much horse-play among the younger men, and much jeering allusion as this man or that man was selected by the captains choosing sides, with such comment as: "Why, Joe, what's the use of you going squirrel hunting? You couldn't hit a cow!" or something not less personal. At the end of it all, the two companies, twenty-one men on a side, separated for the struggle of the day, the tavern-keeper having been meanwhile warned that the supper must be a mighty and a good one.

The two captains, Jones and Granger, conferred but briefly with their companies. Time was precious now. There was swift separation, and armed with anything, from some relic of the War of 1812 to the latest piece from the gunsmith, the men melted away into the woods, singly or by twos—for two men together can hunt squirrels most effectively—each lone man or two hurrying to some ground already decided upon where squirrels were thought to be most plentiful.

Within a radius of three or four miles about Smith's Creek that day the jays and woodpeckers must have thought that Fourth of July had come again, all out of season, for there was a roar and crackle throughout the forest everywhere, and the smell of powder was in the air.

To attempt to tell in detail of the incidents of that day among the forty-two hunters in the game-burdened woods of eastern Michigan forty-five years ago would be a task in vain. Incidents there were in abundance, some droll, some otherwise; but all strenuous, and all partaking of the spirit of the time and the surroundings and the bronzed, strong men. At a little before six o'clock in the evening they came streaming in—the hunters—and by six they were all at hand, for game brought in though but a moment after the appointed hour was not allowed to figure in the count.

There was a great enclosed shed near the tavern, where black-ash hoops for the market were stored in summer, which was now empty, and along each side of this, rude trestles with planks upon them had been placed for the exhibit of the game of the opposing companies. The Jones men came in and deposited their spoils on the trestles to the left, the Granger men placed theirs upon the trestles to the right. Soon each long narrow table had received its furry and feathered burden, and the sight was one calculated to make exceedingly wide open the eyes of the sportsman of to-day.

Meantime, while the hunters were filing in, each captain had disappeared for the time, with some commonplace excuse. Each visited his cache and each found his possession gone. Where were the squirrels of yesterday? The hard work and clever planning of the two honorable captains had already provided old Hank Good-sell with a good meal or two. The two men met in the tavern, each with a blazing face, each half suspicious of the other, took a drink together and went over to the shed.

It was a rule of the squirrel shoots that a committee of six—three from each side—should do the counting alone, the captains being, ex-officio, members of the two committees. The two remaining members from each company were promptly selected and count began. This was the result.

JONES COMPANY

Fox	2
Turkey	11
Ruffed Grouse	19
Woodchuck	1
Squirrel—"barked"	40
Squirrel	248
Total	770

GRANGER COMPANY

Bear	1
Fox	1
Turkey	7
Ruffed Grouse	23
Quail	30
Squirrel—"barked"	25
Squirrel	90
Total	770

It was wonderful, but of course the committee could not know of this coming result until the end of the count was reached. Before that moment, though, the quick eye of Jones had noted that the summaries must be nearly even. Unseen, he thrust into his pocket a black squirrel from the long table of his adversaries. Small benefit seemed likely to accrue to him or his party from that deft feat, for it was the custom to search each man of the committee as he left the counting-place. It is well to be extremely careful, even among old friends, when great sporting events come off and excitement is running high.

The count went on, the end of the second table was nearly reached and Jones was thinking hard. He put his hands behind him as the men moved slowly along, the two committeemen doing the counting, and the captains lagging near and observing closely, and twisted his coat pocket around and got both hands into it, where lay his plunder. Strong fingers tore the skin of the squirrel apart at the back and stripped it clean from head to tail. The hair was swept from the tail by those same fingers and scattered along the earth; and the skin, torn into little patches, found the same resting place, to be ground into the soil of the unfloored shed by the soles of carefully adjusted heavy boots. It was so with the viscera. There remained in the pocket of Jones but a young black squirrel, all ready for the table, save that it was uncooked.

The end of the count was reached and the astonishing result declared. Each captain blazed out expressions of doubt and wrath; Granger, because he had relied upon the accidental bear slain by his party, and Jones for reasons more peculiarly his own. The count must be made over again to insure against all error, and the task was entered upon at once, the Jones game, as before, being counted first.

Lingering a little behind Granger as they followed the four counting and tallying members of the committee came the stalwart Jones. Again his sinewy hands reached the pocket drawn behind him; there was a twitch, a swift subsequent movement, and the hind quarter of a squirrel went into his roomy mouth. His jaws worked vigorously.

"Thought you'd stopped tobacco, Lon," said Granger carelessly, who, though he noted the mastication, was too intent upon the count to pay much attention to anything else.

"Did," was the response, "but I got a hankering and took it up again. Doesn't seem to hurt me any."

A moment later his fingers went swiftly to his mouth and a little handful of white bones was dropped to earth, to be ground as the skin had been beneath the soles of a pair of cowhide boots. And so went all the squirrel.

The end of the second count of the Granger game was reached and then the heavens fell! It did not correspond with the first enumeration. There was one squirrel short. Under the loud protests of Granger the work was repeated with the utmost thoroughness. The enumerators confessed that they must have made a mistake the first time. The Jones company were declared victors in the squirrel shoot by but a single unit, but victors still.

The rage of Granger was something worth the seeing. There had been trickery! The long, bare, floorless shed was searched, but no trace of a squirrel could be found; and besides, the committee had been together all the time. Then each man was searched as thoroughly as ever custom-house officer, keen for diamonds, might have searched some noted smuggler. As the rose—so pure proved they! The doors were opened, the six men filed out, and the result was shoutingly announced. There was silence on one side, wild yells from the other, and a rush for supper.

To tell of that supper and to do it justice would require the skill of him who wrote of one of "Cleopatra's Nights." It was not of the same order of feasting, but it was as enjoyable, and healthier. The moment of pique and anger of the losing party was forgotten. What tales of shots made that October day, and of forest triumphs in the past! What vast consumption of edibles which the tavern, somehow, made more toothsome than anything in the hotel can produce. And how absent-minded the men were next day in the little meeting-houses at the different crossroads. A squirrel shoot is almost a legend now, but a squirrel shoot was one of the days the passing country generation knew of as being as scarlet as the leaves of the October maple, as golden as those of the elm in the same crisp, mellow month.

CAPTAIN
MAYNE REID

A Hunting Party

A hundred years ago, with a most suitable wilderness and an abundance of game not too far removed from the eastern marginal centers of population, it is surprising that sportsmen were willing to travel from fifteen hundred to two thousand miles to hunt and fish. All of which seems to prove that the green grass theory was as prevalent then as it is today. The area traveled by Captain Reid and his fellow sportsmen has been adequately covered in fact and fiction insofar as pioneer movement is concerned, but the hunting under such conditions was a chore rather than a diversion. The country has a different aspect when viewed by a sportsman than it does when surveyed by the settler. Captain Reid is one of those fast-disappearing characters—a round-the-fire storyteller.

O n the western bank of the Mississippi, twelve miles below the *embouchure* of the Missouri, stands the large town of St. Louis, poetically known as the "Mound City." Although there are many other large towns throughout the Mississippi Valley, St. Louis is the true metropolis of the "far west"—of that semi-civilised, ever-changing belt of territory known as the "Frontier."

St. Louis is one of those American cities in the history of which there is something of peculiar interest. It is one of the oldest of North American settlements, having been a French trading port at an early period.

Though not so successful as their rivals the English, there was a degree of picturesqueness about French colonisation that, in the present day, strongly claims the attention of the American poet, novelist, and historian. Their dealings with the Indian aborigines —the facile manner in which they glided into the habits of the latter—meeting them more than halfway between civilisation and savage life—the handsome nomenclature which they have scattered freely, and which still holds over the trans-Mississippian territories—the introduction of a new race (the half blood—peculiarly French)—the heroic and adventurous character of their earliest pioneers De Salle, Marquette, Father Hennepin, &c.—their romantic explorations and melancholy fate—all these circumstances have rendered extremely interesting the early history of the French in America. Even the Quixotism of some of their attempts at colonisation cannot fail to interest us, as at Gallipolis on the Ohio, a colony composed of expatriated people of the French court;—perruquiers, coach-builders, tailors, *modistes*, and the like. Here, in the face of hostile Indians, before an acre of ground was cleared, before the slightest provision was made for their future subsistence, the first house erected was a large log structure, to serve as the *salon du bal!*

Besides its French origin, St. Louis possesses many other points of interest. It has long been the *entrepôt* and *depôt* of commerce with the wild tribes of prairie-land. There the trader is supplied with his stock for the Indian market—his red and green blankets— his beads and trinkets—his rifles, and powder, and lead; and there, in return, he disposes of the spoils of the prairie collected in many a far and perilous wandering. There the emigrant rests on the way to his wilderness home; and the hunter equips himself before starting forth on some new expedition.

To the traveller, St. Louis is a place of peculiar interest. He will hear around him the language of every nation in the civilised world. He will behold faces of every hue and variety of expression. He will meet with men of every possible calling.

All this is peculiarly true in the latter part of the summer season. Then the motley population of New Orleans fly from the annual scourge of the yellow fever, and seek safety in the cities that lie farther north. Of these, St. Louis is a favourite "city of refuge," the Creole element of its population being related to that kindred race in the South, and keeping up with it this annual correspondence.

In one of these streams of migration I had found my way to St. Louis, in the autumn of 18—. The place was at the time filled with loungers, who seemed to have nothing else to do but kill time. Every hotel had its quota, and in every verandah and at the corners of the streets you might see small knots of well-dressed gentlemen trying to entertain each other, and laugh away the hours. Most of them were the annual birds of passage from New Orleans, who had fled from "yellow Jack," and were sojourning here till the cold frosty winds of November should drive that intruder from the "crescent city;" but there were many other *flaneurs* as well. There were travellers from Europe—men of wealth and rank who had left behind them the luxuries of civilised society to rough it for a season in the wild West—painters in search of the picturesque—naturalists whose love of their favourite study had drawn them from their comfortable closets to search for knowledge under circumstances of extremest difficulty—and sportsmen, who, tired of chasing small game, were on their way to the great plains to take part in the noble sport of hunting the buffalo. I was myself one of the last-named fraternity.

There is no country in the world so addicted to the *table d'hôte* as America, and that very custom soon makes idle people acquainted with each other. I was not very long in the place before I was upon terms of intimacy with a large number of these loungers, and I found several, like myself, desirous of making a hunting expedition to the prairies. This chimed in with my plans to a nicety, and I at once set about getting up the expedition. I found five others who were willing to join me.

After several *conversaziones*, with much discussion, we succeeded at length in "fixing" our plan. Each was to "equip" according to his own fancy, though it was necessary for each to provide himself with a riding horse or mule. After that, a general fund was to be "raised," to be appropriated to the purchase of a waggon and team, with tents, stores, and cooking utensils. A couple of professional hunters were to be engaged; men who knew the ground to be traversed, and who were to act as guides to the expedition.

About a week was consumed in making the necessary preparations, and at the end of that time, under the sunrise of a lovely morning, a small cavalcade was seen to issue from the back suburbs of St. Louis, and, climbing the undulating slopes in its rear, head for the far-stretching wilderness of the prairies. It was our hunting expedition.

The cavalcade consisted of eight mounted men, and a waggon with its full team of six tough mules. These last were under the *manège* of "Jake"—a free negro, with a shining black face, a thick full mop, and a set of the best "ivories," which were almost always uncovered in a smile.

Peeping from under the tilt of the waggon might be seen another face strongly contrasting with that of Jake. This had been originally of a reddish hue, but sun-tan, and a thick sprinkling of freckles, had changed the red to golden yellow. A shock of fiery hair surmounted this visage, which was partially concealed under a badly battered hat. Though the face of the black expressed good humour, it might have been called sad when brought into comparison with that of the little red man, which peeped out beside it. Upon the latter, there was an expression irresistibly comic—the expression of an actor in broad farce. One eye was continually on the wink, while the other looked knowing enough for both. A short clay-pipe, stuck jauntily between the lips, added to the comical expression of the face, which was that of Mike Lanty from Limerick. No one ever mistook the nationality of Michael.

Who were the eight cavaliers that accompanied the waggon? Six of them were gentlemen by birth and education. At least half that number were scholars. The other two laid no claim either to gentleness or scholarship—they were rude trappers—the hunters and guides of the expedition.

A word about each one of the eight, for there was not one of them without his peculiarity. First, there was an Englishman—a genuine type of his countrymen—full six feet high, well proportioned, with broad chest and shoulders, and massive limbs. Hair of a light brown, complexion florid, moustache and whiskers full and hay-coloured, but suiting well the complexion and features. The last were regular, and if not handsome, at least good humoured and noble in their expression. The owner was in reality a nobleman—a true nobleman—one of that class who, while travelling through the "States," have the good sense to carry their umbrella along, and leave their title behind them. To us he was known as Mr. Thompson, and, after some time, when we had all become familiar with each other, as plain "Thompson." It was only long after, and by accident, that I became acquainted with his rank and title; some of our companions do not know it to this day, but that is no consequence. I mention the circumstance here to aid me in illustrating the character of our travelling companion, who was "close" and modest almost to a fault.

His costume was characteristic. A "tweed" shooting jacket, of course, with eight pockets—a vest of the same material with four —tweed trousers, and a tweed cap. In the waggon was the hat-box, of strong yellow leather, with straps and padlock. This was supposed to contain the dress hat; and some of the party were merry about it. But no—Mr. Thompson was a more experienced traveller than his companions thought him at first. The contents of the hat-case were sundry brushes—including one for the teeth—combs, razors, and pieces of soap. The hat had been left at St. Louis.

But the umbrella had *not*. It was then under Thompson's arm, with its full proportions of whalebone and gingham. Under that umbrella he had hunted tigers in the jungles of India—under that umbrella he had chased the lion upon the plains of Africa—under that umbrella he had pursued the ostrich and the vicuña over the pampas of South America; and now under that same hemisphere of blue gingham he was about to carry terror and destruction among the wild buffaloes of the prairies.

Besides the umbrella—strictly a weapon- of defence—Mr. Thompson carried another, a heavy double-barrelled gun, marked "Bishop, of Bond Street," no bad weapon with a loading of buck shot, and with this both barrels were habitually loaded.

So much for Mr. Thompson, who may pass for No. 1 of the hunting party. He was mounted on a strong bay cob, with tail cut short, and English saddle, both of which objects—the short tail and the saddle—were curiosities to all of the party except Mr. Thompson and myself.

No. 2 was as unlike No. 1 as two animals of the same species could possibly be. He was a Kentuckian, full six inches taller than Thompson, or indeed than any of the party. His features were marked, prominent and irregular, and this irregularity was increased by a "cheekful" of half-chewed tobacco. His complexion was dark, almost olive, and the face quite naked, without either moustache or whisker, but long straight hair, black as an Indian's, hung down to his shoulders. In fact, there was a good deal of the Indian look about him, except in his figure. That was somewhat slouched, with arms and limbs of over-length, loosely hung about it. Both, however, though not modelled after the Apollo, were evidently full of muscle and tough strength, and looked as though their owner could return the hug of a bear with interest. There was a gravity in his look, but that was not from any gravity of spirits; it was his swarth complexion that gave him this appearance, aided, no doubt, by several lines of "ambeer" proceeding from the corners of his mouth in the direction of the chin. So far from being grave, this dark Kentuckian was as gay and buoyant as any of the party. Indeed, a light and boyish spirit is a characteristic of the Kentuckian as well as of all the natives of the Mississippi Valley— at least such has been my observation.

Our Kentuckian was costumed just as he would have been upon a cool morning riding about the "woodland" of his own plantation, for a "planter" he was. He wore a "Jeans" frock, and over that a long-tailed overcoat of the best green blanket, with side pockets and flaps. His jeans pantaloons were stuck into a pair of heavy horse-leather pegged boots, sometimes known as "nigger" boots; but over these were "wrappers" of green baize, fastened with a string above the knees. His hat was a "broad-brimmed felt," costly enough, but somewhat crushed by being sat upon and slept in. He bestrode a tall raw-boned steed that possessed many of the characteristics of the rider; and in the same proportion that the latter overtopped his companions, so did the steed outsize all the other horses of the cavalcade. Over the shoulders of the Kentuckian were suspended, by several straps, pouch, horn, and haversack, and resting upon his toe was the butt of a heavy rifle, the muzzle of which reached to a level with his shoulder.

He was a rich Kentucky planter, and known in his native state as a great deer-hunter. Some business or pleasure had brought him to St. Louis. It was hinted that Kentucky was becoming too thickly settled for him—deer becoming scarce, and bear hardly to be found—and that his visit to St. Louis had something to do with seeking a new "location" where these animals were still to be met with in greater plenty. The idea of buffalo hunting was just to his liking. The expedition would carry him through the frontier country, where he might afterwards choose his "location"—at all events the sport would repay him, and he was one of the most enthusiastic in regard to it.

He that looms up on the retrospect of my memory as No. 3 was as unlike the Kentuckian, as the latter was to Thompson. He was a disciple of Esculapius—not thin and pale, as these usually are, but fat, red, and jolly. I think he was originally a "Yankee," though his long residence in the Western States had rubbed the Yankee out of him to a great extent. At all events he had few of their characteristics about him. He was neither staid, sober, nor, what is usually alleged as a trait of the true bred Yankee, "stingy." On the contrary, our doctor was full of talk and joviality—generous to a fault. A fault, indeed; for, although many years in practice in various parts of the United States, and having earned large sums of money, at the date of our expedition we found him in St. Louis almost without a dollar, and with no great stock of patients. The truth must be told; the doctor was of a restless disposition, and liked his glass too well. He was a singer too, a fine amateur singer, with a voice equal to Mario's. That may partly account for his failure in securing a fortune. He was a favourite with all—ladies included—and so fond of good company, that he preferred the edge of the jovial board to the bed-side of a patient.

Not from any fondness for buffalo-hunting, but rather through an attachment to some of the company, had the doctor volunteered. Indeed, he was solicited by all to make one of us—partly on account of his excellent society, and partly that his professional services might be called into requisition before our return.

The doctor still preserved his professional costume of black—somewhat russet by long wear—but this was modified by a close-fitting fur cap, and wrappers of brown cloth, which he wore around his short thick legs. He was not over-well mounted—a very spare little horse was all he had, as his funds would not stretch to a better. It was quite a quiet one, however, and carried the doctor and his "medical saddle bags" steadily enough, though not without a good deal of spurring and whipping. The doctor's name was "Jopper"—Dr. John Jopper.

A very elegant youth, with fine features, rolling black eyes, and luxuriant curled hair, was one of us. The hands were well formed and delicate; the complexion silky, and of nearly an olive tint; but the purplish-red broke through upon his cheeks, giving the earnest of health, as well as adding to the picturesque beauty of his face. The form was perfect, and full of manly expression, and the pretty sky-blue plaited pantaloons and close-fitting jacket of the same material, sat gracefully on his well-turned limbs and arms. These garments were of "cottonade," that beautiful and durable fabric peculiar to Louisiana, and so well suited to the southern climate. A costly Panama hat cast its shadow over the wavy curls and pictured cheek of this youth, and a cloak of fine broad cloth, with velvet facings, hung loosely from his shoulders. A slight moustache and imperial lent a manlier expression to his chiseled features.

This young fellow was a creole of Louisiana—a student of one of the Jesuit Colleges of that State—and although very unlike what would be expected from such a dashing personage, he was an ardent, even passionate, lover of nature. Though still young, he was the most accomplished botanist in his State, and had already published several discoveries in the *Flora* of the South.

Of course the expedition was to him a delightful anticipation. It would afford the finest opportunity for prosecuting his favourite study in a new field; one as yet almost unvisited by the scientific traveller. The young creole was known as Jules Besançon.

He was not the only naturalist of the party. Another was with us; one who had already acquired a world-wide fame; whose name was as familiar to the *savans* of Europe as to his own countrymen. He was already an old man, almost venerable in his aspect, but his tread was firm, and his arm still strong enough to steady his long, heavy, double-barrelled rifle. An ample coat of dark blue covered his body; his limbs were enveloped in long buttoned leggings of drab cloth, and a cap of sable surmounted his high, broad fore-head. Under this his blueish grey eye glanced with a calm but clear intelligence, and a singe look from it satisfied you that you were in the presence of a superior mind. Were I to give the name of this person, this would readily be acknowledged. For certain reasons I cannot do this. Suffice it to say, he was one of the most distinguished of modern zoologists, and to his love for the study we were indebted for his companionship upon our hunting expe-dition. He was known to us as Mr. A—— the "hunter-naturalist." There was no jealousy between him and the young Besançon. On the contrary, a similarity of tastes soon brought about a mutual friendship, and the creole was observed to treat the other with marked deference and regard.

I may set myself down as No. 6 of the party. Let a short descrip-tion of me suffice. I was then but a young fellow, educated some-what better than common; fond of wild sports; not indifferent to a knowledge of nature; fond almost to folly of a good horse, and possessing one of the very best; not ill-looking in the face, and of middle stature; costumed in a light hunting-shirt of embroidered buckskin, with fringed cape and skirt; leggings of scarlet cloth, and cloth forage-cap, covering a flock of dark hair. Powder-flask and pouch of tasty patterns; belt around the waist, with hunting-knife and pistols—revolvers. A light rifle in one hand, and in the other a bridle-rein, which guided a steed of coal blackness; one that would have been celebrated in song by a troubadour of the olden time. A deep Spanish saddle of stamped leather; holsters with bearskin covers in front; a scarlet blanket, folded and strapped on the croup; lazo and haversack hanging from the "horn"—*voila tout!*

There are two characters still undescribed. Characters of no mean importance were they—the "guides." They were called respectively, Isaac Bradley and Mark Redwood. A brace of trap-pers they were, but as different from each other in personal appear-ance as two men could well be. Redwood was a man of large dimen-sions, and apparently as strong as a buffalo, while his *confrère* was a thin, wiry, sinewy mortal, with a tough, weazel-like look and gait. The expression of Redwood's countenance was open and manly, his eyes were grey, his hair light-coloured, and huge brown whiskers covered his cheeks. Bradley, on the other hand, was dark—his eyes small, black, and piercing—his face as hairless as an Indian's, and bronzed amost to the Indian hue, with the black hair of his head closely cropped around it.

Both these men were dressed in leather from head to foot, yet they were very differently dressed. Redwood wore the usual buckskin hunting-shirt, leggings, and moccasins, but all of full proportions and well cut, while his large 'coon-skin cap, with the plume-like tail, had an imposing appearance. Bradley's garments, on the contrary, were tight-fitting and "skimped." His hunting-shirt was without cape, and adhered so closely to his body that it appeared only an outer skin of the man himself. His leggings were pinched and tight. Shirt, leggings, and moccasins were evidently of the oldest kind, and as dirty as a cobbler's apron. A close-fitting otter cap, with a Mackinaw blanket, completed the wardrobe of Isaac Bradley. He was equipped with a pouch of greasy leather hanging by an old black strap, a small buffalo-horn suspended by a thong, and a belt of buffalo-leather, in which was stuck a strong blade, with its handle of buckhorn. His rifle was of the "tallest" kind— being full six feet in height—in fact, taller than he was, and at least four fifths of the weapon consisted of barrel. The straight narrow stock was a piece of manufacture that had proceeded from the hands of the trapper himself.

Redwood's rifle was also a long one, but of more modern build and fashion, and his equipments—pouch, powder-horn and belt— were of a more tasty design and finish.

Such were our guides, Redwood and Bradley. They were no imaginary characters these. Mark Redwood was a celebrated "mountain-man" at that time, and Isaac Bradley will be recognised by many when I give him the name and title by which he was then known—viz. "Old Ike, the wolf-killer."

Redwood rode a strong horse of the half-hunter breed, while the "wolf-killer" was mounted upon one of the scraggiest looking quadrupeds it would be possible to imagine—an old mare "mustang."

Our route was west by south. The nearest point with which we expected to fall in with the buffalo was two hundred miles distant. We might travel three hundred without seeing one, and even much farther at the present day; but a report had reached St. Louis that the buffalo had been seen that year upon the Osage River, west of the Ozark Hills, and towards that point we steered our course. We expected in about twenty days to fall in with the game. Fancy a cavalcade of hunters making a journey of twenty days to get upon the field! The reader will, no doubt, say we were in earnest.

At the time of which I am writing, a single day's journey from St. Louis carried the traveller clear of civilised life. There were settlements beyond; but these were sparse and isolated—a few small towns or plantations upon the main watercourses—and the whole country between them was an uninhabited wilderness. We had no hope of being sheltered by a roof until our return to the mound city itself, but we had provided ourselves with a couple of tents, part of the freight of our waggon.

There are but few parts of the American wilderness where the traveller can depend upon wild game for a subsistence. Even the skilled hunter when stationary is sometimes put to his wits' end for "daily bread." Upon the "route" no great opportunity is found of killing game, which always requires time to approach it with caution. Although we passed through what appeared to be excellent cover for various species of wild animals, we reached our first camp without having ruffled either hair or feathers. In fact, neither bird nor quadruped had been seen, although almost every one of the party had been on the look out for game during most of the journey.

This was rather discouraging, and we reasoned that if such was to be our luck until we got into the buffalo range we should have a very dull time of it. We were well provisioned, however, and we regretted the absence of game only on account of the sport. A large bag of biscuit, and one of flour, several pieces of "hung bacon," some dry ox-tongues, a stock of green coffee, sugar, and salt, were the principal and necessary stores. There were "luxuries," too, which each had provided according to his fancy, though not much of these, as every one of the party had had some time or other in his life a little experience in the way of "roughing it." Most of the loading of the waggon consisted of provender for our horses and mules.

We made full thirty miles on the first day. Our road was a good one. We passed over easy undulations, most of them covered with "black-jack." This is a species of dwarf oak, so called from the very dark colour of its wrinkled bark. It is almost worthless as a timber, being too small for most purposes. It is ornamental, however, forming copse-like groves upon the swells of the prairies, while its dark green foliage contrasts pleasantly with the lighter green of the grasses beneath its shade. The young botanist, Besançon, had least cause to complain. His time had been sufficiently pleasant during the day. New foliage fell under his observation—new flowers opened their corollas to his delighted gaze. He was aided in making his collections by the hunter-naturalist, who of course was tolerably well versed in this kindred science.

We encamped by the edge of a small creek of clear water. Our camp was laid out in due form, and everything arranged in the order we designed habitually to follow.

Every man unsaddled his own horse. There are no servants in prairie-land Even Lanty's services extended not beyond the *cuisine,* and for his department he had had his training as the cook of a New Orleans trading ship. Jake had enough to do with his mules; and to have asked one of our hunter-guides to perform the task of unsaddling your horse, would have been a hazardous experiment. Menial service to a free trapper! There are no servants in the prairie-land.

Our horses and mules were picketed on a piece of open ground, each having his "trail rope," which allowed a circuit of several yards. The two tents were pitched side by side, facing the stream, and the waggon drawn up some twenty feet in the rear. In the triangle between the waggon and the tents was kindled a large fire, upon each side of which two stakes, forked at the top, were driven into the ground. A long sapling resting in the forks traversed the blaze from side to side. This was Lanty's "crane"—the fire was his kitchen.

Let me sketch the camp more minutely, for our first camp was a type of all the others in its general features. Sometimes indeed the tents did not front the same way, when these openings were set to "oblige the wind," but they were always placed side by side in front of the waggon. They were small tents of the old-fashioned conical kind, requiring only one pole each. They were of sufficient size for our purpose, as there were only three of us to each—the guides, with Jake and Lanty, finding their lodgment under the tilt of the waggon. With their graceful shape, and snowy-white colour against the dark green foliage of the trees, they formed an agreeable contrast; and a *coup d'oeil* of the camp would have been no mean picture to the eye of an artist. The human figures may be arranged in the following manner.

Supper is getting ready, and Lanty is decidedly at this time the most important personage on the ground. He is stooping over the fire, with a small but long-handled frying-pan, in which he is parching the coffee. It is already browned, and Lanty stirs it about with an iron spoon. The crane carries the large coffee-kettle of sheet iron, full of water upon the boil; and a second frying-pan, larger than the first, is filled with sliced ham, ready to be placed upon the hot cinders.

Our English friend Thompson is seated upon a log, with the hat-box before him. It is open, and he has drawn out from it his stock of combs and brushes. He has already made his ablutions, and is now giving the finish to his toilet, by putting his hair, whiskers, moustache, teeth, and even his nails, in order. Your Englishman is the most comfortable traveller in the world.

The Kentuckian is differently engaged. He is upon his feet; in one hand gleams a knife with ivory handle and long shining blade. It is a "bowie," of that kind known as an "Arkansas toothpick." In the other hand you see an object about eight inches in length of the form of a parallelogram, and of a dark brown colour. It is a "plug" of real "James River tobacco." With his knife the Kentuckian cuts off a piece—a "chunk," as he terms it—which is immediately transferred to his mouth, and chewed to a pulp. This is his occupation for the moment.

The doctor, what of him? Doctor Jopper may be seen close to the water's edge. In his hand is a pewter flask, of the kind known as a "pocket pistol." That pistol is loaded with brandy, and Dr. Jopper is just in the act of drawing part of the charge, which, with a slight admixture of cool creek water, is carried aloft and poured into a very droughty vessel. The effect, however, is instantly apparent in the lively twinkle of the doctor's round and prominent eyes.

Besançon is seated near the tent, and the old naturalist beside him. The former is busy with the new plants he has collected. A large portfolio-looking book rests upon his knees, and between its leaves he is depositing his stores in a scientific manner. His companion, who understands the business well, is kindly assisting him. Their conversation is interesting, but every one else is too busy with his affairs to listen to it just now.

The guides are lounging about the waggon. Old Ike has a new flint in his rifle, and Redwood, of a more mirthful disposition, is occasionally cracking a joke with Mike or the "darkey."

Jake is still busy with his mules, and I with my favourite steed, whose feet I have washed in the stream, and anointed with a little spare grease. I shall not always have the opportunity of being so kind to him, but he will need it the less, as his hoofs become more hardened by the journey.

Around the camp are strewed our saddles, bridles, blankets, weapons, and utensils. These will all be collected and stowed under cover before we go to rest. Such is a picture of our camp before supper.

When that meal is cooked, the scene somewhat changes.

The atmosphere, even at that season, was cool enough, and this, with Mike's announcement that the coffee was ready, brought all the party—guides as well—around the blazing pile of logs. Each found his own platter, knife, and cup; and, helping himself from the general stock, set to eating on his own account. Of course there were no fragments, as a strict regard to economy was one of the laws of our camp.

Notwithstanding the fatigue, always incidental to a first day's march, we enjoyed this *al fresco* supper exceedingly. The novelty had much to do with our enjoyment of it, and also the fine appetites which we had acquired since our luncheon at noon halt.

When supper was over, smoking followed, for there was not one of the party who was not an inveterate burner of the "noxious weed." Some chose cigars, of which we had brought a good stock, but several were pipe-smokers. The zoologist carried a meerschaum; the guides smoked out of Indian calumets of the celebrated steatite, or red claystone. Mike had his dark-looking "dudeen," and Jake his pipe of corn "cob" and and cane-joint shank.

Our English friend Thompson had a store of the finest Havannahs, which he smoked with the grace peculiar to the English cigar smoker; holding his cigar impaled upon the point of his knife-blade. Kentucky also smoked cigars, but his was half buried within his mouth, slanted obliquely towards the right cheek. Besançon preferred the paper cigarette, which he made extempore, as he required them, out of a stock of loose tobacco. This is creole fashion—now also the *mode de Paris*.

A song from the doctor enlivened the conversation, and certainly so melodious a human voice had never echoed near the spot. One and all agreed that the grand opera had missed a capital "first tenor" in not securing the services of our companion.

The fatigue of our long ride caused us to creep into our tents at an early hour, and rolling ourselves in our blankets we went to sleep. Of course everything had been carefully gathered in lest rain might fall in the night. The trail ropes of our animals were looked to: we did not fear their being stolen, but horses on their first few days' journey are easily "stampeded," and will sometimes stray home again. This would have been a great misfortune, but most of us were old travellers, and every caution was observed in securing against such a result. There was no guard kept, though we knew the time would come when that would be a necessary duty.

The prairie traveller never sleeps after daybreak. He's usually astir before that time. He has many "chores" to perform, unknown to the ordinary traveller who rests in the roadside inn. He has to pack up his tent and bed, cook his own breakfast, and saddle his horse. All this requires time, therefore an early start is necessary.

We were on our feet before the sun had shown his disc above the black-jacks. Lanty had the start of us, and had freshened up his fire. Already the coffee-kettle was bubbling audibly, and the great frying-pan perfumed the camp with an incense more agreeable than the odours of Araby.

The raw air of the morning had brought everybody around the fire. Thompson was pruning and cleansing his nails; the Kentuckian was cutting a fresh "chunk" from his plug of "James's River"; the doctor had just returned from the stream, where he had refreshed himself by a "nip" from his pewter flask; Besançon was packing up his portfolios; the zoologist was lighting his long pipe, and the "Captain" was looking to his favourite horse, while inhaling the fragrance of an "Havannah." The guides stood with their blankets hanging from their shoulders silent and thoughtful.

In half an hour breakfast was over, the tents and utensils were restored to the waggon, the horses were brought in and saddled, the mules "hitched up," and the expedition once more on its way.

This day we made not quite so good a journey. The roads were heavier, the country more thickly timbered, and the ground more hilly. We had several small streams to ford, and this retarded our progress. Twenty miles was the extent of our journey.

We encamped again without any of us having killed or seen game. Although we had beaten the bushes on both sides of our course, nothing bigger than the redbird (scarlet tanager, *Piranga rubra*), a screaming jay, or an occasional flight of finches, gratified our sight.

We reached our camp somewhat disappointed. Even old Ike and Redwood came into camp without game, alleging also that they had not met with the sign of a living quadruped.

Our second camp was also on the bank of a small stream. Shortly after our arrival on the ground, Thompson started out afoot, taking with him his gun. He had noticed a tract of marsh at no great distance off. He thought it promised well for snipe.

He had not been long gone, when two reports echoed back, and then shortly after another and another. He had found something to empty his gun at.

Presently we saw him returning with a brace and a half of birds that looked very much like large snipe. So he thought them, but that question was set at rest by the zoologist, who pronounced them at once to be the American "Curlew" of Wilson (*Numenius longirostris*). Curlew or Snipe, they were soon divested of the feathery coat, and placed in Lanty's frying-pan. Excellent eating they proved, having only the fault that there was not enough of them.

These birds formed the topic of our after-supper conversation, and then it generalised to the different species of wading birds of America, and at length that singular creature, the "ibis," became the theme. This came round by Besançon remarking that a species of ibis was brought by the Indians to the markets of New Orleans, and sold there under the name of "Spanish Curlew." This was the white ibis (*Tantalus albus*), which the zoologist stated was found in plenty along the whole southern coast of the United States. There were two other species, he said, natives of the warm parts of North America, the "wood ibis" (*Tantalus loculator*), which more nearly resembles the sacred ibis of Egypt, and the beautiful "sacred ibis" (*Tantalus ruber*), which last is rarer than the others.

Our venerable companion, who had the ornithology of America, if I may use the expression, at his fingers' ends, imparted many curious details of the habits of these rare birds. All listened with interest to his statements—even the hunter-guides, for with all their apparent rudeness of demeanour, there was a dash of the naturalist in these fellows.

When the zoologist became silent, the young creole took up the conversation. Talking of the ibis, he said, reminded him of an adventure he had met with while in pursuit of these birds among the swamps of his native state. He would relate it to us. Of course we were rejoiced at the proposal. We were just the audience for an "adventure," and after rolling a fresh cigarette, the botanist began his narration.

"During one of my college vacations I made a botanical excursion to the south-western part of Louisiana. Before leaving home

I had promised a dear friend to bring him the skins of such rare birds as were known to frequent the swampy region I was about to traverse, but he was especially desirous I should obtain for him some specimens of the red ibis, which he intended to have 'mounted.' I gave my word that no opportunity should be lost of obtaining these birds, and I was very anxious to make good my promise.

"The southern part of the State of Louisiana is one vast labyrinth of swamps, bayous, and lagoons. The bayous are sluggish streams that glide sleepily along, sometimes running one way, and sometimes the very opposite, according to the season of the year. Many of them are outlets of the Mississippi, which begins to shed off its waters more than 300 miles from its mouth. These bayous are deep, sometimes narrow, sometimes wide, with islets in their midst. They and their contiguous swamps are the great habitat of the alligator and the fresh-water shark—the gar. Numerous species of water and wading fowl fly over them, and plunge through their dark tide. Here you may see the red flamingo, the egret, the trumpeter-swan, the blue heron, the wild goose, the crane, the snake-bird, the pelican, and the ibis; you may likewise see the osprey, and the white-headed eagle robbing him of his prey. Both swamps and bayous produce abundantly fish, reptile, and insect, and are, consequently, the favourite resort of hundreds of birds which prey upon these creatures. In some places, their waters form a complete net-work over the country, which you may traverse with a small boat in almost any direction; indeed, this is the means by which many settlements communicate with each other. As you approach southward towards the Gulf, you get clear of the timber; and within some fifty miles of the sea, there is not a tree to be seen.

"In the first day or two that I was out, I had succeeded in getting all the specimens I wanted, with the exception of the ibis. This shy creature avoided me; in fact I had only seen one or two in my excursions, and these at a great distance. I still, however, had hopes of finding them before my return to my friend.

"About the third or fourth day I set out from a small settlement on the edge of one of the larger bayous. I had no other company than my gun. I was even unattended by a dog, as my favourite spaniel had the day before been bitten by an alligator while swimming across the bayou, and I was compelled to leave him at the settlement. Of course the object of my excursion was a search after new flora, but I had become by this time very desirous of getting the rare ibis, and I was determined half to neglect any botanising for that purpose. I went of course in a boat, a light skiff, such as is commonly used by the inhabitants of these parts.

"Occasionally using the paddles, I allowed myself to float some four or five miles down the main bayou; but as the birds I was in search of did not appear, I struck into a 'branch,' and sculled myself up stream. This carried me through a solitary region, with marshes stretching as far as the eye could see, covered with tall reeds. There was no habitation, nor aught that betokened the presence of man. It was just possible that I was the first human being who had ever found a motive for propelling a boat through the dark waters of this solitary stream.

"As I advanced, I fell in with game; and I succeeded in bagging several, both of the great wood-ibis and the white species. I also shot a fine white-headed eagle *(Falco leucocephalus)*, which came soaring over my boat, unconscious of danger. But the bird which I most wanted seemed that which could not be obtained. I wanted the scarlet ibis.

"I think I had rowed some three miles up-stream, and was about to take in my oars and leave my boat to float back again, when I perceived that, a little farther up, the bayou widened. Curiosity prompted me to continue; and after pulling a few hundred strokes, I found myself at the end of an oblong lake, a mile or so in length. It was deep, dark, marshy around the shores, and full of alligators. I saw their ugly forms and long serrated backs, as they floated about in all parts of it, hungrily hunting for fish and eating one another; but all this was nothing new, for I had witnessed similar scenes during the whole of my excursion. What drew my attention most, was a small islet near the middle of the lake, upon one end of which stood a row of upright forms of a bright scarlet colour. These red creatures were the very objects I was in search of. They might be flamingoes: I could not tell at that distance. So much the better, if I could only succeed in getting a shot at them; but these creatures are even more wary than the ibis; and as the islet was low, and altogether without cover, it was not likely they would allow me to come within range: nevertheless, I was determined to make the attempt. I rowed up the lake, occasionally turning my head to see if the game had taken the alarm. The sun was hot and dazzling; and as the bright scarlet was magnified by refraction, I fancied for a long time they were flamingoes. This fancy was dissipated as I drew near. The outlines of the bills, like the blade of a sabre, convinced me they were the ibis; besides, I now saw that they were less than three feet in height, while the flamingoes stand five. There were a dozen of them in all. These were balancing themselves, as is their usual habit, on one leg, apparently asleep, or buried in deep thought. They were on the upper extremity of the islet, while I was approaching it from below. It was not above sixty yards across; and could I only reach the point nearest me, I knew my gun would throw shot to kill at that distance. I feared the stroke of the sculls would start them, and I pulled slowly and cautiously. Perhaps the great heat—for it was as hot a day as I can remember—had rendered them torpid or lazy. Whether or not, they sat still until the cut-water of my skiff touched the bank of the islet. I drew my gun up cautiously, took aim, and fired both barrels almost simultaneously. When the smoke cleared out of my eyes, I saw that all the birds had flown off except one, that lay stretched out by the edge of the water.

"Gun in hand, I leaped out of the boat, and ran across the islet to bag my game. This occupied but a few minutes; and I was turning to go back to the skiff, when, to my consternation, I saw it out upon the lake, and rapidly floating downward!

"In my haste I had left it unfastened, and the bayou current had carried it off. It was still but a hundred yards distant, but it might as well have been a hundred miles, for at that time I could not swim a stroke.

"My first impulse was to rush down to the lake, and after the boat. This impulse was checked on arriving at the water's edge, which I saw at a glance was fathoms in depth. Quick reflection told me that the boat was gone—irrecoverably gone!

"I did not at first comprehend the full peril of my situation; nor will you, gentlemen. I was on an islet, in a lake, only half a mile from its shores—alone, it is true, and without a boat; but what of that? Many a man had been so before, with not an idea of danger.

"These were first thoughts, natural enough; but they rapidly gave place to others of a far different character. When I gazed after my boat, now beyond recovery—when I looked around, and saw that the lake lay in the middle of an interminable swamp, the shores of which, even could I have reached them, did not seem to promise me footing—when I reflected that, being unable to swim, I could *not* reach them—that upon the islet there was neither tree, nor log, nor bush; not a stick out of which I might make a raft—I say, when I reflected upon all these things, there arose in my mind a feeling of well-defined and absolute horror.

"It is true I was only in a lake, a mile or so in width; but so far as the peril and helplessness of my situation were concerned, I might as well have been upon a rock in the middle of the Atlantic. I knew that there was no settlement within miles—miles of pathless swamp. I knew that no one could either see or hear me—no one was at all likely to come near the lake; indeed, I felt satisfied that my faithless boat was the first keel that had ever cut its waters. The very tameness of the birds wheeling round my head was evidence of this. I felt satisfied, too, that without some one to help me, I should never go out from that lake: I must die on the islet, or drown in attempting to leave it!

"These reflections rolled rapidly over my startled soul. The facts were clear, the hypothesis definite, the sequence certain; there was no ambiguity, no supposititious hinge upon which I could hang a hope; no, not one. I could not even expect that I should be missed and sought for; there was no one to search for me. The simple *habitans* of the village I had left knew me not—I was a stranger among them: they only knew me as a stranger, and fancied me a strange individual; one who made lonely excursions, and brought home bunches of weeds, with birds, insects, and reptiles, which they had never before seen, although gathered at their own doors. My absence, besides, would be nothing new to them, even though it lasted for days: I had often been absent before, a week at a time. There was no hope of my being missed.

"I have said that these reflections came and passed quickly. In less than a minute, my affrighted soul was in full possession of them, and almost yielded itself to despair. I shouted, but rather involuntarily than with any hope that I should be heard; I shouted loudly and fiercely: my answer—the echoes of my own voice, the shriek of the osprey, and the maniac laugh of the white-headed eagle.

"I ceased to shout, threw my gun to the earth, and tottered down beside it. I can imagine the feelings of a man shut up in a gloomy prison—they are not pleasant. I have been lost upon the wild prairie—the land-sea—without bush, break, or star to guide me—that was worse. There you look around; you see nothing; you hear nothing: you are alone with God, and you tremble in his presence; your senses swim; your brain reels; you are afraid of yourself; you are afraid of your own mind. Deserted by everything else, you dread lest it, too, may forsake you. There is horror in this—it is very horrible—it is hard to bear; but I have borne it all, and would bear it again twenty times over rather than endure once more the first hour I spent on that lonely islet in that lonely lake.

Your prison may be dark and silent, but you feel that you are not utterly alone; beings like yourself are near, though they be your jailers. Lost on the prairie, you are alone; but you are free. On the islet, I felt that I was alone; that I was not free: on the islet I experienced the feelings of the prairie and the prison combined.

"I lay in a state of stupor—almost unconscious; how long I know not, but many hours I am certain; I knew this by the sun—it was going down when I awoke, if I may so term the recovery of my stricken senses. I was aroused by a strange circumstance: I was surrounded by dark objects of hideous shape and hue—reptiles they were. They had been before my eyes for some time, but I had not seen them. I had only a sort of dreamy consciousness of their presence; but I heard them at length: my ear was in better tune, and the strange noises they uttered reached my intellect. It sounded like the blowing of great bellows, with now and then a note harsher and louder, like the roaring of a bull. This startled me, and I looked up and bent my eyes upon the objects: they were forms of the *crocodilidæ,* the giant lizards—they were alligators.

"Huge ones they were, many of them; and many were they in number—a hundred at least were crawling over the islet, before, behind, and on all sides around me. Their long gaunt jaws and channelled snouts projected forward so as almost to touch my body; and their eyes, usually leaden, seemed now to glare.

"Impelled by this new danger, I sprang to my feet, when, recognising the upright form of man, the reptiles scuttled off, and plunging hurriedly into the lake, hid their hideous bodies under the water.

"The incident in some measure revived me. I saw that I was not alone; there was company even in the crocodiles. I gradually became more myself; and began to reflect with some degree of coolness on the circumstances that surrounded me. My eyes wandered over the islet; every inch of it came under my glance; every object upon it was scrutinised—the moulted feathers of wild-fowl, the pieces of mud, the fresh-water mussels *(unios)* strewed upon its beach—all were examined. Still the barren answer—no means of escape.

"The islet was but the head of a sand-bar, formed by the eddy, perhaps gathered together within the year. It was bare of herbage, with the exception of a few tufts of grass. There was neither tree nor bush upon it: not a stick. A raft indeed! There was not wood enough to make a raft that would have floated a frog. The idea of a raft was but briefly entertained; such a thought had certainly crossed my mind, but a single glance round the islet dispelled it before it had taken shape.

"I paced my prison from end to end; from side to side I walked it over. I tried the water's depth; on all sides I sounded it, wading recklessly in; everywhere it deepened rapidly as I advanced. Three lengths of myself from the islet's edge, and I was up to the neck. The huge reptiles swam around, snorting and blowing; they were bolder in this element. I could not have waded safely ashore, even had the water been shallow. To swim it—no—even though I swam like a duck, they would have closed upon and quartered me before I could have made a dozen strokes. Horrified by their demonstrations, I hurried back upon dry ground, and paced the islet with dripping garments.

"I continued walking until night, which gathered around me dark and dismal. With night came new voices—the hideous voices of the nocturnal swamp; the qua-qua of the night-heron, the screech of the swamp-owl, the cry of the bittern, the el-l-uk of the great water-toad, the tinkling of the bell-frog, and the chirp of the savanna-cricket—all fell upon my ear. Sounds still harsher and more hideous were heard around me—the splashing of the alligator, and the roaring of his voice; these reminded me that I must not go to sleep. To sleep! I durst not have slept for a single instant. Even when I lay for a few minutes motionless, the dark reptiles came crawling round me—so close that I could have put forth my hand and touched them.

"At intervals, I sprang to my feet, shouted, swept my gun around, and chased them back to the water, into which they betook themselves with a sullen plunge, but with little semblance of fear. At each fresh demonstration on my part they showed less alarm, until I could no longer drive them either with shouts or threatening gestures. They only retreated a few feet, forming an irregular circle round me.

"Thus hemmed in, I became frightened in turn. I loaded my gun and fired; I killed none. They are impervious to a bullet, except in the eye, or under the forearm. It was too dark to aim at these parts; and my shots glanced harmlessly from the pyramidal scales of their bodies. The loud report, however, and the blaze frightened them, and they fled, to return again after a long interval. I was asleep when they returned; I had gone to sleep in spite of my efforts to keep awake. I was startled by the touch of something cold; and half-stifled by the strong musky odour that filled the air. I threw out my arms; my fingers rested upon an object slippery and clammy: it was one of these monsters—one of gigantic size. He had crawled close alongside me, and was preparing to make his attack; as I saw that he was bent in the form of a bow, and I knew that these creatures assume that attitude when about to strike their victim. I was just in time to spring aside, and avoid the stroke of his powerful tail, that the next moment swept the ground where I had lain. Again I fired, and he with the rest once more retreated to the lake.

"All thoughts of going to sleep were at an end. Not that I felt wakeful; on the contrary, wearied with my day's exertion—for I had had a long pull under a hot tropical sun—I could have lain down upon the earth, in the mud, anywhere, and slept in an instant. Nothing but the dread certainty of my peril kept me awake. Once again before morning, I was compelled to battle with the hideous reptiles, and chase them away with a shot from my gun.

"Morning came at length, but with it no change in my perilous position. The light only showed me my island prison, but revealed no way of escape from it. Indeed, the change could not be called for the better, for the fervid rays of an almost vertical sun poured down upon me until my skin blistered. I was already speckled by the bites of a thousand swamp-flies and mosquitoes, that all night long had preyed upon me. There was not a cloud in the heavens to shade me; and the sunbeams smote the surface of the dead bayou with a double intensity.

"Towards evening, I began to hunger; no wonder at that: I had not eaten since leaving the village settlement. To assuage thirst, I drank the water of the lake, turbid and slimy as it was. I drank it in large quantities, for it was hot, and only moistened my palate without quenching the craving of my appetite. Of water there was enough; I had more to fear from want of food.

"What could I eat? The ibis. But how to cook it? There was nothing wherewith to make a fire—not a stick. No matter for that. Cooking is a modern invention, a luxury for pampered palates. I divested the ibis of its brilliant plumage, and ate it raw. I spoiled my specimen, but at the time there was little thought of that: there was not much of the naturalist left in me. I anathematised the hour I had ever promised to procure the bird. I wished my friend up to his neck in a swamp.

"The ibis did not weigh above three pounds, bones and all. It served me for a second meal, a breakfast; but at this *déjeûner sans fourchette* I picked the bones.

"What next? starve? No—not yet. In the battles I had had with

the alligators during the second night, one of them had received
a shot that proved mortal. The hideous carcass of the reptile lay
dead upon the beach. I need not starve; I could eat that. Such were
my reflections. I must hunger, though, before I could bring myself
to touch the musky morsel.

"Two more days' fasting conquered my squeamishness. I drew
out my knife, cut a steak from the alligator's tail, and ate it—not
the one I had first killed, but a second; the other was now putrid,
rapidly decomposing under the hot sun: its odour filled the islet.

"The stench had grown intolerable. There was not a breath of
air stirring, otherwise I might have shunned it by keeping to
windward. The whole atmosphere of the islet, as well as a large
circle around it, was impregnated with the fearful effluvium. I
could bear it no longer. With the aid of my gun, I pushed the half-
decomposed carcass into the lake; perhaps the current might carry
it away. It did: I had the gratification to see it float off.

"This circumstance led me into a train of reflections. Why did
the body of the alligator float? It was swollen—inflated with gases.
Ha!

"An idea shot suddenly through my mind—one of those brilliant
ideas, the children of necessity. I thought of the floating alligator,
of its intestines—what if I inflated them? Yes, yes! buoys and
bladders, floats and life-preservers! that was the thought. I would
open the alligators, make a buoy of their intestines, and that would
bear me from the islet!

"I did not lose a moment's time; I was full of energy: hope had
given me new life. My gun was loaded—a huge crocodile that
swam near the shore received the shot in his eye. I dragged him
on the beach; with my knife I laid open his entrails. Few they
were, but enough for my purpose. A plume-quill from the wing of
the ibis served me for a blow-pipe. I saw the bladder-like skin ex-
pand, until I was surrounded by objects like great sausages. These
were tied together, and fastened to my body, and then, with a
plunge, I entered the waters of the lake, and floated downward. I
had tied on my life-preservers in such a way that I sat in the water
in an upright position, holding my gun with both hands. This I
intended to have used as a club in case I should be attacked by the
alligators; but I had chosen the hot hour of noon, when these
creatures lie in a half-torpid state, and to my joy I was not molested.

"Half an hour's drifting with the current carried me to the end
of the lake, and I found myself at the *debouchure* of the bayou.
Here, to my great delight, I saw my boat in the swamp, where it

had been caught and held fast by the sedge. A few minutes more, and I had swung myself over the gunwale, and was sculling with eager strokes down the smooth waters of the bayou.

"Of course my adventure was ended, and I reached the settlement in safety, but without the object of my excursion. I was enabled, however, to procure it some days after, and had the gratification of being able to keep my promise to my friend."

Besançon's adventure had interested all of us; the old hunter-naturalist seemed delighted with it. No doubt it revived within him the memories of many a perilous incident in his own life.

It was evident that in the circle of the camp-fire there was more than one pair of lips ready to narrate some similar adventure, but the hour was late, and all agreed it would be better to go to rest. On to-morrow night, some other would take their turn; and, in fact, a regular agreement was entered into that each one of the party who had at any period of his life been the hero or participator in any hunting adventure should narrate the same for the entertainment of the others. This would bring out a regular "round of stories by the camp-fire," and would enable us to kill the many long evenings we had to pass before coming up with the buffalo. The conditions were, that the stories should exclusively relate to birds or animals—in fact, any hunted game belonging to the *fauna* of the American Continent: furthermore, that each should contribute his quota of information about whatever animal should chance to be the subject of the narration—about its habits, its geographical range; in short, its general natural history, as well as the various modes of hunting it, practised in different places by different people. This, it was alleged, would render our camp conversation instructive as well as entertaining.

The idea originated with the old hunter-naturalist, who very wisely reasoned that among so many gentlemen of large hunting experience he might collect new facts for his favourite science— for to just such men, and not to the closet-dreamer, is natural history indebted for its most interesting chapters. Of course every one of us, guides and all, warmly applauded the proposal, for there was no one among us averse to receiving a little knowledge of so entertaining a character. No doubt to the naturalist himself we should be indebted for most part of it; and his mode of communicating was so pleasant, that even the rude trappers listened to him with wonder and attention. They saw that he was no "greenhorn" either in wood-craft or prairie knowledge, and that was a sufficient claim to their consideration.

There is no character less esteemed by the regular "mountain man" than a "greenhorn"—that is, one who is new to the ways of their wilderness life.

With the design of an early start, we once more crept into our several quarters, and went to sleep.

After an early breakfast we lit our pipes and cigars, and took to the road. The sun was very bright, and in less than two hours after starting we were sweltering under a heat almost tropical. It was one of those autumn days peculiar to America, where even a high latitude seems to be no protection against the sun, and his beams fall upon one with as much fervour as they would under the line itself. The first part of our journey was through open woods of black-jack, whose stunted forms afforded no shade, but only shut off the breeze which might otherwise have fanned us.

While fording a shallow stream, the doctor's scraggy, ill-tempered horse took a fit of kicking quite frantical. For some time it seemed likely that either the doctor himself, or his saddle-bags, would be deposited in the bottom of the creek, but after a severe spell of whipping and kicking on the part of the rider, the animal moved on again. What had set it dancing? That was the question. It had the disposition to be "frisky," but usually appeared to be lacking in strength. The buzz of a horse-fly sounding in our ears explained all. It was one of those large insects—the "horse-bug"—peculiar to the Mississippi country, and usually found near water-courses. They are more terrible to horses than a fierce dog would be. I have known horses gallop away from them as if pursued by a beast of prey.

There is a belief among western people that these insects are propagated by the horses themselves; that is, that the eggs of the female are deposited upon the grass, so that the horses may swallow them; that incubation goes on within the stomach of the animal, and that the chrysalis is afterwards voided. I have met with others who believed in a still stranger theory; that the insect itself actually sought, and found, a passage into the stomach of the horse, some said by passing down his throat, others by boring a hole through his abdomen; and that in such cases the horse usually sickened, and was in danger of dying!

After the doctor's mustang had returned to proper behaviour, these odd theories became the subject of discussion. The Kentuckian believed in them—the Englishman doubted them—the hunter-naturalist could not endorse them—and Besançon ignored them entirely.

Shortly after the incident we entered the bottom lands of a considerable stream. These were heavily timbered, and the shadow of the great forest trees afforded us a pleasant relief from the hot sun. Our guides told us we had several miles of such woods to pass through, and we were glad of the information. We noticed that most of the trees were beech, and their smooth straight trunks rose like columns around us.

The beech *(Fagus sylvatica)* is one of the most beautiful of American forest trees. Unlike most of the others, its bark is smooth, without fissures, and often of a silvery hue. Large beech trees standing by the path, or near a cross road, are often seen covered with names, initials, and dates. Even the Indian often takes advantage of the bark of a beech tree to signalise his presence to his friends, or commemorate some savage exploit. Indeed, the beautiful column-like trunk seems to invite the knife, and many a souvenir is carved upon it by the loitering wayfarer. It does not, however, invite the axe of the settler. On the contrary, the beechen woods often remain untouched, while others fall around them— partly because these trees are not usually the indices of the richest soil, but more from the fact that clearing a piece of beech forest is no easy matter. The green logs do not burn so readily as those of the oak, the elm, the maple, or poplar, and hence the necessity of "rolling" them off the ground to be cleared—a serious thing where labour is scarce and dear.

We were riding silently along, when all at once our ears were assailed by a strange noise. It resembled the clapping of a thousand pairs of hands, followed by a whistling sound, as if a strong wind had set suddenly in among the trees. We all knew well enough what it meant, and the simultaneous cry of "pigeons," was followed by half a dozen simultaneous cracks from the guns of the party, and several bluish birds fell to the ground. We had stumbled upon a feeding-place of the passenger-pigeon *(Columba migratoria)*.

Our route was immediately abandoned, and in a few minutes we were in the thick of the flock, cracking away at them both with shot-gun and rifle. It was not too easy, however, to bring them down in any considerable numbers. In following them up we soon strayed from each other, until our party was completely scattered, and nearly two hours elapsed before we got back to the road. Our game-bag, however, made a fine show, and about forty brace were deposited in the waggon. With the anticipation of roast pigeon and "pot-pie," we rode on more cheerily to our night camp. All along the road the pigeons were seen, and occasionally large flocks whirled over our heads under the canopy of the trees. Satiated with the sport, and not caring to waste our ammunition, we did not heed them farther.

In order to give Lanty due time for the duties of the *cuisine,* we halted a little earlier than usual. Our day's march had been a short one, but the excitement and sport of the pigeon-hunt repaid us for the loss of time. Our dinner-supper—for it was a combination of both—was the dish known in America as "pot pie," in which the principal ingredients were the pigeons, some soft flour paste, with a few slices of bacon to give it a flavour. Properly speaking, the "pot pie" is not a pie, but a stew. Ours was excellent, and as our appetites were in a similar condition, a goodly quantity was used up in appeasing them.

Of course the conversation of the evening was the "wild pigeon of America," and the following facts regarding its natural history —although many of them are by no means new—may prove interesting to the reader, as they did to those who listened to the relation of them around our camp-fire.

The "passenger" is less in size than the house pigeon. In the air it looks not unlike the kite, wanting the forked or "swallow" tail. That of the pigeon is cuneiform. Its colour is best described by calling it a nearly uniform slate. In the male the colours are deeper, and the neck-feathers present the same changeable hues of green, gold, and purple-crimson, generally observed in birds of this species. It is only in the woods, and when freshly caught or killed, that these brilliant tints can be seen to perfection. They fade in captivity, and immediately after the bird has been shot. They seem to form part of its life and liberty, and disappear when it is robbed of either. I have often thrust the wild pigeon, freshly killed, into my game-bag, glittering like an opal. I have drawn it forth a few hours after of a dull leaden hue, and altogether unlike the same bird.

As with all birds of this tribe, the female is inferior to the male, both in size and plumage. The eye is less vivid. In the male it is of the most brilliant fiery orange, inclosed in a well-defined circle of red. The eye is in truth its finest feature, and never fails to strike the beholder with admiration.

The most singular fact in the natural history of the "passenger," is their countless numbers. Audubon saw a flock that contained "one billion one hundred and sixteen millions of birds!" Wilson counted, or rather computed, another flock of "two thousand two hundred and thirty millions!" These numbers seem incredible. I have no doubt of their truth. I have no doubt that they are *under* rather than *over* the numbers actually seen by both these naturalists, for both made most liberal allowances in their calculations.

Where do these immense flocks come from?

The wild pigeons breed in all parts of America. Their breeding-places are found as far north as the Hudson's Bay, and they have been seen in the southern forests of Louisiana and Texas. The nests are built upon high trees, and resemble immense rookeries. In Kentucky, one of their breeding-places was forty miles in length, by several in breadth! One hundred nests will often be found upon a single tree, and in each nest there is but one "squab." The eggs are pure white, like those of the common kind, and, like them, they breed several times during the year, but principally when food is plenty. They establish themselves in great "roosts," sometimes for years together, to which each night they return from their distant excursions—hundreds of miles, perhaps; for this is but a short fly for travellers who can pass over a mile in a single minute, and some of whom have even strayed across the Atlantic to England! They, however, as I myself have observed, remain in the same woods where they have been feeding for several days together. I have also noticed that they prefer roosting in the low underwood, even when tall trees are close at hand. If near water, or hanging over a stream, the place is still more to their liking; and in the morning they may be seen alighting on the bank to drink, before taking to their daily occupation.

The great "roosts" and breeding-places are favourite resorts for numerous birds of prey. The small vultures (*Cathartes aura* and *Atratus*), or, as they are called in the west, "turkey buzzard," and "carrion crow," do not confine themselves to carrion alone. They are fond of live "squabs," which they drag out of their nests at pleasure. Numerous hawks and kites prey upon them; and even the great white-headed eagle (*Falco leucocephalus*) may be seen soaring above, and occasionally swooping down for a dainty morsel. On the ground beneath move enemies of a different kind, both biped and quadruped. Fowlers with their guns and long poles; farmers with waggons to carry off the dead birds; and even droves of hogs to devour them. Trees fall under the axe, and huge branches break down by the weight of the birds themselves, killing numbers in their descent. Torches are used—for it is usually a night scene, after the return of the birds from feeding,—pots of burning sulphur, and other engines of destruction. A noisy scene it is. The clapping of a million pair of wings, like the roaring of thunder; the shots; the shouts; men hoarsely calling to each other; women and children screaming their delight; the barking of dogs; the neighing of horses; the "crash" of breaking branches; and the "chuck" of the woodsman's axe, all mingled together.

When the men—saturated with slaughter, and white with ordure—have retired beyond the borders of the roost to rest themselves for the night, their ground is occupied by the prowling wolf and the fox; the raccoon and the cougar; the lynx and the great black bear.

With so many enemies, one would think that the "passengers" would soon be exterminated. Not so. They are too prolific for that. Indeed, were it not for these enemies, they themselves would perish for want of food. Fancy what it takes to feed them! The flock seen by Wilson would require eighteen million bushels of grain every day!—and it, most likely, was only one of many such that at the time were traversing the vast continent of America. Upon what do they feed? it will be asked. Upon the fruits of the great forest—upon the acorns, the nuts of the beech, upon buckwheat, and Indian corn; upon many species of berries, such as the huckleberry *(whortleberry)*, the hackberry *(Celtis crassifolia)*, and the fruit of the holly. In the northern regions, where these are scarce, the berries of the juniper tree *(Juniperus communis)* form the principal food. On the other hand, among the southern plantations, they devour greedily the rice, as well as the nuts of the chestnut-tree and several species of oaks. But their staple food is the beechnut, or "mast," as it is called. Of this the pigeons are fond, and fortunately it exists in great plenty. In the forests of Western America there are vast tracts covered almost entirely with the beech-tree.

As already stated, these beechen forests of America remain almost intact, and so long as they shower down their millions of bushels of "mast," so long will the passenger pigeons flutter in countless numbers amidst their branches.

Their migration is semi-annual; but unlike most other migratory birds, it is far from being regular. Their flight is, in fact, not a periodical migration, but a sort of nomadic existence—food being the object which keeps them in motion and directs their course. The scarcity in one part determines their movement to another. When there is more than the usual fall of snow in the northern regions, vast flocks make their appearance in the middle States, as in Ohio and Kentucky. This may in some measure account for the overcrowded "roosts" which have been occasionally seen, but which are by no means common. You may live in the west for many years without witnessing a scene such as those described by Wilson and Audubon, though once or twice every year you may see pigeons enough to astonish you.

It must not be imagined that the wild pigeons of America are so "tame" as they have been sometimes represented. That is their character only while young at the breeding-places, or at the great roosts when confused by crowding upon each other, and mystified by torchlight.

Far different are they when wandering through the open woods in search of food. It is then both difficult to approach and hard to kill them. Odd birds you may easily reach; you may see them perched upon the branches on all sides of you, and within shot-range; but the *thick* of the flock, somehow or other, always keeps from one to two hundred yards off. The sportsman cannot bring himself to fire at single birds. No. There is a tree near at hand literally black with pigeons. Its branches creak under the weight. What a fine havoc he will make if he can but get near enough! But that is the difficulty; there is no cover, and he must approach as he best can without it. He continues to advance; the birds sit silent, watching his movements. He treads lightly and with caution; he inwardly anathematises the dead leaves and twigs that make a loud rustling under his feet. The birds appear restless; several stretch out their necks as if to spring off.

At length he deems himself fairly within range, and raises his gun to take aim; but this is a signal for the shy game, and before he can draw trigger they are off to another tree!

Some stragglers still remain; and at them he levels his piece and fires. The shot is a random one; for our sportsman, having failed to "cover" the flock, has become irritated and careless, and in all such cases the pigeons fly off with the loss of a few feathers.

The gun is reloaded, and our amateur hunter, seeing the thick flock upon another tree, again endeavours to approach it, but with like success.

When the conversation about the haunts and habits of these birds began to flag, some one called for a "pigeon story." Who could tell a pigeon story? To our surprise the doctor volunteered one, and all gathered around to listen.

"Yes, gentlemen," began the doctor, "I have a pigeon adventure, which occurred to me some years ago. I was then living in Cincinnati, following my respectable calling, when I had the good fortune to set a broken leg for one Colonel P———, a wealthy planter, who lived upon the bank of the river some sixty miles from the city. I made a handsome set of it, and won the colonel's friendship for ever. Shortly after, I was invited to his house, to be present at a great pigeon-hunt which was to come off in the fall. The colonel's plantation stood among beech woods, and he had therefore an annual visitation of the pigeons, and could tell almost to a day when they would appear. The hunt he had arranged for the gratification of his numerous friends.

"As you all know, gentlemen, sixty miles in our western travel is a mere bagatelle; and tired of pills and prescriptions, I flung myself into a boat, and in a few hours arrived at the colonel's stately home. A word or two about this stately home and its proprietor.

"Colonel P——— was a splendid specimen of the backwoods gentleman—you will admit there *are* gentlemen in the backwoods." (Here the doctor glanced good-humouredly, first at our English friend Thompson, and then at the Kentuckian, both of whom answered him with a laugh.) "His house was the type of a backwoods mansion; a wooden structure, both walls and roof. No matter. It has distributed as much hospitality in its time as many a marble palace; that was one of its backwoods' characteristics. It stood, and I hope still stands, upon the north bank of the Ohio— that beautiful stream—'La belle riviere,' as the French colonists, and before their time the Indians, used to call it. It was in the midst of the woods, though around it were a thousand acres of 'clearing,' where you might distinguish fields of golden wheat, and groves of shining maize plants waving aloft their yellow-flower tassels. You might note, too, the broad green leaf of the Nicotian 'weed,' or the bursting pod of the snow-white cotton. In the garden you might observe the sweet potato, the common one, the refreshing tomato, the huge water-melon, cantelopes, and musk melons, with many other delicious vegetables. You could see pods of red and green pepper growing upon trailing plants; and beside them several species of peas and beans—all valuable for the colonel's *cuisine*. There was an orchard, too, of several acres in extent. It was filled with fruit-trees, the finest peaches in the world, and the finest apples—the Newton pippins. Besides, there were luscious pears and plums, and upon the espaliers, vines bearing bushels of sweet grapes. If Colonel P—— lived in the woods, it cannot be said that he was surrounded by a desert.

"There were several substantial log-houses near the main building or mansion. They were the stable—and good horses there were in that stable; the cow-house, for milk cattle; the barn, to hold the wheat and maize-corn; the smoke-house, for curing bacon; a large building for the dry tobacco; a cotton-gin, with its shed of clapboards; bins for the husk fodder, and several smaller structures. In one corner you saw a low-walled erection that reminded you of a kennel, and the rich music that from time to time issued from its apertures would convince you that it *was* a kennel. If you had peeped into it, you would have seen a dozen of as fine stag-hounds as ever lifted a trail. The colonel was somewhat partial to these pets, for he was a 'mighty hunter.' You might see a number of young colts in an adjoining lot; a pet deer, a buffalo-calf, that had been brought from the far prairies, pea-fowl, guinea-hens, turkeys, geese, ducks, and the usual proportion of common fowls. Rail-fences zigzaged off in all directions towards the edge of the woods. Huge trees, dead and divested of their leaves, stood up in the cleared fields. Turkey buzzards and carrion crows might be seen perched upon their grey naked limbs; upon their summit you might observe the great rough-legged falcon; and above all, cutting sharply against the blue sky, the fork-tailed kite sailing gently about."

Here the doctor's auditory interrupted him with a murmur of applause. The doctor was in fine spirits, and in a poetical mood. He continued.

"Such, gentlemen, was the sort of place I had come to visit; and I saw at a glance that I could spend a few days there pleasantly enough—even without the additional attractions of a pigeon-hunt.

"On my arrival I found the party assembled. It consisted of a score and a half of ladies and gentlemen, nearly all young people. The pigeons had not yet made their appearance, but were looked for every hour. The woods had assumed the gorgeous tints of autumn, that loveliest of seasons in the 'far west.' Already the ripe nuts and berries were scattered profusely over the earth offering their annual banquet to God's wild creatures. The 'mast' of the beech-tree, of which the wild pigeon is so fond, was showering down among the dead leaves. It was the very season at which the birds were accustomed to visit the beechen woods that girdled the colonel's plantation. They would no doubt soon appear. With this expectation everything was made ready; each of the gentlemen was provided with a fowling-piece, or rifle if he preferred it; and even some of the ladies insisted upon being armed.

"To render the sport more exciting, our host had established certain regulations. They were as follows:—The gentlemen were divided into two parties, of equal numbers. These were to go in opposite directions, the ladies upon the first day of the hunt accompanying whichever they chose. Upon all succeeding days, however, the case would be different. The ladies were to accompany that party which upon the day previous had bagged the greatest number of birds. The victorious gentlemen, moreover, were endowed with other privileges, which lasted throughout the evening; such as the choice of partners for the dinner-table and the dance.

"I need not tell you, gentlemen, that in these conditions existed powerful motives for exertion. The colonel's guests were the *élite* of western society. Most of the gentlemen were young men or bachelors; and among the ladies there were *belles;* three or four of them rich and beautiful. On my arrival I could perceive signs of incipient flirtations. Attachments had already arisen; and by many it would have been esteemed anything but pleasant to be separated in the manner prescribed. A strong *esprit du corps* was thus established; and, by the time the pigeons arrived, both parties had determined to do their utmost. In fact, I have never known so strong a feeling of rivalry to exist between two parties of amateur sportsmen.

"The pigeons at length arrived. It was a bright sunny morning, and yet the atmosphere was darkened, as the vast flock, a mile in breadth by several in length, passed across the canopy. The sound of their wings resembled a strong wind whistling among tree-tops, or through the rigging of a ship. We saw that they hovered over the woods, and settled among the tall beeches.

"The beginning of the hunt was announced, and we set forth, each party taking the direction allotted to it. With each went a number of ladies, and even some of these were armed with light fowling-pieces, determined that the party of their choice should be the victorious one. After a short ride, we found ourselves fairly 'in the woods,' and in the presence of the birds, and then the cracking commenced.

"In our party we had eight guns, exclusive of the small fowling-pieces (two of these), with which a brace of our heroines were armed, and which, truth compels me to confess, were less dangerous to the pigeons than to ourselves. Some of our guns were double-barrelled shot-guns, others were rifles. You will wonder at rifles being used in such a sport, and yet it is a fact that the gentlemen who carried rifles managed to do more execution than those who were armed with the other species. This arose from the circumstance that they were contented to aim at single birds, and, being good shots, they were almost sure to bring these down. The woods were filled with straggling pigeons. Odd birds were always within rifle range; and thus, instead of wasting their time in endeavouring to approach the great flocks, our riflemen did nothing but load and fire. In this way they soon counted their game by dozens.

"Early in the evening, the pigeons, having filled their crops with the mast, disappeared. They flew off to some distant 'roost.' This of course concluded our sport for the day. We got together and counted our numbers. We had 640 birds. We returned home full of hope; we felt certain that we had won for that day. Our antagonists had arrived before us. They showed us 726 dead pigeons. We were beaten.

"I really cannot explain the chagrin which this defeat occasioned to most of our party. They felt humiliated in the eyes of the ladies, whose company they were to lose on the morrow. To some there was extreme bitterness in the idea; for, as I have already stated, attachments had sprung up, and jealous thoughts were naturally their concomitants. It was quite tantalising, as we parted next morning, to see the galaxy of lovely women ride off with our antagonists, while we sought the woods in the opposite direction, dispirited and in silence.

"We went, however, determined to do our best, and win the ladies for the morrow. A council was held, and each imparted his advice and encouragement; and then we all set to work with shot-gun and rifle.

"On this day an incident occurred that aided our 'count' materially. As you know, gentlemen, the wild pigeons, while feeding, sometimes cover the ground so thickly that they crowd upon each other. They all advance in the same direction, those behind continually rising up and fluttering to the front, so that the surface presents a series of undulations like sea-waves. Frequently the birds alight upon each other's backs, for want of room upon the ground, and a confused mass of winged creatures is seen rolling through the woods. At such times, if the sportsman can only 'head' the flock, he is sure of a good shot. Almost every pellet tells, and dozens may be brought down at a single discharge.

"In my progress through the woods, I had got separated from my companions, when I observed an immense flock approaching me after the manner described. I saw from their plumage that they were young birds, and therefore not likely to be easily alarmed. I drew my horse (I was mounted) behind a tree, and awaited their approach. This I did more from curiosity than any other motive, as, unfortunately I carried a rifle, and could only have killed one or two at the best. The crowd came 'swirling' forward, and when they were within some ten or fifteen paces distant, I fired into their midst. To my surprise, the flock did not take flight, but continued to advance as before, until they were almost among the horse's feet. I could stand it no longer. I drove the spurs deeply, and galloped into their midst, striking right and left as they fluttered up round me. Of course they were soon off; but of those that had been trodden upon by my horse, and others I had knocked down, I counted no less than twenty-seven! Proud of my exploit, I gathered the birds into my bag, and rode in search of my companions.

"Our party on this day numbered over 800 head killed; but, to our surprise and chagrin, our antagonists had beaten us by more than a hundred!

"The gentlemen of 'ours' were wretched. The belles were monopolised by our antagonists; we were scouted, and debarred every privilege.

"It was not to be endured; something must be done. What was to be done? counselled we. If fair means will not answer, we must try the opposite. It was evident that our antagonists were better shots than we.

"The colonel, too, was one of them, and he was sure to kill every time he pulled trigger. The odds were against us; some plan must be devised; some *ruse* must be adopted, and the idea of one had been passing through my mind during the whole of that day. It was this:—I had noticed, what has been just remarked, that, although the pigeons will not allow the sportsman to come within range of a fowling-piece, yet at a distance of little over a hundred yards they neither fear man nor beast. At that distance they sit unconcerned, thousands of them upon a single tree. It struck me that a gun large enough to throw shot among them would be certain of killing hundreds at each discharge; but where was such a gun to be had? As I reflected thus, 'mountain howitzers' came into my mind. I remembered the small mountain howitzers I had seen at Covington. One of these loaded with shot would be the very weapon. I knew there was a battery of them at the Barracks. I knew that a friend of mine commanded the battery. By steamer, should one pass, it was but a few hours to Covington. I proposed sending for a 'mountain howitzer.'

"I need hardly say that my proposal was hailed with a universal welcome on the part of my companions; and without dropping a hint to the other party, it was at once resolved that the design should be carried into execution. It was carried into execution. An 'up-river' boat chanced to pass in the nick of time. A messenger was forthwith despatched to Covington, and before twelve o'clock upon the following day another boat on her down trip brought the howitzer, and we had it secretly landed and conveyed to a place in the woods previously agreed upon. My friend, Captain C———, had sent a 'live corporal' along with it, and we had no difficulty in its management.

"As I had anticipated, it answered our purpose as though it had been made for it. Every shot brought down a shower of dead birds, and after one discharge alone the number obtained was 123! At night our 'game-bag' counted over three thousand birds! We were sure of the ladies for the morrow.

"Before returning home to our certain triumph, however, there were some considerations. To-morrow we should have the ladies in our company; some of the fair creatures would be as good as sure to 'split' upon the howitzer. What was to be done to prevent this?

"We eight had sworn to be staunch to each other. We had taken every precaution; we had only used our 'great gun' when far off, so that its report might not reach the ears of our antagonists; but how about to-morrow? Could we trust our fair companions with a secret? Decidedly not. This was the unanimous conclusion. A new idea now came to our aid. We saw that we might dispense with the howitzer, and still manage to out-count our opponents. We would make a depository of birds in a safe place. There was a squatter's house near by: that would do. So we took the squatter into our council, and left some 1500 birds in his charge, the remainder being deemed sufficient for that day. From the 1500 thus left, we might each day take a few hundred to make up our game-bag just enough to out-number the other party. We did not send home the corporal and his howitzer. We might require him again; so we quartered him upon the squatter.

"On returning home, we found that our opponents had also

made a 'big day's work of it;' but they were beaten by hundreds. The ladies were ours!

"And we kept them until the end of the hunt, to the no little mortification of the gentlemen in the 'minority:' to their surprise, as well; for most of them being crack-shots, and several of us not at all so, they could not comprehend why they were every day beaten so outrageously. We had hundreds to spare, and barrels of the birds were cured for winter use.

"Another thing quite puzzled our opponents, as well as many good people in the neighbourhood. That was the loud reports that had been heard in the woods. Some argued they were thunder, while others declared they must have proceeded from an earthquake. This last seemed the more probable, as the events I am narrating occurred but a few years after the great earthquake in the Mississippi Valley, and people's minds were prepared for such a thing.

"I need not tell you how the knowing ones enjoyed the laugh for several days, and it was not until the colonel's *réunion* was about to break up, that our secret was let out, to the no small chagrin of our opponents, but to the infinite amusement of our host himself, who, although one of the defeated party, often narrates to his friends the story of the 'Hunt with a Howitzer.' "

V E R N E   A T H A N A S

Royal Elk

In some of the stories created for diversion, hunting is the means rather than the end. So let it be with this one. Verne Athanas is a professional writer and an amateur hunter, but there must be occasions when he wishes these activities were in reverse. "Royal Elk" is a diversion, but a most pleasant one, and it offers stout proof that as a hunter, Athanas is not such an amateur.

They rode out in predawn grayness, traveling light with only their rifles and personal gear. The packstring had already gone ahead to set up camp. Ace, the guide, rode alongside David Harbin. "Ride much?"

"Once before," David admitted. "I was about twelve."

"Only way to get to the good huntin'," said Ace. Then quietly, "Get down an' walk ten minutes ever' hour or so."

"Thanks," said David, ready to dismount any time.

Morton Sperling rode as one born to the saddle. His Western hat was wider and taller than Ace's and looked harder used. He wore a sheepskin coat, woolly side in, scratched leather out. He chewed one of his dollar cigars, as cheerful as a berserker in battle. A rugged type, J. Morton Sperling. The story was that he'd left home at nineteen, after a battle with his Old Man, had boomered around as a harvest hand and oil-field roughneck—even as a semi-pro baseball player—until his father had suffered a disabling stroke, and Morton had come home to run the business. Sperling Tool and Steel had prospered since, for Morton Sperling was a big, vital driver. He stood six feet tall and weighed just over 200, and little of it was fat. How he had ever sired a daughter like Karen, David thought he would never know.

They had left the company's DC-3 hulking in the cold wind on the back-country landing strip, the golden ST&S colophon gleaming on either flank; Ace had met them and driven them many more rough miles in a four-wheel-drive station wagon to the lodge where they'd stayed overnight. Now they rode through high elk country, where rocky peaks had at least a nodding acquaintance with the angels, and ice water leaped quickly through its stony stream beds. Ace pulled up, and David dismounted; Ace pointed something out to Morton Sperling, who said, "Yeah. But have you got me a 'Boone' elk lined up?"

"Sure hope so, Mr. Sperling."

"Hope, hell! I'm after a bull to go in the book, this time."

"Well, we'll sure try, Mr. Sperling."

"Sure. . . . Davey, what the hell you doing back there? You're holding up the parade."

"Just stretching my legs a little," said David, wishing then he hadn't said it, because Morton's look made it sound like an excuse. He stood a rawboned six-two and weighed in around 185, which made him look skinnier than he was, but no one besides his mother had gotten away with calling him "Davey" in the last fifteen years or so.

"Well, come on," said Morton Sperling, and David resignedly climbed into the saddle of the strong, good-natured animal. He wore his deer-hunting outfit—red plaid cap, lumber jacket, wool pants and eight-inch boots with two pairs of socks, and glad to have them at this elevation. He didn't look dashing, but he was fairly comfortable—from the saddle up. They halted again, while Ace tested a ford, and David again dismounted, moving stiffly and gingerly, and his legs didn't feel right at all. Morton Sperling turned to give him a long considering look, but said nothing.

Confucius say, David reminded himself, *young man who court boss's daughter got lots more trouble than man who not court boss's daughter. But I didn't know Karen was Morton Sperling's daughter when I met her.*

Ignorance never excuse, said Confucius, or maybe Blackstone. Anyway, would it make any difference?

Yes, it would. I am twenty-six years old, and I have knocked around enough and she is The One. I wish she wasn't his daughter, because I am beginning not to like him very much. Now they are

*getting so far ahead I'm going to have to climb up on this big
damned horse to catch up.*

They rode into the camp in late afternoon. David dismounted
without groaning. He even managed to keep the upper lip stiff as
Morton Sperling swung athletically down, favoring him with
another speculative look. David decided to die just a little bit
before complaining.

Ace came to help unsaddle and said straight-faced, "Remember
once I didn't ride any for about a year, an' when I went back to it
I had to soak that damn saddle in whisky for a week 'fore it quit
hurtin'." David groaned appropriately, and Ace grinned.

There were two small sleeping tents and a larger one which was
cookhouse, dining hall and lounge. There was another guide,
called Clint, and the cook, referred to only as Beargrease. Clint was
twenty years older than Ace, who was David's age, and Beargrease
was ageless, little bigger than a fourteen-year-old boy, brown and
thin and leathery. He limped heavily on one leg, and a brown-
paper cigarette jutted constantly from the corner of his mouth.

The coffee was hot and the dinner hearty, and David gratefully
slid an ache exactly six feet and two inches long into his thick down
sleeping bag, the ache precisely measurable because it extended
from his head to his heels. He was nearly asleep when Morton
Sperling jostled the cot, undressing in the narrow space. Too tired
to be really irritated, David turned his head from the glare of the
electric lantern Morton had switched on. Surely it was no more
than ten minutes later that Beargrease dragged a stick on the canvas
in a horrible ripping sound and called, "Grub's ready. Come an'
eat it, or I throw it away!"

Breakfast was bacon and eggs and hash-brown potatoes and
coffee as authoritative as a good shaking by the scruff of the neck.
Then they were moving out on horseback in the darkness, Morton
and Clint disappearing to one side, David's mount following Ace's
through some means of its own; David feeling as if he had been
dropped twenty feet and landed astraddle a log—a big, rough log.

He was glad to dismount. Ace took a battered lever-action rifle
from his saddle sheath after picketing the horses, and said quietly,
"It'll be about a mile. Make it as quiet as you can."

They moved through the dark loom of scattering timber, stopped
where a rugged outcropping of rock overlooked one of the small
meadows and there waited out the coming of day. Deep gray turned
light gray, and then a touch of violet came, and they could see the

fringing of timber across the glade. Somewhere a squirrel chattered, and a small bird went yeep-yeep-dee and something small skittered briskly among the rocks below them. Far across the basin a purple mountain's bleak shoulder blushed pink and then yellow, and they could see the meadow now, see the bleached grass (a bleached, gray windfall snag) dissolving into it as if in water. Somewhere, distantly to the left, a coarse, screeching yell went up, a wild and savage sound that brought David around, staring.

Ace grinned, his own eyes shining, and he whispered, "Big 'un. That's some old gran'pappy bull elk buglin'. Sit tight, now."

Ace scanned the opposite side of the meadow with a binocular. David checked his rifle's safety lock, then cheeked the weapon and used his telescopic sight to extend his vision. The four-power glass showed depth and detail in shadowed pockets impenetrable to the naked eye.

Then Ace said, in a soft exhalation of sound that didn't carry beyond six feet, "Yonder, through the break; no, a little more left; see it, there?"

Even at that range, through the scope they looked enormous; two cow elk, and then another, calf size; they moved across an arm of grass reaching back into the timber, crossed it in perhaps a dozen strides from shelter to shelter. Cream-bellied, dark-necked, brown-backed, enormous. The calf stopped in the clear area, sampled the meadow grass, tore up a mouthful and looked back. David lowered the rifle.

"No horns," he said, and then at Ace's quick grunt looked back just in time to see the bull cross at a swinging trot, high-shouldered, heavy-rumped, his great crest of antlers poised weightlessly. There wasn't time for anything, really—the bull took the crossing in half a dozen reaching strides, the calf, as he came abreast, capering with an odd, long-shanked, knobby-kneed springing gait alongside. David didn't even get the safety off.

He glanced at Ace, feeling like a fool. Ace gave him a tight little grin and murmured, "That was fast," and lifted the binocular again, swinging past the projecting snag, watching intently.

He said tautly, not lowering the glasses from his eyes. "Get set. There's a little opening—see? Maybe they'll stop, maybe not. Be ready. I guess it maybe 250 to 275. Don't shoot 'less he stops. Don't shoot 'less you're steady on."

David swung himself a bit to the right. He snugged the sling loop high on his left arm, leaned into the rifle, elbows on knees, the cross hairs showing broad and black. He took a breath, felt a tremor coming all through him, waiting with his thumb on the safety.

The first cow walked into his sights as calmly as her barnyard namesake. As she paused, the second one shouldered past, then raised her head to look across, seemingly right into the scope. David felt his whole body seize up in a spasm of non-movement, and then the scope wobbled the whole length of her—past her nose, back past her rump. She moved on, and the calf came shambling, not stopping, and David had to breathe or suffocate, and the air came out of his lungs in a sound like a steam whistle, he was sure.

He took a breath, and another, and the cross hairs wavered, and then the bull was there, standing, and Ace sighed, "Ah'h-h," almost soundlessly, and the scope wavered, wavered, but only across the broad shoulder, now, and he raised the horizontal hair a trifle and took up his squeeze while the scope wavered, wavered, and then the rifle shouted its jubilant roar and rammed his shoulder back.

He lost the bull and the whole sight picture, and he slammed the bolt back, forward, down, leaning into the butt plate, putting his weight against the steadying leather sling, and then he could see the bull, down and kicking. He heard Ace's jubilant whoop in his ear, and the bull made one last convulsive struggle upward and fell back, and suddenly the scope was sweeping in great uncontrollable arcs.

Ace ran like an eager hunting hound, toward a break in the rocky rim which gave rough access to the bowl of the meadow. David got up, feeling weak and shaky.

The closer he got, the bigger the bull became. The massive head was propped atilt by the great curved antlers, four points to the side, the mane thick and shaggy, black-coffee brown; he was big as a horse, lying there, rank as a goat; Ace walked clear around and came back and struck David a rough comradely blow on the shoulder.

"Man," he said, "that's a bull!"

David swallowed and nodded dumbly. Ace looked at him. "First one for you?"

"Yes."

Ace grinned widely and reached behind his hip and brought out a heavy, wickedly curved knife. "Turn around," he said. "This costs you your shirttail."

Not quite comprehending, David turned, and Ace went under his heavy jacket, yanked out his shirttail and haggled it off with the knife. David did not protest, though it was a fine wool shirt, his best heavy hunting shirt. And suddenly, the whole ridiculous ceremony was no more ridiculous than an ancient Sioux's murmured prayer, as he loosed his arrow at a buffalo, "My brother, I am sorry that you die." For the Sioux knew, in his dim pagan way, the unchanging affinity between hunter and quarry. The words perhaps were perfunctory, but the meaning was there, bone-deep—marrow-deep. Not much of a sacrifice, a shirttail, offered in an air more of rough horseplay than propitiation, but welling from the same deep secret and ancient spring.

Then, just as suddenly, Ace was again a lean and whang-tough sometime rancher-farmer-hunting guide, and he said, "Man, I guess we show 'em who brings in fresh liver for supper first!" And the shirttail impaled on an antler tine was just a tag end of hound's-tooth checked wool, and there was the rough and red-handed butcher's work of transforming the great wild carcass into manageable quarters of elk beef.

David put the rifle aside and unsheathed his knife.

The massive quarters hung on the meat pole, and the smell of frying liver and onions was heavy on the downward side of the cook tent when Morton and Clint rode in just before dark. Morton dismounted and walked over to the head, propped at the foot of one of the trees supporting the meat pole.

"Won't make Boone and Crockett," he said.

Ace, who had been rather ostentatiously touching up the hide, turned, half grinning, then stopped grinning and said nothing. He cut a look at Clint, and at David, and then very carefully turned back to his rather pointless, careful scraping. Clint, stolid as an Indian, threw a stirrup across the saddle and started loosening latigos. He looked once at Ace, and David had a feeling that a silent comment passed between them, though neither moved a muscle of his tanned face. Beargrease stuck his head out the cook tent.

"If yer gonna warsh," he said, "y'd better warsh, 'cause the grub's ready to eat."

They ate, and no one spoke, beyond asking for something he couldn't reach. Morton Sperling seemed to be completely untouched by silence, oblivious to mood. He ate heartily, drank three cups of coffee and lighted one of his enormous cigars.

"Good meal," he said perfunctorily.

"Well, yeah," said Beargrease. "I kinda like a mess of fresh liver an' onions m'self."

Ace made a sound that almost wasn't a sound at all, and Morton turned his head slowly, but Ace had his face hidden behind his uptilted tin cup.

David got his rifle rod and cleaning dope and carefully swabbed out and oiled the bore of his rifle. He wiped down all the metal with an oily cloth and cased it. Morton Sperling said carelessly, "Run a rag through mine, will you, Davey? If it's not too much trouble."

"No trouble," said David evenly. He got up, put his own rifle away, walked around the table and got Morton's rifle, within Morton's reach, and took it back to his own seat. He swabbed out the bore—which didn't need cleaning—ran a final dry patch through it, wiped it down carefully with the oiled cloth and put it back where he had gotten it. He heard no thanks.

He did not consider himself entirely a fool. He had known from the moment of the invitation to this trip that Morton Sperling had more than a pleasant outing in mind. As yet he honestly had no inkling what. *So O.K. Confucius say—ah, the hell with it!* And just possibly with J. Morton Sperling and his eight million dollars, or whatever, too. He went back to his chair and sat down.

As they finished breakfast, Morton Sperling said, "Saddle 'em all, Clint. We'll take Ace and Davey along."

David said, "I got my elk, remember?"

"Well, I didn't," said J. Morton Sperling. "With your dumb luck, you might just bird-dog one up for me."

David did not look around, but he felt the rest of them were watching him. "Maybe," he said, keeping it quiet. He finished his coffee. When he did look, no one was looking.

Outside, Morton said. "Where's your gun?"

"In the tent."

"Well, *get* it! You might fall down and break a leg and have to fire a signal shot or something."

"Now there's a thought," said David. He got the rifle and put it in the saddle sheath.

They rode longer this time; the blush-pink tip of the peak was visible before they pulled up. Clint and Morton conferred, low-voiced, to one side. The glory of another high-country sunrise unfolded about them, David absorbing it with only half his senses, resentfully aware of the irritation which he shouldn't really permit to spoil this experience, but still unable to dispel it.

Clint came over. "We're headin' up to the rockslide," he said to Ace. "Give us an hour. You cut on over to Stumphole Meadow and then come on through. You jump anythin' good, why, bring it past close an' slow."

Ace said straight-faced, "Sho. You want it crossin' right or left?" Clint looked at him and said a bad word and went back to lead off through the timber.

They crossed three or four of the small saddle-blanket meadows, the tawny-brown grass smelling like sweet, cured hay in the clean morning air, the aspen leaves riotously yellow and steadily ashimmer. They climbed a long open slope and rode onto a stony shoulder, where Clint pulled up and dismounted.

"I'll shinny on up to the ledge," he said. He took a powerful telescope from a saddlebag, and started up a steep narrow ravine that scarred the flank of the mountain like a cruel and crooked knife slash.

Morton Sperling made no conversation. He moved away, stopped with one foot propped on a stone while he scanned the basin below with a proprietary air. He looked lean, tough and brown; competent enough to be literally lord of all he surveyed here. His four-day beard was as thick and gray as a clipped steelwire brush, but the assurance of his movements put the lie to the gray's being any sign of age.

David took his rifle and walked away at right angles, no more desiring Morton's company than the man did his, apparently. He found a seat on a rock a couple of hundred yards from the horses, with another uptilted for a back rest, and he propped his elbows on his knees and used his rifle scope as a spyglass. Almost directly below, the slope shouldered upward, broke and then fell away; a natural pass lay close before him. There was no really clean approach, however; like the rest of the high basin, the little aspen meadows were interspersed, helter-skelter, all through the timber, thin or thick.

An hour passed. The sun was warm on his shoulders now, and the vista below him was breath-taking in its reach and color. He had sat silent so long that a small striped squirrel of some kind now paid him no more heed than the rock he sat on and went frisking about his business, passing and repassing within a yard.

Bright-eyed but not bushy-tailed, David was thinking, and then he was aware of motion at the corner of his eye, and he turned his head to see Morton Sperling running through the scattered boulders of the rocky shoulder like a halfback breaking into a broken field off left tackle, running for the horses in their little pocket perhaps two hundred yards distant. Then he saw David watching, and he plunged to a halt and gestured violently out and down, and as David followed the pointing arm he saw the bull elk standing, as if he had been there forever, just at the edge of the near timber, as still as an immense statue.

The first impression was of size. His own big four-point bull might have been plumper of body, for this bull was lean, and his great bulk was muscle and not fat; lean, scarred, brutally muscular, and his mane was shaggy and long and black, and his great crown of antlers was almost unbelievable. A royal bull he was, seven points to the side, main beams thick as a man's arm, great tines curved and pointed, shading from near black to yellowed ivory at the tips, the whole great burdensome weight poised on the thick muscular neck as easily, as weightless, as a bird's own feathers.

He was not afraid. Alert he was, with a wild alertness, but he had no fear in him, either of Ace, if it had been he who had driven him here, or of the others, whose scent he was apparently sampling as he raised that immense, breath-stopping head and tasted the air currents eddying over him.

Perhaps it was only seconds. It seemed longer. Then Morton Sperling roared imperiously, "Take him, damn it! Take him! That's a Boone bull if I ever saw one!"

David's boot scuffed slightly as he brought up his knee. His elbows slid into place, and the cross hairs were before his eye, and the great royal bull leaped at him, four times magnified. He could see the eye, brown and yellow, and the ringleted mane and the steel-cable muscles writhing under the scarred shoulder hide as it made its first lunge into motion; and even that was in dignity, more of sensible retreat than fearful flight. He took the trigger all the way back, and the rifle did not fire, for he had not chambered a cartridge; down deep, almost subconsciously, he had known that. He had known he wasn't going to kill that bull because it wasn't his bull; but Morton Sperling was watching, so he made a disgusted shake of the head and slapped the bolt up, and then was truly disgusted with himself and slapped the bolt down, not picking a cartridge out of the magazine with it, just cocking the firing pin with that up-and-down motion. Then he lifted the scope off the great bull and watched, unmoving, as the bull made his powerful lumbering run, across the opening below, over the crest of the little pass, into the straggling timber, past another opening, and then he was gone, as if he had never been, and David pointed the rifle up and pulled the trigger and let the firing pin fall on the empty chamber. He heard Morton Sperling coming, not running but in long, purposeful walking strides, and he stood and turned to face him.

He couldn't read Morton's expression. His face was bleak and tough and showed nothing at all. He looked at David with cold and impersonal eyes, and he reached out and took the rifle out of his hands without request or apology.

He flicked open the bolt and looked into the empty chamber, at the glinting brass-cased cartridges in the magazine. His lips pulled back from his teeth, and he looked at David, grinning that small, impersonal, unmirthful wolf's grin. He tossed the rifle back to him.

"Buck fever," he said.

"No," said David. "No, it wasn't buck fever."

"Then what the hell was it?" demanded Morton Sperling.

"He wasn't mine," said David.

"What the hell difference does that make? We've got two elk licenses—we get two bull elk to fill 'em—nobody knows the difference."

"I'd know," said David.

Morton Sperling stared at him. Clint came down out of the end of the slashed gully in a scramble and a rattling of rocks, half running, half breathless. "Didn't you get a shot at him?"

"No," said Morton Sperling. Then he wheeled away from David. He said to Clint, "What do you think?"

Clint's observant eye took in Morton's rifle still in its saddle scabbard, flicked to David and back and Clint said neutrally, "No tellin'. He might run half a mile—or twenty."

"O.K., let's go." Sperling swung away and said without looking around, "You can tell Ace to go on back to camp."

Ace came finally, riding the royal bull's track. He came to where it had stopped, read the lunge, the run—in its tracks as plain as print—and then he came on. "Nobody got a shot at him?"

"No," said David. "They went on after it. Said we could go on back to camp."

"Sho," said Ace without expression.

Beargrease came out, saw they carried nothing they hadn't

carried out that morning and said, "Hell of a pair of hunters you are," and went back into his tent.

David helped Ace unsaddle. Once Ace said very casually, "You work for him?" and David, knowing who, said, "That's right."

"Hard man to work for?"

David considered only a moment. "No," he said honestly. "He hasn't been." He wondered, during a short silence, whether Ace was going to pursue the matter, then decided he wasn't.

Clint and Morton came in after dark, Morton grinning wolfishly around his cigar, the head and cape of the royal elk leaving Clint precious little saddle room. Morton, as expansive as a wealthy sardine in his own private can, broke out a bottle of top-notch whisky and bought everybody a drink; he sat at the table and savored his drink and his cigar and his triumph while Clint told of their long careful stalk and a masterful shot and a clean kill; even Beargrease pushed his pots and pans to the back of the stove to listen.

David went outside when the story was finished and the grub was being reheated. The great head was swung to the meat pole so that it seemed to look down at him, and he raised his tin cup and toasted it silently with the last of the excellent whisky. And maybe it was the whisky on an empty stomach, but he thought of untimely death—and decided that a physical death was no worse than the death of an ideal. He thought of the brutal shocking death by bullet—and thought it was no worse than the nibbling away, the sloughing off of strengths and wisdoms and powers. There is no place for the wild ones to grow old and die in ease and comfort and dignity. The bullet was more merciful than time. For he had died in strength, brought down only by great strength. He had not died in weakness, one cruel winter soon, his proud antlers fallen, foundered in some drift, waiting weak and without pride while the circling coyote plucked up the courage to come near enough to tear at the faint life pulsing just under slack, starved hide.

And that was a neat bit of rationalizing, he told himself, as Morton Sperling came out of the tent and toward him. David started to turn away, and Morton said, "David," and he turned back. Morton came close in the darkness and said, "You think I'm the biggest slob in Christendom, don't you?"

"Since you brought it up," said David quietly, "yes."

"All right, then, I'll apologize for that."

"Don't bother."

Morton Sperling snapped on the electric lantern he was carrying, sent the strong beam up to spotlight the enormous head. He said quietly, "I've been after this old bull a good long while now. I think I've earned him."

"Fine," said David. "I'm glad you got him." Morton Sperling snapped off the light, and darkness swooped back on them—stark blackness to their unadjusted eyes.

Out of that blackness Morton said, "I suppose you're thinking of quitting."

"I am quitting. My letter of resignation will be on your desk the first morning you get back."

"And how about Karen?"

"I'm going to marry her, if she'll have me. If she won't—because of you—well, that's just too bad." He was glad of the thick blackness then because he wasn't sure he could keep misery out of his face under Morton's close scrutiny.

There was a short silence, and then Morton Sperling said, "No. You're not quitting. Consider the letter torn up before I see it."

"That won't change it. I said it, and you heard it. That's all there is to it."

Morton snapped on the light, pointing it at the ground, so that its bounced light illuminated their faces. He looked tough, but there was another expression on his face too.

"No. I put you over the jumps. I didn't do it for fun. I had to know. I have no son, David. I've only the one daughter. And I'm just you-know-what enough to make sure that she gets the man she deserves, if I had to break my back or yours in the test. Maybe I came pretty close to doing both. But I beg you most humbly to give me a chance to prove that I'm not what you think I am. That's asking a lot, and I know it'll take time. But I won't accept your resignation, not until you've seen Karen, and not till you've had time to think it over."

David said carefully, "Suppose I'd shot that elk when you yelled at me?"

"Why," said Morton Sperling gently, "then I would very likely have accepted your resignation." He smiled faintly. "You don't really think I'm such a stupid you-know-what as to leave my rifle on the saddle like that, do you?"

David said, "You went to a hell of a lot of trouble."

"It's worth a lot of trouble to find out some things." Morton stood, looking at him steadily. "So now I'll get down on my knees and bark like a fox if that's what it takes. But you are not getting away from me."

The mental picture of J. Morton Sperling down on his knees barking like a fox almost fractured David. Despite himself, he grinned.

Morton Sperling grinned back, and it was like a granite boulder cracking.

"O.K.," said David suddenly. "O.K. I didn't want to quit. But you made such an obnoxious you-know-what of yourself that I couldn't have lived with myself if I didn't."

Strangely, Morton Sperling let out a long sighing breath. "Son," he said, "I think you and I will get along all right. Now let's get the hell out of this cold. It'll take me five years to get back in the good graces of Clint and Ace, likely. Come on, I don't dare go in there without you. Old Beargrease would likely poison me."

"Sure," said David. "Right with you."

Together they walked to the tent, glowing with light and warmth.

RAY P. HOLLAND

Hungarian Partridge and Prairie Chicken

The author of *Nip And Tuck* is not as well known today as he was to the last generation, to whom he was mentor and guide in many phases of the sport, but his books occupy a handy place on many a shooter's shelf. Holland was one of the few outdoor writers who could weave painless instruction into his stories. He had the rare faculty of taking his readers with him into the field.

Few dogs were as traveled as Nip and Tuck. Aside from the many trips north, south, east and west they made after the various game birds native to this country, they both went to Saskatchewan with me, where the game was prairie chickens of two species—pinnated and sharp-tailed grouse—and Hungarian partridge. In fact, Nip made this trip three times. Poor old Tuck didn't fit in; so he went only the first time.

On that first trip I had great fun baiting the train crew and amusing the passengers. At division points the train would stop twenty minutes. I made it a point to be in the baggage car, ready to take the dogs out the minute the train stopped. They were such a good-looking pair of pointers that they attracted a great deal of attention. Both were under such perfect control that I was able to put on a show at every stop where there was any room for them to run. Anyone who has made the trip knows that at most stops there is plenty of room and little else.

When the big Canadian National transcontinental train came to a stop, I would be ready to come down the steps of the baggage car with the two dogs on a split leash. They were so full of go that they would actually drag me along the platform. As soon as I got a little way in front of the engine and at the edge of the crowd I would unsnap them and motion them on. The way they left there would have pleased the heart of any field-trial fan. If it was open prairie, I would let them race two hundred yards before I would whistle them back. I couldn't do this where there were woods, for fear Tuck might go hunting and leave me stranded.

Every new train crew would warn me not to turn the dogs loose, for fear I would either lose them or have to remain while the train went ahead. I will admit that I was a little nervous at times, when the spruce forest was close, but I had no trouble and a lot of fun. One afternoon, however, I got a good scare. I had turned them loose, and they had raced down a long grass-covered embankment and out across a big flat.

It was about four o'clock in the afternoon on the last lap home. The next morning we would be in Montreal. About a hundred yards from the station out on this flat was a small red building, probably a pump house belonging to the railroad. I had cast the dogs out and whistled them back twice, and time was about up. On what was to be the last run, Tuck cut over and disappeared behind this building. I waited long enough for him to show and then gave the whistle for them to come in. Nip came racing in, but Tuck couldn't hear me. I whistled again, and again, but no Tuck.

It looked as if I was going to spend the night in this God-forsaken place where there was nothing but the railroad property and a shack or two. I called Tuck by name and kept on whistling. To help matters, the engine-man called to me that I had better get him in, because time was about up. I knew Tuck was behind that house. I didn't believe he could have gone on to the woods, keeping the house in line with me so I couldn't see him.

"Have I time to run out there and back?" I asked the engineer.

"Nope," he replied. "Time's almost up."

Just then I saw Tuck cautiously peeking around the corner of the building.

"Come in here to me!" I shouted, and as though he had heard me for the first time he jumped into a run and came right up to me to have the leash snapped on his collar.

I had looked forward with a good deal of anticipation to taking these dogs to the prairies. Here would be a country where they could really run. Tuck would be in his element and so would Nip, for that matter, as I had been reliably informed that we could expect to fly fifty coveys of partridges in a day. Shedd and I discussed the prospects of the two dogs on the way out, and we both voted that Tuck would probably win any medals we might have to bestow.

I had heard from friends that no dog could handle Hungarians without a great deal of experience, but I discounted this, and I still discount it. A dog with a choke-bore nose and brains in his head can handle them. Nip and Tuck would have handled them on their first trip except for one thing: namely, the fact that they were both retrievers.

These partridges, which lie so tight in England, have changed their habits since coming to the New World. Probably due to scant cover, they usually run like ostriches. I say "usually," for once in a great while a covey scattered and lay well that first year. Two years later, with heavy ground cover, they lay much better.

The pair would cut out across the stubble, and bang! they would nail a covey of partridges. Shedd and I would start toward them, and as we neared the dogs we would see partridge heads start coming up out of the stubble and then the whole covey would move off at double-quick time. Well, anybody could guess what my shot-breaking pointers did then. They undoubtedly said to themselves or to each other, "It's a whole covey of cripples! Come on! Let's go!"

One dog or the other would bust every covey they found before we could get to them. They would not chase. They were both perfectly steady to wing. But to see that flock of birds running away from them was more than either dog could stand. Tuck never did learn to take it.

The sharp-tailed grouse were just as hard to handle as the Huns. We usually found them in the small clumps of willows around old buffalo wallows. Often we would see them from the car. There was little or no cover in many of these clumps, and the chickens would be running around under the brush like so many domestic fowl. And Tuck knew exactly what to do where domestic fowl were under consideration.

Nip and I worked out a little plan of our own for these Huns, and it was very successful. In fact, the next year I was shooting one afternoon with Charlie Newberry, and after Nip had done his stuff to my complete satisfaction Charlie said it was the best and most unusual piece of dog work he had ever seen.

One of the first things I had taught the dogs when they were little was to heel, and I had kept them right up to snuff in this most important command. There is nothing easier than to teach a dog to walk behind you, or heel. Simply take him on leash and carry a light switch in your right hand. Every time the puppy's nose comes up even with your knee, switch him on the nose and say "Heel!" He has to come along because you are leading him. If he tries to pass you, he hears the same command each time and gets switched on the nose. In a remarkably short time a green puppy can be taught to follow along behind you.

This afternoon Charlie Newberry and I were hunting a big stretch of golden stubble on foot. Nip quickly had a covey nailed, and we started for him. Now, these partridge would often lie well enough for the dog; but when the gunners got within long shoot-ing distance from the dog, the birds would start to run. As they were usually from twenty-five to thirty yards ahead of the dog, the gun didn't have a chance if the dog broke. If the dog followed slowly, the chances were still bad.

When we got within fifty yards of Nip, I saw him start to draw ahead carefully, and I knew the birds were moving. Just loud enough for him to hear me I said, "Heel, boy!"

All the tenseness of the pointing dog left Nip. He crouched low and then slipped back to me, taking up his position almost on my heels. Along we walked, Nip watching around the side of my leg, waiting for the birds to jump. We got to within thirty yards before they took the air, and Nip had the nearest dead bird back to me before it seemed possible. Furthermore, he knew how many birds were down and where they were, and he didn't quit until we had put three partridges in the bag.

We developed this system, which is different from anything I know of in ordinary bird-dog practice, and it proved to be death on Huns. I doubt if I could have called Nip off his point. I knew from experience that he could not be called off pheasants. But here was something different for his canine mind to fathom. I wasn't calling him away. He knew that I knew he had birds. I gave him a command that he had been obeying almost all his life, and he knew that I was going to shoot some of the birds for him to bring in. Therefore, being his Boss, I must be right, and back behind me he could come. Then he would walk as if on eggs until the guns popped.

It is remarkably easy to teach a dog to do a certain thing if you can get him to understand you. Most dogs want to please their masters, but few masters have the patience and the ability to train a dog.

Charlie Newberry has a beautiful setter. The dog retrieved perfectly so long as his birds were dead. If the bird had any life in it, this dog refused to touch it. Charlie said several good trainers had tried to teach this dog to retrieve a live bird, without success. There was nothing to lose if I failed; so I thought I would have a try.

Taking a winged bird, I called the setter to me and showed him the bird. I got down on my knees by him and kept turning the bird loose and grabbing it before it could run out of my reach. This was a lot of fun, and the setter watched the performance with great interest. In less than five minutes he was all excited. Not only was he following the bird with his eyes, but he was dancing around daring me to miss it once. Then I grabbed at the bird and purposely missed it. Quicker than a flash he had it and handed it to me as much as to say: "Go on with the game. This is a lot of fun."

We played a while longer, and he never failed to grab the bird the minute he saw it had gotten away from me. Later Charlie told me that this dog never gave him any more trouble. He brought in the cripples just as nicely as he brought in the dead ones.

Harry Felt, with whom we all hunted in Saskatchewan, had a little setter bitch that knew the Huns from the ground up. She and Nip made a good team. This little Llewellin had her own methods, which were not at all orthodox. She would circle a clump of willows wide around the outside. If she smelled birds, she would stop and stand out in the stubble, wagging her tail. That usually meant "shove up the safeties." She had learned that she could not go up and nail these birds down; she knew they would flush, and this was her method of getting the best of them.

Tuck's method was the same one that he started out with, and I finally had to give him up. I know of nothing more discouraging than to have a beautiful bird dog pull up on game with all the style in the world and then jump in on the game before you can get near him. It is bad enough with a pup; but when an old dog does it, you are tempted to kill him. When it so happens that you think about as much of this particular dog as you do of your right hand, it certainly is bad for your liver.

I decided that maybe he would listen to me when I yelled "Whoa!" if I could get him tired enough. Instead of spelling him off with other dogs I kept him going from early in the morning, right straight through. I certainly gave him a day of it without any success. I killed a good number of his birds—when he flushed them, they frequently came my way—but I didn't get him down where I could handle him. He was having lots of fun, anyway. Along about three o'clock he brought me a nice green-headed mallard that he had found in the stubble. Someone had shot the bird that morning and had been unable to find it.

Hungarians, like the other upland game birds, handle better in the mornings and evenings than they do in the middle of the day. They are out feeding at that time, and the dog can pick up the scent more easily. So about four o'clock I put Tuck down for a final fling. He had been at it pretty hard all day, and I felt that surely now he was tired enough to mind me when I called to him, even if he did see a field full of bobbing heads running through the stubble.

I saw the old boy throw up his head into the wind and swing up toward a "clump," as the patches of willow growth are called. Before he reached the willows he froze solid, as stylish a point as anyone ever saw. He was about 150 yards from me. I started for him; and when I got to where I thought he could hear me I began cautioning him in a low voice. He held perfectly until I got within about thirty yards of him. Then he exploded, and like a flash he was in the clump and chickens and Huns were boiling out. If there was one bird in that clump, there were forty.

After he was sure they were all out, he swung around by me just to reassure me it was nothing serious and that he would soon have another covey. He raced off through the stubble, and as I watched him I could not help but marvel at his stamina. Then I noticed he was not running with his usual stride. I saw him stagger. He went down, got up and went down again.

I got to him as soon as I could, and sat down in the stubble and Russian thistles alongside him. For a minute I was afraid he was done for, but after a little rest he wanted to go on and finish the day. Instead I put my gun through the back of my hunting coat and, picking the old fellow up, I carried him back to the car.

It was almost a two-mile hike; and when I put the big thick-head down, instead of jumping in he dashed around the car and took off across the stubble, bent on finding more birds in spite of me. Of such stuff are good dogs made.

SAXTON POPE

Grizzly Bear

The shade of Robin Hood now stalks the forests of a score of states, for hunting with the bow and arrow has been accepted with enthusiasm by a legion of hunters during the past ten years. But most of the new devotees of the long bow are satisfied to loose their shafts at game that is not apt to bite back. Saxton Pope, who substituted the bow for the rifle in another generation, was primarily interested in the killing power of his arrow on dangerous game. He has proved, at least to his own satisfaction, that a broadhead arrow, accurately and forcefully directed, has suitable lethal powers. Occasionally, not being completely foolhardy, he had a rifleman near, just in case he found his nerves impaired the accuracy of the shaft. It is a matter of record that even the rifleman behind him was occasionally troubled by nerves. Pope found the arrow to be effective on most African game, but this story shows what it can do on our own big carnivore—the grizzly.

The very idea of shooting grizzly bears with the bow and arrow strikes most people as so absurd that they laugh at the mention of it. The mental picture of the puny little archery implements of their childhood opposed to that of the largest and most fearsome beast of the Western world produces merriment and incredulity.

Because it seemed so impossible, I presume, this added to our desire to accomplish it.

Ever since we began hunting with the bow, we had talked of shooting grizzlies. We thought of an Alaskan trip as a remotely attainable adventure, and planned murderous arrows of various ingenious spring devices to increase their cutting qualities. We estimated the power of formidable bows necessary to pierce the hides of these monsters. In fact, it was the acme of our hunting desires.

We read the biography of John Capen Adams and his adventures with the California grizzlies, and Roosevelt's admirable descriptions of these animals. They filled out our dreams with detail. And after killing black bears we needed only the opportunity to make our wish become an exploit.

The opportunity to do this arrived unexpectedly, as many opportunities seem to, when the want and the preparedness coincide.

The California Academy of Sciences has in its museum in Golden Gate Park, San Francisco, a collection of very fine animal habitat groups, among which are deer, antelope, mountain sheep, cougars, and brown bear. While an elk group was being installed, it happened that the taxidermist, Mr. Paul Fair, said to me that the next and final setting would be one of grizzly bears. In surprise, I asked him if it were not a fact that the California grizzly was extinct. He said this was true, but the silver-tip bear of Wyoming was a grizzly and its range extended westward to the Sierra Nevada Mountains; so it could properly be classified as a Pacific Coast variety. He cited Professor Merriam's monograph on the classification of grizzlies to prove his statements. He also informed me that permit might be obtained from Washington to secure these specimens in Yellowstone National Park.

Immediately I perceived an opportunity and interviewed Dr. Barton Everman, curator of the museum, concerning the feasibility of offering our services in taking these bears at no expense to the academy. Incidentally, we proposed to shoot them with the bow and arrow, and thereby answer a moot question in anthropology. The proposition appealed to him, and he wrote to Washington for a permit to secure specimens in this National Park, stating that the bow and arrow would be used. I insisted upon this latter stipulation, so that there should be no misunderstanding if, in the future, any objection was raised to this method of hunting.

In a very short time permit was given to the academy, and we started our preparations for the expedition. This was late in the fall of 1919, and bear were at their best in the spring, just after hibernation; so we had ample time.

It was planned that Mr. Compton, Mr. Young, and I should be the hunters, and such other assistance would be obtained as seemed necessary. We began reviewing our experience and formulating the principles of the campaign.

Our weapons we now considered adequate in the light of our contact with black bears. We had found that our bows were as strong as we could handle, and ample to drive a good arrow through a horse, a fact which we had demonstrated upon the carcasses of recently dead animals.

But we decided to add to the length of our arrowheads, and use tempered instead of soft steel as heretofore. We took particular pains to have them perfect in every detail.

Then we undertook the study of the anatomy of bears and the location and size of their vital organs. In the work of William Wright on the grizzly, we found valuable data concerning the habits and nature of these animals.

In spite of the reputation of this bear for ferocity and tenacity of life, we felt that, after all, he was only made of flesh and blood, and our arrows were capable of solving the problem.

We also began preparing ourselves for the contest. Although habitually in good physical condition, we undertook special training for the big event. By running, the use of dumbbells and other gymnastic practices, we strengthened our muscles and increased our endurance. Our field shooting was also directed toward rapid delivery and the quick judgment of distances on level, uphill, and falling ground. In fact, we planned to leave no factor for success untried.

My brother, G. D. Pope, of Detroit, being a hunter of big game with the gun, was invited to join the party, and his advice was asked concerning a reliable guide. He gladly consented to come with us and share the expenses. At the same time he suggested Ned Frost, of Cody, Wyoming, as the most experienced hunter of grizzly bears in America.

About this time one of my professional friends visited the Smithsonian Institution at Washington, where he met a member of the staff, who inquired if he knew Doctor Pope, of San Francisco, a man that was contemplating shooting grizzlies with the bow and arrow. The doctor replied that he did, whereat the sage laughed and said that the feat was impossible, most dangerous and foolhardy; it could not be done. We fully appreciated the danger involved—therein lay some of the zest. But we also knew that even should we succeed in killing them in Yellowstone Park, the glory would be sullied by the popular belief that all park bears are hotel pets, live upon garbage, and that it was a cruel shame to torment them with arrows.

So in my early correspondence with Frost, I assured him that we did not want to shoot any tame bears and that we would not consider the trip at all if this were necessary. He assured us that this was not necessary, and reminded us that Yellowstone Park was fifty miles wide by sixty miles long, and that some of the highest portions of the Rocky Mountains lay in it. The animals in this preserve, he said, were far from tame and the bears were divided into two distinct groups, one mostly composed of black and brown with a few inferior specimens of grizzlies that frequent the dumps back of the camps and hotels, and another group of bears that never came near civilization, but lived entirely up in the rugged mountains and were as dangerous and wary as those in Alaska or any other wild country. These bears wander outside the park and furnish hunting material throughout the neighboring state. He promised to put us in communication with grizzlies that were as unspoiled and unafraid as those first seen by Lewis and Clarke in their early explorations.

After explaining the purposes of our trip and the use of the bow, Ned Frost agreed that it was a real sporting proposition and took up the plan with enthusiasm. I sent him a sample arrow we used in hunting, and his letter in reply I take the liberty of printing. It is typical of the frontier spirit and comes, not only from the foremost grizzly hunter of all times, but discloses the man's bigness of heart:

My dear Doctor:

Your letter of the 18th was received a day or so ago, and last night I received "Good Medicine" [a hunting arrow] on the evening train, and I feel better away down deep about this hunt after a good examination of this little Grizzy Tickler than I have at any time before. I have, by mistake, let it simmer out in a quiet way that I was going to see what a grizzly would really do if he had a few sticks stuck in his innerds, and my friends have been giving the Mrs. and me a regular line of farewell parties. Really, I think it has been a splendid paying thing to do; pork chops are high, you know, and I really feel I am off to the good about nine dollars and six bits worth of bacon and flour right now on this deal. Maybe I'll be in debt to you before green-grass if I don't look out.

Well, anyway, here is hoping we will all live through it and have a dandy time. Don't worry about coming to blows with the bear; I have noticed from long experience that it is not the times that you think a bear is going to give you trouble that it happens, but always when least expected. I have trailed wounded grizzlies time and time again, and was more or less worried all the while, but never had one turn on me yet. Then, too, I have had about three experiences with them that made my hair stand straight up, and when it finally settled, it had more *frost* in it than ever before; and let me add right here, that one of the worst places I ever got into was when I had sixteen of the best bear dogs that were ever gotten together, I believe, after an old she-grizzly, and I was like you, thought they would hold the bear's attention. *But,* don't let any notion like this get you into trouble. Now, I am not running down dogs as a means of getting bear; I love them and would now have a good pack if it was possible to run them in the game fields of this state, but you don't want to think that they can handle a grizzly like they do a black bear. In fact, I would place no value on them whatsoever as a safeguard in case a grizzly got on the pack, and I am speaking from experience, mind you. No, a good little shepherd would do more than a dozen regular bear dogs, but there is only about one little shepherd like I speak of in a lifetime.

If you can use the bow from horseback, here is a safe proposition, and I believe a practical one, too. But I don't feel that there is really so much danger in the game after all, as it is only once in a great while that any bear will go up against the human animal, and then is most likely to be when you are not expecting it at all. Don't worry about it. What I am thinking about most is to get the opportunity to get the first arrow into some good big worthy old boy that will be a credit to the expedition.

There are lots of grizzlies in the park all right, and some of them are not very wild, but if you get out away from the hotels a few miles, they are not going to come up and present their broadsides to you at thirty yards. So, as I say, I am thinking mostly about the chances of getting the opportunities. I don't know, of course, just how close you can place your arrows at thirty yards, and it is getting the first hole into them that I am most interested in now. I feel that we ought to get some good chances, as I have seen so many bear in the park; but, of course, have never hunted them and don't know just how keen they will be when it comes right down to getting their hides. There are some scattered all over the park that will rob a camp at night, and some of them will even put up a fight for it, but most of them will beat it as soon as one gets after them.

It would be impossible, I believe, to keep dogs still while watching a bait, as they would get the scent of any approaching bear, and then you would not be able to keep them quiet, and they would most likely scare the bear out of the country. I can rustle a few dogs to take along if you want them, and pretty good dogs, too; but I am not strong for them myself, only in this way, to put them on the trail of a bear and take a good horse apiece, so that we could get up to the chase and have a chance to land on him. This might be a good thing to try if all others failed.

I know how you feel about killing clean with the bow and not having any shooting, and I can assure you that I would let 'em get just as close as you want them, and not feel any concern about their getting the best of anybody, and you would have a chance to use the bow well in this case; but I am more prone to think they will beat it off with a lot of your perfectly good arrows than anything else.

Yours truly,
Ned Frost

It was apparent from the first that dogs were of little use in taking grizzly. It would be necessary to shoot from blinds set conveniently near bait. Frost assured us that bears of this variety, when just out of hibernation and lean, would run out of the country if chased by a pack of dogs, and incidentally kill all that they could catch. In the fall of the year, when the bears are fat, they refuse to run, but wade through the pack, which is unable to keep him from attacking the hunter.

As an example of this, he related an instance where he started a grizzly with eight or ten Russian bear hounds, and chased the beast about thirty miles. As he followed on horseback, he found one after the other of his dogs torn to pieces, disemboweled, and dismembered. At last, he came upon the bear at bay in deep snow, against a high cliff. Only two of his hounds were left, and one of these had a broken leg. Mad with vengeance, Frost shot the grizzly. It charged him at forty yards. In quick succession he fired five bullets in the oncoming bear, seemingly with no effect. Up to his waist in the snow, he was unable to avoid its rush. It came on and fell dead on his chest, with the faithful hound hanging to it in a desperate effort to save his master.

This is one of the three or four maulings that Ned has received in his hunting experiences, which, he says, "have added frost to my golden locks." The dog became a cherished pet in the family for many years.

Frost killed his first bear when fourteen years of age, and has added nearly five hundred to this number since that time.

It is characteristic of the grizzly that he will charge upon the slightest provocation, and that nothing will turn him aside from his purpose. Later we found this particularly true where the female with cubs is concerned.

Instances of this are too well known to recount, but one coming under our own experience was related to me by Tom Murphy, the bear hunter of California.

In early days in Humboldt County, there lived an old settler named Pete Bluford, who was a squaw man. He shot a female grizzly with cubs within a quarter of a mile of what are now the town limits of Blocksburg. The beast charged and struck him to the ground. At the same time she ripped open the man's abdomen. Bluford dropped under a fallen tree, where the bear repeatedly assaulted him, tearing at his body. By rolling back and forth as the grizzly leaped over the log to reach him from the other side, he escaped further injury. Worried by the hunter's dog, she finally ceased her efforts and wandered off. The man was able to reach home in spite of a large open wound in his abdomen, with protruding intestines. This was roughly sewed together by his friend, Beany Powell. He recovered from the experience and lived many years with the Indians of that locality. As an example of Western humor, it is related that Beany Powell, when sewing up the wound with twine and a sack needle, found a large lump of fat protruding from the incision, of which he was unable to dispose; so he cut it off, tried out the grease in the frying-pan and used it to grease his boots.

Old Bluford became a character in the country. He was, in fact, what is colloquially known as "an old poison oaker." This is an individual who sinks so low in the scale of civilization that he lives out in the backwoods or poison oak brush and becomes animal in type. His hair grew to his shoulders, his beard was unkempt, his finger nails were as long as claws and filthy with dirt. Rags of unknown antiquity partially covered his limbs, vermin infested his body and he stayed with the most degraded remnants of the Indians.

One cold winter they found him dead in his dilapidated cabin. He lay on the dirt floor, his ragged coat over his face, his hands beneath his head, and two house cats lay frozen, one beneath each arm. These old pioneers were strange people and died strange deaths.

In our plans to capture grizzlies we took into consideration the proclivity of this beast to attack. We knew his speed was tremendous. He is able to catch a horse or a dog on the run. Therefore, it is useless for a man to try to run away from him. There is no such thing as being able to climb a tree if the animal is at close quarters. Adams has shown that it is a mistake to attempt it. One only stretches himself out inviting evisceration in the effort.

We decided if cornered either to dodge or to lie flat and feign death. So we practiced dodging, our running being more for the purpose of gaining endurance and to follow the bear if necessary.

Ishi, the Yana Indian, said that grizzlies were to be overcome with arrows and if they charged, they were to be met with the spear and fire. So we constructed spears having well-tempered blades more than a foot in length set upon heavy iron tubing and riveted to strong ash handles six feet in length. Back of the blade we fashioned quick lighting torches of cotton waste saturated with turpentine. These could be ignited by jerking a lanyard fastened to a spring faced with sandpaper. The spring rested on the ends of several matches. It was an ingenious and reliable device.

The Esquimaux used a long spear in hunting the polar bear. It was ten or twelve feet in length. After being shot with an arrow, if the bear charged, they rested the butt of the spear on the ground, lowered the point and let the bear impale himself on it.

When the time came to use our weapons, Ned Frost dissuaded us from the attempt. He said that he once owned a pet grizzly and kept it fast with a long chain in the back yard. This bear was so quick that it could lie in its kennel, apparently asleep, and if a chicken passed within proper distance, with incredible quickness she reached out a paw and seized the chicken without the slightest semblance of effort. And when at play, the boys tried to stick the bear with a pitchfork, she would parry the thrusts and protect herself like a boxer. It was impossible to touch her.

The fire, Frost thought, might serve at night, but in the daylight it would lose its effect. So he insisted that he would carry a gun to be used in case of attack. On our part, we stipulated that he was to resort to it only to prevent disaster and protested that such an exigency must be looked upon by us as a complete failure of our plans. We knew we could not stop the mad rush of a bear with our arrows, but we hoped to kill at least one by this means and compromise on the rest if necessary.

Indians, besides employing the spear, poisoned arrows, and fire, also used protected positions, or shot from horseback. We scorned to shoot from a tree and were told that few horses could be ridden close enough, or fast enough, to get within bowshot of a grizzly.

Inquiry among those qualified to know led to the estimate of the number of all bears in the Park to be between five hundred and one thousand. Considering that there are some three thousand square miles of land, that there were nearly sixty thousand elk, besides hundreds of bison, antelope, mountain sheep, and similar animals, this does not seem improbable. I am aware that recent statements are to the effect that there were only forty grizzlies there. This is palpably an underestimate, and probably takes into account only those that frequent the dumps. Frost believes that there are several hundred grizzlies in the Park, many of which range out in the adjacent country. So we felt no fear of decimating their ranks, and had every hope of seeing many. In fact, their number has so increased in recent years that they have become a menace and require killing off.

During the past five years four persons have either been mauled or killed by grizzlies in Yellowstone. One of these was a teamster by the name of Jack Walsh. He was sleeping under his wagon at Cold Springs when a large bear seized him by the arm, dragged him forth and ripped open his abdomen. Walsh died of blood poison and peritonitis a few days later.

Frost himself was attacked. He was conducting a party of tourists through the preserve and had just been explaining to them around the campfire that there was no danger of bears. He slept in the tent with a horse wrangler by the name of Phonograph Jones. In the middle of the night a huge grizzly entered his tent and stepped on the head of Jones, peeling the skin off his face by the rough pressure of his paw. The man waked with a yell, whereupon the bear clawed out his lower ribs. The cry roused Frost, who having no firearms, hurled his pillow at the bear.

With a roar, the grizzly leaped upon Ned, who dived into his sleeping bag. The animal grasped him by the thighs, and dragged him from the tent out into the forest, sleeping bag and all. As he carried off his victim, he shook him from side to side as a dog shakes a rat. Frost felt the great teeth settle down on his thigh bones and expected momentarily to have them crushed in the powerful jaws. In a thicket of jack pines over a hundred yards from camp, the bear shook him so violently that the muscles of the man's thighs tore out and he was hurled free from the bag. He landed half-naked in the undergrowth several yards away.

While the frenzied bear still worried the bedding, Frost dragged himself to a near-by pine and pulled himself up in its branches by the strength of his arms.

The camp was in an uproar; a huge fire was kindled; tin pans were beaten; one of the helpers mounted a horse and by circling around the bear, succeeded in driving him away.

After first aid measures were administered, Frost was successfully nursed back to health and usefulness by his wife. But since that time he has an inveterate hatred of grizzlies, hunting them with grim persistency.

It is said that nearly forty obnoxious grizzlies were shot by the Park rangers after this episode and Frost was given a permit to carry a weapon. We found later that he always went to sleep with a Colt automatic pistol strapped to his wrist.

We planned to enter the Park in two parties. One, comprised of Frost, the cook, horse wrangler, my brother, and his friend, Judge Henry Hulbert, of Detroit, was to proceed from Cody and come with a pack train across Sylvan Pass. Our party consisted of Arthur Young and myself; Mr. Compton was unexpectedly prevented from joining us by sickness in his family. We were to journey by rail to Ashton. This was the nearest point to Yellowstone Station on the boundary of the reservation that could be reached by railroad in winter.

We arrived at this point near the last of May, 1920. The roads beyond were blocked with snow, but by good fortune, we were taken in by one of the first work trains entering the region through the personal interest and courtesy of the superintendent of the Pocatello division.

We had shipped ahead of us a quantity of provisions and came outfitted only with sleeping bags, extra clothing, and our archery equipment. This latter consisted of two bows apiece and a carrying case containing one hundred and forty-four broad-heads, the finest assembly of bows and arrows since the battle of Crecy.

Young had one newly made bow weighing eighty-five pounds and his well-tried companion of many hunts, "Old Grizzly," weighing seventy-five pounds. He later found the heavier weapon too strong for him in the cold weather of the mountains, where a man's muscles stiffen and lose their power, while his bow grows stronger.

My own bows were seventy-five pounds apiece—"Old Horrible," my favorite, a hard hitter and sweet to shoot, and "Bear Slayer," the fine-grained, crooked-limbed stave with which I helped to kill our first bear. Our arrows were the usual three-eighths birch shafts, carefully selected, straight and true. Their heads were tempered steel, as sharp as daggers. We had, of course, a few blunts and eagle arrows in the lot.

In the Park we found snow deep on the ground and the roads but recently cleared with snow plows and caterpillar tractors. We traveled by auto to Mammoth Hot Springs and paid our respects to Superintendent Albright, and ultimately settled in a vacant ranger's cabin near the Canyon. Here we awaited the coming of the second party.

Our entrance into the Park was well known to the rangers, who were instructed to give us all the assistance possible. This cabin soon became a rendezvous for them and our evenings were spent very pleasantly with stories and fireside music.

After several days, word was sent by telephone that Frost and his caravan were unable to cross Sylvan Pass because of fifty feet of snow in the defile, and that he had returned to Cody where he would take an auto truck and come around to the northern entrance to the Park, through Gardner, Montana.

At the expiration of three days he drove up to our cabin in a flurry of snow. This was about the last day in May.

Frost himself is one of the finest of Western types; born and raised in the sagebrush country, a hunter of big game ever since he was large enough to hold a gun. He was in the prime of life, a man of infinite resource, courage, and fortitude. We admired him immensely.

With him he had a full camp outfit, selected after years of experience, and suited to any kind of weather.

The party consisted of Art Cunningham, the cook; G. D. Pope, and Judge Henry Hulbert. Art came equipped with a vast amount of camp craft and cookery wisdom. My brother came to see the fun, the Judge to take pictures and add dignity to the occasion. All were seasoned woodsmen and hunters.

We moved to more commodious quarters, a log cabin in the vicinity, made ourselves comfortable, and let the wind-driven snow pile deep drifts about our warm shelter while we planned a campaign against the grizzlies.

So far, we had met few bears, and these were of the tourist variety. They had stolen bacon from the elevated meat safe, and one we found in the woods sitting on his haunches calmly eating the contents of a box of soda crackers. These were the hotel pets and were nothing more than of passing interest to us.

Contrary to the usual condition, no grizzlies were to be seen.

The only animals in evidence were a few half-starved elk that had wintered in the Park, marmots, and the Canadian jay birds.

We began our hunts on foot, exploring Hayden Valley, the Sour Creek region, Mt. Washburn, and the headwaters of Cascade Creek.

The ground was very wet in places and heavy with snow in the woods. It was necessary, therefore, to wear rubber pacs, a type of shoe well suited to this sort of travel.

Our party divided into two groups, usually my brother and the Judge exploring in one direction while Young and I kept close at the heels of Frost. We climbed all the high ridges and swept the country with our binocular glasses. From eight to fourteen hours a day we walked and combed the country for bear signs.

Our original plan was to bring in several decrepit old horses with the pack train and sacrifice them for bait. But because of the failure of this part of our program, we were forced to find dead elk for this purpose. We came across a number of old carcasses, but no signs that bear had visited them recently. Our first encounter with grizzly came on the fourth day. We were scouting over the country near Sulphur Mountain, when Frost saw a grizzly a mile off, feeding in a little valley. The snow had melted here and he was calmly digging roots in the soft ground. We signaled to our party and all drew together as we advanced on our first bear, keeping out of sight as we did so.

We planned to go rapidly down a little cut in the hills and intercept him as he came around the turn. Progressing at a rapid pace, Indian file, we five hunters went down the draw, when suddenly our bear, who had taken an unexpected cut-off, came walking up the ravine. At a sign from Ned, we dropped to our knees and awaited developments. The bear had not seen us and the faint breeze blew from him to us. He was about two hundred yards off. We were all in a direct line, Frost ahead, I next, Young behind me, and the others in the rear. Our bows were braced and arrows nocked.

Slowly the bear came feeding toward us. He dug the roots of white violets, he sniffed, he meandered back and forth, wholly unconscious of our presence. We hardly breathed. He was not a good specimen, rather a scrawny, long-nosed, male adolescent, but a real grizzly and would do as a starter.

At last he came within fifty yards, stopped, pawed a patch of snow, and still we did not shoot. We could not without changing our position because we were all in one line. So we waited for his next move, hoping that he would advance laterally and possibly give us a broadside exposure.

But he came onward, directly for us, and at thirty yards stopped to root in the ground again. I thought, "Now we must shoot or he will walk over us!" Just then he lifted his head and seemed to take an eyeful of Young's blue shirt. For one second he half reared and stared. I drew my bow and as the arrow left the string, he bounded up the hill. The flying shaft just grazed his shoulder, parting the fur in its course. Quick as a bouncing rubber ball, he leaped over the ground and as Young's belated arrow whizzed past him, he disappeared over the hill crest.

We rose with a deep breath and shouted with laughter. Ned said that if it had not been for that blue shirt, the bear would have bumped into us. Well, we were glad we missed him, because after all, he was not the one we were looking for. It is a hard thing to pick grizzlies to order. You can't go up and inspect them ahead of time.

This fiasco was just an encouragement to us, and we continued to rise by candle light and hunt till dark. The weather turned warmer, and the snow began to melt.

At the end of the first week we saw five grizzlies way off in the distance at the head of Hayden Valley. They were three or four miles from us and evening was approaching, so we postponed an attack on them. Next morning, bright and early, we were on the ground again, hoping to see them. Sure enough, there they were! Ned, Art and I were together; my brother and the Judge were off scouting on the other side of the ridge. It was about half past eight in the morning. The bears, four in number this time, were feeding in the grassy marshland, about three miles up the valley. Ned's motto has always been: "When you see 'em, go and get 'em."

We decided to attack immediately. Down the river bank, through the draws, up into the timber we circled at a trot. It was hard going, but we were pressed for time. At last we came out on a wooded point a quarter of a mile above the bears, and rested. We knew they were about to finish their morning feeding and go up into the forest to lay up for the day. So we watched them in seclusion.

We waxed our bowstrings and put the finishing touches on our arrowheads with a file.

Slowly the bears mounted the foothills, heading for a large patch of snow, where Frost thought they would lie down to cool before entering the woods. It seems that their winter coat makes them very susceptible to heat, and though the sun had come out pleasantly for us, it was too hot for them. There was an old female and three half-grown cubs in their third year, all looking big enough for any museum group.

At last they settled down and began to nuzzle the snow. The time had come for action. We proposed to slip down the little ravine at the edge of the timber, cross the stream, ascend the hill on the opposite side, and come up on our quarry over the crest. We should thus be within shooting distance. The wind was right for this maneuver, so we started at once.

Now as I write my muscles quiver, my heart thumps and I flush with a strange feeling, thinking of that moment. Like a soldier before a battle, we waded into an uncharted experience. What does a man think of as he is about to enter his first grizzly encounter? I remember well what passed through my head: "Can we get there without alarming the brutes?" "How close will they be?" "Can we hit them?" "What will happen then?"

Ned Frost, Young and I were to sneak up on four healthy grizzlies in the open, and pit our nerve against their savage reaction. Ned had his rifle, but this was to be used only as a last resort, and that might easily fail at such short range.

As we walked rapidly, stepping with utmost caution, I answered all the questions of my subconscious fears. "Hit them? Why, we will soak them in the gizzard; wreck them!" "Charge? Let them come on and may the best man win!" "Die? There never was a fairer, brighter, better day to die on." In fact, "Lead on!" I felt absolutely gay. A little profanity or a little intellectual detachment at these times is of material help in the process of autosuggestion. As for Young, he was silent, and possibly was thinking of camp flapjacks.

Halfway up the hill, on the opposite side of which lay our grizzlies, we stopped, braced our bows, took three arrows apiece from our quivers, and proceeded in a more stealthy approach.

Young and I arranged ourselves on each side of Frost, abreast with him. Near the top Ned took out a green silk handkerchief and floated it in the gentle breeze to see if the wind had changed. If it had, we might find the bears coming over the top to meet us. Everything was perfect, so far! Now, stooping low we crept to the very ridge itself, to a spot directly above which we believed the bears to be. Laying our hats on the grass and sticking our extra arrows in the ground before us, we rose up, bows half drawn, ready to shoot.

There on the snow, not over twenty-five yards off, lay four grizzly bears, just like so many hearth rugs.

Instantly, I selected the farthest bear for my mark and at a signal of the eye we drew our great bows to their uttermost and loosed two deadly arrows.

We struck! There was a roar, they rose, but instead of charging us, they rushed together and began such a fight as few men have seen. My bear, pinioned with an arrow in the shoulder, threw himself on his mother, biting her with savage fury. She in turn bit him in the bloody shoulder and snapped my arrow off short. Then all the cubs attacked her. The growls and bellowing were terrific.

Quickly I nocked another arrow. The beasts were milling around together, pawing, biting, mad with rage. I shot at my bear and missed him. I nocked again. The old she-bear reared on her haunches, stood high above the circling bunch, cuffing and roaring, the blood running from her mouth and nostrils in frothy streams. Young's arrow was deep in her chest. I drove a feathered shaft below her foreleg.

The confusion and bellowing increased, and, as I drew a fourth arrow from my quiver, I glanced up just in time to see the old female's hair rise on the back of her neck. She steadied herself in her wild hurtling and looked directly at us with red glaring eyes. She saw us for the first time! Instinctively I knew she would charge, and she did.

Quick as thought, she bounded toward us. Two great leaps and she was on us. A gun went off at my ear. The bear was literally knocked head over heels, and fell in backward somersaults down the steep snowbank. At some fifty yards she checked her course, gathered herself, and attempted to charge again, but her right foreleg failed her. She rose on her haunches in an effort to advance, when, like a flash, two arrows flew at her and disappeared through her heaving sides. She faltered, wilted, and as we drew to shoot again, she sprawled out on the ground, a convulsed, quivering mass of fur and muscle—she was dead.

The half-grown cubs had disappeared at the boom of the gun. We saw one making off at a gallop, three hundred yards away. The glittering snowbank before us was vacant.

The air seemed strangely still; the silence was oppressive. Our nervous tension exploded in a wave of laughter and exclamations of wonderment. Frost declared he had never seen such a spectacle in all his life; four grizzly bears in deadly combat; the din of battle;

the wild bellowing; and two bowmen shooting arrow after arrow into this jumble of struggling beasts.

The snow was trampled and soaked with blood as though there had been an Indian massacre. We paced off the distance at which the charging female had been stopped. It was exactly eight yards. A mighty handy shot!

We went down to view the remains. Young had three arrows in the old bear, one deep in her neck, its point emerging back of the shoulder. He shot that as she came at us. His first arrow struck anterior to her shoulder, entered her chest, and cut her left lung from top to bottom. His third arrow pierced her thorax, through and through, and lay on the ground beside her with only its feathers in the wound.

My first arrow cut below the diaphragm, penetrated the stomach and liver, severed the gall ducts and portal vein. My second arrow passed completely through her abdomen and lay on the ground several yards beyond her. It had cut the intestines in a dozen places and opened large branches of the mesenteric artery.

The bullet from Frost's gun had entered at the right shoulder, fractured the humerus, blown a hole an inch in diameter in the chest wall, opened up a jagged hole in the trachea, and dissipated its energy in the left lung. No wound of exit was found, the soft nose copper-jacketed bullet apparently having gone to pieces after striking the bone.

Anatomically speaking, it was an effective shot, knocked the bear down and crippled her, but was not an immediately fatal wound. We had her killed with arrows, but she did not know it. She undoubtedly would have been right on us in another second. The outcome of this hypothetical encounter I leave to those with vivid imaginations.

We hereby express our gratitude to Ned Frost.

Now one of us had to rush off and get the rest of the party. Judge Hulbert and my brother were in another valley in quest of bear. So Ned set off at a rapid tramp across the bogs, streams, and hills to find them. Within an hour they returned together to view the wreckage. Photographs were taken, the skinning and autopsy were performed. Then we looked around for the wounded cub. Frost trailed him by almost invisible blood stains and tracks, and found him less than a quarter of a mile away, huddled up as if asleep on the hillside, my arrow nestled to his breast. The broken shaft with its blade deep in the thorax had completely severed the head of his humerus, cut two ribs, and killed him by hemorrhage from the pulmonary arteries. Half-grown as he was, he would have made an ugly antagonist for any man.

His mother, a fine mature lady of the old school, showed by her teeth and other lineaments her age and respectability. In autumn she would have weighed four or five hundred pounds. We weighed her in installments with our spring scales; she registered three hundred and five pounds. She was in poor condition and her pelt was not suitable for museum purposes. But these features could not be determined readily beforehand. The juvenile Ursus weighed one hundred and thirty-five pounds. We measured them, gathered their bones for the museum, shouldered their hides, and turned back to camp.

That night Ned Frost said, "Boys, when you proposed shooting grizzly bears with the bow and arrow, I thought it a fine sporting proposition, but I had my doubts about its success. Now I know that you can shoot through and kill the biggest grizzly in Wyoming!"

Our instructions on leaving California were to secure a large male *Ursus Horribilis Imperator*, a good representative female, and two or three cubs. The female we had shot filled the requirements fairly well, but the two-year-old cub was at the high school age and hardly cute enough to be admired. Moreover, no sooner had we sent the news of our first success to the Museum than we were informed that this size cub was not wanted and that we must secure little ones.

So we set out to get some of this year's vintage in small bears. Ordinarily, there is no difficulty in coming in contact with bears in Yellowstone; in fact, it is more common to try to keep some of the hotel variety from eating at the same table with you. But not a single bear, black, brown, or silver-tipped, now called upon us. We traveled all over that beautiful Park, from Mammoth Hot Springs to the Lake. We hunted over every well-known bear district. Tower Falls, Specimen Ridge, Buffalo Corrals, Mt. Washburn, Dunraven Pass (under twenty-five feet of snow), Antelope Creek, Pelican Meadows, Cub Creek, Steamboat Point, and kept the rangers busy on the lookout for bear. From eight to fifteen hours a day we hunted. We walked over endless miles of mountains, climbed over countless logs, plowed through snow and slush, and raked the valleys with our field glasses.

But bears were as scarce as hen's teeth. We saw a few tracks but nothing compared to those seen in other years.

We began to have a sneaking idea that the bear had all been

killed off. We knew they had been a pest to campers and were becoming a menace to human life. We suspected the Park authorities of quiet extermination. Several of the rangers admitted that a selective killing was carried out yearly to rid the preserve of the more dangerous individuals.

Then the elk began to pour back into the Park; singly, in couples, and in droves they returned, lean and scraggly. A few began to drop their calves. Then we began to see bear signs. The grizzly follow the elk, and after they come out of hibernation and get their fill of green grass, they naturally take to elk calves. Occasionally they include the mother in the menu.

We also began to follow the elk. We watched at bait. We sat up nights and days at a time, seeing only a few unfavorable specimens and these were as wild and as wary as deer. We found the mosquitoes more deadly than the bear. We tracked big worthy old boys around in circles and had various frustrated encounters with she-bears and cubs.

Upon one occasion we were tracking a prospective specimen through the woods, proceeding with great caution, when evidently the beast heard us. Suddenly, he turned on his tracks and came on a dead run for us. I was in advance and instantly drew my bow, holding it for the right moment to shoot. The bear came directly in our front, not more than twenty yards away and being startled by the sight of us, threw his locomotive mechanism into reverse and skidded towards us in a cloud of snow and forest leaves. In the fraction of a second, I perceived that he was afraid and not a proper specimen for our use. I held my arrow and the bear, with an indignant and disgusted look, made a precipitous retreat. It was an unexpected surprise on both sides.

They say that the Indians avoided the Yellowstone region, thinking it a land of evil spirits. In our wanderings, however, we picked up on Steamboat Point a beautiful red chert arrow-head, undoubtedly shot by an Indian at elk years before Columbus burst in upon these good people. In Hayden Valley we found an obsidian spear head, another sign that the Indian knew good hunting grounds.

But no Indian was ever so anxious to meet grizzly as we were. We hunted continually, but found none that suited us; we had to have the best. Frost assured us that we had made a mistake in ever trying to get grizzlies in the Park—and that in the time we spent there we could have secured all our required specimens in the game fields of Wyoming or Montana.

A month passed; the bears were beginning to lose their winter coats; our party began to disintegrate. My brother and the Judge were compelled to return to Detroit. A week or so later Ned Frost and the cook were scheduled to take out another pary of hunters from Cody and prepared to leave us. Young and I were determined to stick it out until the last chance was exhausted. We just had to get those specimens.

Before Frost left us, however, he packed us up to the head of Cascade Creek with our bows and arrows, bed rolls, a tarpaulin, and a couple of boxes of provisions.

We had received word from a ranger that a big old grizzly had been seen at Soda Butte and we prepared to go after him. At the last moment before departure, a second word came that probably this same bear had moved down to Tower Falls and was ranging between this point and the Canyon, killing elk around Dunraven Pass.

Young and I scouted over this area and found diggings and his tracks.

A good-sized bear will have a nine-inch track. This monster's was eleven inches long. We saw where he made his kills and used certain fixed trails going up and down the canyons.

Frost gave us some parting advice and his blessing, consigned us to our fate, and went home.

Left to ourselves, we two archers inspected our tackle and put everything in prime condition. Our bows had stood the many wettings well, but we oiled them again. New strings were put on and thoroughly waxed. Our arrows were straightened, their feathers dried and preened in the sun. The broad-heads were set on straight and sharpened to the last degree, and so prepared we determined to do our utmost. We were ready for the big fellow.

In our reconnaissance we found that he was a real killer. His trail was marked by many bloody episodes. It seemed quite probable that he was the bear that two years before burst in upon a party of surveyors in the mountains and kept them treed all night. It is not unlikely that he was the same bear that caused the death of Jack Walsh. He seemed too expert in planning murder. We saw by his tracks how he lay in ambush watching a herd of elk, how he sneaked up on a mother elk and her recently born calf on the outskirts of the band, and with a great leap threw himself upon the two and killed them.

In several places we saw the skins of these little wapiti licked clean and empty of bodily structure. No other male grizzly was permitted to enter his domain. He was, in fact, the monarch of the mountain, the great bear of Dunraven Pass.

We pitched our little tent in a secluded wood some three miles from the lake at the head of Cascade Creek, and began to lay our plan of attack. We were by this time inured to fatigue and disappointment. Weariness and loss of sleep had produced a dogged determination that knew no relaxation. And yet we were cheerful. Young has that fine quality so essential to a hunting companion, imperturbable good nature, never complaining, no matter how heavy the load, how long the trail, how late or how early the hour, how cold, how hot, how little, or how poor the food.

We were there to win and nothing else mattered. If it rained and we must wait, we took out our musical instruments, built up the fire and soothed our troubled souls with harmony. This is better than tobacco or whiskey for the purpose. In fact, Young is so abstemious that even tea or coffee seem a bit intemperate to him, and are only to be used under great physical strain; and as for profanity, why, I had to do all the swearing for the two of us.

We were trained down to rawhide and sinew, keyed to alertness and ready for any emergency.

Often in our wanderings at night we ran unexpectedly upon wild beasts in the dark. Some of these were bears. Our pocket flashlights were used as defensive weapons. A snort, a crashing retreat through the brush told us that our visitant had departed in haste, unable to stand the glaring light of modern science.

We soon found that our big fellow was a night rover also, and visited his various kills under the cloak of darkness. In one particularly steep and rugged canyon, he crossed a little creek at a set place. Up on the side of this canyon he mounted to the plateau above by one of three possible trails. At the top within forty yards of one of these was a small promontory of rock upon which we decided to form a blind and await his coming. We fashioned a shelter of young jack pines, constructed like a miniature corral, less than three by six feet in area, but very natural in appearance. Between us and the trail was a quantity of down timber which we hoped would act as an impediment to an onrushing bear. And the perpendicular face of our outcropping elevated us some twelve or thirteen feet above the steep hillside. A small tree stood near our position and offered a possibility in case of attack. But we had long ago decided that no man can clamber up a tree in time to escape a grizzly charging at a distance less than fifty yards. We could be approached from the rear, but altogether it was an ideal ambush.

The wind blew steadily up the canyon all night long and carried our scent away from the trail. Above us on the plateau was a recently killed elk which acted as a perpetual invitation to bears and other prowlers of the night.

So we started watching in this blind, coming soon after dusk and remaining until sunrise. The nights were cold, the ground pitiless, and the moon, nearly at its full, crept low through a maze of mist.

Dressed in our warmest clothing and permitting ourselves one blanket and a small piece of canvas, we huddled together in a cramped posture and kept vigil through the long hours. Neither of us smoked anyway, and of course, this was absolutely taboo; we hardly whispered, and even shifted our positions with utmost caution. Before us lay our bows ready strung, and arrows, both in the quiver belted upright to the screen and standing free close at hand.

The first evening we saw an old she-bear and her two-year-old cubs come up the path. They passed us with that soft shuffling gait so uncanny to hear in the dark. We were delighted that they showed no sign of having detected us. But they were not suited to our purpose and we let them go. The female was homely, fretful and nervous. The cubs were yellow and ungainly. We looked for better things.

Bears have personality, as obvious as humans. Some are lazy, some alert, surly, or timid. Nearly all the females we saw showed that irritability and irascible disposition that go with the cares of maternity. This family was decidedly commonplace.

They disappeared in the gloom, and we waited and waited for the big fellow that some time must appear.

But morning came first; we stole from our blind, chilled and stiffened, and wandered back to camp to breakfast and sleep. The former was a fairly successful event, but the latter was made almost impossible by the swarms of mosquitoes that beset us. A smudge fire and canvas head-coverings gave us only a partial immunity. By sundown we were on our way again to the blind, but another cold dreary night passed without adventure.

On our way to camp in the dim light of early dawn, a land fog hung low in the valley. As we came up a rough path there suddenly appeared out of the obscurity three little bear cubs, not thirty-five yards away. They winded us, squeaked and stood on their hind legs, peering in our direction. We dropped like stones in our tracks, scarcely breathing, figuratively frozen to the ground, for instantly the fiercest-looking grizzly we ever saw bounded over the cubs and straddled them between her forelegs. Nothing could stop her if she came on. A little brush intervened and she could not locate us plainly for we could see her eyes wander in search of us; but her trembling muscles, the vicious champing of her jaws, and the guttural growls, all spoke of immediate attack. We were petrified. She wavered in her intent, turned, cuffed her cubs down the hill, snorted and finally departed with her family.

We heaved a deep sigh of relief. But she was wonderful, she was the most beautiful bear we had ever seen; large, well proportioned, with dark brown hair having just a touch of silver. She was a patrician, the aristocrat of the species. We marked her well.

Next day, just at sunset, we got our first view of the great bear of Dunraven Pass. He was coming down a distant canyon trail. He looked like a giant in the twilight. With long swinging strides he threw himself impetuously down the mountainside. Great power was in every movement. He was magnificent! He seemed as large as a horse, and had that grand supple strength given to no other predatory animal. Though we were used to bears, a strange misgiving came over me. We proposed to slay this monster with the bow and arrow. It seemed preposterous!

In the blind another long cold night passed. The moon drifted slowly across the heavens and sank in a haze of clouds at daybreak. Just at the hush of dawn, the homely female and her tow-headed progeny came shuffling by. We were desperate for specimens, and one of these would match that which we already had. I drew up my bow and let fly a broad-head at one of the cubs. It struck him in the ribs. Precipitately, the whole band took flight. My quarry fell against an obstructing log and died. His mother stopped, came back several times, gazed at him pensively, then disappeared. We got out, carried him to a distant spot and skinned him. He weighed one hundred and twenty pounds. My arrow had shaved a piece off his heart. Death was instantaneous.

We packed home the hind quarters and made a fine grizzly stew. Before this we had found that the old bears were tough and rancid, but the little ones were as sweet and tender as suckling pigs. This stew was particularly good, well seasoned with canned tomatoes and the last of our potatoes and onions. Sad to relate the better part of this savory pot next day was eaten by a wandering vagabond of the *Ursus* family. Not content with our stew, he devoured all our sugar, bacon, and other foodstuffs not in cans, and wound up his debauch by wiping his feet on our beds and generally messing up the camp. Probably he was a regular camp thief.

That night, early in the watch, we heard the worthy old boy come down the canyon, hot in pursuit of a large brown bear. As he ran, the great animal made quite a noise. His claws clattered on the rocks, and the ground seemed to shake beneath us. We shifted our bows ready for action, and felt the keen edge of our arrows. Way off in the forest we heard him tree the cowardly intruder with such growls and ripping of bark that one would imagine he was about to tear the tree down.

After a long time he desisted and, grunting and wheezing, came slowly up the canyon. With the night glasses we could see him. He seemed to be considerably heated with his exercise and scratched himself against a young fir tree. As he stood on his hind legs with his back to the trunk and rubbed himself to and fro, the tree swayed like a reed; and as he lifted his nose I observed that it just touched one of the lower branches. In the morning, after he had gone and we were on our way to camp, we passed this very fir and stretching up on my tip toes, I could just touch the limb with my fingers. Having been a pole vaulter in my youth, I knew by experience that this measurement was over seven feet six inches. He was a real he-bear! We wanted him more than ever.

The following day it rained—in fact, it rained nearly every day near the end of our stay; but this was a drenching that stopped at sunset, leaving all the world sweet and fragrant. The moon came out full and beautiful, everything seemed propitious.

We went to the blind about an hour before midnight, feeling that surely this evening the big fellow would come. After two hours of frigidity and immobility, we heard the velvet footfalls of bear coming up the canyon. There came our patrician and her royal family. The little fellows pattered up the trail before their mother. They came within range. I signalled Young and we shot together at the cubs. We struck. There was a squeak, a roar, a jumble of shadowy figures and the entire flock of bears came tumbling in our direction.

At that very moment the big grizzly appeared on the scene. There were five bears in sight. Turning her head from side to side, trying to find her enemy, the she-bear came towards us. I whispered to Young, "Shoot the big fellow." At the same time, I drew an arrow to the head, and drove it at the oncoming female. It struck her full in the chest. She reared; threw herself sidewise, bellowed with rage, staggered and fell to the ground. She rose again, weakened, stumbled forward, and with great gasps she died. In less than half a minute it was all over. The little ones ran up the hill past us, one later returned and sat up at its mother's head, then disappeared in the dark forever.

While all this transpired, the monster grizzly was romping back and forth in the shaded forest not more than sixty-five yards away. With deep booming growls like distant thunder, he voiced his anger and intent to kill. As he flitted between the shadows of the trees, the moonlight glinted on his massive body; he was enormous.

Young discharged three arrows at him. I shot two. We should have landed, he was so large. But he galloped off and I saw my last arrow, at the point blank range of seventy-five yards, fall between his legs. He was gone. We thought we had missed the beast and grief descended heavy upon us. The thought of all the weary days and nights of hunting and waiting, and now to have lost him, was very painful.

After our palpitating hearts were quiet and the world seemed peaceful, we got out of our blind and skinned the female by flashlight. She was a magnificent specimen, just right in color and size for the Museum, not fat, but weighing a trifle over five hundred pounds. My arrow had severed a rib and buried its head in her heart. We measured her and saved her skull and long bones for the taxidermist.

At daybreak we searched for the cubs and found one dead under a log with an arrow through his brain. The others had disappeared.

We had no idea that we hit the great bear, but just to gather up our shafts, we went over the ground where he had been.

One of Young's arrows was missing!

That gave us a thrill; perhaps we had hit him after all! We went further in the direction he had gone; there was a trace of blood.

We trailed him. We knew it was dangerous business. Through clumps of jack pines we cautiously followed, peering under every pile of brush and fallen tree. Deep into the forest we tracked him, where his bloody smear was left upon fallen logs. Soon we found where he had rested. Then we discovered the fore part of Young's arrow. It had gone through him. There was a pool of blood. Then we found the feathered butt which he had drawn out with his teeth.

Four times he wallowed down in the mud or soft earth to rest and cool his wound. Then beneath a great fir he had made a bed in the soft loam and left it. Past this we could not track him. We hunted high and low, but no trace of him could we find. Apparently he had ceased bleeding and his footprints were not recorded on the stony ground about. We made wide circles, hoping to pick up his trail. We searched up and down the creek. We cross-cut every forest path and runway, but no vestige remained.

He was gone. We even looked up in the tree and down in the ground where he had wallowed. For five hours we searched in vain, and at last, worn with disappointment and fatigue, we lay down and slept on the very spot where he last stopped.

Near sundown we awoke, ate a little food, and started all over again to find the great bear. We retraced our steps and followed the fading evidence till it brought us again to the pit beneath the fir tree. He must be near. It was absolutely impossible for any animal to have lost so much blood and travel more than a few hundred yards past this spot. We had explored the creek bottom and the cliffs above from below, and we now determined to traverse every foot of the rim of the canyon from above. As we climbed over the face of the rock we saw a clot of dried blood. We let ourselves down the sheer descent, came upon a narrow little ledge, and there below us lay the huge monster on his back, against a boulder, cold and stiff, as dead as Caesar. Our hearts nearly burst with happiness.

There lay the largest grizzly bear in Wyoming, dead at our feet. His rugged coat was matted with blood. Well back in his chest the arrow wound showed clear. I measured him; twenty-six inches of bear had been pierced through and through. One arrow killed him. He was tremendous. His great wide head; his worn, glistening teeth; his massive arms; his vast, ponderous feet and long curved claws; all were there. He was a wonderful beast. It seemed incredible. I thumped Young on the shoulder: "My, that was a marvelous shot!"

We started to skin our quarry. It was a stupendous job, as he weighed nearly one thousand pounds, and lay on the steep canyon side ready to roll on and crush us. But with ropes we lashed him by the neck to a tree and split him up the back, later box-skinning the legs according to the method required by the museum.

By flashlight, acetylene lamp, candle light, fire light and moonlight, we labored. We used up all our knives, and having neglected to bring our whet-stones, sharpened our blades on the volcanic boulders, about us. By assiduous industry for nine straight hours, we finished him after a fashion. His skin was thick and like scar tissue. His meat was all tendons and gristle. The hide was as tight as if glued on.

In the middle of the night we stopped long enough to broil

some grizzly cub steaks and brew a pot of tea; then we went at it again.

As we dismembered him we weighed the parts. The veins were absolutely dry of blood, and without this substance, which represents a loss of nearly 10 per cent of his weight, he was nine hundred and sixteen pounds. There was hardly an inch of fat on his back. At the end of the autumn this adipose layer would be nearly six inches thick. He would then have weighed over fourteen hundred pounds. He stood nearly four feet high at the shoulders, while his skull measured eighteen and a half inches long; his entire body length was seven feet four inches.

As we cleaned his bones we hurled great slabs of muscle down the canyon, knowing from experience that this would be a sign for all other bears to leave the vicinity. Only the wolves and jays will eat grizzly meat.

At last we finished him, as the sun rose over the mountain ridges and gilded all the canyon with glory.

We cleaned and salted the pelts, packed them on our backs, and, dripping with salt brine and bear grease, staggered to the nearest wagon trail. The hide of the big bear, with unskinned paws and skull, weighed nearly one hundred and fifty pounds.

We cached our trophies, tramped the weary miles back to camp, cleaned up, packed and wandered to the nearest station, from which we ordered a machine. When this arrived we gathered our belongings, turned our various specimens over to a park ranger, to be given the final treatments, and started on our homeward trip.

We were so exhausted from loss of sleep, exertion and excitement, that we sank into a stupor that lasted almost the entire way home.

The California Academy of Sciences now has a handsome representative group of *Ursus Horribilis Imperator*. We have the extremely satisfactory feeling that we killed five of the finest grizzly bear in Wyoming. The sport was fair and clean, and we did it all with the bow and arrow.

HAROLD
McCRACKEN

The Alaskan Grizzly

Although more widely known for his exploration than his activities as a hunter, McCracken was apparently a hunter at heart. Forty years ago, when he was collecting Alaskan game animals, it was not possible to charter an amphibian at Anchorage to put you down, with full equipment, at the spot where the game you sought was reputedly in abundance. Had such facilities been available, it is questionable whether McCracken would have employed them, for he had a penchant toward doing things the hard way. Modern terminology varies where the identity and nomenclature of the big bears are concerned, and what McCracken calls the Alaskan grizzly would be, these days, merely lumped in with the Alaskan brown. The scientific name, however, is *Ursus gyas,* where the Peninsula bear is concerned.

The great Alaskan grizzly—the Kodiak brown bear *(Ursus middendorffi)* and its even larger Alaska Peninsula brother *(Ursus gyas)*—is probably as far famed as either the African lion or the Bengal tiger. And yet, probably less is known of its life history than of any of the other larger mammals. He is, nevertheless, a sort of fictitious byword at the hearths of all those hunter-sportsmen who enjoy the savor of genuine hazard in their quest for sport and trophies. A beast whom most prefer to "talk" about hunting, rather than face in mortal combat. And his one thousand to two thousand pounds of brawn and power is unquestionably the embodiment of all that even the most adventurous care to seek. He is supreme in size, in brute power, as well as in physical dexterity, sagacity, and pernicious damnableness in the animal kingdom. And this, not in the mere belief of a casual observer, but weighed and tried on the scales of science. To go into details regarding the life history, the "whys" and "whens" and "hows" of his life career, would entail a goodly volume, which, though immensely interesting in every detail, would be far too cumbersome in such a place as this.

His home is that long, slightly curved arm that reaches out from the southwestern corner of Alaska, separating the North Pacific Ocean from the Bering Sea, and dabbling off in the spattered Aleutian Islands. The Alaska Peninsula is today one of the most wild, least visited and less known of all the districts on this continent.

But in reality, the Alaska Peninsula is, for the most part, a terribly wild Garden of Eden. Its waterways boast more fine fish than any other similar sized section of the globe; on its rounded undulating hills and tundra lands are great herds of caribou, the finest of edible flesh; it is carpeted with berry bushes; there are fine furred animals in abundance; millions of wildfowl, duck, geese, eiders, seals, sea lions; big bears—everything necessary for the welfare and happiness of primitive man. It is a truly primitive land.

While the great Alaska Peninsula bear is a carnivore, or flesh-eater—and what applies to this bear also applies in many respects to his brothers, the sub- and sub-sub-species of other districts of Alaska—yet he has frequently and correctly been called "the great grass-eating bear" and also "the great fish-eating bear." All animals subsist in the manner and on the foods that demand the least efforts, hazard and inconvenience to their life and comforts. Thus the bears of the Alaskan Peninsula have chosen fish and grass and berries as their main diet of food, varied with an occasional caribou, a seal or meal from the carcass of a dead whale or walrus washed up on the beach. During most of the months of the year, the streams are choked with salmon, affording him an inexhaustible supply until well into the middle of the winter. And as hibernation is for the most part only an alternative for existing under winter conditions, when it is hard or sometimes impossible to get food, and as the Alaska Peninsula is in winter moderated by the warming Japan Current, making it quite mild and livable for old Gyas, he is forced to spend but a relatively short period in the "long sleep." This increased activity, together with the abundance of fine food, accounts for the unusual size to which the bears of that district grow.

And he is very much aware of his size and strength; and the fact that he has had no outside natural enemy through the line of his ancestors has made him aggressive, haughty and overbearing, fearing nothing and crushing all that impedes his way.

Thus the Alaska Peninsula grizzly is to be found a most unscrupulous fighter, and his acquaintance with man and his high-powered rifles is as yet too short and limited to have impressed upon his brute mind that here is a most powerful mortal enemy. He usually charges when wounded, more than frequently when a female with very young cubs is suddenly surprised or attacked, and occasionally when watching a fresh "kill" or "cache" and surprised. And if old Gyas decides to fight, woe betide our bold Nimrod unless he is a good shot and non-excitable, or accompanied by someone who possesses these valuable faculties. For a wounded grizzly will not stop for one to reload his gun, nor pause to be shot at until the vital spot is struck. He means blood! Fifty bullets that are not placed in the proper place will not stop him; and you can't back out once he accepts your challenge. Not that one is certain of being charged by every Alaskan grizzly that he fells; I have had even females retreat until knocked down. But these cases are really the exception, and the experiences of practically all the old bear hunters of that district—I have known most of them—will bear me out in the statement that these Alaskan grizzlies almost invariably charge under the three circumstances I have cited.

The natives of Alaska do not often go to look for these big bears. They have a great deal of respect for them—as all others have who know them.

We are at King Cove, a native village near the site of the once famous village of Belkovski, center of the sea otter hunting grounds of old. We are about six hundred miles southwest of Kodiak, the nearest town of over fifteen white inhabitants, and very near the extreme western end of the Alaska Peninsula, and almost due north of Honolulu by location. And here, where the traveler is almost never seen, we will start out to hunt for the biggest of carnivora —start it by incidentally being shipwrecked, almost drowned and getting a foot severely frozen.

It was on the morning of Wednesday, November 1, 1916, that I left King Cove in a twenty-eight-foot covered-over powerboat with Captain Charlie Madsen. We headed for the Isanotski Straits, at the end of the peninsula, and the Bering Sea country, where I intended hunting Grant's Barren Ground caribou and the big grizzlies at several desirable localities near the end of the peninsula.

It was cloudy; looked like another snowstorm; but the wind being from the north, rave it might and the low hills of the mainland would protect us until we reached the end of the peninsula, where we could hunt bear and wait for more favorable winds. But the winds of the North are most fickle!

It was a most magnetic sight as we plied out towards the cape at the entrance of the bay, sending flock after flock of salt-water ducks flopping off over the swelling surface of the blue-green sea. An occasional seal could be seen plunging headlong into the water from the jut of a reef or an outcrop of the rocky shoreline. The hills were gray, dappled with the first settling snows of winter, and the clouds were heavy and leaden-looking.

As we rounded the cape the swells became more pronounced, carrying a deep, rolling, green-sided trough. But our boat plied steadily on, plunging its nose fearlessly into the rising waves.

Breasting some five miles of rocky coastline, we rounded the second cape at the entrance to Cold (Morofski) Bay, which protrudes some twenty-five miles back into the peninsula, almost making what is to the west an island and what is to the east the end of the peninsula. As we had expected, the wind was raging out of the bay to seaward. But heading the boat's nose towards Thin Point, about ten miles distant, we started fighting our way to the protection of the opposite cape.

Madsen had been watching the sky with misgiving and shortly announced that the wind was changing to the southwest.

I naturally inquired what would be the best course to pursue, knowing that it undoubtedly meant more storm and that we would soon be in the thick of it.

"Cap" decided we would take a chance on reaching Thin Point before the wind had swung to the southwest and thrown the storm in our faces. Once behind the cape we would be safe.

But we were not halfway across when the wind, swinging out past the protection of the peninsula and clashing against the tide, was soon lashing the sea into a stormy havoc. Diving into one great swell, the wind toppled its crest over the boat, washing overboard the hatch-cover and pouring a volume of water into the hold upon our supplies and outfit. I got on deck and endeavored to get a piece of canvas nailed over the open hatchway before another big one should pour its volume into the boat, at the same time clinging as best I could to the pitching vessel.

In the midst of all this, and as if to impress more forcibly upon us our insignificance in this big affair, our engine stopped. Gas engines are hellish things anyhow, and always buck in just the wrong place. But one must act quickly in a case such as this, and almost before I knew it the boat's sail was up and we were racing back before the wind, toward the entrance to the bay we had not long left.

I took the rope and wheel, while Madsen endeavored to get the engine running again, though vainly. But the wind was now coming in such gusts that each one nigh turned our boat onto its nose. It was also snowing and sleeting, almost hiding the outline of the coast.

A gust hit our sail, turning the boat clear on its side, taking water over the rail, and we narrowly escaped finding ourselves in the arms of Neptune himself. Madsen left the engine and decided we would run before the wind and tack into King Cove Bay.

We crossed the entrance to the bay, driven at top speed towards the opposite cape and the line of rocky reefs.

Going as close to as safe, the sail was drawn in with an endeavor to throw it to the opposite side, thus turning the boat. But the wind was too strong and the sea too rough, and try as we might, we would only be driven helplessly on towards the reef where the waves were dashing their foam and spray high in the air. Then a big wave took the flopping sail, pulling the boat over onto its side until the canvas was torn from end to end. As a last resort, the anchor was thrown out; this failed to catch sufficiently to hold us and was regained at great difficulty when we saw that hitting the reef was inevitable.

The first rock of the reef that the boat hit jammed its head through the bottom of the hull and we clambered out into the big dory we were towing and started for shore through the narrow, raging channels in the reef. But this being an open boat, it soon swamped in the breakers and we were forced to take to the water and make shore as best we could. Swimming was impossible, but keeping our heads above the water as best we could, and riding the waves, we were soon washed up on the rocky shore, like half-drowned rats.

To build a fire was impossible for lack of material; we must wait until the boat washed over the reef and was driven ashore. So, wet and cold, and facing a biting snow and sleet and rain-pelleted wind, we walked back and forth over the rocks and waited.

Through all this, while we had been battling with the elements, for our very lives, I had noticed with no small interest how very

little the storming and havoc had inconvenienced the little creatures that made their homes in or about the sea. The ducks swam
about, quacking, and apparently thoroughly enjoying their buoyant existence. So even storms at sea, it seemed, were a mere matter
of relativity and part of the everyday life of those that made their
home thereon.

Eventually the boat came ashore—it was fortunately high tide—
and getting aboard we got out block and tackle, sunk our anchor
as a deadman, and pulled the boat up as best we could. Supplies
and everything were drenched and several planks in the hull were
smashed.

When we had done all that we could we started for the village—
a hard hike. It was well after dark when we reached the squatty
barrabaras, or native dirt huts, of King Cove, and we were wet and
tired and miserable—ready for a meal and the blankets.

As I began to thaw out, however, I found that part of my right
foot had frozen—the leather boots I had been wearing having
shrunk and stopped the circulation of blood, causing the freezing.
I was laid up for over a week with my foot, though it took Madsen,
with the assistance of several natives, somewhat longer to get the
boat repaired and back to the village.

Such are but a bit of the "pleasures" that often come with hunting big bear at the western end of the Alaskan Peninsula.

I was especially fortunate in making a one-day bag of four of
these Alaska Peninsula bears, a big female and her three yearling
cubs, the latter being as large as quite mature Southern brown
bears I have gotten.

Deciding to spend a day alone in the hills after caribou, I took
the .30-40 Winchester—in consideration of the bear—and followed the beach of a lagoon or bay to its head about two and half
miles from the village. From the head of the lagoon a valley rose
at an easy pitch for about two miles to a low divide on the opposite
side of which was a large valley extending out onto the Pacific.
This was a very good place for caribou.

At the head of the lagoon I stopped to shoot some salt-water
ducks with a .22 Colt revolver, but had fired but a few shots when
I was attracted by the bawling of a bear. Glancing in the direction
of the sound, I saw a brown bear making a speedy, somewhat noisy,
getaway up through the alders from where he had been no doubt
eating salmon in the creek a few hundred yards upvalley from me.
He was then a good five hundred yards distant and in the alders. I
fired, hoping at least to turn him back down the hillside, but he

made the top of the ridge and went over it out of sight. I started a speedy climb up through the alders towards the top, not far from where he went over. By the time I reached this, Mr. Ursus had gone down the other side and was making a "hiyu clattewa" along the opposite side of the valley. I started up the ridge toward an open space in the alders with the intent of hurrying down to the creek and descending it with hopes of heading the bear off or getting a shot at him while crossing a wide rock slide a few hundred yards below. But I had not gone a dozen steps when I saw three other bears coming along at a good pace on quite the same course that Number One had taken. This was somewhat more of a "bear party" than I had really anticipated inviting myself to!

I felt quite certain that they would cross a small saddle through which the previous one had passed, and I decided to wait until they had come out of this and were somewhat below me before chancing a shot. I was alone, I remembered.

Squatting down in the alders, I waited with gun ready and, I must say, nerves tense. The first one to come through the saddle was the old female, a big, high-shouldered brute that strode in a manner indicating it was looking for me every bit as much as I was waiting for it. She was followed by her other two yearlings—big fellows almost as tall and as broad as they were long. Being alone, and feeling that the female would undoubtedly fight, I deemed it most wise to play doubly safe. Conditions were fortunately in my favor. The wind was from seaward, and the alders were heavy enough to conceal me from her none-too-good eyesight, and it would be difficult for her to determine from just which direction the report of my rifle came. The dispatching of the old one was of course my first move. The rest would be comparatively easy. I did not have an opportunity of a good shot, however, until the three had reached the creek bed and crossed and started up along the other side. I slipped into a heavy clump of alders and waited. She was not then, I was quite sure, aware of my whereabouts at least. She lumbered slowly along, yet ever watchful, I could see. Coming out in a little open space she stopped and made an apparent survey of the surrounding vicinity. I took a coarse bead and let drive at her shoulder. I could fairly hear the bullet slap into her. With a nasal bellow she wheeled and made a vicious swipe at the nearest yearling. I fired again, at which she wheeled and charged madly along the hillside opposite me. She went into a small ravine and in a moment came up into sight on one side and stopped, snout swaying high in the air to catch a scent of danger. I steadied my aim, and at the report she went down in a heap and rolled out of sight. "A bullseye!" I thought, and breathed a sigh of relief.

The two cubs had made off in the opposite direction, stopping occasionally to look about. I knocked down one of these at the second shot, breaking his back, though he raised on his forelegs and bawled for all he was worth. I was about to let him have another, when out of the ravine came Mrs. Ursus, mad and apparently as much alive as ever, although dragging her right foreleg. She scrambled through the alders straight for the bawling cub. Greatly surprised and a little uneasy, I again let drive at her. She threw her head to one side, at the same time letting forth another nasal cry. At my next shot she wheeled completely around and charged along the mountainside for a short distance with head held high and every nerve strained to its utmost to locate the cause of her molestation—snarling and bawling in a manner that made me perspire uncomfortably. She was desperate and no doubt calling upon the souls of all her past ancestors to assist her in locating the peculiar new enemy. Then she charged back to the cub. Finally she made a dash almost straight in my direction.

One does not fully appreciate the thrills of real bear hunting until he has experienced just such circumstances as this. To be alone in such a case is a quite different matter from being in company—poor though it may be.

She at last came to a standstill, standing half sidelong to me, and I clamped the gold bead square on her neck and let drive. She went down, got up and, tearing a few alders up by the roots, unwillingly sank in a heap. She had finished her career as a big brown bear on the Alaska Peninsula.

The rest was quite easy and uneventful.

With the assistance of three natives I skinned the four, took the necessary measurements for mounting, and brought the pelts in by boat. The natives, however, made a second trip, bringing in every bit of the meat of all four, salting it down for winter use. The pelts were in fine condition and beautiful specimens, the large one measuring a full ten feet. They are now in the Ohio State Museum.

It was on Sunday, November 19, 1916, that I bagged the original "bearcat"—one of the largest bears ever killed on the continent.

We were hunting around the eastern side of Frosty Peak, a high volcanic mountain towering between Morzhovi and Morofski Bays and about ten miles from the Pacific. This is about twenty miles from King Cove, near the end of the peninsula, and a very good place for big bears. It was a *big* one that I wanted now; and though numerous tracks and one medium-sized bear were seen, none were bothered until the original "bearcat" was found. That took two days under Old Frosty.

I had previously been hunting Grant's Barren Ground caribou on the Bering Sea side of the peninsula and before we landed at the foot of Frosty Peak on our return there was a good twelve inches of snow on the ground. In places it had already drifted to a depth of five feet. Bear hunting was quite an easy matter—though a little unpleasant on account of the snow and cold—as it was a small matter to track the animals. The streams were still open and full of salmon, but a small percentage of the bruins had sought their winter quarters, the pads of their big clawed feet having beaten paths along the iced shores of the stream where they came periodically to gorge themselves.

It was late afternoon of the second day under Frosty Peak that we found the fresh trail of our longed-for quarry. We had been investigating the broad alder-patched table of one of the valleys that cut up toward the pinnacle of Old Frosty. There were numerous tracks along the creek where the brownies had been feasting on the silver salmon, though no fresh ones of a really large bear. But as we came well up to the head of the valley we saw the well-distinguished trail of an unquestionably large bear where it had made its way up through the snow on the mountainside into a heavy growth of alders. This was at the very foot of the peak and in the highest growth of alders. Upon reaching the tracks we were well satisfied that they could have been made only by the paw and claw of just the bear that we were seeking. Although it was evident that he had been in no special hurry in making the climb, yet it was all that a six-foot man could possibly do to step from one track to the next.

To the left of the alder patch was a comparatively open track of rocky ground, with only a spare patch of brush here and there. It was certain that he could not, if still in the thicket, escape in that direction without being noticed. But on the right there was a low ridge, the opposite side of which dipped down into a deep wide ravine. The alders extended to within a few yards of this ridge, and to see the other side it was necessary to mount to the top of it. Also, it was quite probable that the bear had already gone over this ridge and might then be high up in the canyon near to its hibernation quarters.

Being unable to locate the bear with my glasses, I decided to make a complete detour around the patch, to be assured whether or not he was still in there.

So leaving Charlie on the flat below, I took the two natives and started up through the alders on the trail of old Ursus. As soon as possible, we mounted the ridge at the right and went along the extent of it to assure ourselves that the bear had not crossed. This he had not. But to make doubly sure that he was still in the alder patch, we went above and around it to complete the circle about the place. He was without question lying somewhere in that thicket.

Upon reaching the flat, and as a last resource, we fired several volleys up through the alders. Then one of the natives spotted him standing in a thick growth of the alders, where he had gotten up and was looking inquiringly down at us. We moved down opposite to him and I fired from the shoulder. He started off along the mountainside, like an animal that has just broken from its cage. Then I fired again. Mounting a little knoll in the open, he peered dubiously down at us—in unmistakable defiance. I held on him full in the chest for my next shot, at which he let out a bellow and came for us.

My shots had hit, though he had not so much as bit or clawed at the wound on either occasion—merely jumped slightly. He was then about 200 yards distant, though I was well aware of the short time that it would take him to cover that distance. And he was a big fellow—looked more like a load of hay than a bear, coming down the mountainside.

I had previously told the others not to shoot until I called for help, as I was anxious to fell this big brute singlehanded. But on he came, and though try as I might, I could not stop him. My shots seemed to be taking no effect whatever. And then, when he had come about half the distance, I yelled "Shoot!" And I'd have liked to have done so long before. The four guns spoke simultaneously, but old Gyas kept coming.

I squatted down in the snow, and resting my elbows on my knees, decided to take the long chance—a shot for the head. I was confident that Madsen could stop him before he reached us, and determined to take a chance shot of dropping him in a heap. The two natives, however, were not so confident and began to move backward, shooting as they went.

He turned an angle to cross a small ravine, and while he was mounting the opposite side at a decreased pace I held just forward of the snout. The first shot missed, as I saw a small flit of snow where it hit just in front of him. But at the second shot he dropped in a heap, falling on his belly with his nose run into the snow. After waiting for some moments to make certain he was beyond the trouble point, we climbed up through the alders to where he lay. The others stood by with guns ready while I went up and poked him with the end of my own gun. He was dead.

This had all taken but a few moments, though relatively it seemed a great deal longer.

He was indeed a big fellow—a genuine bearcat. We gutted him, and as it was then getting late, hit for camp. The next morning we went back to skin the animal—and no small task it was!

He had been hit twelve times, we found. Nine of the shots had entered the neck and shoulder and two in the head and one in the abdomen. One bullet had hit him squarely in the mouth, shattering the tops of his lower teeth on one side, piercing the tongue and lodging in the back of his throat. Four of the .30 caliber leads were retrieved from the shoulder, where they had not so much as reached the bone. The shot that stopped him struck well up on the brain box, but squarely enough to break the casing of the bone and penetrate the skull, though only a part of the lead entered the brain, the most of it spattering off in the fleshy part of the head. It was a lucky shot on an even more lucky day!

We estimated his live weight at from 1,600 to 1,800 pounds, and the skin at twelve feet in length. The actual measurements of the tanned skin, however, as made by Chas. A. Ziege, noted taxidermist of Spokane, Wash., are: eleven feet four inches maximum length, by ten feet six inches spread of forelegs. The skull, measured one year after killing, eighteen and one-quarter inches, or one-half inch under the world record, according to Washington, D.C., authorities.

R U S S E L L   A N N A B E L

Blue Ghosts of the Moraine Hills

The acquisition of statehood has not prevented Alaska from carrying on as the last wilderness frontier of this country. Few writers know this frontier more thoroughly than Russell Annabel. It was not easy to make a selection from Annabel's wildlife gleanings, but this one had the advantage of being different, in that it involved a game animal with which few experienced hunters are familiar.

T his is gonna be a cinch," panted my friend Bud Davis as he eased a shell into the chamber of his '06. "The only way that bear could get off the point without stopping lead would be to grow wings and fly off."

We had just completed a mean two-mile stalk and were lying at the rim of a wild-rose jungle, a hundred feet above the head of Knik River. On our right sheered a wall of shattered, turquoise-green glacier ice, while on our left the ground sloped down steeply to a barren granite point that jutted into the muddy, fast-flowing current of the stream. At the farther end of the point, hopefully investigating a whistler's den, was a medium-size glacier bear— about a two-hundred-pounder. The animal had a pelt to make your eyes bug out; solid blue from head to heels, the fur so long that you could see it winnow in the wind. As Bud had hunted glacier bears four seasons in a row without getting a shot at one, he naturally was determined to make a sure thing of the advantage we seemed to have over this particular bear.

"Don't see a chance for anything to go wrong," he muttered, manifestly endeavoring to convince himself. "There isn't any cover on the point, not even a bush he could hide behind. And if he heads back this way, he's gotta come right past me. I couldn't miss."

He slipped the safety latch, took a dead rest over a rock, and whistled so the bear would turn and expose its shoulder. It was a good old-fashioned, time-tried trick. Most experienced hunters probably would have used it in the circumstances. But instead of reacting normally, the bear pulled one of the slickest, most unusual stratagems I ever saw. It cast one startled glance in our direction, saw that it was cornered, and then bounded to the edge of the point and, whuffing hoarsely, jumped off. We heard it hit the water twenty feet below, and a moment later saw it bobbing down the middle of the channel, riding the current rips like a seal. Bud said later he had the animal fairly and squarely in the ring of his sight, but there was no use in shooting, because we couldn't possibly have recovered the trophy. The bear presently disappeared round a bend. At first neither of us was able to speak. Then Bud sighed and stood up.

"Typical," he moaned. "Absolutely typical. The double-crossing blue sons-of-guns were misnamed. They should of been called jinx bears."

I agree with him. Plenty of guides and sportsmen, myself among them, believe that the blue bear is the most difficult animal on the continent to hunt successfully. Wary, smart, lucky, invariably found in extreme rugged country, it is unsurpassed in its talent for keeping out of sight. So little accurate information is available concerning it that our top-flight wildlife authorities seem unable even to agree as to its proper classification. Some contend that, like the cinnamon, it is a color variation of the black bear. Others are inclined to think it may be a separate species. Still others assert it is the only animal known to be in a swift process of evolution; that is, they believe it to be a black bear changing rapidly into something else. To further complicate the picture, Indian hunters —whose opinions in such matters generally are pretty shrewd— hold that the blue bear is simply a small variety of grizzly that changes color with the seasons. They say it emerges from hibernation a light yellow, almost white, and becomes blue only when its fall pelt comes in.

Despite the fact that there are areas in which the animals are fairly plentiful, the record of blue-bear hunting consists largely in hard-luck yarns, alibis, and profane resolutions to "get one next time if it takes until freeze-up." I know a Southern judge, for example, who made two straight blue-bear hunts without so much as seeing one of the animals. Then, while taking a bath one morning in a pool near his camp in the moraine hills, he heard a sound on the bank and looked up to see a handsome sky-blue bear standing there gazing calmly down at him. The startled judge eased out of the water and dashed buck-naked through fifty yards of devil's club to get his rifle. But when he returned with the gun he found, of course, that the bear had departed even more rapidly in the opposite direction. Whereupon his honor declared the entire species in contempt of court and swore he would get one of the animals if it took the rest of his life. He hasn't yet, however, succeeded in carrying out this project, although his guide informs me he is working hard at it.

And there was the New York banker who, a day or two before the season opened, came upon three blue bears sleeping beside the trail, and then hunted a solid month without seeing another one. And the member of the Explorer's Club who emptied his rifle at a distant black bear, and a moment later was almost run over by a blue bear that had been hiding in a thicket behind him.

My own experiences with the elusive little moraine spooks haven't deviated far from the usual pattern. Two years ago, for instance, near the mouth of Jim Creek, I had a brief skirmish with one of the animals which considerably reduced my professional amperage. I was coming down from the Chugach Lake and had halted on the bank of Jim Creek ford to smoke a cigarette before tackling the swift, muddy, bone-chilling chute of water. Suddenly, some four hundred yards below me, I saw the bear in question gallop out into a shallow, willow-bordered slough, chasing a school of salmon. It was an especially striking animal, light blue—nearly maltese—with gray flanks and a bald face. It caught one of the salmon, carried it ashore, and lay down at the water's edge to eat it. Concluding that this was my golden opportunity, one for which I had long waited, I doused my cigarette and began what should have been a quick, easy stalk. The wind was strongly in my favor, the bear had not seen me, and the roar of the stream was loud enough to cover the sound of my progress through the bankside willows.

But when I stepped out of the brush at the margin of the slough, the bear was nowhere in sight. The salmon lay beside the water, still alive, slapping its tail against the wet sand; and from this spot the bear's trail went up over the shoulder of a dune and down toward a dense stand of jackspruce. The animal had been running.

It took me ten minutes to find out what had gone wrong. Grounded on the bar point, within a few yards of the place where the bear had lain down to eat the salmon, was the cigarette I had thrown away. The bear, of course, had scented it the moment it drifted down to him, and had known what it meant. To say that I was humiliated would only half describe my feelings.

Then there was an incident that happened during a hunt Hal Johnson and I made in the Pinnacle Lake country. Getting up at daybreak one morning, Hal sighted an animal swimming across the lake toward camp and shook me awake to tell me about it.

"It's probably a beaver," I said, hoping he wouldn't insist that I get up to look at it.

"Makes a mighty big wake for a beaver," Hal said doubtfully. Then, a moment later: "A beaver's ears don't stand up, do they?"

They don't, not on any beaver I ever saw. So I crawled out of my robe for a look. The first pink wash of dawn was on the quiet water, and swimming in a sort of lane between the reflections of two giant peaks was a bear. He was a little fellow, and presumably he had come across from the farther shore, some eight hundred yards distant. As he drew near the beach he winded us, and thrust himself half out of the water and blew sharply. Against the pale shine of the lake his coat was coal-black. I asked Hal if he wanted the animal and he said no, that he had all the black-bear trophies he intended to take; so I thought it would be a good idea to give the bear a scare. Otherwise he might hang around and find opportunity to loot the camp. The most convenient missile happened to be a shoeing hammer I had used the evening before and left lying on the woodpile. Snatching it up, I ran down the beach as the bear landed, waving my arms and shouting.

He was really scared. Without even pausing to shake himself, he let out a moan and tore up the bank, heading for cover. I threw the hammer in his general direction as he fled into a group of dead cottonwoods, and for a moment it sounded as if he was going to knock the entire stand of trees down. It was very funny. Hal and I laughed so hard that we couldn't go back to sleep. After breakfast I went down to look for the hammer. I found it, and as I stooped to pick it up I saw something that took all the comedy out of the reception we had given the bear. Snagged on a broken limb was a tuft of blue hair. It was a good three inches long, soft as silk, with a double wave in it such as you sometimes see in mountain-goat wool. Being wet, I suppose, was what had made the bear look black.

"The trophy of a lifetime," Hal moaned when he saw it, "and what do you do? You shag it out of camp. What a guide!"

And there was an enlightening affair that took place one fall at the head of the Matanuska. I had packed in from tidewater in the hope of getting some photographs of blue bear. There were not, so far as I could discover, any such photographs in existence. Plenty of northern wildlife shutterbugs could dig into their negative files and produce passable shots of any arctic or subarctic fauna you might choose to name, from crested sea parrots to musk-oxen —except that when you mentioned blue bear they would shake their heads sadly and inform you that a good shot of a blue bear would be in a class with eighty-inch moose heads, fifty-inch ram trophies, and twelve-foot Kodiak pelts. So I thought that if I could find a blue bear and get some really fine pictures of the animal, it would be the outstanding feat of my career as a woodsman.

I made camp in the last timber below the glacier and during the following two weeks scouted the area thoroughly, extensively, and altogether unsuccessfully. One morning when I had just about reached the conclusion that the hunt was a bust, I sighted two cubs, apparently grizzlies, on a pea-vine bar between the river and some big cottonwoods. They were catching grasshoppers, or at any rate were trying to catch grasshoppers. Their method was to locate one of the fat green hoppers and then make an elaborate stalk from different angles, finishing with a joyous rush that usually brought them together in head-on-collision. One of the cubs was brown, while the other was palomino—yellow with silver points. As they were unaware of my presence and the wind was blowing from them to me, I had no difficulty in approaching within fair telephoto range.

But before I could pick them up in the finder and make an exposure, the cubs charged another grasshopper, ran into each other again, and this time began to fight—rolling over and over, biting, clawing, and snarling like demons. They tumbled into a wash, and presently one of them, getting the worst of the fight, let out a loud, urgent squall. At once there was a snort back in the timber, followed by a great crashing of undergrowth. Obviously mamma was coming and I knew she would wind me and blame me for the trouble her cubs had got into. I tossed the camera under a windfall and made for the only hospitable tree in sight. As I pulled myself up among the first limbs, the she bear passed me, blowing like a horse, her hackles so stiffly erect that she looked humpbacked. She was a glacier bear, a typical specimen. Her pelt, so glossy that it shone in the sunlight, was a deep, rich blue, yielding to black on the rump and legs, with a sprinkling of silver along the top line of her shoulders.

She slapped the cubs apart and hazed them down the bars, halting every few yards to look back and growl. It was hard to believe the three were of the same species, let alone members of the same family. Possibly the explanation of their wide difference in coloring was that glacier-bear cubs do not shed out the first summer and therefore do not get their blue pelts until they are fourteen or fifteen months old. Anyhow, that was the only explanation I could think of. I've told a number of old-time bear-hunters about the incident, and none have offered a more reasonable answer. Of course, I didn't get any pictures. Nor have other camera hunts I have made produced even one photograph of a blue bear. I haven't, in fact, ever seen a photograph of a wild blue bear, and I doubt that one exists. Which state of affairs, incidentally, provides an interesting challenge to the increasing legion of wildlife photographers—and also accounts for the absence of photographs for this chapter.

Both the Indian and the white hunters of the north maintain that the blue bear is as short-tempered as the grizzly and as prone to charge when crowded. An example of this characteristic occurred during a wolf-trapping expedition I made as a youngster with Starvation Smith. Starvation is a tall, lean, bushy-whiskered old-timer who acquired his unusual nickname in the Happy River country, during a community moose hunt that the residents of Susitna Station made there one winter for meat when the annual supply ship had failed to arrive. Starvation was appointed cook for the expedition, despite his earnest protests that he didn't know anything about cooking except how to boil beans, fry bacon, and make sourdough flapjacks. The hunters didn't believe him, but they soon discovered he not only had told the truth but actually had somewhat overestimated his cooking ability. After a half-dozen meals they summarily ejected him from the cook-tent, and thenceforth he was known as Starvation Smith.

Well, we were at the head of the Nelchina, trapping wolves in July by virtue of a special permit, and one morning, while running a line we had put out along the river, we found a blue bear caught in a snare. Alive and full of fight, the animal was roaring at the top of its lungs and throwing gravel in all directions. Although the game commission at this time was committed to the dubious policy of cutting down the black and glacier bear population of the territory, this bear was so thin and ragged—worthless as a trophy —that we decided to release it if we could figure out a way to do so.

"Looks like there's just one way to do it," Starvation said presently, when he had surveyed the situation. "I'll have to shoot the snare off." He motioned to a log jam piled against some huge granite boulders. "I'll do it from there. You climb a tree and stay put."

So I found a perch in a gaunt hangman's cottonwood growing on the edge of the bench and watched Starvation prepare for his sharpshooting stunt. When he was all set, with the bear standing in the right position, he squinted through the sights of his .30/40 and pulled. It was a good shot. The soft-nose clipped the steel wire behind the lock as neatly as it could have been done with pliers. This was the bear's cue to beat it. But instead, without an instant's hesitation, it charged. Before Starvation could chamber another cartridge, the animal was on the jam, hidden momentarily by a projecting tangle of logs. Taken by surprise, Starvation acted on what he later admitted was sheer panicky impulse. He laid his rifle down, turned, and jumped into the river. Fifty yards below, a gravel bar reached out from the inside of a bend, and Starvation —flailing the water with more energy than science—made a landing on the tip of it. The bear batted his rifle around a moment, bit the stock and forearm, then swaggered off the jam, growling, and headed up the bank, where it disappeared into the timber.

"I didn't know you were such a strong swimmer," I said when Starvation had recovered his gun and I had slid out of the tree. "Man, you plowed through the water like a beaver."

"W-well, the f-fact is," Starvation said, shivering violently and looking around for dry wood with which to start a fire, "I'm kind of s-surprised about that myself. Because right up to the time the b-bear chased me into the d-damned river, I was of the opinion that I c-couldn't swim a lick."

In the matter of the blue bear's orneriness, however, I have seldom heard of anything to equal a display Slim Watson and I witnessed one fall during a flight over the southern shed of the Endicotts. We were following the course of a nameless Arctic stream, cruising along a few hundred feet above the bars, when we sighted a glacier bear digging into a cut-bank, apparently trying to excavate a whistler's den. This was Slim's first chance for a close-up look at a blue bear, so he banked, flattened the propeller out so the ship wouldn't fall off, and flew in a tight circle about the animal, twenty feet or so above it. The bear's reaction to this was surprising.

Instead of fleeing as we had expected, the animal rolled over on its back, lips curled to show its fighting teeth, and reached up with all four paws, ready to grapple with us.

Amazed and delighted by this show of ferocity, Slim edged the ship closer and suddenly slanted a wing at the bear. Just as the wing dipped, the bear bounded into the air and grabbed at the ship with its front paws. It came so close to getting a hold on the wing that, expecting a crash, I ducked under the instrument panel. Slim zoomed the ship up in a climbing turn and when he had leveled off he glanced at me and I saw he was as scared as I was.

"Some bear," I said.

"If they're all that tough," Slim stated, "it's no darned wonder the old-timers rate 'em as dangerous game."

Blue bear are so elusive and so difficult to hunt that you seldom hear of a sportsman going out for them alone. The animals in most cases are hunted in connection with other game, usually mountain goats or high-country grizzlies. They inhabit the barren wastes of rock in the vicinity of the vast glacier systems that sprawl over the Coast Range, the southern slope of the Alaska Range, and the Endicotts. They subsist on the scanty vegetation that, during the brief summer, grows along the moraine dumps and the Alpine streamlets, and on parka squirrels and marmots, which they capture by digging them out of their burrows. There are a few accounts of their having killed sheep and the young of mountain goats. Prospectors and others who journey back into the bleak ice-torn fastnesses of the peaks have told of being stalked by the blue bear. It has been claimed that on occasions the animals will charge without provocation.

My friend Wasilla Stepan told me once that a blue bear circled him repeatedly in an alder jungle on the upper Talkeetna River, roaring and popping its teeth threateningly.

"I got one shot at him," Wasilla said, "and I didn't hear him any more, but I don't know whether I killed him or not. I didn't try to find out. I went away from there as fast as I could. Blue bears are bery bad. I think maybe they all are clazy."

Probably the two likeliest blue-bear ranges are Yakataga Basin and the sweep of moraine hills lying below Ruth and Eldridge Glaciers. The former area is accessible by boat or airplane from Cordova, while the latter can be reached by canoe from Chulitna

Station on the Alaska Railroad. Fall hunts are preferable because at this season the bears are in characteristic blue pelage, whereas during the spring season it would be difficult, if not impossible, to distinguish between a grizzly and a glacier bear without killing the animals and examining their skulls and teeth. Since the game commission has decided, doubtless because it was necessary to take a stand somewhere in the matter, that the blue bear actually is a color phase of the black, there is no closed season and no bag limit on the animal in most parts of the territory.

In outfitting for a blue-bear hunt, I suggest that you include equipment for preserving the skeletons of any kills, as specimens are needed for study. The effort required to bring them out probably would gain a hunter the enduring gratitude not only of wildlife authorities but of zoologists who are seeking to unravel the somewhat complicated relationships of our many species, subspecies, and varieties of bear.

Tex Cobb claims he once hit upon an emergency method of identifying blue-bear skulls which deserves a place in the record of scientific achievement. According to the tale, a certain world-famous naturalist was making a study of Alaskan bears and as a part of the undertaking had engaged Tex to collect skulls of the animals for him. Tex says he gathered together and shipped several crates of brown, black, and grizzly skulls, but when he tried to find a glacier-bear skull he discovered he was up against a difficult proposition. He worked through the Chickaloon Mountains, across the Nelchina country, and down to the Big Susitna—arriving there in September, his clothes in rags and his grub nearly gone—before he got on the track of one. Two prospectors coming down the river on a raft told him they had killed a glacier bear the previous fall and that the skull was under their cache on Loon Creek, twenty miles back upstream.

Fired with renewed zeal, Tex headed up the bars, and reached the cache after dark, in the teeth of the season's first snowstorm. By the light of a birch-bark torch he pawed through a frozen litter of chips, bones, tin cans, and other odds and ends of debris and succeeded, to his considerable surprise and confusion, in finding not one but six bear skulls. As he couldn't carry all of them with him, the problem was strictly one of identification. To make the matter worse, the six skulls were nearly of a size, and none had any special peculiarity or distinguishing feature that Tex could see, save that one was that of an old, old bear, the teeth worn down to mere stumps.

"Well, I looked 'em over careful," Tex told me afterward, "and by the time the torch was burned out, I had the situation all solved. The skull with the wore-down teeth was the one. Anyhow, I was willing to gamble hit was. So I packed hit down to tidewater an' shipped hit. An' sure enough, Doctor What's-his-name wired back from New York that hit was a glacier-bear skull all right, an' that he was plenty glad to get hit."

"I still don't see how you were able to pick it out," I said.

"Shucks, hit was simple. Jest a case of usin' my head. You've hunted glacier bears, ain't you?"

I said I had.

"Well, then you oughta know that if there is one critter in the north that's likely to live long enough to wear hits teeth down to the gums, hit's the dang, tricky son-of-a-gun of a glacier bear."

It's a fact!

E DISON M ARSHALL

In the Land of the Sladang

No difference of opinion, not even one involving horse races, will
ever equal in vehemence the debate between experienced hunters,
qualified and otherwise, as to what constitutes the most dangerous game. The fact that circumstance and habitat enter the picture is not relevant. A number of sportsmen who have run the
gamut from rabbits to elephants insist that the wild buffalo,
whether his home be Africa or Asia, puts the hunter in the most
interesting and exciting situation. Of the buffalos the "sladang"
or "seladang" of Asia is the giant of his kind, and, so many insist,
the Number One trophy of the hunter. Edison Marshall has
earned the reputation of being a thinking hunter, so his opinion
is offered as expert evidence.

For two years I had been living on big game memories. True, I
had an abundant stock. The walls of the big trophy room
were adorned with horns and pelts, every one of which recalled
some sharper, more vital moment on some far-off trail. To the left
of the fireplace hung the great head of Osborn's caribou—massive
antlers with an odd back-spike—my first real trophy. I had only to
shut my eyes to return to a long glade in the dark spruce forests
of the Selkirk Mountains and the old herd bull tossing his horns
with the light of November dawn on his white mane.

In ten years, the big game fever had cost me not only two years'
time, but a generous percentage of my income and more cold and
broiling heat and discomfort and insect bites than any sane man
would tolerate for a thousand trophies. It had led me into moderate
danger, had made me work like a bullock, and sent me to the

loneliest and least habitable corners of the world. Yet it had given me, in all, a hundred or so brief moments of intense existence, of life at highest pitch.

As I looked at the caribou horns memories came thronging. My first guide, Dean Cochran—queer mixture of savant and frontiersman—who followed his trap lines on winter days and read Schopenhauer at night. A yellow horse that literally sat down on his tail in every quagmire we crossed. An old scout named Kibbe, part of whose face had been shorn away by the paw of a grizzly. The curious notched line of the spruce trees against the twilight sky . . .

There on the floor lay my first grizzly—and once more the waters of the Iskut, tributary to the great Stikine, gurgled by the canoe. How hard I hunted for that fellow! With what cruel cunning I caught and heaped spawned-out salmon on the river bank to draw him forth from the devil-club thickets where I could not go! Then how at last I stole upon him—great shaggy forest king and little frail-boned *Homo sapiens* with his wicked little gun!

As my eye roamed to the big moose head over the fireplace, the scene changed. The waters flowing through the black forest gave way to the gray pools of the beaver meadows, yellow and sear under October skies. From the jackpine thickets beyond came a long wild call . . . The guide answered through the birchbark horn—and into the open strode a black giant with ungainly head and swinging antlers.

Why is it that the sight of big game leaves such an indelible etching on the memory? The light is often dim—the animal has the advantage of protective coloration—yet the hunter can always recall the scene with an uncanny vividness. And why is he not content with that wonderful memory-picture—quick with life, imbued with the primal spirit of the outdoors—instead of trying to seize it in his hands and staining them with blood?

There was another bearskin in the center of the room. It dwarfed every other trophy—the head alone as big as a chair. Instantly the walls receded and became towering cliffs, guarding a secret valley somewhere behind Mount Pavlof on the road to Siberia. Out of those cliffs little streams plunged like wild white horses, but there was never a tree to redeem the desert of crag and tundra, and not one gleam of sunlight through the gray desolate clouds. The monster, one of twenty-six Kodiak bears seen in a single day in Lost Valley, lay asleep on an old snowbank. I came upon him in his unguarded hour—and now all that remains of him is a fur rug for visitors to tread on and hardly notice. Yet he was no doubt one of the largest bears ever killed by a sportsman. His pelt, laid out naturally on the ground, was a full twelve feet.

As the eye sweeps around the trophy room, the continents pass in review. The walrus ivories and the polar-bear skin call back the glittering drift-ice north of Barrow, and the Eskimos beating through the surf in their kayaks. The lion skins on the floor and a tobacco humidor made of a rhino's foot call up the green dongas, the flat-topped mimosa groves, and the endless yellow veldt baked by a tropic sun.

Now was the time to go again. I began studying maps, oiling up and admiring my rifles, reading with bitter jealousy the adventures of other hunters in regions I had not yet visited. When I started to write to guides, receiving their frequently misspelled but strangely eloquent replies, my civilized jig was up until further notice. The best letter I received was from Francis Defosse—an intelligent, exciting description of a new, happy hunting ground in French Indo-China.

Like most Americans, I knew very little about this vast jungle lying between India and China. I knew vaguely that it could be entered through the port of Saigon, that it contained a French colony and two considerable kingdoms, Anam and Cambodia, and that Theodore Roosevelt, Jr., had been there in 1929; also, that it remained one of the few virgin game-fields in the world. Almost every large mammal found in India is also found in Anam—and, I think, under more picturesque conditions.

There was a corner in a trophy room where a large tiger skin would fit nicely. I had always craved a tiger—the very word has a glamour and calls up mental images of steaming jungles and a great striped killer gliding through like the shadow of doom—and he was the one great carnivore I had never hunted. My first idea was to make this trip purely a tiger hunt, devoting no attention to the other large game animals of Indo-China. Certainly I had no desire to kill the small-tusked Asiatic elephant. He is too old and too wise and too grand to lay low with five cents' worth of lead. To kill an Indian rhinoceros would be, to my thinking, an offense against the whole world of sport, so rare has the species become.

The Indian buffalo is an easy trophy in the dry season, but I proposed to go at the height of the rains. I would take any leopard that came along, of course, and I would like a head of sambur, the big stag of Kipling's jungle books; but at first I took no interest in the remaining two big game animals of Indo-China, the banteng and the sladang.

What is a sladang? I had a very dim idea. In an old animal book over which I used to pore as a child I had seen a picture of what seemed to be a large stag-like brute with bull horns called the gaur, the Indian name for the sladang, but his description was as vague as the picture was fantastic. But as the weeks went by, I began to hear more and more about this great wild ox of the jungle. To my amazement I learned that he was the biggest horned animal in the world—larger than our giant moose, far larger than the African buffalo, equally as large as the great aurochs, the extinct bison of Caesar's day. Moreover, the old hunters spoke of him with marked respect. He was not only hard to hunt in the black fastnesses of the jungle, but he was savage tempered as a rhino with a festering tooth. The old shikaris spoke civilly to him who had shot a sladang. A germ of an idea began to take root in my brain—that the sladang would share honors with the tiger in my hunt, and that quite possibly he was the finest big game trophy in the whole world of sport.

Fellow sportsmen will like to know the kind of outfit that I brought from home. I made the usual number of mistakes, but on the whole did well enough. In the way of guns, I took a heavy side arm in case of close work with a king cobra, a light shotgun for jungle fowl and small game, and a .35 caliber pump-action rifle, a quick and nippy little piece with surprising killing power.

I selected this gun from my list first, because I am used to the pump action, and second, because it combines lightness, positive action and sudden death all in one piece. I felt I could take only one rifle, as I knew there would be no end of red tape in getting firearms into Indo-China, and the little .35 was my pick. It was not nearly heavy enough for tigers or sladang, but I expected to buy a .404 Mauser in Saigon.

I took binoculars, but never looked through them once. The range of vision in the jungles of the sladang is never over one hundred yards, and is frequently less than forty feet. In the way of footgear I had moccasins reaching well to the knee, to guard against the little krait and the common cobra that sometimes loiter by the trail. In view of tropical rains I carried rather heavy rain-proof breeches, but this was a mistake. The lighter the khaki the better. The hunter is bound to be wet through by the torrential rains, and heavy canvas chafes the skin raw. Medicines, a small surgical outfit and a tourniquet in case of a cobra bite, a strong headlight, and plenty of tobacco and chocolates completed my rig.

I sailed from Seattle and disembarked at Hongkong, in southern China. Here I boarded the French ship *Athos*, and three days later arrived at Saigon, the chief port of Indo-China. Francis Defosse and his son Louis, my two guides, met me on the dock.

Francis Defosse is known wherever sportsmen gather. He had lived in the jungle for more than twenty years, first as a market hunter, then as a guide. Before that he was a soldier, and the mark was still upon him in the set of his shoulders and the free swing of his stride. Like so many white hunters, he is an able naturalist and a man of keen intelligence. I had come alone on this expedition, but as soon as I met Defosse and his son I knew that I would have no need for other company. The elder Defosse spoke English fluently in addition to his native French, Anamese and two of the Moi dialects—the language of the savages in whose country we meant to penetrate.

I have met only one man, old Bwana Cottar in Africa, who has seen and lived more adventure than Francis Defosse. He has watched over the gnawed-off trunk of a native to kill the man-eater that had snatched him from his village gate. He was once tracked more than two miles by three terrible avengers—bull elephants he had wounded. He has been tossed by a buffalo and left for dead.

As a rule, Americans do not think of Frenchmen as natural outdoor men. We forget the voyageurs of Quebec and the deep-voiced guides on the salmon lakes of northern Maine. Francis Defosse is of the school of Audubon. A tall blue-eyed man, he can out-tramp, outshoot, and outrough-it many an English guide in Africa, and is on a par with our own Western and Alaskan frontiersmen.

The figure of Louis Defosse, Francis' son, will loom large in this narrative and must be described in detail. His mother is an Anamese woman, as his Oriental features reveal. He was just twenty, but he spoke all the tongues known to his father and in addition several other Moi dialects.

This boy was born and raised in the jungle. Somehow he made me think of Kipling's Mowgli. While he didn't speak the languages of birds and beasts, at least he knew many of their secrets. In eleven big game trips, I have met only one other man possessing this curious intimacy with wild things—a feeling about animals mystic and indescribable—and he was a quarter-breed Indian named Mauf Hamilton, in the Quesnel Lake country of British Columbia. Of books, Louis knows little, but the dim pages of the wild he can read as he runs. Finally, he has the curious capacity to put himself in an animal's place and thus know what that animal will do, where he will go, and how to hunt him.

The Mois regard Louis with superstitious reverence. Most French can not handle them—they have successfully withstood the encroachments of French law and civilization, and still live in complete savagery—but Louis can do with them what he likes. In case of war, I believe he could enlist them all, provided he led them in person.

Somehow we got through the red tape of the French customs. I was allowed to import my firearms and buy a .404 Mauser. With the help of half a dozen rickshaws we got our supplies to the train and headed north into the kingdom of Anam. Within a few hours we were traveling through dense jungle. From a village called Soui-Kiet we packed into oxcarts and said farewell to civilization.

Thank heaven no automobile can penetrate the jungles of Anam. The roads are rough trails laid out in the immemorial past by various unknown races who came and flourished and died away; and although they are half up and half down, a two-wheeled cart can somehow get along. Perched on the cart rode a dozen Mois—little brown men of the jungle, naked save for G strings, but smiling and chattering and keen for the trip.

These boys would do the skinning, the boma-building, the load-carrying and all the other tasks which in the North Country the guides and hunters do for themselves. They were pleased by the prospect of big wages—twenty cents a day in our money—and even more delighted by the promise of good feeding. Some of them had their wives—rather unprepossessing women, naked to the waist—and there was even a baby or two in the mothers' pack-sacks. Apparently a hunting trip of this kind was quite a break in the monotony of their lives.

I liked the little heathens from the start. They reminded me of our primitive Gulla darkies on the coastal plain of Carolina. Their idea of what made a rifle shoot was peculiarly childlike—that the force of the hammer knocked the bullet through the barrel something after the manner that their own bow-strings propelled an arrow—and they judged the power of a rifle by the loudness of the click when it was snapped on an empty chamber. Gunpowder meant nothing to their simple souls. When a hunter fired and failed to kill his game, they obligingly blamed it on some flaw in the magic of the gun rather than on the hunter's aim.

They did not know one end of a rifle from the other, but they apparently regarded it with a great deal of superstitious reverence. I noticed that when they were sent on errands in the jungle, they went far more willingly if they were permitted to carry a firearm in their hands. Whether or not it was loaded was a matter of indifference.

They could not tell time, but they loved to hold my watch to their ears and hear it tick. Their jabber was baffling—in my whole trip I learned only one word of their language. But they worked like buffaloes and were nippy and ready to go any hour of the day or night.

For uncounted centuries these little people have fought the jungle. The sambur eat their rice; tigers kill their buffalo calves and, more frequently than is pleasant to contemplate, man-eaters creep upon them in the twilight and crush their skulls with one chain-lightning sweep of a sledge-hammer paw; elephants destroy their little plantations. But still the fight goes on, the same as when they first wandered here from some lost birthplace in Malaysia.

They hew little fields out of the thick jungle, till them a year or two, then forsake them and move on. They build their queer community houses, on high stilts; in the firelight they perform ceremonial dances, offer sacrifices to their numerous gods, and drink themselves into oblivion on their fiery rice-brew. The race may die out in a few years—slain by the white man's nearing civilization—but certainly it will never change its ways.

In describing the outfit, it would be a grave oversight not to mention Cooky and his boy. Cooky was, as a matter of course, Chinese. His son was a racial mystery defying any ethnologist to solve. He was fully three shades darker than his father, but his features looked Caucasian. These two prepared the curry, fought the ants, and did the washing. In addition to all his other duties, Cooky, Sr., prophesied every morning as to the day's bag, and I must admit that his predictions were most uncannily close.

The outfit afforded three little stallions, smaller than Western mustangs, for the two guides and myself to ride. Amid a downpour of rain—a rain that lashed through the trees like bayonets and changed the trail first to one long mud-puddle, then to a rushing river—we headed into the jungle.

I shall never forget that first day's ride. When the rain stopped, as suddenly as it had begun, I found myself in what seemed a haunted forest. The trees were gigantic, with naked trunks fifty—seventy-five—some of them a hundred feet high. Newly washed by rain, the vegetation was an indescribable rich green, save for an occasional flash of vivid color provided by a nameless flower or a gaudy butterfly. From the treetops hung creepers like giant pythons; unseen birds chattered and screamed in the branches. Mostly the thorn thickets and the underbrush restricted the vision to a few yards, but occasionally we came out on open glades, as lovely as the park lands in the high mountains of the North.

For some hours I saw no sign of game. If we had trusted only to our eyes, we might have thought we were in an uninhabited desert. Yet the feeling came over me that these dense thickets through which I rode were fairly teeming and breathing with living things. I knew that furtive eyes were watching me as I rode by, and that the grass was springing up from light feet that had just crept away.

As evening drew on and the brown shadows turned purple, I was more and more conscious of invisible life all about me. Once the thickets crashed beside the trail, where a wild boar fled from his meal of fallen fruit. Once a silver pheasant flashed between the trees. Once I saw a little brown face, strangely human, peering at me from a low branch, but it vanished as if by magic.

Late in the afternoon I saw Defosse swing over his horse and peer at something on the trail. When I rode up, I saw a four-toed track nearly as big as a saucer.

"A pretty big fellow," Defosse said.

It looked enough like the lion tracks I had seen in Africa that I could recognize it. "Looks pretty fresh," I said.

"He crossed here about five minutes ago." Without another word, Defosse mounted and rode on.

But a pleasant little thrill stole up my back when I thought that an old dream had come true, and I was in tiger country at last.

Too much has already been written about the insect pests of Indo-China. Even in the rainy season they are not so bad as painted. With proper nets and a can or two of poison they can be kept well under control.

The skeeters make night-watching over bait one big scratchy torment, but they have nothing of the resourcefulness and general cussedness of Alaskan skeeters. I did have one painful experience with the ants—little red fellows, with nippers out of all proportion to their size. I failed to put kerosene rags around the legs of my cot, and one infernal night they invaded my bed. While I slept the sleep of exhaustion they bit me only occasionally—just enough to make me dream I was being torn to pieces by red-hot pinchers—but when at last I wakened and stirred, they all tackled me at once. Four thousand of them bit me in my tenderest places. The dance that I performed, alone in the moonlight, would have done credit to any sacrificial devil-dance of the Mois.

The next-sized ant was a black fellow, incredibly ferocious. He only desired to be left alone, but one night I was unfortunate enough to put my naked foot into one of his roving bands, to be attacked with tigerish fury. They actually stung like hornets.

And speaking of hornets, there is a curious hazard to be encountered in Indo-China that I had never met before. This winged demon does not attack the hunter, but is obsessed with the notion of making a nest in his gun-barrel! The little black hole appeals to her, somehow. In an hour she will have it well plugged with dirt, in which is buried a paralyzed worm. When her larvae hatch, they will find their meal fresh and ready for them. One such hornet made her nest in a hole in the metal case of my razor stropper. An obstructed rifle barrel is no joke, as every hunter knows; so when I leaned my weapon in the tent, I always stopped the barrel with the business end of a cartridge.

In every tropic country the hunter encounters scorpions. Now a scorpion is closely related to the spiders. He has a hooked projection at the end of his elongated tail with which he can inject a minute drop of venom into his victim. Fortunately the dose is too small to do more than paralyze the immediate area of the bite for a period of an hour or more.

These little blighters are too devilish common in Indo-China. Twice I caught them in my bed, twice in my trunk, and twice they caught me in the hand. The sting is somewhat similar to the sudden thrust of a red-hot needle, but this is a very mild comparison. I defy the strongest and most silent man not to yell like a Comanche Indian when, without the slightest warning, a scorpion turns back his tail and gets to work.

Far in the jungle we made our camp. We wakened in the dark dawn and breakfasted by lantern light. My two guides went scouting for game signs. I summoned the old tracker—a gray-haired savage whose name I never could learn to pronounce but which sounded like a gurgle deep in the throat—and took a stroll out from camp.

I have hunted in the big forests of the North and the wide veldts of the far South, but these lush and leafy jungles seemed to offer an entirely new experience. Unless I can carry my readers into them, into the shadowy depths, the hunted glades, this narrative will fail in its purpose and become a mere recital of bloodshed. The North Woods are awesome, and somber. The veldt is sun-baked, cruel, somehow accursed. But in describing the jungle, the only term that seems to fit is sinister. It is altogether too richly beautiful, too green, and inviting. The pools under the arching trees are limpid and lovely—but you must not drink the cool water! You see no stir of movement and hear no sound. It is hard to guess that Striped Death may be lurking only twenty yards away. Unless you search diligently, you will never find the little krait hiding in the dust. Yet you find yourself curiously on guard. You do not relax and stand daydreaming, as on the good green hills of our native land. You keep moving and watching, and frequently you glance over your shoulder. Your good sense tells you that you are in no real danger—only rarely does any wild creature make an unprovoked attack—but your heart is thumping with excitement and your blood tingles pleasantly as it spurts through your veins. You have come here seeking excitement—when all is said and done—and suddenly you know that the red gods mean to give it to you. Here is The Land of the Sladang. It is one of the three great happy hunting grounds in the wild world.

I am not a good tracker, and a third-rate hiker, but I have one asset which has always proved a great advantage in hunting—a quick, strong eye. In a very little while I began to look through the leafy screen and see marvelous sights beyond. Presently a black creature that I could not identify crossed an open glade at a distance of a hundred yards. It did not move like a four-legged animal, yet it looked as big as a small deer. Then I guessed the truth—a wild peacock. Hereafter we saw these marvelous big birds every day.

I saw squirrels, jungle fowl, parrots, wild pigeons. There were dozens of other birds of which even the white hunters do not know the name, and are known only by jaw-breaking Latin appelations in ornithological tomes. I saw a porcupine, and once the fluffy tail of a mongoose wiggled behind a bush. Once something that looked like a small dead branch on the ground came to life and wiggled away.

It was a cobra (cobra de capello of the black variety). Although they were fairly common in the woods, it was unusual to see one on the first day's hunt. They are little to be feared—although their bite is often fatal, they keep out of man's way—and are not to be confused with the terrible, malignant king cobra, which is possibly the most dangerous large creature in the world. The king cobra is not only likely to attack without provocation, but is incredibly swift and ferocious.

Many living things had crossed my trail the preceding night. There were tracks of banteng, the big red ox of the jungle park lands—an animal large as the African buffalo, but a runt compared to the mighty sladang. Here a leopard had crouched in ambush; there a sambur buck, the great dun stag of Kipling's *Jungle Books*, had stolen out of the dense thickets to feed in the open glades. There were tracks of the little red barking deer, an animal no longer than the Thompson's gazelle in Africa.

Finally I found some tracks that I could not identify. They looked like deer tracks seen through the wrong end of a microscope—the little cloven hoof could rest with ease on a dime. I could not understand the tracker's explanations, but I soon guessed that the tracks were those of the mouse-deer—the smallest hoofed animal in the world. He is not so big as many a hearty jack rabbit on eastern Oregon plains.

We flushed one of these little fellows presently. It went bounding off with surprising speed. I had no desire to kill any of them; but one of the guides procured a buck later for the table.

I was not to go back to camp with a clean gun-barrel. A glimmer of brown through the thickets revealed itself as a barking deer, much desired for the pot. A quick shot and I sent him scampering off. I could hardly believe I had missed him at that range, but there was not a drop of blood. Plainly, I had forgotten how sharp and intent the gaze must be along a gun-barrel. The tracker looked at the weapon with disapproval. When I pretended, with expansive gestures, to find and fix something wrong with the sights, he appeared better satisfied.

When we reached camp, we had good news from the scouts. There was considerable tiger sign, including the print of "the Old Man." Naturally I wanted to know who "the Old Man" might be. Well, he was an especially big tiger, with a track nearly as big as a tea plate, that the guides had seen in these jungles on and off for the past four years. They knew him because one toe turned sideways, showing in the track.

What chance did I have of getting this old veteran? About one in a hundred, Defosse said—dismiss the idea! He was wary as an old wolf. He almost never touched baits, but killed his own meat.

Anyway, he was just passing through the country—one big track after another—and might be thirty miles away by now. But there were other tigers available, doubtless as big and fine.

Defosse let the matter drop, but it continued to linger in my mind. Someone, some time, would get that old fellow—and carry home his skin as an enduring memento of a glorious day—and if luck broke just right . . . Yet it was only a chance in a hundred.

The scouts had found the fresh trail of a big elephant herd. Better yet, they reported that there was at least one small herd of sladang in the thick jungle between our camp and the river.

At lunch we planned our campaign. The first duty was to lay out baits for tigers. From the Moi villages, we could buy old, worn-out buffaloes. There was no cruelty here; a quick bullet through the brain saved them the lingering death otherwise their fate.

Usually, it is necessary first to attract the tiger with a dead sambur. I have never liked the idea of killing game animals for bait, but Defosse explained that there would be little if any loss to the wild life of the country. The tiger would simply devour the meat we gave him, instead of killing for himself. Big game hunting is not nearly as bloody a business as a big pigeon shoot, but any attempt to excuse it is likely to be hypocritical. To procure a rare trophy, some lesser lives must be taken, if only to supply camp meat for guides and camp help.

That night Louis strapped a headlight on his forehead, and he and I rode in the oxcart out of the firelight deep into the fastnesses of the jungle. I shall never forget my first taste of night hunting. We followed the old trails, the cart pitching and listing like a ship in a heavy sea. All the way the light showed magic vistas—little green glades under the huge trees; dense brush coverts; dark waters still rippling from some wild thing that had just submerged; tangles of vines and creepers like great serpents; a shadow flicking across the beam of light and fading into shadows. But for a long time we saw no live thing except fireflies, glimmering through the trees.

It was a creepy feeling—to be riding through the utter dark in tiger country. Actually only a confirmed man-eater, rare in any jungle, and familiar to the point of contempt with Moi carts, would jump in with us and jump out with one of us. But we might meet wild elephants. These are very touchy and unpredictable animals. Also I was afraid that a green viper might be on some of the low branches that we set shaking.

Presently, the light picked up two gleaming eyes. But Louis

identified the animal as a civet cat—a creature the size of our lynx —and we let it go in peace. Shortly after, we saw the eyes of what might be a leopard but was probably a barking deer. We needed meat; so Louis unloosed his old shotgun, loaded with buckshot. We heard the animal fall. A moment later the boys picked up a young buck, shot through the neck.

No sambur showed itself that night. I thought it must be due to the noise of the oxcart, but Louis said that this seemed to fascinate the animals rather than frighten them. They would stand staring, in dumb curiosity, while the rumbling monster wheeled by.

We scouted for sladang the following day, and soon after nightfall boarded the oxcart again. Tonight I would wear the headlight, and try my hand at what was for me a new and difficult sport. The eyes of any animal are a small target, as every hunter knows. Worse still, they are likely to disappear as the light ray catches the sights of the rifle. Louis explained that I must aim below the target with a full bead.

An hour later, the ray picked up two little twin moons, blue as sapphire. Instead of following Loius' instructions, I slowly raised my rifle and, as the eyes winked out behind the glaring sights, pulled the trigger.

We heard a rustle as of some animal running off. It seemed patent to everyone that I had missed, as was to be expected. Yet I was not quite convinced. As I pulled the trigger, I had the assurance of a dead aim—a curious feeling, half instinct, half perception, known to every experienced hunter. The sights had been right, and the gun had fired smoothly. So I walked over and had a look around.

It was another animal that had run away. The one I had fired at lay dead in the flickering light, a bullet through the center of his neck, just below the head. It was a splendid sambur buck.

I had no idea that the jungle stag was so large. I judged his weight at close to four hundred pounds. He was not only a bait but a trophy. I knew a corner in the trophy-room where his odd-shaped horns would fit—and they would always recall me to the pitch-black jungle, and two miniature blue moons. The eyes had seemed to shine from an immense distance; as a matter of fact, the range was less than forty yards.

At once we turned back toward camp, but the hunt was not to end without first-chop adventure. In a dense thicket, half a mile from the wickiups, the scythe-like sweep of my light cut across two little circles of green fire. I peered steadily. Presently the two eyes gleamed plain and true. I decided it was a sambur; so I made no move to raise my rifle.

"Jump off and fire!" Louis whispered.

"But we don't want another deer," I protested under my breath.

"It may not be a deer. Do as I tell you!"

When guides speak like that they mean business. Besides, even a tenderfoot could see something different about those incandescent orbs that affected the spine and the short hairs of the scalp. Perhaps I merely imagined a brighter, fiercer glare than I had seen in the gentle eyes of the sambur. The eyes of the sambur had appeared a limpid blue. These were like the green flame of burning gas . . .

At that moment I was nearer to an understanding of Blake's mystic poem than ever before. But I was not thinking of poetry. My heart was leaping, partly because of the suppressed excitement in Louis' hushed tone—a thrill contagious as terror itself in the blackness under the trees—and partly because of the wild intensity of those green lanterns. I knew something thrilling and magnificent and terrifying was going to take place in something short of ten seconds.

It is rare to happen upon one of the great beasts of prey. They are rarely seen except from a carefully prepared ambush, or else when driven from their secret lairs by an army of beaters. In a thousand nights' hunting, Defosse had shined the eyes of only a dozen tigers. Yet my heart kept yelling "Tiger! Tiger!" and this was one of the unforgettable moments of my life.

Just as I leveled the rifle the eyes winked out. Thinking that the glittering sights had eclipsed them, I touched the trigger. The rifle roared—and then there came a terrifying answer from the stillness.

It *was* a tiger! Although I had had no experience with the big cats—had never seen one out of a zoo—I instantly recognized this voice. True, it was not at all like the half-hearted growls one hears before the tiger cage in the circus. It was not even similar to the roar of a lion that I had heard, thirty feet from the boma, one night on the moonlit veldt. No animal other than the great beautiful lord of the jungle could make a noise like that.

It was a snarl and a growl and a roar mingled in one blast of fury and pain. I don't know what it did to Louis, but it shook me to the marrow of my bones. If the tiger had charged that instant, I would have been a pushover. I would hardly have had time to work my bolt, let alone find my aim by a wobbling headlight. Quick-shooting Louis would have had to get me out of that fix, if I were to go home in one piece. The suspense, the darkness, the savage roar right on the heels of my rifle report, and the sure knowledge that there was a wounded tiger thirty yards away in the deep thicket was enough to raise the hair of old Bwana Cottar himself.

An instant before, there had been two Mois waiting behind us. When they heard the tiger, they waited no more. Just what happened to them in the next few seconds we were never to find out. They were congenitally afraid of the black jungle at our rear, but they did not linger on that account. Louis, the tiger, and I were left alone.

The big cat did not charge. We heard the thicket crash as he bounded off—music to my ears. The volume and ferocity of the beast's roar showed that there was plenty of life in him yet, and I needed a little breather before having any more business with tigers. True, I might only have scratched him and we would lose him altogether, but Louis said without offering any evidence that the beast had been seriously wounded. If so, we could track him in the morning. If he were only consoling me, he needn't bother. I preferred daylight tigers.

As we stood straining into the dark, all I could hear was the apoplectic thumping of my own heart. Louis did not make a sound. He was thinking things over. Then I found out what it meant to be hunting with a Mowgli.

"Let's go after him," he whispered.

What a grim joke, I thought. It was not even in very good taste.

"Don't be funny at a time like this."

"I mean it. It's safer now than it will be in daylight. Then he can hide and ambush us. We'd never see him in the brush until he's almost on top of us. His stripes blend with the leaves." This last he spoke in a slightly pedantic tone, like a naturalist to a troop of boy scouts.

"Oh, hell."

"But tonight the light will pick him up. If he's strong enough to fight, he'll have his head up, listening and watching for us. We're bound to shine his eyes at a safe distance."

I did not believe the words; only swayed to the conviction in Louis' voice. The reasoning was perfectly sound—animal eyes light up like beacons in the beam from a head lamp—but the whole idea objectionable in the extreme. Since then, I have told other hunters to try it; they remarked that theoretically it is the perfect answer to trailing wounded tigers in heavy cover, but I could tell from their eyes that they would not dream of doing such a damn fool thing. Neither would I, in my right mind. Yet I let that nocturnal jungle brat, Louis, talk me into it.

Rather, he hypnotized me by his manner of complete confidence that I would comply. Moreover, he signaled for me to lead the way. I cannot remember his gesture—he must have made one, since he certainly did not employ words for the revolting suggestion—and I would like to have a flashlight photograph of it, revealing a bit of French grace, while I stood there bug-eyed and gasping. Of course it was the hunter's province to take the shot, the guide's to back him up. The way I was to go was in the general direction of the wounded tiger's flight.

My legs, like a mechanical man's, obeyed. The rest of me was in open but impotent rebellion. What a ghastly march! Unless I swung my headlight very slowly, turning my head at a snail's pace, scanning every thicket, the beam might fail to pick up the ambushed beast; but this procedure left great areas in total blackness for great, horrifying periods of time. Nor was there the slight doubt that if alive and able, the giant cat would charge. We had heard him stop out there in the dark; a sure sign that he had come to bay; his next move was certain. The only question was just when.

In about ten minutes, we gained about a hundred feet. Then suddenly, there were two great blazing emeralds a hundred feet beyond. But the monarch of the fastnesses of the night had lost his most formidable advantage; he could not now see us unseen; he was revealed to us behind the blinding blaze of my head lamp. A tiger does not charge until he has marked down his target. He gave one powerful bound toward us and again stopped, dazzled by the light. We saw him standing with his head high, dauntless, craving a clear sight of his foe.

I got my rifle leveled, resisted the frightful impulse to shoot too quick, and the front sight shone in a dead line along the barrel to his breast. At the roar of the piece he crumpled, his twin flames dark.

A tiger had been killed. The lord of the jungle had fallen. It was a real tiger lying dead in his thickets, striped, ruffed, fanged, bewhiskered. I could not feel that he was merely a head of big game; I could not put in words how I did feel about him, to cause such exultation in my heart. I had known he dwelt in this gorgeous wilderness, skulking unseen even by its other denizens until he rushed forth and slew, gayly painted, deadly armed, a beast of awful symmetry and immeasurable power. I wanted other trophies of the chase and the new dramatic experiences of their pursuit but from hence forward, so long as the passion lived, tigers would be my main quarry. This was the most worthwhile hunting I could ever do. I knew now why the most impassioned hunters would pursue and prize one or two heads each of other magnificent beasts, but never turn from the tiger trail. Sport was somehow an inadequate word for the chase of this royal game.

My tiger was a mature male. In Louis' and my hysteria, we guessed that he would peg out nine feet six inches unskinned; actually he fell half a foot short of that figure. The two Mois came up yelling with excitement and we heaved his four hundred pounds into the oxcart.

All the way to camp, we behaved like lunatics and on arriving there the excitement by no means died down. What happened that night was further proof that tiger hunting is the greatest thrill in all the jungles. The Chinese cook went into raptures and did incantations with a whisker. The little dark Mois came screeching out of bed and danced and pranced with joy about their fallen foe. *They* knew about tigers. These were not just striped animals that ate deer, pigs, cows, buffaloes, and people. Instead they were demons of the forest. The men howled curses at his head and patted the gun that had brought him low. One rather pretty Moi girl salaamed to it.

In fact it was my gun, not I, that received the main credit for the victory. However, my stock had risen sharply, and the head man addressed a long speech to me which Louis said contained a flattering proposal. Francis Defosse was greatly pleased to have a first-class trophy in camp. He even cut down the odds against my getting the Old Man—maybe not a hundred to one, more like ten to one. The huge beast had left his fresh print in a nullah only four miles from our camp. Now there was a real tiger—a Royal Tiger!

Jugs of rice-liquor and bottles of cognac and Georgia corn flowed freely. Francis, as befitting his dignity, went to bed about two o'clock; but most of us saw the sun rise. It was a memorable night.

In the next few days, we had various minor adventures. We flushed the sambur from his bed beside the woodland pools; we met a herd of red wild oxen, large as the African buffalo and second only to the great sladang among the horned animals of the world; we scared the wild boar from their gluttonous feeding under the fruit trees. Night after night, we heard wild elephants trumpeting in their thick jungles of palm. One evening we found them in the tall elephant-grass of an abandoned Moi plantation and stampeded them, blaring and squealing.

One incident that the two Defosses regarded as trifling gave me a real fright. I was stalking through the jungle, alone except for two Mois, trying to glimpse an elephant herd that was crashing brush and trumpeting in a near-by palm thicket. Not ten feet in front of me, there rose a wicked hiss as from a steam jet. Then an evil, ugly, flat head rose out of the grass on two feet of yellow-brown snake. Obviously, this was only a small part of his flagitious length.

I have no innate horror of snakes and after my first jump to the rear did not feel in the least afraid of him. That could have been a disastrous mistake. While I was certain this was a small king cobra, at the time I had either not heard or could not believe that they were much more dangerous at this distance than a diamond-back rattler. The Moi behind me jabbered and gestured for me to shoot—in fact he seemed as alarmed as if we had run into a tiger—but I rather enjoyed his excitement in contrast to my fine pose of imperturbability. Instead of shooting his head off with my rifle, I handed the gun to the boy and drew my pistol. It was a beautiful target, and I was going to show my companions a pretty feat.

Unfortunately, I was not a good pistol shot. By careful aim, I could hit a tin can at forty feet; at less than twenty feet, I missed the devil's head and only creased his neck. Instead of wiggling away, he dropped flat and darted toward me!

Defosse told me later that this should not have surprised me— that it was quite characteristic of that most malignant of creatures, the king cobra. When he felt the sting of the bullet, his cold blood turned malignant. He lives on other snakes; his deepmost instinct is to pursue and kill. Surprise was no word for it. As I sprang back, I fired again, missing the reptile clean. At the roar, he stopped and raised his evil head again.

The Mois and I continued our retreat. The snake is living in that patch of jungle yet for all I know, probably a dozen feet long by now—I judged his length at about nine—and sudden death for any living being, short of an elephant, into whom he sets his fangs. Defosse was rather irritated with me for not finishing him off. He told me that although king cobras were quite rare, they were his chief source of worry in going through heavy cover.

"A big one on the opposite bank of a river bit an Anamese girl," he related. "I heard her scream, and scrambling into a handy boat, I got to her in at least five minutes. She was already prostrated, and within five minutes more she was dead."

It was Defosse's opinion that the king cobra is the most danger-ous large animal in the world. He is aggressive in the extreme, lightning fast, and hideously venomous. Later I learned that even elephants are not completely safe from these demoniac reptiles. They have been known to die from being bitten on the thin-skinned ends of their trunks; according to report, a fine shikari elephant was killed by a king cobra bite on the eyelid when no less than Edward, Prince of Wales, was aboard his broad back. A king cobra does not strike like a rattler; he chews at his victim, sinking his fangs several times in the course of a second or two, and administering a frightful jolt of poison. Defosse told me that he did not know of a single case where a human being survived the bite of a king cobra. Paralysis set in so quickly that even a resource-ful, cool-headed white man, carrying a tourniquet and antivenom, could not save himself.

One of the biggest frights of Defosse's life had been to waken from a nap in an open-ended shanty to find a twelve-foot king cobra cooling off in the rain trough under the eaves.

No venomous snake visited our camp, but we had another ex-citing caller almost every night. This was a middle-sized leopard —or panther, as they are commonly called in Asia. For that mat-ter, Americans almost always speak of a black leopard as a panther, perhaps from the mistaken notion that he is a different breed of animal, instead of being born often in the same litter with the spotted leopards. Our visitor, one of many leopards ranging the territory, had taken a fancy to some of the worthless dogs belonging to the Mois.

The natural antipathy between the leopard and the domestic dog is almost as bitter and malign as that between the dog and the wolf. It is a well-known fact in all the hunting lands of the Old World that a leopard will spend night after night, with tireless persistence, trying to ambush this hereditary enemy. Not that he is particularly fond of canine chops. Ordinarily, meat is meat to a leopard; like all other wild things, he will take the line of least resistance. The cat that haunted our camp lay for our dogs either through some feline notion of sport, or because of a congenital hatred for the whole canine clan. Certainly he was not starving; the country around was thronging with barking deer and wild pig. The leopard himself was an active animal in his prime; we caught glimpses of him from time to time.

The show would always start sometime after midnight. The whinnying of the horses and the sullen lowing of the oxen would waken me. Then the dogs would begin to howl. Presently they would come sneaking, bellies on the ground, into my tent, and the terror of the wild was in their eyes. I would get up, put on my headlight, and sneak about camp; but although more than once I saw evil blue eyes burning in the darkness, they always winked out before I could shoot.

The Asiatic leopard is a fine trophy, but hard to take. He is a night feeder, and usually kills his own meat. It is not worth while to try to lie in wait for him with dead bait. Sometimes he can be killed by the hunter tying out a live goat or dog and waiting in ambush with a flashlight, but even this is a doubtful ruse. If he comes at all, he springs on the animal, tears the rope from its neck in one jerk, and is gone. If the rope holds, he suspects the trap and vanishes as quickly and as mysteriously as he came. The hunter rarely has time to flick on his light and shoot. He is very unlikely to get the leopard, but he has every possibility of getting a dose of jungle fever, plus enough mosquito and ant bites to spoil the sport.

Yet one evening, I had a first-rate chance at a leopard skin. Francis Defosse, scouting from an auxiliary camp, sent word that one of the big cats had attacked the carcass of a sambur laid down for tigers. I rode over to join him, arriving in the middle of the afternoon. We planned to steal up on the carcass just before dark, with the hope of catching the leopard at his meal.

But we started a little too soon. The jungle night had only begun to fall when we dipped into the little glade where the bait lay. We should have waited, but sounds that we heard from the thicket excited us and made us hurry on. The jungle cocks, which make it their business to keep track of their ancient enemies, were cackling like so many domestic hens in the trees. We assumed that the leopard was already at the feast.

Francis dropped behind—the fewer the feet, the better the chance of a successful stalk. I crept on to the bait. But just as I was peering through the vines, there came a harsh cough beside me, like a dull saw going through a board; then the little rustle-rustle of branches as some light-footed, sinuous animal stole away.

I had come just too soon. The leopard had drawn near the bait, but with his usual caution had stopped to reconnoiter. No doubt he had seen me stealing through the thickets.

Even so, the jungle did not send me home without a tremor. The god that rules the Indo-China forests is the god of the unexpected—nothing ever turns out quite as planned, and there is a series of surprises for the invading hunter from dawn till dark. Its idea seems to be to kill the alien if possible and, if not, to make him a nervous wreck from insects, jungle fever, and excitement.

As I was gazing forlornly after the vanished leopard, there was a sudden crash of branches over my head, and a heavy body struck the earth not twenty feet off. I think I made the record standing broad jump. It was a large civet cat that instantly dashed away into the woods.

Obviously, he had been snatching a hasty meal on the bait. When he sensed the approach of his big cousin, he took to the tree. The leopard had scared him. I had scared the leopard, and he had scared me. Such is life in the Indo-China jungle—one scare after another for the entire population of man and beast.

One of the two chief objectives of my hunt was to get a sladang —the sladang of Malaya, with a slightly more humped nose than the black bison of India. Defosse would consider the trip nearly a failure unless I did so. While there was nothing like tiger hunting in the long run, there was nothing like a bull sladang in the place of foremost honor in a trophy room. Any tenderfoot with fair luck could get a tiger, he said, but a lot of luck and usually a good deal of skill and determination were needed to bring down the largest, noblest horned animal on earth.

The name had a thrilling ring in my ear. I admired the way Defosse rolled it off his tongue. He told me of how some previous hunters had taken specimens—always in a voice of respect. He described the animal's elusive ways, his great size—standing between six and seven feet at the shoulders—his implacable ferocity. This was the Land of the Sladang! So I began hunting him by day and dreaming of him by night.

Of course, the sladang comes in numerous grades. Possibly a cow, anyway a young bull, is better than none. Next in rank are the herd bulls, animals in their prime, well-horned, not yet so overgrown and vicious tempered as to be exiled from their fellows. Of course, the best of all are the lone bulls, living solitary lives in the

374 — HUNTING TRAILS

deep of the jungle. They are the largest, the meanest, and by far the most wary. When a herd bull detects the sound of a breaking twig in the thickets, he is likely to think it one of his own stray calves and continue feeding. But when the old lone patriarch hears the slightest rustle of a leaf, he is on his feet and listening. At the slightest warning, he slips like a black ghost into the mesh of vines and naught is left but his big track, cut deep in the soft earth.

Almost every day, Francis Defosse and I hunted the sladang feeding grounds. Lest any of my readers think that I was on a "hunting trip de luxe," I shall describe one typical day. The cook wakened me at four-thirty. To make safe, I flashed my searchlight on the ground under the cot before I reached for my boots. Probably I found nothing more serious than a swarm of ants; perhaps a scorpion on the leg of my cot, his tail all aimed and primed to jab in the hand. And there was always the possibility of a little krait, lying unseen in the dust. One that the boys killed had seemed to me the most deadly instrument for his inches I had ever seen, unless it were the small poisoned Borneo dagger, with a slick little hilt to hold daintily in the fingers, that an old Army officer gave me a few years before.

My servant entered (my old Alaskan guides will shudder at this) and shook out my garments one by one. The idea is to knock loose any small reptiles and large insects that may be camping there for the night. Even this violent treatment is not always effective for scorpions. I remember one malignant little fiend that had laid his ambush in the sleeve of my raincoat and had declined to be shaken out. When I thrust in an arm, he thrust his dart into my thumb.

Dressed in light khaki and boots, I joined Defosse in the mess-shack. I put away two piquant eggs from the cook's store and other provender, and with two naked Mois to carry the tea-flasks (tea keeps sweet on the trail, whereas boiled water takes on assorted flavors; we used it even for brushing our teeth), the lunch, and the raincoats, we pushed out into the gray dawn. In ten minutes our clothes were soaking wet with dew.

After an hour's stiff hike, we headed into the elephant grass. The sun found us here, and dried out our dew-soaked clothes. But twenty minutes later they were soaking wet again—this time from sweat. It trickled from the forehead, ran down our arms and legs, soaked through our pockets, and wet our matches. The jungle under the arching trees is usually delightfully cool, but the ten-foot elephant grass under the June sun resembled a combination of a Turkish bath and a blast furnace. This hellish spot was the feeding ground of the sladang.

We crisscrossed the plain, looking for tracks. Perhaps we were lucky enough, this particular morning, to find the spoor of a small herd. We took the trail swiftly and silently. Then began the real work of the day.

Morning after morning we followed this course. Often we searched in vain, finding nothing but stale spoor. Often we followed the wary herd until the afternoon rains—a regular feature of the landscape at this time of the year—wiped out the tracks. Often my clumsy step flushed the herd just too soon, and we would hear the great beasts stampeding through the jungle.

Defosse, fifty years old, stood six feet, and was lean and tireless as a panther. I was fourteen years younger, and shorter both of leg and breath. Trying to keep up with him wore out my feet; having to wait for me wore thin his patience. He could weave through the thorn thickets where I either crashed like a buffalo or hung up like a snared rabbit. Tropical thorns are as vicious compared to the American variety as tigers are to mountain lions. I was punctured and tattooed from head to foot.

Yet these morning hunts remained indescribably wonderful. Often we saw deer at the woodland pools; peacocks strutted in the glades as on the lawns of England; there were gorgeous flowers although without perfume and gaudy birds without song.

Sometimes we heard a distant crashing and tumult that I thought was an elephant stampede. But Defosse would laugh and point overhead. Through the branches would come an army of monkeys swinging from the top of one tree to the lower part of the next, racing along the limbs, performing all sorts of gymnastic feats. When they caught sight of us, they would stop and set up a clamor that could be heard a mile. They would chatter and scold at us, peer at us with their strange, sad faces, break sticks and drop them, and then without rhyme or reason dash away.

Defosse was the best of companions and his wilderness lore a constant source of delight. He took interest not only in the game, but in all the living things of his beloved jungle—strange trees, unknown birds, small mammals. Quite unexpectedly one morning, we flushed a herd of sladang. We heard them break from the jungle into the elephant grass. At top speed, Defosse and I sprinted to cut them off. Somehow we got through the thorns and thickets in time. My heart was pounding like a bass drum and my eyes were full of sweat as we came out on the edge of the plain to see the whole herd a hundred yards beyond. They had stopped to look back at us.

This was my first big chance—perhaps my only chance. The vast shoulders of the herd bull loomed above the five-foot grass, a clear target. I took a quick aim and heard the bullet thwack against his hide.

But the bull ran off. Almost instantly the tall grass hid him from sight. We followed a short distance, but found no sign of blood. My heart did not pound any more. It had gone down into my boots.

Maybe what I had thought was the thwack of the bullet had been only an echo. Yet Defosse looked more puzzled than disgusted. "Where did you hold?" he asked.

"About twelve inches from the top of his back, in the region of his shoulder."

"That's too high. I should have warned you. You can't drop a sladang with a bullet in the ridge of his back—there's nothing there but muscle and great flanges of his vertebrae. There's no use trying to follow that herd. They'll hardly stop till they get to Siam."

We trudged home, two weary and discouraged men. That night Defosse warned me that I had better not count on a sladang. My alloted time was half gone, the beasts were scarce this season, and hunting conditions unfavorable. I had better lower my sights for a banteng. After all, a big banteng bull was an excellent and by no means an easy trophy. In reply, I took a painful pledge. It was to get on the water wagon—in this case the tea wagon—until I had some big horns in camp. This was no small sacrifice to the hunting gods. The big jolt of Georgia corn or cognac just before the evening meal was a wondrous comfort to a tired, sore-footed hunter. But to forego it would not only give me a kind of reversed Dutch courage to keep trying, it would also spur Defosse to his utmost efforts. The point was, that when I took my snifter, he never failed to join me. His own bottle was empty, and of course he would not tap mine so long as I remained, literally, a teetotaler. It was a Spartan test for us both.

Yet my chances continued to fade day by day. We found nothing but stale tracks, cold dried dung. Apparently the last herd had left the country. It looked certain now that I would leave the country, tail feathers dragging, without the horns of this grandest of game. It was a sickening prospect.

One morning, both Louis and Francis went scouting farther into the virgin north. I took two of the Mois, one of whom was a first-rate tracker, and the three of us headed for the great tangle of elephant grass and thorn jungle five miles west of camp. But apparently, it was the same old story—great dunghills half covered by anthills, and the tracks washed dim by a week's rains.

We left camp at five-thirty. By eight o'clock, I was wet through with a mixture of sweat and dew, the sun was changing the elephant grass plains into one great double boiler, and I was seriously considering giving up and returning to camp for a full day's sleep. But crossing an old trail, I noticed a big bovine track in the mud of yesterday's rains.

I noticed the track before either of my keen-eyed savages. This was a certain satisfaction—as any tenderfoot will understand. The track looked fresh to me, and of a challenging size.

Still, a lone track is often deceiving, especially in the mud. It might be that of a tame ox, or even a big banteng bull. The boys looked at it and uttered a series of grunts. I thought I saw signs of excitement in their dark, impassive faces.

"Sladang?" I asked.

But they did not understand. Strange as it may seem, in all their contacts with Defosse and French officials, they have never learned to recognize one white man's word. True, "sladang" was originally a Malay word, but it is now used throughout southeastern Asia instead of the older word, "gaur."

They shook their heads; so I tried again.

"Banteng?"

Again they shook their heads. So I resorted to sign language. I indicated a very large animal, then a smaller one, with a free gesture portraying the sweeping horns. Their grunts and nods indicated that this was, indeed, a very large animal—still there was no telling whether he was black or red—sladang or banteng—or whether they knew themselves. However, it was a lone track—the mark of a solitary bull. In any event it was my last chance for big horns.

I signaled to the boys to take the trail. At once we went filing through the jungle, the old tracker in front, myself second, and the water boy third. The two native trackers stole along almost like shadows. I managed my big boots and clumsy khaki as carefully as I could.

Before long, we found a huge pile of warm dung. The animal had passed not more than a half hour before. Defosse had told me that both the sladang and banteng lie down about nine o'clock for morning naps. Obviously, this beast had finished his feeding and was seeking some cool, safe retreat in the thick heart of the jungle. The dung was in one pile, not strewn along the trail, showing that he was taking his time and had not been alarmed. He could not be more than two miles ahead of us.

It was a thrilling prospect. Moreover, I was glad to be on my own—without either Louis or Francis Defosse to back me up. My chances of overtaking the monster were considerably less—but if I did succeed, it would be the kind of lone victory I really needed. The only rifle was the big .404 in my hand. There was no body-guard, no experienced woodsman to make the decisions and support me. The two boys would help me track the beast to his lair, but we could not exchange one word, and in the final roundup they would be interested spectators, nothing more.

The trail led us into one of the darkest and weirdest jungles I had yet seen. The trees were covered with creepers, and great vine stalks dangled like pythons. A peacock flew up from under our heels, and my heart flew into my mouth. A wild boar grunted in the thickets; a little mouse deer fled from our path.

It was just about nine when we came to a little clear water stream. Here the trail circled, crossing and recrossing, a sign that the beast was seeking a place to lie down. And then, without warning, we heard a mighty crashing fifty yards ahead. A black shape burst through the brush.

It was a sladang—and he had heard my clumsy feet. Apparently our great chance was lost.

But there was a rift in the trees twenty yards farther through which the bull might pass. I hopped upon a near-by anthill, the butt plate of the .404. jumping against my shoulder. The same second the great black brute burst through the vines and emerged into open forest.

Still it was the slimmest kind of a chance. Actually all I saw was a black shape racing away between the tree trunks and the broken underbrush. I caught one glimpse of his sweeping horns, big shoulders, and straining loins.

I don't remember aiming or touching the trigger. Both of these things can be instinctive; but certainly it was snap-shooting of the riskiest kind. The gun roared—the animal disappeared in the farther thickets—and I aimed a mental kick at my own backside.

Why had I shot so recklessly? It had been only a tenth chance for anyone but an expert; we might have bided our time, followed him till evening, and caught him feeding. Cursing myself, sick to my stomach with disgust and disappointment, I walked up to examine the ground.

As the three of us crept through the little glade, the old tracker stopped and pointed to the ground. What a double-barreled thrill! On the green leaves was a small smear of blood. Somewhere in the thick jungle beyond ran a wounded sladang!

Now began one of the longest, certainly the toughest, and by all odds the most thrilling trek of my big game hunting career. There was no more blood—not one drop. Right from the start I was faced with the possibility that my bullet had merely scratched the animal. And because I could not talk with my little brown companions or read what they could from the tracks, I had no idea what to expect.

Was the big bull running or walking? After we had followed him an hour, this became a vital question. If he were still running, it was positive proof that he was not badly hurt and we were wasting our time. One would think that the merest tenderfoot could answer this; but here I failed completely. The tracks were often dim, sometimes in the mud, sometimes on sun-baked ground, sometimes in high grass. On my own hook, I could not have followed them at all, much less interpreted them.

I tried to find out from the boys, acting out the animal running, then walking. They grinned appreciatively, evidently thinking I had either gone crazy or was putting on some kind of show for their benefit. Even this rudimentary idea failed to reach them. They nodded and smiled whether I either walked or ran.

We moved too cautiously at first. I recalled all I had heard of the fury of a wounded sladang. Moreover, the ground was his, not ours. There were a thousand places where he could lurk in ambush and have his horns under us before I could raise my rifle. By going so slowly, perhaps we were throwing away our only chance.

After a time, we gained courage. We plowed through the ten-foot elephant grass and crashed into the thickets. Once, we thought we heard him running but it was only a big sambur buck, disturbed in his midday lair.

We had started the trek at nine. At noon we were apparently no nearer to our wounded quarry. There was no warm dung to encourage us, not one drop of blood. The boys began to appear discouraged. They pointed to the gathering clouds and shook their heads. If the rains broke on time—they usually began shortly after noon—they would wipe out the tracks and end the hunt.

The trail led us through mud bogs, across the steaming grass plains, up and over creek banks, deep into the black heart of the jungle. I saw more game than any day of my hunt—barking deer, sambur, wild hog, banteng. And now I began to fight fatigue. I had been tramping since five-thirty, and seven hours under the tropic sun on a trail like this is a day's work even for a hardened woodsman. By half-past one I was bitterly and painfully tired. My feet were swollen and raw. And still not one drop of blood or the least sign to encourage us on.

The trail became hard to follow. Often we lost it in the dense grass, often confused it with stale trails. At two o'clock came the first sprinkling of rain.

The boys stopped and told me in sign language that the animal had escaped; that we might as well turn back to camp. But I ordered them to follow on. The way I wanted that sladang passed all reason; it was really a terrible obsession. There came a sharp shower of rain. At any moment now, the big afternoon downpour might begin. The boys were tiring, losing interest.

Just before three o'clock we lost the trail, and had to encircle a patch of grass to find it again. I resolved to try for a half hour more, then head for camp. How far camp was, or in what direction, I had not the slightest idea, but could trust the little brown men to find their way. By giving up the hunt at half-past three, it might be that we could reach the huts soon after dark. The trail had doubled and redoubled; certainly there would be a short cut home.

This thought had hardly formed when the tracks turned from the grassy plain into a patch of jungle. The younger boy was now walking in front. He pushed through the thickets thirty feet ahead of me. And then without the least warning, the top blew off.

What I had wanted was to find the beast dead. I was too tired to crave excitement. As if for that reason, it arrived in barrels! The events of the next few seconds were so explosively and so swiftly crowded upon each other that it is difficult to reconstruct them. My senses could hardly take them all in. The scene was instinct with violence and peril and a revelation of the savage power of the jungle—truly the kind of crisis that overtakes a big game hunter rarely in all his days.

There rose a yell of terror, a bellow of rage. Thirty feet ahead, through a rift in the trees, I saw the boy spring to the left and knew from his all-out wrench that he was leaping for his life. Instantly, he disappeared from view and a second later, a great black shape lunged by the opening.

This was the end of the trail. With noble courage, the sladang bull had come to bay. He had fled as far as he would, then joined battle with us. He had chosen the ground—a fairly open glade sixty feet long—taking his stand at one end and facing his back trail. There he had waited for his pursuers to push through into the open.

Even so, his brute brain had betrayed him. He had sought a clean view of his foe; he did not know we carried a weapon that could destroy him from a distance. Had he laid his ambush in the blind elephant grass, his revenge would be almost sure.

The instant the Moi tracker had entered the open ground, the bull had charged. Fast as I could I ran down the trail to his help. In that second or two the action had blazed to white heat. The terrified tracker had evidently dodged around one tree with the bull close behind him and now was reaching for another. I saw his frantic hands, his body tense, almost distorted; his naked foot grasped for the trunk. This was a sharp scene in the sudden glare. The sladang bull was surging toward him, in that violent rocking horse gait that cattlemen know. His head was lowered and starting a great sweeping movement of his horns. The glade that formed the backdrop for this terrific drama was green and beautiful and still.

The thought jumped through my mind, "I can't shoot quick enough." It was not in words that took time, but in an instantaneous vision of shooting too late. My rifle was on the way to my shoulder but went off in my hands. Swinging the barrel in the general direction, I had blazed at the black mass.

The bullet weighed four hundred grains and struck a two ton blow. Hitting him in the flank, it appeared to shove him sideways and almost knock him down. Above his lowered horns, I saw the boy grab the trunk of the tree and appear to run up it like a monkey. The bull's hind hoofs scrabbled to keep his balance, his forequarters swung toward me. That brought him up facing me, not more than ten feet distant.

My hand was racing to work the bolt and throw in another shell. It was a long bolt and the action seemed to take a nightmare length of time, but I could not run and dodge like a Moi tracker. I was too slow and awkward to climb a tree and the only boost I could count on was from the horns of the sladang.

The shell ran in quickly and smoothly and the bolt shot home. That was cutting it mighty fine. At the same instant, he discovered me, another enemy, in one glare of his fierce eyes. With a snort, he moved to attack. I saw his knees bend—almost seem to cave in—as his huge thighs propelled him forward.

This was to be the all but sublime finish of a game begun when I first yearned for a sladang bull. No denouement could be more fitting than our facing each other at ten feet, both in extreme exertion, I straining to shoot, he to strike. But his lowering head presented a perfect target. My rifle swung too fast for him, out and a little down, then blazed.

That was the end of the sladang. The bullet pierced his forehead, an inch or two to the right of the left eye, and a little low. Crashing through the heavy bones, the shot destroyed the animal's brain and killed him instantly. He rolled over almost at my feet.

I think I let out a cataleptic yell as the bull toppled, then stood there unable to move or make a sound. When the tracker climbed nimbly down from his tree and came up grinning, I was in profound reverie and unable at first to emerge. The other boy appeared, no doubt out of a tree behind the arena. They patted me and my gun, grunting their pleasure, but were no longer excited. They did not seem to think that anything unusual had happened. That was what brought me, with a great start of surprise, to a realization of the truth.

It had already dawned on me that the specimen was nothing special in the way of a sladang. Although solitary and hence more wary, he did not have the massive, blunt horns of a veteran, rather the long, very handsome ones, blue with ivory-colored tips of a bull just entered into his prime. Francis Defosse had previously described the difference. He was apart from the herd because the leader would not stand for his rivalry and he had not yet won a herd of his own. But his taking today could well be the adventure of a hunter's lifetime. It did not seem to me that I would ever meet such thunder and lightning on the hunting trail again.

Actually on this very trip, I had been fated for another knockdown and drag-out fracas with the foe almost in arms' reach, but that would arise from an incredible piece of folly on my part. It would be the result of breaking a rule as fixed as that of not dragging a loaded gun through a fence. I would save my bacon only from long dexterity with a pump gun. This affair with the sladang was in a different class from messes blundered into with dangerous wild animals, which are only too common. It was a perfect big game adventure. It was like a well-contrived play with a smashing climax—indeed a very simple and powerful episode, in a perfect setting. Such drama with such a happy ending is extremely rare on the hunting grounds. It was no wonder that I ever afterward considered the great sladang the single finest big game trophy in the world. Francis Defosse was of the same opinion and he was to be greatly impressed not with me but with the whole event. Other hunters have since told me how he would take them to that very glade where the big bull made his last charge, say with some punctilio, "Here is where Mr. Mar-*shall* killed his sladang," and point out the spots featured in the fight.

Alas, though, there was to be an anticlimax. We were miles and miles from camp. Maybe in the long view, this went with the rest, to make me all the more appreciative of my trophy, but that stand was too grand for me to take at the time.

We measured the horns with my pocket tape. They were forty inches across the outside curve. My first bullet at the beginning of the chase had entered the right buttock and had quartered into the left flank without emerging, a crippling but by no means a fatal wound and from which the bull would have no doubt completely recovered. We cut boughs and covered him from head to foot to hide him from passing vultures.

Then I pronounced the only Moi word I knew. It sounded like "nee-yah" and meant camp. If pronounced with not quite the proper inflection, it could mean a long knife, a piece of bark, or a baby. The boys nodded, greatly pleased with me for these remarkable linguistics, more pleased with themselves for understanding. They blazed a few trees to mark the spot, then went questing into the woods for some sort of orientation.

I do not know what it was. They did not look at the sun nor for moss on the trees; they appeared to keep glancing at the sky. The same instant both of them tossed their heads in the same childish exultant gesture. Grunting, they pointed in the same direction. I beckoned for them to lead the way. Maybe we had circled back toward camp and they had recognized a landmark!

I was wrong about that. We were the devil's own way from camp and I think they traveled on some sort of psychic radio beam. They went straight as bees to the hive, pigeons to the roost. Almost the sky fell down in rain, rain that roared through the jungle, washing out every trail, dimming every scene: it didn't matter to them. It fell in drenching sheets, soon the darkness in blinding folds. One of the Mois got behind me so I wouldn't straggle; the other took my rifle to lighten my step. Some of my New York friends had compared modern big game hunting to a Cook's Tour! I wished they had to walk just one mile of this weary trail.

Camp might show up any time, I thought. I would see its lights, and then the Chinese cook rushing about his thatch hut, fixing me a hot supper. Instead, long after dark, long after I thought I had about slogged my last, we came to a rude bridge over a deep-cut creek. I recognized one of its broken logs. We were still five miles from home.

But I had shot a sladang! Only a handful of hunters could say that, and wouldn't Defosse be surprised! It seems incredible and silly that this fact alone kept me going when again and again I was tempted to huddle beside a tree trunk while the boys went after an oxcart to lug me in. I made up a little game to play with the urbane Frenchman. I composed a delightful dialogue.

Those last five miles took three awful hours. I was reeling with exhaustion when I entered Defosse's hut and it was no trouble at all to put on a long face.

"You'd had a long day, and I hoped you'd had some luck," he told me, plainly and deeply disappointed. "Now you'd better get off those wet clothes and have some supper."

"Not until I've had three fingers of mellow Georgia corn," I answered in dejected tones.

"I think that's a good idea, and I'll join you." He was careful not to remind me of my pledge.

"Well, it's not necessary for me to be on the wagon any longer."

It took about five seconds for this to sink in.

"You shot something!"

"You ain't foolin'."

"A banteng?" I had been talking banteng for several days.

"No."

"A sladang!" He jumped to his feet. "A herd bull!"

"No herd bull, by God!"

"A lone bull! *Finis la guerre!* The great solitary one! *Magnifique! Magnifique!*"

It was the first time I had heard this self-contained, cold-nerved Frenchman mix up his languages and sputter with excitement.

But that night I paid the penalty for my walk in the rain. My mouth turned furry and my pulse raced with jungle fever. With twenty grains of quinine in me, I hunted sladang the rest of the night, chasing them over illimitable forests and through tree high elephant grass, only to have them circle and charge me from the rear. Doctors have since told me that the parasite of malaria was even then in my veins, and this was our first skirmish.

Clearheaded and fit in the morning, I went with Defosse in the oxcart to retrieve the sladang head and as much as we could use of the beef. The Mois directed us straight to the spot where the giant lay. Actually, he was not the "great solitary one" that Defosse meant—a superannuated bull divorced from the herd—but full-grown and a trophy of which any nimrod, let alone a tenderfoot, could be proud.

Only twenty days remained to round out my bag. I resolved to devote them entirely to tigers, with maybe a leopard thrown in, and not go philandering after banteng, rare deer, wild hogs, or elephant. The banteng was only a smaller red imitation of his huge black cousin. Deer and wild boar were mere tiger victuals in Indo-China. I still could not bring myself to hunt Asiatic elephants, although Defosse told me that some of the bulls carried magnificent ivories, and when old and ill-tempered, became rogues of the worst description.

All preparations had been made for my campaign. Side camps had been established, and a line of baits thrown out. Every day, the scouts visited these baits to see if a tiger had been there. Two days after the sladang hunt, the old tracker came in with word that a small tiger or a large leopard had begun to feed on one of our buffalo baits, six miles from camp. He knew that the animal was no great shakes in size, first by the tracks, and second because he had made no effort to drag the bait away. Any considerable tiger would at least haul the meat as far as the chain would permit and, if the bait were fairly ripe, would tear the carcass loose and drag it perhaps a hundred yards into heavy thickets.

Louis and I at once rode to investigate. Leaving our horses a half mile from the bait, we made a careful stalk. When we were still fifty yards distant, we knew that this was no false alarm, and at least a minor and maybe a major thrill was in the making.

Jungle fowls were cackling nervously from the lower limbs of the trees. High overhead an unseen monkey chattered in rage.

The big cat was no doubt on the bait. Another real live tiger, miraculously emerging from his mysterious, forbidden, magic world of dimness and darkness and deviltry, maybe for me to hold his skin in my hand. I caught a glimpse of Louis' slanted eyes, glittering with excitement. Yet twenty yards from the screen the boys had built across the trail, he gestured for me to go on alone!

He wanted to be there, in the blaze, and knew that the main of my heart wanted him there, to back me up in a mess. Yet a kind of a jungle priest, more like a Mowgli, master of the jungle, he was going to let me shoot one of his terribly beautiful band in all the excitement possible. After all, for the present, I bought his bread. He and his civilized father had contracted to provide an outlander with varied and tremendous thrills. His excuse was that one pair of feet would make less noise than two. At the least suspicious sound reaching the big cat's hair-trigger ears, he would bound into the thickets beside the bait, then dematerialize. Actually the noise would have been the same—all made by me; Louis could walk like a leopard. He knew the prize would count more with me if I took it alone.

Stalking is a breath-taking business. Children playing hide-and-seek know that; they yelp with excitement. A strong-living tiger must almost explode with suspense as he steals upon his prey. Tigers and lions and leopards have immense adrenal glands to key them up to the mark: mine was no slouch, it seemed, by the way it was shooting fire. The sound of meat-tearing grew louder. I could hear the clamp of the beast's jaws as he chewed. I tried not to rustle a leaf. My spine was one crackling tremor.

I looked through the screen. There were no black stripes on a yellow hide but there were most beautiful black spots. It was a leopard on the bait. Shafts of sunlight slanted through rifts in the treetops and he made as gorgeous a wildwood picture as a chrono camera could seek. But I could not carry it away in my memory unstained by blood.

It was a moving picture. His round muscles moved with a wonderful silky smoothness under his decorated hide. He ate like a tomcat, tearing off steaks, then raising his head to chew. He was perhaps ten yards away. I began easing my rifle to my shoulder. Then I had to swing it up fast, because he suddenly froze into a painted statue. Then he turned his head until his baleful green eyes were staring straight into mine.

My gun roared. As usual, I did not remember aiming. But the leopard dropped like a poled ox—like the deer he had slain with the neck-breaking power of his whizzing maul, never knowing what hit him.

That made a sladang, a tiger, and a leopard on the drying rack. Defosse had written me that I could reasonably count on three tigers of varied sizes, plus the rest no large bag for a four months' overall trip; with extra good luck I could take more. Actually the country at that time was overstocked with tigers, but threatened by a scarcity of horned game. Tigers are good survivors even in hard-hunted territories; they are far more cunning than wild oxen and water buffaloes, and themselves play havoc with deer and wild pig. If I needed a better excuse to shoot as many as I could, it was that tigers are really a formidable enemy of man. Many take to hanging around the villages, preying on cattle and domestic buffaloes. Only a few become out-and-out man-eaters, but Americans would be shocked to know how many native children, playing at the edge of the fields while their parents are at work, are carried off.

In teeming India, most of these tragedies are never reported. Old people, dropping behind on the lonely roads, frequently never reach home. Ten thousand human lives a year lost to wild beasts in India alone is by no means an extravagant estimate—there may be twice this number, counting babies stolen and devoured by wolves. If I killed three tigers, I could hazard a likely guess that I had saved at least that many people in the long run and certainly a considerable herd of goats, cattle, work-buffaloes, pigs, and ponies for desperately poor natives. If any big game hunting serves a humanitarian purpose, it is the pursuit of tigers. Lions in sparsely settled East Africa are not in a class with tigers on the jungle fringe in India. Actually Indo-Chinese tigers fall short of it too, since the country is less thickly populated and the natives seemed better able to defend themselves and their livestock than do the hapless Indian villagers.

So when the scouts brought word of another tiger feasting on one of my baits, we were all as excited as before. Was he a big fellow? Apparently not—he had failed to move the bait. Then there was no chance of his being the Old Man of whose prodigious pelt I had never stopped dreaming. No, the Old Man was too wary to come to dead bait; anyway, he had not been spotted lately. Someone, sometime, would be lucky enough to kill the old monarch, but it would be an accidental meeting in the jungle.

This news reached us just before dark. Nothing could be done that night, but soon after dawn we started to the bait. In this case, stalking was out of the question. In the dense brush, the cat would be sure to hear us before we could get a shot. So, instead of creeping like snakes through the vines, we tramped up boldly, talking and breaking brush. We wanted to scare him far enough that he could not watch our movements from some hidden thicket. We knew he would not desert his feast for good.

Ten yards from the buffalo carcass, the boys had built a shelter of sticks and palm leaves. Camouflaged with vines, no animal and few men would suspect that it was anything but a green bush. True, it was in no way a fortress. That an enraged tiger could not break into it and fork the hunter out of it—provided of course the shooting iron did not function properly—was absurd. The theory was that a wounded tiger would not locate a hunter so well hidden. This was predicated on another theory—that tigers never trail or locate an enemy by scent. This arbitrary limiting of a tiger's talents seems mightily theoretical when the big cat comes creeping about the blind.

One ham of the buffalo had been nearly eaten off. This ought to indicate a fair-sized tiger, but the tracks told a different story. They did not seem much larger than leopard tracks. Eager to please, the Mois had stretched the facts considerably, and perhaps a real pukka tiger-hunter would have returned to camp. I could not. I was too obsessed by the striped killers, big or little. It was not to be a very exciting experience, I thought, but would help some. So the boys left me in the blind with a tea flask, a lunch box, a book, and my gun, and went jabbering off to persuade the listening tiger that the coast was clear.

Would the beast return to his feast in open day? In this respect, the tiger differs from his African cousin, the lion. He regards the carcass as strictly his own property, a meal ticket to save him the trouble of hunting for a matter of three or four days, and makes frequent daylight visits to keep away thieves. The lion, on the other hand, shares his feast with his pals. It is not extraordinary to see half a dozen lions feeding on the same zebra. Not that the lion is a gentleman and the tiger a hog. The lion lives in open country, and he knows perfectly well that there is no use in hoarding his victuals. Any bones left after the first night's feast will be picked clean by the vultures and carried away by hyenas in the morning.

I settled down on the little bench the boys had made. Little noises came sneaking out of the jungle. At best it was only a young tiger. To experience such sensations, a racing heart and a prickling skin and icy inwards, was surely the mark of a tenderfoot.

My eyes were glued to the peephole. Some leaves trembled faintly ten yards from the bait. The vines parted with the most magical silence and grace. Then a tawny shape that might be a leopard's began to emerge. Boldly the beast strode into the clearing —not a leopard, but as miserable a little tiger as was weaned the year before. It was hardly larger than the spotted demon, had the lines of a tigress, and I was half ashamed to shoot her. However, as the sunlight struck her, she blazed up marvelously. Certainly she had a fine, high-colored pelt.

She stopped beyond the buffalo carcass and was so short-legged that only her head remained in plain sight. This she turned slowly, to survey the scene. Fairly cool for once, indeed overconfident, I leveled at her head, the easiest of targets and pressed the trigger. Down she went, with no sound of a death struggle—plainly brain-shot. This was practically child's play, I thought.

I crawled out of the blind and slogged around the carcass for a look at my trophy. I had brought my gun from instinct, in spite of the bright sun, the clear day, the pushover tiger. Just as I reached the buffalo's half-devoured rump, the thought flashed through my mind that I knew better than this—that no big game hunter short of an idiot ever approached fallen game of the dangerous varieties without due caution—and maybe I made the first movement to alert my gun. It was in the cards for me to confess the folly and think no more about it. The tigress was due to be dead with a bullet through her brain.

Actually that little remorse came almost—within a half second, by a generous estimate—too late. The tigress was not dead. As it happened, she was only stunned by the ball quartering through her lower jaw and coming out her cheek. She was lying there with her eyes open, had heard me barging around the buffalo, and the instant that I came in sight, she jumped at me.

She was only a little tiger with a smashed jaw but plenty big enough to wind up this big game hunt here and now.

I was carrying the pump-action thirty-five. On seeing the size of the cat's tracks, I had used it instead of the .404, although taking the big piece into the blind for emergencies. It happened that most of my bird-shooting had been done with a pump-action twenty-gauge shotgun, with the same kind of safety button: I was quick and handy with it from long experience. Doubtless, that fact saved me a mauling and only too likely, a funeral. The brute's claws were as rank with poison as a full-grown tiger's. The gun was on safe, but I was used to pushing the button as I raised. I haven't the least memory of doing any such thing, or throwing up the rifle or of aiming—in fact, there was no time or very little need to aim, with the cat coming about eight feet away. Did she come fast! She was one streak of yellow. By what exercise of habit God knows, the gun went off.

The next I knew I was running backward with startling speed, the tiger crumpled on the ground. I ran into some vines and kept thrusting at them until securely lodged. Then I emptied my gun at the fallen beast and was feverishly loading it for another volley when a suspicion that this was no way for a *shikari* to act crossed my jellied brain. My advance on the stone-dead, shot-riddled little tigress would have been ludicrous to any imperturbable English sahib. Actually of the five frantic bullets I had fired since her attack, two were clean misses. Of the three hits, I could not tell which had crumpled her—presumably a fairly well-centered breast shot. If so, she had taken off the ground, aiming for my head, when it blasted home.

The yarn I told Defosse explained the odd distribution of the bullet wounds fairly plausibly. Craving his good opinion of my hunting, I have never until this moment confessed the truth.

Up until now, my bag had been just ordinary compared to the superlative thrills in its taking. Although my sladang was too young to be counted first rate, the chase had been long, tough, and with a gloriously exciting and happy ending. My night hunt with Louis for the wounded tiger had given me an unforgettable experience and him a good time. My idiotic behavior with the little tigress had furnished me a scare of first water, not even very pleasant to look back on, yet surely a valuable and invigorating memory. In addition, I had a fair leopard—four trophies for five weeks' hunting. If I could get one more in the ten days that remained, the trip could be considered a fair success on the basis of bag alone.

My belief remains that five trophies constitute only a modest bag for an American going clean halfway around the world, employing two licensed guides and a tribe of Mois, spending four months in the overall journey and no few hard-earned shekels. Most experienced hunters take at least one of the six species of dangerous Indo-Chinese game and a few extras. If I could be content with a big banteng bull or a small-tusked elephant, the chance of success was good. Instead, Francis Defosse agreed with me that we should spend the remaining days trying for another, perhaps a royal, tiger.

Although not aware of it then, throughout the remainder of my big game hunting career I was always going to be trying for one more tiger. This is true of almost every *shikari* who has ever leveled a gun at one of these gorgeous felines. They are the headiest drink in all the jungles.

Our luck began bad, and grew worse. I got a shot at a fine tiger creeping away from a bait, an open, easy mark, but only succeeded in scaring him into the next province. All our baits but one melted away, devoured by insect larvae and the scavengers of the woods. The one remaining, an old decrepit plow buffalo mercifully shot, was already ripe and would hardly last out the trip. Every morning we had ridden over to look at it with hungry, hopeful eyes, but there were no big four-toed tracks near by, no haunch devoured. Once a big tiger had crossed within a hundred yards of it and gone on his way.

Four mornings before the end, the old cook counted on his fingers and pronounced his incantations. "Catchee luck today," he told me.

"I'm going to kill a tiger?"

"Maybe no kill, catchee luck all same."

This was a much better augury than I can make practical fellows believe. Our Chinese cook came as close to being a sure-fire prophet as I had ever known. He hit a great deal oftener than he missed. I believed him to be a real psychic. It was as if he had seen with an inward eye what we saw when we reached the bait—one ham of the buffalo eaten off, the carcass dragged the length of the chain, and the tracks of a good-sized tiger in the wet ground.

The Mois rushed me into the blind and noisily departed. I heard their voices die away, then the silence of the jungle seep in about me.

It was a wonderful silence, instinct with unheard sound. Almost from the first moment of my wait, I had a feeling of impending action, suppressed excitement. Maybe this was merely frayed nerves. The jungle had taken a lot out of me in my six weeks' stay; fever lay dormant in my bones; I had lived harder and more intensely than ever in my life before. My senses were most curiously sharpened. Little rustlings, I would have hardly noticed ordinarily, startled and alarmed me. Also, I was more afraid of tigers than when I had known them only by hearsay—that wicked little demon of a female had taught me that. This particular tiger might be a man-eater. The protection afforded me—my blind and my rifle—might not be enough against a cunning giant cat accustomed to hunting human prey. The shelter had been thrown together hastily by the Mois while Defosse was off scouting. If he stole on me from the rear . . .

Yes, this was mainly frayed nerves. But there were innumerable false alarms to make them taut. Sometimes they turned out to be birds, hopping in the branches of near-by thickets, or maybe a wandering gust of air, or a few stray raindrops falling from the leaves. Sometimes I heard steps—unmistakable steps—but what animal was creeping by I never knew. Once a long green lizard popped his sharp head over the top of my blind and looked down at me in amazement. For an instant, I thought it was a krait.

Presently I began to have company. The first was a flock of jungle fowl that trooped out of the forest to pick up larvae around the buffalo. There was something very homey about this. They were precisely like the dark, nondescript, undersized domestic poultry that we see in Georgia around the doors of the darkies' cabins and call "nigger chickens." They scratched and cackled and the roosters chased each other and the hens precisely as they do in every colored farmer's back yard.

There was a perfectly good reason for this resemblance. The jungle fowl of southern Asia is the ancestor of all domestic chickens. By artificial selection, many types have been evolved, from big Rhode Island Reds to little bantams. But selection stops when the colored man of Georgia begins to raise poultry. After a few generations of free and easy mingling of all types of chickens, naturally the birds revert to the original type. In other words, our southern darkies are raising jungle cock without knowing it.

The birds slipped back into the thickets to give right of way to a ferret-like animal I could not identify. Later, a company of monkeys passed overhead, with a great crashing of branches and wild cries. Then two magnificent peacocks joined the jungle fowl.

About noon, I had a much less pleasant visitor. It approached with a slinky sound in the thickets, more noise than a tiger would make, indeed indicating a rather heavy animal, yet without revealing even a tawny glimpse. I became very much excited, and when still the creature remained unseen, deeply uneasy. Presently it pushed out of the vines—a truly ghastly looking brute common in these wilds, and yet the first that had given me a clear view of his revolting self.

A veranus lizard, first cousin to the famous dragon lizards of the Dutch East Indies, it was eight or nine feet long. Its skin was marked like a snake's, in bands and geometric designs; its feet made me think of a Chinese dragon's; its long tail was ever twisting and turning; it had a darting tongue and its sickening mouth opened deeply in an idiotic fashion. It crawled to the carcass, thrust its long, hideous head down the neck, braced itself with its tail and four legs, and pulled and tugged until it tore loose a mouthful of rotten meat. When the head emerged, it was covered with blood and altogether the most revolting object these eyes had ever rested on. It choked and gulped over the obscene fare, then crawled around to the hind end of the dead bull and repeated the performance. Down into the torn entrails stretched that reptilian neck; up it would come with carrion dangling from its jaws. In the meantime, he never straightened out his snaky body. The tail was all over the place, twitching and curling like a serpent's.

I watched him about an hour. When thoroughly sick of him, I heard the brush rustle again, louder than before. Out came another dragon, much larger than the first—at least ten feet long. As he passed upwind from me, I almost fell off my seat; the sewer-boats in Shanghai harbor had nothing on him.

The other paid him no mind at first. He was used to the smell, and as Francis told me later, all veranus lizards are stone-deaf. The big brute came peering with white, witless eyes. Then with a coughing sound, he charged his fellow, chasing him off into the woods. I heard them both go crashing off and they were gone at least half an hour on their dim-witted affairs. Then the big fellow returned and duplicated the dainty feeding of the other. In a few minutes, the smaller one showed up, only to be chased away again.

Smaller specimens came to the feast but were not allowed to share it. Sometimes half a dozen were in sight and others twisting and turning in the shrubbery all about my blind. When I tried to read, their sudden, explosive coughs and violent movements scared me half out of my wits. The rains broke early in the afternoon, a storage tank that contained a young lake suddenly smashing. Although there were palm leaves over my head, numerous trickles and an occasional cold jet chilled and discouraged me. The hours passed, the sun declined, and the tiger did not return.

Louis waited until the light had failed before he drove up to the blind in the oxcart. He wanted to give me every chance, he said—it was slim enough at best. The rough road jolted my tired, cramped bones. Five times his headlight picked up the eyes of large animals: I didn't want them to be tigers—my nerves and eyes were too tired and jumpy—likely they were sambur or barking deer. They might have been great sladang for all I knew. The creeks were up with the rains and sometimes washed into the cart at the fords.

I was up before dawn, watching the cook make his auguries. No tiger today, he told me. Yet I returned to the blind, to find that the tiger had come after dark, and made a tremendous meal. The carcass was half devoured, the rest melting away from the attacks of millions of flies. Unless the beast gave me a shot today, it was in the cards for me to go home without him.

Again the veranus lizards kept me ghastly company. The jungle chickens picked up larvae, monkeys passed overhead, a barking deer wandered within forty feet of my blind, great peacocks flashed in the sunlight. The rains came, followed by a great stillness. The light began to fail.

Half an hour before dark the two veranus lizards feeding on the bait crept stealthily away. They had been coming and going all day; it might mean nothing. But only a second later, a rank, musky smell began to fill the glade. Even if I had never visited a zoo, I would have suspected its source. It was a very strong, intensely exciting smell. When deer caught it, they ran for their lives. When great sladang detected it on the breeze, they lowered their huge bossed horns.

The tiger was very close. He was an old, rank male. He was creeping about the clearing, looking and listening; he was seeing if there was any suspicious change since he was there; he was no young tiger to blunder into an ambush. For that matter, only old large males gave forth that powerful scent. He might be the Old Man, for all I knew. Maybe the middle-sized tiger that had left the tracks near the bait had been driven away and the Old Man had come for the broken meats.

My heart was thumping out of all keeping with the apparent issue—whether I would get a shot at a jungle beast. I think it was the way the hearts of cave men thumped, when they smelled the sabertooth outside their cavern doors. My gun seemed a little thing, my blind a treachery; yet I truly ached to have the beast show himself and put an end to the almost unbearable suspense. He did not. The light slowly failed. The rank smell slowly dimmed.

Then I heard Louis coming for me in the oxcart.

"We'll try again tomorrow," he said.

"Hell, yes. I'll get him tomorrow sure."

My servant wakened me from troubled dreams. It was tomorrow, and the last roundup so far as my Indo-Chinese adventure was concerned. But the cook came beaming to the table, bringing my venison breakfast-steak. "Velly good luck today," he told me. "Massa shoot Number One tigel!"

I needed all the luck there was around. In fact, a sensible man, seeing the outlook, would have called it a washout, headed for camp and America. The bait was reduced to a few gnawed bones and torn bits of hide. Surely the tiger would not return for these miserable scraps, when the jungle teemed with game. Anyway, I dreaded another long day in the cramped space of a palm-leaf blind, with no prospect ahead but defeat.

Louis too appeared discouraged, when he had surveyed the scene. Yet I'd better stay, he told me. "The tiger may not come here, but it's a dead cinch he won't come to camp," he added. "And I believe he's a fine tiger, old and wary, perhaps a bigger tiger than those tracks we saw would indicate." We had not looked for new tracks, lest we disturb the ground in some way to make him suspicious.

"There's no bait for him to come to," I said.

A dreamy expression I had seen before came into Louis' Mongoloid face. He was exerting his jungle-born, jungle-fed imagination—putting himself in the tiger's place. "Yes, I think he'll come back, and earlier than usual. He'll want to clean up these little scraps to stay his stomach before going hunting. You stay here and watch like the devil."

"How about coming at three o'clock and fixing me a flashlight and some kind of mosquito protection, so I can lay for him all night?"

This demented proposal struck him as quite sound. "I'll think it over," he promised; and herding me quickly into my cell, rode away.

The long watch began. It was drearier than the day before, otherwise unchanged. After hours of watching veranus lizards and trying to ease cramped limbs, the hour approached three. A sprinkling of rain pattered down. I listened for Louis—aching at least for a little company—but he did not come, and at four I gave him up. Anyway, I would be glad to escape the nightlong misery of a hopeless vigil. The sun dropped low, the daylight dimmed; soon it would be too dark to see my sights. The wild pigeons had begun to fly to their roosts.

About six o'clock I was watching two veranus lizards quarreling over the scraps of bait. A flock of a dozen or more jungle fowl were picking up larvae. Presently, both lizards crawled rather hastily away. Although stone-deaf, perhaps their darting tongues were sense organs—I had heard so, somewhere. For a moment, I sat tense, watching the chickens. Always quick to detect the nearing presence of an enemy, they continued to scratch and scuttle about. So I eased my tired knees so carelessly that they banged against the palm-leaf wall of the shelter. With that damage done, I picked up my tea flask and took a long drink unmindful of the gurgle.

At that instant, I smelled the tiger. The reek poured into my blind, unbelievably strong, and came from immediately behind me. Undoubtedly the beast was standing, looking and listening, only a few feet distant. An instant later, the jungle fowl flew up in great alarm, straight from me. They lighted in trees beyond the clearing and began to cackle in wild excitement. It was the same frantic *kut-kut-kut-degockit* that clamors from the barnyard when a stray skunk strolls near. I sat petrified, afraid to try to turn and look behind me through the palm leaves, terrified not to. I thought anything might happen next—and nothing did.

Only the rank smell slowly faded away.

As the moments passed, I became more and more convinced that I had muffed my only chance. No doubt the tiger had been standing just behind my blind when I had made the telltale sounds; suspicious, he had withdrawn into the forest. He would not come back until after dark. Already the light was almost too dim for shooting. Still I sat tense, in the grip of extreme excitement. The strain on my nerves and lungs and heart seemed almost unbearable.

The light failed steadily. I could still see the broken white bones of my bait, but the jungle beyond had become a dark wall. Already it was doubtful if I could see my sights. But at six-thirty, when it was almost too dark to shoot, a huge yellow circle suddenly appeared on the dark curtain of the thickets beyond the bait. For a hair-raising second, I could not identify it. It could not be the head of a tiger because it was too big. . . .

It was the head of a tiger. Its seeming gigantic size was a most curious optical illusion—a matter of mistaken judgment of distance. The dusk had caused those thickets to appear very far away. Actually, they were scarcely forty feet. Unconsciously, I expected the tiger's head to be reduced to fit that illusion of distance—a common trick of the mind.

An instant later, the tiger pushed boldly into the open—he too appearing colossal. What a moment in any man's life!

My gun was leaning against the boma, trigger guard up. I felt for it blindly, still watching that stupendous beast. I thrust my finger against the safety lever, and found that I could not move it —that apparently it had been already thrust over, making the gun ready to fire. Normally, I would have investigated this curious thing. It is a strict rule with me never to set down a firearm unsafe. But in my excitement I had apparently left the gun cocked.

Slowly, I eased up the weapon and thrust the barrel through the loophole. By pushing it all the way out, I could dimly make out the sights. Leveling them at the great yellow head, I pulled the trigger.

The gun did not go off! The trigger was locked. What a sickening anticlimax! Panic came mighty close as I thought the gun was out of order and I was helpless either to kill the tiger or prevent him if he took the notion of killing me. Half out of my head, I took a quick glance at the gun and in a few heart-stopped seconds understood what had happened. The gun had been safe all the time. Because it was upside down, I had pushed in the wrong direction. Somehow I managed to press the button and level the gun again.

The tiger was still standing quietly by the broken bones, calmly gazing in my direction. I saw that great yellow head along the sights. . . .

As I squeezed, the gun blazed in the twilight. Brainshot, the tiger sprang up on his hind legs, his immense forepaws high in the air—a most strange and dramatic scene—then crashed down. Such was the illusion of magnitude that he seemed to be thrown from a great height.

Of course I gave him a second shot, then a third and a fourth. After five minutes' steady quivering, I fired two shots into the air to give the prearranged signal that the tiger was dead. As it turned out, Louis and the boys were at that moment less than a half mile from the blind, coming to take me home from a lost hope.

Calming down a little, I crawled out of the blind to look at the tiger. He lay doubled up, his size hard to judge, yet plainly he was a full-grown male. It was only a short time after that the rumble of the oxcart and then the ring of Louis' voice breached the twilight silence.

"Is the tiger dead?" For Louis was not going to barge into the gloom in the face of a wounded killer.

"Yes, he's dead."

"He looks pretty big to me."

Louis fixed and turned on his headlight. However, we did not pause to examine the trophy closely: we were afraid the larvae from the bait might get into the fur. The Mois bound the front feet, then the rear, and thrust a pole between them. Four of the boys got under the pole and heaved.

Until then I had not ventured the guess that this was a royal tiger. I had suspected it, but was waiting for Louis to give his opinion. When the four boys could barely lift the animal off the ground, Louis gave me a great, wondering glance. He and I had to help carry the huge striped carcass to the cart. It filled the eight-foot box snugly as a coffin, with a good length of his tail hanging out behind.

Louis gave an odd little grunt. "He's a big tiger," he told me. Then, after a long, wide-eyed stare, "I believe he's one of the biggest tigers I ever saw."

We let it go at that, and started for camp. But all the way, Louis and I kept glancing at our prize, and always he seemed to grow in size. By the time we reached the tents, we thought it worthwhile to send a message to Francis Defosse, at the scout camp five miles away. Four boys carried it, one with a rifle to hold in his hands to give them comfort. They did not ask if the gun was loaded, nor did they care. They couldn't shoot if they had met a battalion of tigers. So great was its magic in their sight that all the beasts of the jungle would flee from their trail.

Francis Defosse arrived about midnight. He walked all around the tiger with a grave, almost solemn, expression. He had written the beast off at the end of my second day's watch and had never for a moment believed the Mois' story of a truly royal tiger.

"That's the biggest tiger that has ever been taken in this district," he told me in a funny, formal way.

"Is it the Old Man?"

"I think so. Certainly it isn't the tiger that made those tracks."

Both Louis and I had been ready to swear that this was the Old Man. However, Francis was a little doubtful even at first, and when he looked for a broken front claw to account for the Old Man's slew-toed track, he could not find it. Actually, the fine and fitting denouement did not pan out. Months later, he wrote me that the Old Man was back on the job—killing buffaloes and cattle, and leaving his unmistakable print on the Moi trails. My tiger had newly wandered into this district from some other jungle and had frightened the middle-sized beast from the kill.

He pegged out nine feet, ten inches unskinned, a truly royal tiger. His pelt was over eleven feet.

As far as I know, the Old Man still ranges those noble jungles, growing in girth and cunning, killing in the night, sleeping in the day, the trophy of a lifetime for the lucky hunter who levels his sights at his great, ruffed head. But I had memories that I would not trade for his great pelt. One was the scene of a sladang in the act of hooking a terrified Moi. One was of a wounded tiger "burning bright in the forests of the night." The last and best was of my giant as he sprang to his full height in the second of his doom. It was good hunting.

F. D. DUNCAN

With Slashing Tusks

Only in one small corner of New Hampshire and another in North Carolina can the American hunter expect to bring about an encounter with a wild boar, and in both these areas there is usually a tree handy. In the Far East habitat of the tusker there are few such escape routes, which makes the sport more interesting—and dangerous. Just how much of both are involved Duncan's tale makes clear.

While any big game animal may be dangerous now and then, there are some that are dangerous all the time. Take, for instance, a beast weighing four hundred pounds or more, one with knife-edged tusks, great speed, savagery, cunning, and inborn cussedness. Such is the great Asiatic wild boar. When you are charged by this formidable creature you need nerves of steel and the ability to think and act quickly—without those qualities you may well be facing death. Poor Frenchy was to learn that grim lesson.

When, that autumn, rumors of a huge gray boar, said to be ranging among the hills back of Chinkiang, China, began to trickle in, I was sure that before long Randall would show up. Together we had had many a good hunt in those hills, and had brought out some fine specimens.

Moreover, I guessed that my head coolie had been doing a little conniving with Randall's head coolie. It was a way they had, for each was as keen for a hunt as we were. They would see to it that word of the great gray boar (they called him "Old Big") would come to us in roundabout fashion, while they'd wait, in bland innocence, for us to take the bait.

Randall had charge of the Customs station on the other side of the river. He was a grand hunting companion—a splendid shot, a true sportsman, as steady as a rock in dangerous situations, and possessed of a rare sense of humor. Yes, I knew that Randall would come over, and I'd be glad to see him.

It is useless to go after wild boar until the trees and bushes are fairly clear of foliage. Prior to that, the chances are all with the game. Even when the limbs and twigs are bare it is hard enough to see the great pigs, for their coloring blends in with their surroundings and they are adept at hiding. It is difficult to believe, but often a hunter has been within twenty feet of a wild boar weighing from three hundred to four hundred pounds and has never known it. So it was early in December when Randall showed up.

It was like him to drop in casually, talk about everything under the sun except wild boar until it was about time to leave, and then, in a very offhand manner, ask if I'd heard about a huge boar back in the hills—and if I didn't think something ought to be done about it. Just as casually I expressed appropriate surprise and interest, hemmed and hawed, and finally agreed to go hunting with him during the holiday week, just after New Year's.

We were more than ordinarily keyed up when we started off on our trip, and the thrill of anticipation didn't lessen when, back in the hills, we began to hear stories of Old Big at first hand. Almost every bush cutter had come across his tracks, and some of them had seen him. They were unanimous in saying that he was one of the very biggest of his kind, so there was little sleep for hunters or coolies that first night. There was much excited talk; everyone seemed in a fever of expectation. Any wild boar hunt is dangerous —we all knew that—and now we were after a monster. But our coolies had implicit confidence in the marksmanship and courage of their white hunters, and it was up to Randall and me not to let them down.

That is a broken country of hills and valleys, and heavily brushed. We had hunted it before and knew where our game might be, but in a vast area like that, a search for one particular animal seems an almost hopeless thing. We combed favorite cover, thrashed through likely valleys, and wearily climbed ridge after ridge without incident. Again and again we came across the astounding tracks of Old Big; their size, and the way they were deeply pressed into the earth by his great weight, made us tingle all over. We all realized that this was not a boar to fool with. He was old, wise, and savage, undoubtedly as ready to attack as to flee. Such a boar may hide, skulk, dodge, and slip away all day long when such tactics are possible. Then, if you come upon him suddenly where he cannot escape before being seen, look out! He'll charge, grinding his tusks and foaming at the mouth, bent upon your destruction.

All that first day was spent in tramping over miles of tough country. We saw plenty of game, and twice spotted small bands of boar, but they were far out of sporting range. Neither of us wanted to wound an animal we could not bag.

The second day brought a lot of action and excitement. Randall caught a fleeting glimpse of a large boar as it flashed through an opening in the cover across a valley, and he got in a quick shot. The boar staggered, almost fell, then raced into the bush. His trail was clearly marked with blood, indicating a hit well up in the chest, and there was froth high on the bushes he'd passed. Whether Randall had made a lung shot or not, that boar was able to travel fast, and when, after a long chase, he took to cover we were just about worn out.

There are always bush cutters on the hillsides, and these men are of great help to hunters, for they quickly notice any moving animal. Usually they are able to tell you where a wounded boar has gone, and where it is likely to stop and hide. We now met one of them and he told us he'd seen our quarry—"he is not Old Big" —plunge into a thick patch of cover at the edge of a wide valley; he was certain that the brute had not come out.

We soon found that the beast's place of refuge was perfect for a kill. A wild boar usually runs uphill instead of down, and here was an open space, covered with the usual brown grass, just above the thicket in which Randall's boar was hidden. Randall went on ahead to watch this opening, while I took the beaters down the slope to start the drive at the foot of the hill.

Hitherto that boar had flitted from brier patch to wooded covert, always keeping far ahead of us, and moving on before we got anywhere near. But now that we wanted him to come out he was stubborn and refused to move. The beaters set up an awful din, screeching with all their might, beating the brush with clubs, and heaving rocks into the densest cover, places they dared not enter. For a long time nothing happened. It is hard, nerve-racking work to beat a thicket like that, not knowing where the quarry is, and expecting and dreading a charge at any moment. The briers were almost impenetrable; we scrambled over rocks, tripped and fell, every man of us tense. Each knew what would happen if the boar should decide not to run, but await a favorable moment to charge. I did my best to keep all the beaters in sight so that I would have a chance to stop a charge before it became deadly. The coolies were all unarmed, and I admired their courage. Their only defense was their numbers, the noise they made—and their faith in us.

There came the familiar yell—"La-li! La-li!"—which means "Over there!" The warning is too general to help you much, but even with the most careful training I have never been able to get the men to be more specific. So now I first had to locate the particular beater who was yelling, and then wait until he decided to point.

The boar did what we hoped he would. Slipping noiselessly through the cover with an ease that's astonishing in so large an animal, he made his way to the edge of the brush at my left, and was now streaking across the open, near the top of the hill. For a moment it looked as though he would escape—for while he was within easy rifle shot of Randall, a small knoll hid him from the hunter. But Randall was gifted with true hunting instinct, and sized up the situation as soon as he had heard the beater's shouted warning. At once he picked out the man who had yelled, caught his gesture toward the moving boar, and realized that to get a shot he must run to the top of the knoll. It is a trying test of nerve and steadiness to run rapidly and then make a good shot without a moment's pause, but Randall did just that. The boar was clearing the top of a very steep rise at the far edge of the open space, and in an eyelid's flicker he would have been out of sight. But Randall caught the big brute over his rifle sights, pulled the trigger, and sent a high-powered bullet crashing through the great, long-snouted head. The boar keeled over, and lay wildly pawing the air with his feet.

A great yell of joy went up from the coolies, for all of them were able to see the finish. But the thrills were not yet over. Randall trotted forward, knife in hand, intending to cut the boar's throat to bleed him. He seized the brute by a front leg to make his cut. The touch had an immediate and surprising effect. The boar, lying at the edge of a very steep, smooth pitch, heaved and kicked violently. Randall, taken by surprise, didn't let go of the leg and was swung off his feet; then boar and man started rolling together down the slope. We knew the boar was too far gone to be able to do any serious damage, and the scene was so ludicrous that the coolies and I flopped down in the brush and laughed until we cried.

Boar and hunter rolled clear across the open space until brought to an abrupt halt by a small tree. Randall rose to his feet with much dignity, looked at us reproachfully, and then finished his sticking job. That ended the day's hunt. We had bagged a fine specimen with a splendid head, and all hands were happy as we started back for camp. The coolies kept saying to one another— "Tomorrow we get Old Big."

That night my head coolie looked up a friend of his who lived not far away, and from him got definite information as to where our great boar was likely to be. Soon after daylight we started out, passing through deep and thicket-filled valleys that looked like excellent boar country, enough to convince us that my coolie's friend knew what he was talking about. We often came across Old Big's tracks, some of them fresh, and by the time we were ready to start our first drive, everyone was on edge with anticipation.

On a boar hunt of this sort a considerable number of coolies are needed to act as beaters. All the cover must be combed, for otherwise the game is likely to lie hidden until the drive has passed, and then sneak noiselessly off to the rear. The line of beaters is arranged in such a way that the boar will be driven toward an open slope where a shot is possible. When Randall and I hunted together one of us would go on ahead to take a position commanding the open slope, while the other worked with the beaters. We found this advisable because the coolies alone would naturally be timid about going into the heaviest cover, and it's in such places that the game usually is hidden. Furthermore, if the boar tries to slip away to the rear, there is possibility that the hunter with the coolies will get a shot. So, this time I was with the coolies, while Randall was at the top of the ridge.

The thickets were full of game—mostly river deer and pheasants. We did not fire at them, for we were after boar. But somebody, just over the ridge, began to shoot at the game we were driving out. We heard the sharp cracks of a rifle, occasionally varied with the boom of a shotgun. We were puzzled and none too well pleased. Who could it be?

We went to the top of the ridge and looked down the other side. To our dismay we saw "Frenchy" and a group of coolies on the hill below. Frenchy was also a worker at the Customs station, and though he was very fond of hunting he was also very poor at it.

Whenever he could he'd join a hunting party, but no party ever took him along if it could be avoided. He was a bad shot, a bad sport, and a general nuisance, though he meant well. We did not want him with us that day, so we signaled to our coolies, and dropped back over our hill where we'd be out of sight.

Hunting is full of surprises, which is one of the things that endear it to a sportsman. We had worked that valley thoroughly. But as I looked down toward the bottom of the rise, watching as a hunter always should, I saw a great gray shape slipping through the brush. To our utter amazement there was Old Big himself, coming out of the very cover we had just been through. He was enormous—just as big as we had expected him to be—and in plain sight, though far out of range. None of us who saw him can ever forget him; we were overwhelmed by his tremendous size, his evident age, and the terrible ferocity that was made plain by every look and action. We stood spellbound while he leisurely trotted out of sight. When he disappeared a great sigh came from all of us.

Old Big did not seem alarmed, and the head coolies were confident that he would not go far. A deep, open valley separated the mountain he rounded from the one beyond. The coolies believed he would not cross that valley, so our plans were made accordingly. Randall was to go into the cover with the coolies while I went over the mountain to form a welcoming committee of one should the monster come out. The great boar had made us forget Frenchy. Furthermore, as I crossed the rise, he was nowhere in sight. For a stand I selected a knob that commanded the entire mountainside. Randall and the beaters skirted the hill base and began their drive in the cover that Old Big had entered. Prospects looked excellent for us to bag the biggest boar any of us had ever seen.

Randall, the coolies, and I were all ready to act promptly in the event of any emergency that might arise where the hunt was under our control. But who could have foreseen the swift, tragic, and uncontrollable rush of events that was to leave us dazed and saddened?

I heard the shouts of the drivers as they beat the cover around the hill; I followed the course of the coolies by their yells as they pushed through the brush. Then, when I heard the familiar "La-li!" and the excitement in those Chinese voices, I knew that our men had started Old Big himself. I felt myself go taut. Would the boar come my way?

But suddenly, maddeningly, from beyond the knoll that hid the far side of the hill, there came the unexpected roar of a shotgun, followed by another. Then a coolie screeched a yell or terrified warning, and after that came a sound such as I hope never to hear again. It was the cry of a man in mortal pain and fear. At once I thought of Frenchy, blundering and inefficient, there in the path of that great wild boar. In the distance I heard Randall yell, and then the crash of his rifle, again and again. Tense and alert, I went forward as fast as I could travel, but be sure that I did not go so hurriedly that I neglected to watch for every movement and sound.

Thanks to good old Lau Wong I had a bit of warning. I heard him yell my name twice in quick succession, and I put myself on guard. The next second there came over the hill above me a raging, maddened monster, an irresistible thunderbolt running with the speed of a deer, four hundred pounds of death and destruction. Old Big's bristles stood on end and made him look twice his size. His tusks were slashing and dripping with foam and blood.

I *had* to be steady. My bullet took him in the base of the skull, and never did an animal die more quickly. The force of his rush carried him over the short grass for some distance, and then he came to a stop on his side, dead when he reached there.

But at the moment there was no time to pause over him. I rushed beyond the knoll to where an awed and horror-stricken group stood around Frenchy. The thing that had always been a possibility on each of our boar hunts had now actually happened. The wounds left by the big boar's tusks were bad enough, but not necessarily fatal—a man can take a tremendous amount of tearing and mauling if the wounds are clean. But a boar's tusks never are clean. With them he grubs in the earth for such roots and tubers as he likes to eat, and the soil of China crawls with deadly germs.

We bandaged Frenchy's wounds as best we could, made a rude stretcher, and started for home. The boar, magnificent trophy as he was, was almost forgotten. We hurried as fast as we could to get Frenchy to the hospital, but our fears were well founded. Blood poison set in, and a few days later we followed his casket to the little foreign cemetery beside the river.

For many years I hunted wild boar and other big game in China, and have seen many fine trophies brought in. Old Big was not only the most formidable animal I have ever faced, but the finest trophy. And he was responsible for the only really serious accident that I ever have seen happen on a hunt. But one is too many. I do not care to see another.

JIM CORBETT

The Bachelor of Powalgarh

If there were still opportunities to be paid to hunt tigers, the long line of applicants would stretch from here to there, but it becomes increasingly apparent that the golden age of big game hunting is now in the past. Many of us who are still able to take to the field with a gun were gathering in pheasants and grouse while Corbett was hunting tigers—or arranging for them to hunt him— as a professional. *Man-Eaters of Kumaon* is the work of a professional writer as well as a professional hunter, and the "Bachelor" provided one of the most interesting episodes of an exciting career.

Three miles from our winter home, and in the heart of the forest, there is an open glade some four hundred yards long and half as wide, grassed with emerald green and surrounded with big trees interlaced with cane creepers. It was in this glade, which for beauty has no equal, that I first saw the tiger that was known throughout the United Provinces as "The Bachelor of Powalgarh," who from 1920 to 1930 was the most sought-after big game trophy in the province.

The sun had just risen, one winter's morning, when I crested the high ground overlooking the glade. On the far side, a score of red jungle fowl were scratching among the dead leaves bordering a crystal-clear stream, and scattered over the emerald-green grass, now sparkling with dew, fifty or more chital were feeding. Sitting on a tree stump and smoking, I had been looking at this scene for some time when the hind nearest to me raised her head, turned in my direction, and called; and a moment later the Bachelor stepped into the open, from the thick bushes below me. For a long minute he stood with head held high, surveying the scene, and then with slow unhurried steps started across the glade. In his rich winter coat, which the newly risen sun was lighting up, he was a magnificent sight as, with head turning now to the right and now to the left, he walked down the wide lane the deer had made for him. At the stream he lay down and quenched his thirst, then sprang across and, as he entered the dense tree jungle beyond, called three times in acknowledgment of the homage the jungle folk had paid him, for from the time he had entered the glade every chital had called, every jungle fowl had cackled, and every one of a troupe of monkeys on the trees had chattered.

The Bachelor was far afield that morning, for his home was in a ravine six miles away. Living in an area in which the majority of tigers are bagged with the aid of elephants, he had chosen his home wisely. The ravine, running into the foothills, was half a mile long, with steep hills on either side rising to a height of a thousand feet. At the upper end of the ravine there was a waterfall some twenty feet high, and at the lower end, where the water had cut through red clay, it narrowed to four feet. Any sportsman, therefore, who wished to try conclusions with the Bachelor, while he was at home, would of a necessity have to do so on foot. It was this secure retreat, and the Government rules prohibiting night shooting, that had enabled the Bachelor to retain possession of his much sought-after skin.

In spite of the many and repeated attempts that had been made to bag him with the aid of buffalo bait, the Bachelor had never been fired at, though on two occasions, to my knowledge, he had only escaped death by the skin of his teeth. On the first occasion, after a perfect beat, a guy rope by which the machan was suspended interfered with the movement of Fred Anderson's rifle at the critical moment, and on the second occasion the Bachelor arrived at the machan before the beat started and found Huish Edye filling his pipe. On both these occasions he had been viewed at a range of only a few feet, and while Anderson described him as being as big as a Shetland pony, Edye said he was as big as a donkey.

The winter following these and other unsuccessful attempts, I took Wyndham, our Commissioner, who knows more about tigers than any other man in India, to a fire track skirting the upper end of the ravine in which the Bachelor lived, to show him the fresh pug marks of the tiger which I had found on the fire track that morning. Wyndham was accompanied by two of his most experienced shikaris, and after the three of them had carefully measured and examined the pug marks, Wyndham said that in his opinion the tiger was ten feet between pegs, and while one shikari said he was 10 feet five inches over curves, the other said he was ten feet six inches, or a little more. All three agreed that they had never seen the pug marks of a bigger tiger.

In 1930 the Forest Department started extensive fellings in the area surrounding the Bachelor's home and, annoyed at the disturbance, he changed quarters; this I learned from two sportsmen who had taken out a shooting pass with the object of hunting down the tiger. Shooting passes are only issued for fifteen days of each month, and throughout the winter, shooting party after shooting party failed to make contact with the tiger.

Towards the end of the winter an old dak runner, who passes our gate every morning and evening on his seven-mile run through the forest to a hill village, came to me one evening and reported that on his way out that morning he had seen the biggest pug marks of a tiger that he had seen during the thirty years of his service. The tiger, he said, had come from the west and, after proceeding along the road for two hundred yards, had gone east, taking a path that started from near an almond tree. This tree was about two miles from our home, and was a well-known landmark. The path the tiger had taken runs through very heavy jungle for half a mile before crossing a wide watercourse, and then joins a cattle track which skirts the foot of the hills before entering a deep and well-wooded valley; a favorite haunt of tigers.

Early next morning, with Robin at my heels, I set out to prospect, my objective being the point where the cattle track entered the valley, for at this point the tracks of all the animals entering or leaving the valley are to be found. From the time we started Robin appeared to know that we had a special job in hand and he paid not the least attention to the jungle fowl we disturbed, the kakar (barking deer) that let us get quite close to it, and the two sambur that stood and belled at us. Where the cattle track entered the valley the ground was hard and stony, and when we reached this spot Robin put down his head and very carefully smelled the stones, and on receiving a signal from me to carry on he turned and started down the track, keeping a yard ahead of me; I could tell from his behavior that he was on the scent of a tiger, and that the scent was hot. A hundred yards further down, where the track flattens out and runs along the foot of the hill, the ground is soft;

here I saw the pug marks of a tiger, and a glance at them satisfied me we were on the heels of the Bachelor and that he was only a minute or two ahead of us.

Beyond the soft ground the track runs for three hundred yards over stones, before going steeply down onto an open plain. If the tiger kept to the track we should probably see him on this open ground. We had gone another fifty yards when Robin stopped and, after running his nose up and down a blade of grass on the left of the track, turned and entered the grass which was here about two feet high. On the far side of the grass there was a patch of clerodendron, about forty yards wide. This plant grows in dense patches to a height of five feet, and has widely spread leaves and a big head of flowers not unlike horse-chestnut. It is greatly fancied by tiger, sambur, and pig because of the shade it gives. When Robin reached the clerodendron he stopped and backed towards me, thus telling me that he could not see into the bushes ahead and wished to be carried. Lifting him up, I put his hind legs into my left-hand coat pocket, and when he had hooked his forefeet over my left arm, he was safe and secure, and I had both hands free for the rifle. On these occasions Robin was always in deadly earnest, and no matter what he saw, or how our quarry behaved before or after fired at, he never moved and spoiled my shot, or impeded my view. Proceeding very slowly, we had gone halfway through the clerodendron when I saw the bushes directly in front of us swaying. Waiting until the tiger had cleared the bushes, I went forward expecting to see him in the more or less open jungle, but he was nowhere in sight, and when I put Robin down he turned to the left and indicated that the tiger had gone into a deep and narrow ravine near by. This ravine ran to the foot of an isolated hill on which there were caves frequented by tigers, and as I was not armed to deal with a tiger at close quarters, and further, as it was time for breakfast, Robin and I turned and made for home.

After breakfast I returned alone, armed with a heavy .450 rifle, and as I approached the hill, which in the days of the long ago had been used by the local inhabitants as a rallying point against the Gurkha invaders, I heard the boom of a big buffalo bell, and a man shouting. These sounds were coming from the top of the hill, which is flat, and about half an acre in extent, so I climbed up and saw a man on a tree, striking a dead branch with the head of his axe and shouting, while at the foot of the tree a number of buffaloes were collected. When he saw me the man called out, saying I had just arrived in time to save him and his buffaloes from a shaitan of a tiger, the size of a camel, that had been threatening them for hours. From his story I gathered that he had arrived on the hill shortly after Robin and I had left for home, and that as he started to cut bamboo leaves for his buffaloes he saw a tiger coming towards him. He shouted to drive the tiger away, as he had done on many previous occasions with other tigers, but instead of going away this one had started to growl. He took to his heels, followed by his buffaloes, and climbed up the nearest tree. The tiger, paying no heed to his shouts, had then set to pacing round and round, while the buffaloes kept their heads towards it. Probably the tiger had heard me coming, for it had left only a moment before I had arrived. The man was an old friend, who before his quarrel with the Headman of his village had done a considerable amount of poaching in these jungles with the Headman's gun. He now begged me to conduct both himself and his cattle safely out of the jungle; so telling him to lead on, I followed behind to see that there were no stragglers. At first the buffaloes were disinclined to break up their close formation, but after a little persuasion we got them to start, and we had gone halfway across the open plain I have alluded to when the tiger called in the jungle to our right. The man quickened his pace, and I urged on the buffaloes, for a mile of very thick jungle lay between us and the wide, open watercourse beyond which lay my friend's village and safety for his buffaloes.

I have earned the reputation of being keener on photographing animals than on killing them, and before I left my friend he begged me to put aside photography for this once, and kill the tiger, which he said was big enough to eat a buffalo a day, and ruin him in twenty-five days. I promised to do my best and turned to retrace my steps to the open plain, to meet with an experience every detail of which has burned itself deep into my memory.

On reaching the plain I sat down to wait for the tiger to disclose his whereabouts, or for the jungle folk to tell me where he was. It was then about 3 P.M., and as the sun was warm and comforting, I put my head down on my drawn-up knees and had been dozing a few minutes when I was awakened by the tiger calling; thereafter he continued to call at short intervals.

Between the plain and the hills there is a belt, some half-mile wide, of the densest scrub jungle for a hundred miles round, and I located the tiger as being on the hills on the far side of the scrub

—about three-quarters of a mile from me—and from the way he was calling it was evident he was in search of a mate.

Starting from the upper left-hand corner of the plain, and close to where I was sitting, an old cart track, used some years previously for extracting timber, ran in an almost direct line to where the tiger was calling. This track would take me in the direction of the calling animal, but on the hills was high grass, and without Robin to help me there would be little chance of my seeing him. So instead of my going to look for the tiger, I decided he should come and look for me. I was too far away for him to hear me, so I sprinted up the cart track for a few hundred yards, laid down my rifle, climbed to the top of a high tree and called three times. I was immediately answered by the tiger. After climbing down, I ran back, calling as I went, and arrived on the plain without having found a suitable place in which to sit and await the tiger. Something would have to be done, and in a hurry, for the tiger was rapidly coming nearer; so, after rejecting a little hollow which I found to be full of black stinking water, I lay down flat in the open, twenty yards from where the track entered the scrub. From this point I had a clear view up the track for fifty yards, to where a bush, leaning over it, impeded my further view. If the tiger came down the track, as I expected him to, I decided to fire at him as soon as he cleared the obstruction.

After opening the rifle to make sure it was loaded, I threw off the safety catch and with elbows comfortably propped and resting on the soft ground, waited for the tiger to appear. I had not called since I came out on the plain, so to give him direction I now gave a low call, which he immediately answered from a distance of a hundred yards. If he came on at his usual pace, I judged he would clear the obstruction in thirty seconds. I counted this number very slowly, and went on counting up to eighty, when out of the corner of my eye I saw a movement to my right front, where the bushes approached to within ten yards of me. Turning my eyes in that direction I saw a great head projecting above the bushes, which here were four feet high. The tiger was only a foot or two inside the bushes, but all I could see of him was his head. As I very slowly swung the point of the rifle round and ran my eyes along the sights I noticed that his head was not quite square on to me, and as I was firing up and he was looking down, I aimed an inch below his right eye, pressed the trigger, and for the next half-hour nearly died of fright.

Instead of dropping dead as I expected him to, the tiger went straight up into the air above the bushes for his full length, falling backwards onto a tree a foot thick which had been blown down in a storm and was still green. With unbelievable fury he attacked this tree and tore it to bits, emitting as he did so roar upon roar, and what was even worse, a dreadful blood-curdling sound as though he was savaging his worst enemy. The branches of the tree tossed about as though struck by a tornado, while the bushes on my side shook and bulged out, and every moment I expected to have him on top of me, for he had been looking at me when I fired, and knew where I was.

Too frightened even to recharge the rifle for fear the slight movement and sound should attract the attention of the tiger, I lay and sweated for half an hour with my finger on the left trigger. At last the branches of the tree and the bushes ceased waving about, and the roaring became less frequent, and eventually, to my great relief, ceased. For another half-hour I lay perfectly still, with arms cramped by the weight of the heavy rifle, and then started to pull myself backwards with my toes. After progressing for thirty yards in this manner, I got to my feet and, crouching low, made for the welcome shelter of the nearest tree. Here I remained for some minutes, and as all was now silent I turned and made for home.

Next morning I returned, accompanied by one of my men, an expert tree-climber. I had noticed the previous evening that there was a tree growing on the edge of the open ground and about forty yards from where the tiger had fallen. We approached this tree very cautiously, and I stood behind it while the man climbed to the top. After a long and careful scrutiny he looked down and shook his head, and when he rejoined me on the ground he told me that the bushes over a big area had been flattened down, but that the tiger was not in sight.

I sent him back to perch on the tree with instructions to keep a sharp lookout and warn me if he saw any movement in the bushes, and went forward to have a look at the spot where the tiger had raged. He had raged to some purpose, for, in addition to tearing the branches and great strips of wood off the tree, he had torn up several bushes by the roots, and bitten down on others. Blood in profusion was sprinkled everywhere, and on the ground were two congealed pools, near one of which was lying a bit of bone two inches square, which I found on examination to be part of the tiger's skull.

No blood trail led away from this spot, and this, combined with the two pools of blood, was proof that the tiger was still here when I left and that the precautions I had taken the previous evening were very necessary, for when I started on my "getaway" I was only ten yards from the most dangerous animal in the world—a freshly wounded tiger. On circling round the spot I found a small smear of blood here and there on leaves that had brushed against his face. Noting that these indications of the tiger's passage led in a direct line to a giant semul tree [1] two hundred yards away, I went back and climbed the tree my man was on in order to get a bird's-eye view of the ground I should have to go over, for I had a very uneasy feeling that I should find him alive: a tiger shot in the head can live for days and can even recover from the wound. True, this tiger had a bit of his skull missing, and as I had never dealt with an animal in his condition before I did not know whether he was likely to live for a few hours or days, or live on to die of old age. For this reason I decided to treat him as an ordinary wounded tiger, and not to take any avoidable risks when following him up.

From my elevated position on the tree I saw that, a little to the left of the line to the semul tree, there were two trees, the nearer one thirty yards from where the blood was, and the other fifty yards further on. Leaving my man on the tree, I climbed down, picked up my rifle and a shotgun and bag of a hundred cartridges, and very cautiously approached the nearer tree and climbed up it to a height of thirty feet, pulling the rifle and gun, which I had tied to one end of a strong cord, up after me. After fixing the rifle in a fork of the tree where it would be handy if needed, I started to spray the bushes with small shot, yard by yard up to the foot of the second tree. I did this with the object of locating the tiger, assuming he was alive and in that area, for a wounded tiger, on hearing a shot fired close to him, or on being struck by a pellet, will either growl or charge. Receiving no indication of the tiger's presence I went to the second tree, and sprayed the bushes to within a few yards of the semul tree, firing the last shot at the tree itself. After this last shot I thought I heard a low growl, but it was not repeated and I put it down to my imagination. My bag of cartridges was now empty, so after recovering my man I called it a day and went home.

When I returned next morning I found my friend the buffalo man feeding his buffaloes on the plain. He appeared to be very much relieved to see me, and the reason for this I learned later. The grass was still wet with dew, but we found a dry spot and there sat down to have a smoke and relate our experiences. My friend,

---

[1] *Bombax malabaricum,* the silk cotton tree.

as I have mentioned, had done a lot of poaching, and having spent all his life in tiger-infested jungles tending his buffaloes, or shooting, his jungle knowledge was considerable.

After I had left him that day at the wide, open watercourse, he had crossed to the far side and had sat down to listen for sounds coming from the direction in which I had gone. He had heard two tigers calling; he had heard my shot followed by the continuous roaring of a tiger, and very naturally concluded I had wounded one of the tigers and that it had killed me. On his return next morning to the same spot, he had been greatly mystified by hearing a hundred shots fired, and this morning, not being able to contain his curiosity any longer, he had come to see what had happened. Attracted by the smell of blood, his buffaloes had shown him where the tiger had fallen, and he had seen the patches of dry blood and had found the bit of bone. No animal in his opinion could possibly live for more than a few hours after having a bit of its skull blown away, and so sure was he that the tiger was dead that he offered to take his buffaloes into the jungle and find it for me. I had heard of this method of recovering tigers with the help of buffaloes but had never tried it myself, and after my friend had agreed to accept compensation for any damage to his cattle I accepted his offer.

Rounding up the buffaloes, twenty-five in number, and keeping to the line I had sprinkled with shot the previous day, we made for the semul tree, followed by the buffaloes. Our progress was slow, for not only had we to move the chin-high bushes with our hands to see where to put our feet, but we also had frequently to check a very natural tendency on the part of the buffaloes to stray. As we approached the semul tree, where the bushes were lighter, I saw a little hollow filled with dead leaves that had been pressed flat and on which were several patches of blood, some dry, others in process of congealing, and one quite fresh; and when I put my hand to the ground I found it was warm. Incredible as it may appear, the tiger had lain in this hollow the previous day while I had expended a hundred cartridges, and had only moved off when he saw us and the buffaloes approaching. The buffaloes had now found the blood and were pawing up the ground and snorting, and, as the prospect of being caught between a charging tiger and angry buffaloes did not appeal to me, I took hold of my friend's arm, turned him round, and made for the open plain, followed by the buffaloes. When we were back on safe ground I told the man to go home, and said I would return next day and deal with the tiger alone.

The path through the jungles that I had taken each day when

coming from and going home ran for some distance over soft ground, and on this soft ground, on this fourth day, I found the pug marks of a big male tiger. By following these pug marks I found the tiger had entered the dense brushwood a hundred yards to the right of the semul tree. Here was an unexpected complication, for if I now saw a tiger in this jungle I should not know—unless I got a very close look at it—whether it was the wounded or the unwounded one. However, this contingency would have to be dealt with when met, and in the meantime worrying would not help, so I entered the bushes and made for the hollow at the foot of the semul tree.

There was no blood trail to follow so I zigzagged through the bushes, into which it was impossible to see further than a few inches, for an hour or more, until I came to a ten-foot-wide dry watercourse. Before stepping down into this watercourse I looked up it, and saw the left hind leg and tail of a tiger. The tiger was standing perfectly still with its body and head hidden by a tree, and only this one leg visible. I raised the rifle to my shoulder, and then lowered it. To have broken the leg would have been easy, for the tiger was only ten yards away, and it would have been the right thing to do if its owner was the wounded animal; but there were two tigers in the area, and to have broken the leg of the wrong one would have doubled my complications and difficulties, which were already considerable. Presently the leg was withdrawn and I heard the tiger moving away, and going to the spot where he had been standing I found a few drops of blood—too late now to regret not having broken that leg.

A quarter of a mile further on there was a little stream, and it was possible that the tiger, now recovering from the wound, was making for this stream. With the object of intercepting him, or failing that, waiting for him at the water, I took a game path which I knew went to the stream and had proceeded along it for some distance when a sambur belled to my left, and went dashing off through the jungle. It was evident now that I was abreast of the tiger, and I had only taken a few more steps when I heard the loud crack of a dry stick breaking as though some heavy animal had fallen on it; the sound had come from a distance of fifty yards and from the exact spot where the sambur had belled. The sambur had in unmistakable tones warned the jungle folk of the presence of a tiger and the stick therefore could only have been broken by the same animal, so getting down on my hands and knees I started to crawl in the direction from which the sound had come.

The bushes here were from six to eight feet high, with dense foliage on the upper branches and very few leaves on the stems, so that I could see through them for a distance of ten to fifteen feet. I had covered thirty yards, hoping fervently that if the tiger charged he would come from in front (for in no other direction could I have fired), when I caught sight of something red on which the sun, drifting through the upper leaves, was shining; it might only be a bunch of dead leaves; on the other hand, it might be the tiger. I could get a better view of this object from two yards to the right so, lowering my head until my chin touched the ground, I crawled this distance with belly to ground, and on raising my head saw the tiger in front of me. He was crouching down looking at me, with the sun shining on his left shoulder, and on receiving my two bullets he rolled over on his side without making a sound.

As I stood over him and ran my eyes over his magnificent proportions it was not necessary to examine the pads of his feet to know that before me lay the Bachelor of Powalgarh.

The entry of the bullet fired four days previously was hidden by a wrinkle of skin, and at the back of his head was a big hole which, surprisingly, was perfectly clean and healthy.

The report of my rifle was, I knew, being listened for, so I hurried home to relieve anxiety, and while I related the last chapter of the hunt and drank a pot of tea, my men were collecting.

Accompanied by my sister and Robin and a carrying party of twenty men, I returned to where the tiger was lying, and before he was roped to a pole my sister and I measured him from nose to tip of tail, and from tip of tail to nose. At home we again measured him to make quite sure we had made no mistake the first time. These measurements are valueless, for there were no independent witnesses present to certify them; they are, however, interesting as showing the accuracy with which experienced hunters can judge the length of a tiger from his pug marks. Wyndham, you will recall, said the tiger was ten feet between pegs, which would give roughly ten feet six inches over curves; and while one shikari said he was 10 feet five inches over curves, the other said he was ten feet six inches or a little more. Shot seven years after these estimates were made, my sister and I measured the tiger as being ten feet seven inches over curves.

I have told this story at some length, as I feel sure that those who hunted the tiger between 1920 and 1930 will be interested to know how the Bachelor of Powalgarh met his end.

J . A . H U N T E R

Clients, Brave and Otherwise

The "white hunter" of Africa has become a legend—although still a living one—on the dark continent, and it may come as something of a surprise to many to learn that the occupation is not all beer and skittles. Many of the so-called great stories of African hunting are as familiar to hunters as Mother Goose. In the stories I have selected on Africa, of which this is one, I have tried to avoid the familiar and bring out some of the reality. An outstanding hunter, unfortunately, is not necessarily a graphic writer, but J. A. Hunter seems to possess the ability to present a clear picture of the African scene and the creatures that populate it—wild and allegedly civilized.

I spent much of my next twenty years as a white hunter, generally outfitting in Nairobi and going everywhere from the Belgian Congo to Southern Abyssinia. During those years I guided the Prince and Princess Schwarzenberg, the Baron and Baroness Rothschild, many of the lesser Continental nobility, a number of rajahs and maharajahs, and a scattering of American millionaires. I also guided many sportsmen in very moderate circumstances who had spent years saving up enough money so they could have a go at African big game.

Like most white hunters, I was usually employed by one of the big organizations in Nairobi that makes a business of outfitting safaris for clients. Although I have worked for several of these organizations, I spent most of my time with Safariland, Inc., a company that has been in operation since the turn of the century and has arranged safaris for Radclyffe Dugmore, the Martin Johnsons, the Aga Khan, and in recent years MGM's *King Solomon's Mines*. Safariland keeps a number of white hunters on its payroll and during the boom years of the twenties, as soon as one of us returned from safari, he was immediately sent out on another.

I never knew beforehand if my next client would be a nervous individual who merely wanted to camp a few miles outside of Nairobi so he could later boast of having been "on safari through the wilds of Africa" or a keen sportsman who was willing to risk his life to obtain a fine trophy. Whatever my clients wanted, I did my best to provide, whether it was a record head or an easy tour of the game country.

It has been said that a white hunter must combine "the expert lore of an Indian scout, the cool nerve of a professional soldier, and the ability to mingle easily with the rich and aristocratic." One of the most successful white hunters with Safariland put the matter to me somewhat differently. "Hunter," he said, "you must always remember that only ten per cent of your work is hunting. Ninety per cent is keeping your clients amused." Now I was never much of a clubman and so Safariland tried to send me out with sportsmen who were mainly interested in obtaining trophies. But during the rush seasons no such distinction could be made. Then I had to learn to study my clients and try to gratify their whims. This I did —up to certain limits.

Among my first aristocratic clients were a French count and his countess who wanted a few African trophies for their château in Normandy. It was fashionable for the European nobility to be able to say that they had been big-game hunting in Africa and we white hunters profited by the fad. With the help of Safariland, I arranged a luxury safari for the couple. I saw to it that we had big, comfortable tents divided up into several small dressing and bathrooms. The couple had eight trained native boys as their personal servants and I took along enough supplies to stock a small hotel. Before we left, the count made it clear that the only commodity he was interested in was a plentiful supply of whiskey. I took along more whiskey bottles than I did cartridges and it was well I did so. We could have done without the cartridges, but without the whiskey I fear I'd have had a dead count on my hands and no mistake.

A few days out, I spotted a fine black-maned lion and took my clients over to him. When the countess saw the lion, she screamed and wanted to go back to Nairobi. The count lifted his gun with shaking hands and then asked anxiously, "Suppose I shoot and don't kill, what does he do, eh?"

"He may charge, but I'll stop him with my rifle," I told the gentleman.

The count shook his head. "I think I need a drink," he said and off we went back to camp. That was all the lion hunting the count did. But that evening the couple called me in to have drinks with them.

"I have thought of a clever idea," said the count. "You are a hunter, no? So you go and hunt. I will stay here and you get me nice trophies to show my friends."

I agreed that this was an excellent suggestion, saving us all time and worry. I got them several good trophies and the countess posed on each one for photographs wearing her shooting togs and holding her rifle. She always asked me anxiously, "Hunter, how do I look?" I knew little about such matters but I always told her she looked very well indeed and my answer seemed to please her. The countess wanted her husband to pose on a few of the trophies, but he was seldom in a condition to sit up long enough for the camera to click. So she and I spent most of the time together, wandering about the veldt and having tea by the banks of a stream or under one of the big acacia trees.

One evening after I had turned in, the flap of my tent opened and the countess came in wearing a lace Parisian nightgown that covered her but poorly and carrying a beer glass full of whiskey. She sat down on the edge of my cot, offered me a drink, and then took one herself. "Hunter, my friend, I am lonely," she told me sadly. "Countess, where's your husband?" I asked her. She looked at me a long time. "Hunter, you Englishmen ask the strangest questions," she said and flounced out of my tent. For the next few days she was a bit cool toward me, but when the safari was over both she and the count kissed me as they said goodbye. A very affectionate couple. I enjoyed meeting them.

It is a curious fact that some people lose their heads when they go into the bush and forget ordinary conventions. They seem to feel that they have escaped from civilization and all its responsibilities. Women succumb to this strange state of mind more often than men. I have seen carefully reared ladies whose conduct shocked even the broadminded natives. There is much of the savage in all of us, but a man will work out his primitive instincts by shooting while a certain type of woman often turns to sex.

Usually the white hunter is the object of her devotion. In the bush a white hunter cuts a fine figure. He is efficient, brave, and picturesque. These ladies never stop to think how this dashing individual would appear on the dance floors of London or in a Continental drawing room. One of the greatest scandals of Kenya came about as the result of a lady's unwise attachment to a white hunter.

This tragedy occurred near the turn of the century. The white hunter involved was internationally known, having established a reputation by killing several man-eating lions. One of the parties he guided consisted of a wealthy man and his attractive young wife. When the safari returned to Nairobi, the husband was not with them. The hunter announced that his client had shot himself with a revolver while delirious. However, the hunter could not stop his native boys from talking and the story got around that the man had met with foul play. The government sent a police officer to investigate. The officer backtracked the safari and found where the client had been buried. He dug up the body and discovered that the man had been shot in the back of the head by a heavy-caliber rifle. Meanwhile, the hunter and the dead man's wife had left the country. As far as I know, they were never heard of again. I believe that the American writer Ernest Hemingway based his famous story "The Short and Happy Life of Francis Macomber" on this incident.

After this case, the conduct of white hunters with their clients was carefully checked. Any suspicion of a scandal was enough to deprive a hunter of his license and ruin him for life. Although such careful supervision is no doubt a good thing, yet it occasionally puts a hunter in awkward positions.

I was once guiding a German baron who had a very handsome wife and was insanely jealous of her. He hired an ex-major in the German Army to stay with the lady at all times. This male chaperon earned his pay, for he never let the baroness out of his sight. The major was a trustworthy man but a bit heavy-footed and he made so much noise clumping along that he scared all the game away. This annoyed the baroness, who was a very keen sportswoman, but if she ordered the major away, he refused to go, looking suspiciously at the lady and me all the while. As the baron did not go out in the bush much, we usually had the major along and so we got little hunting done. One afternoon I mentioned to the baroness that there was a donga near the camp that usually held several lions. At supper that evening, she told her husband about the spot, adding, "Hunter says that the cover is so thick that taking three people would be dangerous."

She gave me a kick under the table as she spoke so I nodded my head and said, "Yes, I have my doubts if three can make it." I was always a poor liar, so the major glared at us and said he was coming too, cover or no.

Next morning we started off to the donga. We put up no lion, but there was a fine warthog and the baroness wanted his tusks. The major stood on one side of the ravine and the baroness on the other, while I went in to drive the beast out.

I had taken only a few steps when I heard the baroness shout, "Hunter, come quick!" Thinking a lion had her, I ran to the spot, throwing off the safety catch on my rifle. I burst through some little bushes and there was the baroness standing there stark naked except for her knickers. For an instant I thought she was mad. Then I saw her desperately pulling safari ants off her body. These ants are terrible things, half an inch long, with jaws like pincers. I have been attacked by them myself in the bush and, like the baroness, I tore off my clothes to get at the creatures, for no one can stand the torture of their bites.

I spent several minutes pulling ants off the baroness. Then I had to scrape her body with the back of my knife blade to get out the insects' heads, for the ants will let themselves be pulled apart rather than relax their grip. The lady had just gotten her clothes on again when the major came bursting through the bush on us.

"What's going on here?" he screamed.

"John and I were doing a little hunting together," said the baroness casually. The major glared at us, but there was nothing he could say. Later I sat down on the ground and shook as though I'd had a close call with a rhino, for if the man had come upon us a few minutes before, he would have reported the matter to the baron and I would have lost my hunter's license for sure and certain. Under the circumstances no one would have believed either the lady or myself. Such are the perils of the veldt with clients.

I do not wish to give the impression that a white hunter's duties are merely to keep out of scrapes with beautiful women. Much of his work is the prosaic task of organizing the equipment necessary for a two or three months' trip "into the blue." In the case of a large safari, this is a tremendous undertaking. Some clients travel with a small city of tents equipped with generators to supply electricity. Each tent has its own bathtub, toilet facilities and an Electrolux icebox. To keep the cars and trucks in running condition, the equivalent of a small machine shop is taken along. Six-and seven-course meals that would not disgrace the best hotels in Paris or London are served regularly with a choice of several dishes and the best of wines. With such elaborate safaris, usually two or even three white hunters go along: one to handle the supplies and trucks, one to keep the clients entertained and one to find game.

As was only natural, the clients who wanted the luxury of these big safaris were seldom greatly interested in hunting. I remember guiding a rajah who refused to step out of his touring car to shoot a rhino which, I believe, carried a world's record horn. The rajah was afraid of getting the cuffs of his trousers wet in the tall grass. He insisted on trying to approach the animal in his car and the rhino took fright and galloped way.

Yet a short time after I was with this rajah, I had the privilege of guiding Commander Glen-Kidston, a British sportsman, who wanted to go to the Northern Frontier after oryx, a large straight-horned antelope. We took with us nothing but the barest essentials. In the desert country along the Abyssinian border the heat was so terrible that the rhinos scooped hollows in the sand during the day to bear the strain. The country was being continually raided by Abyssinian slave traders and bandits. We could hear their war parties go past our camp at night, but although they must have known we were there they never bothered us. The local natives lived in such terror of strangers that the poor creatures urinated with fear when I spoke to them. Very few safaris ever penetrated that country and it was easy to see why. Water was more precious than gold. The natives dug in the ground for it and considered themselves well paid for an hour's hard work by a few mouthfuls of dirty seepages. At one camp, robbers stole our water bags. We had to punch holes in our cans of beans and drink the stale fluid out of them until we reached the next water hole. In return for all our trouble, Commander Glen-Kidston managed to bag what was at that time the world's record oryx and a greater kudu that was a Kenya record.

Until that time I had been receiving fifty pounds a month as a white hunter. After I returned from that safari, my salary was gradually increased to two hundred pounds. At that time, this was considered top salary for a white hunter.

I have always liked to guide sportsmen who were interested in getting fine trophies. I was guiding Mrs. Dorothy McMartin when she bagged a record Hunter's hartebeest. I helped Major Bruce get a Thomson gazelle with 16¾ inch horns. I, myself, have shot a roan antelope with horns just one-half inch short of the record and have the head of a record suni gazelle that I collected in the Nyeri Forest. Yet I must say that in recent years the passion for trophy hunting has reached a point that I consider ridiculous. For a man to spend weeks or months hoping to get an animal with perhaps another quarter-inch of horn or a half an inch more of span simply to see his name in Rowland Ward's *Records of Big Game* seems to me a bit foolish.

Records are often freak animals and the trophy instead of being a particularly fine specimen is actually deformed. Record rhino horns are often long, thin things like overgrown knitting needles, not at all an impressive trophy from my point of view. I prefer a really fine natural horn, thick, powerful, and of reasonable length. Such a trophy gives a far better idea of the animal and the strength of his weapon. By the same token a buffalo with no boss— the boss being the thick, central base to which the horns proper are attached—will often have an extra length of horn. Yet such an animal bears no more relation to a true buffalo bull than a circus giant does to a strong, well-developed average man. These malformations may be of interest to a zoologist but I cannot see that they have a proper place among the trophies of a sportsman.

Some sportsmen carry their craze for world records to an amazing length. I remember talking to a man who had come back with a gigantic leopard skin measuring over ten feet. As an eight-foot leopard is very unusual, I could not believe my eyes when I saw this monster hide. Later when the owner was not around, I had the chance to examine the skin more closely. The man's native boys had very cleverly let into the center of the hide a four-foot strip of leopard skin from another trophy, matching the design so perfectly and doing such an expert job on the sewing, that not until I turned the skin over and examined the bottom did I detect the trick.

I soon learned to study my clients carefully before we started out into the bush. During my first few months as a white hunter, I would merely guide my client up to a good trophy and then expect him to do the rest. I found this was not a good practice. Some men would panic, others would show unwise boldness, many would fire wildly at the animal regardless of where they hit him. Then I would have a wounded rhino or elephant on my hands. So I tried to find out what sort of man I had as my client and laid my plans accordingly.

Sometimes having a client who is afraid of big game works out very well for the white hunter. I once guided a Swiss millionaire who was greatly impressed by the fine, 150-pound elephant tusk that hung in the Nairobi railway station. "I want you to find me an elephant like that," he informed me on our first meeting. I told the man that he was some thirty years too late, for big ivory like that is not common. However, it so chanced that after a few days in the bush we came on a bull carrying magnificent tusks, at least equal to those in Nairobi. After a careful hunt, we came up with him. My client fired. His bullet chipped the bull's right tusk and the elephant turned and ran. My client, thinking the elephant was charging him bolted in the opposite direction. When I finally caught up with the man he was too paralyzed by funk to go after the bull. Yet he kept muttering. "Those tusks! I must have those tusks!" Finally I went after the bull myself and dropped him. My client was so delighted that he presented me with a fine car. I am enough of a Scotsman to find safaris like that very pleasant.

Other clients were brave to the point of rashness. While I was lion hunting with two Canadians, we went out one morning to visit our baits. We stopped at one bait and saw it was undisturbed. While we were looking at it, the wind shifted and carried our scent into a patch of tall grass a few yards away. Suddenly three heavy-maned lions stood up in the grass. They had been feeding on their own kill a short distance from our bait.

We were between the lions and a heavily bushed river bank. The lions rushed past us, intent on reaching the cover. Before I could move, the two Canadians had tumbled out of the car and were racing after the lions. The men and lions sprinted across the open ground that led to the river, the lions lashing themselves with their tails as they ran as though to whip up fresh energy. Then one lion veered to the left, racing across the plains in gigantic bounds. Instantly both sportsmen pulled up in their stride and threw up their magazine rifles. They fired at the two remaining lions, which tumbled head over heels like shot hares. These two young men played at hunting very much as they might have played at football.

Rashness in my clients was always a source of concern to me for no one knows what a wild animal may do. A professional hunter learns to expect a certain type of animal to behave in a certain way and nine times out of ten he will be right. But there is always the tenth animal and he is the danger. No one can say that an animal will never perform a certain action unless it is something that the animal is physically incapable of doing. Sometimes an animal will show completely unexpected ferocity. At other times, he will be remarkably tolerant of humans. Rhinos are generally considered to be among the most bad-tempered of all African big game, but I once saw a rhino deliberately avoid goring a man who was at his mercy.

I was guiding a rajah who never moved without his personal secretary and doctor. The doctor carried a regular medical clinic around with him, most of the drugs being potent aphrodisiacs as the rajah was afraid of losing his manhood from the hardships of African life. In the bush, the doctor became a sort of general factotum, struggling along under a heavy cinema outfit to record the rajah's triumphs, while his pockets bulged with bottles of medicines, packets of herbs, and pills.

On one occasion, we were hunting buffalo. The rajah and I were in front while the doctor and the secretary lagged behind. We came on a herd with a fine bull and the rajah fired. At the sound of the shot, the herd panicked and dashed off through the thorny bush. The rajah was sure he had hit the bull and I was equally sure he had missed. I had not heard the familiar "sough-zup" of a bullet striking flesh.

Eager to prove their patron right, the doctor and the secretary set off to look for bloodstains on the ground. While they were wandering about, a bull rhino came trotting out of the bush toward the doctor. The animal had evidently been disturbed by the stampeding buffalo and was looking for a quieter spot. If the doctor had stood still, all would have been well, but instead he screamed and raced for the startled secretary, apparently hoping the rhino would take off in pursuit of the other man. The secretary quickly realized what was happening and made for the nearest tree. He flattened himself against the stem like a poster and yelled "Go away! Go away!" to the frantic doctor.

The rhino had stopped for a moment when the doctor began to run. Then he started after him, making rooting motions in the air with his horn. The doctor put up a fine sprint, for his heart was in it, but the rhino easily overtook him. The doctor was in line with the rhino so I could not shoot but I soon saw that the beast was not making a serious charge. There is always some degree of safety in a rhino's coming unexpectedly on a man instead of vice versa for the beast is not unduly alarmed. The doctor ran through the thorn trees screaming "Help!" while the rhino galloped behind, encouraging his victim to fresh efforts by an occasional jab of his horn. As the doctor became so weak he could only stagger, the rhino slowed down to a trot, still keeping behind him. I became so interested in this performance that I forgot all about shooting the bull and watched with curiosity while the rhino chivied the man through the scrub. At last, tiring of the sport, the rhino trotted off and the doctor returned to us, sweating and exhausted. His first words were, "I have had much troubles."

Perhaps a hunter's most disagreeable task is to guide a man who behaves like a stoat in a henhouse, killing for the very love of causing destruction. I have done my share of shooting but always with a purpose. Yet some men delight in killing simply for the pleasure of seeing death. Often a client would say to me. "Hunter, I am allowed three hundred animals on my license and as yet I have only shot two hundred. Are you sure I can get the rest in the next few days?" However, with most of them the mania soon passes. I have guided several Americans who came over hoping for the big bag, only to throw their rifles away after a few days and devote the rest of the trip to photography.

I remember, particularly, a story told me by Mr. Jack Holliday, an American whose encouragement was largely responsible for my writing this book. He and Roy Home, his guide, were on the track of a very fine bull elephant. Contrary to the opinion of many hunters, it is my belief that the size of an elephant's spoor does not indicate the size of his ivory. Often an elephant with a comparatively small footprint will carry better tusks than a giant. "Down-at-the-heel" footprints usually mean that the bull is old and therefore has big tusks. The bull's imprints showed he was a grand old chap and probably had magnificent ivory. After a long and very hard track, Jack and Roy found him standing by the bank of a stream. He must have heard some sound, for his great ears were spread to the uttermost to listen and his trunk raised to scent the wind. His tusks were two of the finest Roy had seen in many years of hunting. He made an unforgettable picture as he stood there in the forest, noble and unafraid, his ivory gleaming against the slate blue of his body. Jack slowly raised his rifle. He is an excellent shot and Roy stood waiting for the bull to drop. Instead, Holliday lowered his rifle and with a shake of his head said, "I can't do it, he's too fine to kill." They turned and left the bull standing there, watching them with his wise, old eyes.

Very few sportsmen will pass up a fine trophy for sentiment after spending weeks of hard work to get the animal. Yet I have seen it happen. I took out a young Yale student who was very keen to get a bongo, one of the finest and rarest of the forest antelope. Now almost the only way to get a bongo is to run the animal down with dogs. My client and I had a long, hard trek to a native village deep in the forest and I told the headman that we needed dogs for a bongo hunt. He willingly supplied me with a scratch pack of a dozen village dogs, shabby little brutes but keen on a trail. We started out and after several false starts we heard the dogs barking and the villagers shouting. Tearing our way through the thick undergrowth, we found the dogs had bayed a fine bongo in a little stream. The buck was standing up to his knees in the water with one foot raised, challenging his tormentors to come any closer. Around him was the baying pack, flanked by the yelling natives.

"There's your trophy," I said pointing.

My client raised his gun and then lowered it again. "I can't shoot that poor beast. He hasn't a chance with all those dogs and people around him. It isn't sporting."

Back we went without our trophy to the intense irritation, I may add, of the natives, who had been counting on a fine dinner of bongo steaks.

An amusing and harmless type of fool is the self-proclaimed expert on African game. I attended a dinner in Nairobi where one such individual was giving us a long discourse on game animals. Later, someone handed him a collection of game pictures, among them a photograph of a male hyena. The man nodded intelligently,

"Ah, yes, a very fine bull hyena," he assured the group. As the hyena is a doglike animal this was like speaking of a "bull" fox terrier, but I thought it best to keep my own counsel.

I was with another man who took great pride in his shooting. He had the best of firearms and talked knowingly about muzzle velocity, calibers and ammunition. One day we happened on a herd of warthogs and the pigs broke across the plain at full gallop, their tails carried straight up in the air as is the custom of the beasts. My client threw up his magazine rifle and opened fire on the pigs. I watched with great interest while his bullets went high, wide and every other way except among the porkers. After the barrage had finished and I was thinking what a good thing it was that in the wilds of Africa you seldom heard of accidents from traveling bullets, my client turned to me and said, solemnly: "Hunter, I hope you don't disapprove of this slaughter, but I like blotting out these swine because they spread disease." I assured him I had no objections. Privately, I only wished I would never be any closer to death than those warthogs were.

Some clients may be headaches but they are also a pleasure to be with. I remember a young English girl called Fay, barely out of her teens, whose greatest joy was to be on safari. Much snow has fallen on the summit of Kilimanjaro since I took this girl hunting, but I can picture her before me now, dressed in semi-cowboy fashion, a silk bandana loosely tied around her dark hair, ends tucked into a shirt blouse, while a fancy-headed pigskin belt was wound round her slim waist to hold her cartridges. Fay was a true open-air girl; a fine angler, an excellent shot and a splendid rider. Her horses and dogs adored her. Vim and dash surrounded her like a light around a lamp. No matter what came up Fay was game for it.

When we started off on safari, I hired a number of donkeys from the local natives as pack animals. The donkeys hated the smell of a European. Hours were wasted and tempers frayed getting the nervous brutes loaded but at last it was accomplished. In no very good mood, I ordered the safari to start. The donkeys refused to budge. Fay quickly solved that problem. From some hidden recess of her luggage she produced an Australian stock whip with a short, thick handle and coils made of pleated kangaroo hide. The weapon looked absurdly heavy in Fay's small hand and I had no idea she could use it. The next thing I knew, she had cracked the ten-foot lash with a report like an elephant rifle across the donkey's backs. The donkeys scattered like beads, bucking and kicking. In an instant their loads were under their bellies. Before the boys could grab their heads, all our kit was scattered across the veldt. Four hours of hard work was destroyed in ten seconds. I turned on Fay in a rage but she was sitting on the ground screaming with laughter. Between her howls of mirth she managed to gasp out, "Hunter, what are you looking so glum about?" Dullness was not her failing.

The donkeys did not prove a success so I engaged an oxcart to carry our supplies. This cart was a heavy vehicle and moved slowly, the yelling native driver cracking his giraffe-thonged whip constantly and the ponderous oxen throwing their weight into the yoke as the driver called them each by name. Traveling by oxcart was far too slow a means of progress for the lively Fay. "We'll never get there at this rate," she told me. "You and I will go ahead in my car." As there were no roads where we were headed, I doubted if a car could make the journey, but Fay had an old Studebaker that she assured me could go anywhere. We loaded up the old car with the more important camping supplies. I perched on top of the load and off we went with Fay at the wheel.

In a few minutes, I decided I had made a mistake in not staying with the oxcart. Fay's Studebaker seemed to have the properties of a modern jeep and Fay always drove at high speed no matter what the country. We tore through thorn bushes, the branches flicking me from either side. We rushed through streams at such a rate we had no chance of getting stuck in the mud and reached the other side by sheer momentum. On the open plains, Fay really let the car out. We were tearing along at a terrific speed when the car hit an old antbear hole. Up went the load with me on top of it. When the load came down the car had shot from under and was speeding off across the plains leaving a wake of churned up grass and dry leaves. I made a perfect landing on top of the load just where nature intended, with my pipe still clutched between my teeth.

Fay had covered a good two miles before discovering my absence and then only because some more kit bounced off. Back she came at full tilt, and found me still sitting on the load, smoking my pipe. She drew up with a scream of brakes, leaped out of the car and stood regarding me, arms akimbo. "Hunter, what kind of a game are you playing?" she demanded severely.

Fay was a magnificent shot. Elephant and lion were her particular game. She favored a d/b .360 No. 2 rifle made by William Evans of London, and as in my opinion this gun was too light for elephants, I made a point of taking her hunting in open bush where we could see the bulls a fair distance off. A good shot can easily drop an elephant with a light rifle if the animal is in the open and the hunter can aim carefully at the bull's earhole. In thick bush where the bull may charge you at close quarters, it is a different matter. Then you need a heavy gun that will stop the animal with a frontal brain shot.

Fay had unlimited energy and could hunt all day and play all night. I was not so gifted. One evening we returned to camp after tramping through the bush since dawn, and after a quick meal, I went to bed. Fay did the same, but with her superabundance of spirits she could not sleep. We were sharing the same small tent, for our boys had not come yet with the slow moving oxcart that held our other tents and the bulk of the equipment. After tossing about for a few minutes, Fay swung her feet out of the cot and called: "Hunter, I'm bored. Get up and talk to me." I pretended to be asleep, for I was tired and had no wish for an all-night session of drinking and talking with the lively girl. Fay called to me again. Then I heard her mutter. "I'll wake him up." The next moment a knapsack full of cartridges hit me on the side of the head while

Fay shouted, "Don't be so stuffy! Get up and amuse me." Knowing when I was beaten I got up.

I fear that as an all-night companion I was less satisfactory than as hunter, for on our next safari Fay brought along a handsome young man she had picked up in Nairobi. I could not imagine what a girl like Fay could see in the chap for he was a very poor shot, but from what she told me I gathered he had other qualities not immediately apparent. This seemed an ideal arrangement for Fay could hunt with me during the day and spend the evenings with her escort. Unfortunately, Fay was an impulsive girl and insisted that her friend share her enthusiasm for hunting. The man did not like to use a heavy-caliber gun because the kick hurt his shoulder so he borrowed a .275 of Fay's while she took her trusty .360. We were after lions, so these fairly light rifles were usable, but I took along my .475 in case we should meet an elephant or rhino.

We were going single file along a game trail that led through the heart of some tall grass. Suddenly we saw ahead of us a lone bull buffalo grazing. Now the African buffalo is a very formidable animal. When he charges with lowered head the only mark for a hunter is his thick forehead, protected by the wide boss of the horns. Nothing but a heavy-caliber rifle will stop the charge.

I was quite willing to withdraw and leave this bull to his grazing but Fay would have none of it. She was determined that her sweetheart should return to Nairobi saying he had shot a buffalo. "Hit him in the shoulder, dear," she whispered. "If he doesn't drop, I'll nail him for you."

The young man nervously raised his rifle and fired. He hit the bull high. Instantly, the buffalo wheeled and charged us at terrible speed. We could see nothing but the wide horns rushing at us along the narrow path. With admirable coolness, Fay raised her rifle and put two shots into the beast's forehead. She might as well have been throwing spitballs. When Fay saw the animal was still coming, she dropped her rifle and threw herself into her lover's arms.

With the two of them locked together in a close embrace on the narrow trail, I couldn't get around the idiots to shoot. The bull was almost on us. I could see the white foam on his black chest and the ridges on his great horns. If the two thousand pounds of animal hit us, we would be knocked flat and trampled into the ground. When the horns seemed only a couple of yards away I managed to force the barrel of my rifle between the two sweethearts and fired. The bull came crashing down, throwing foam and blood over Fay's trousers. The shock of the fall was so great that I believe both Fay and her friend thought the bull had hit them. After a few seconds, Fay opened her eyes and saw the bull lying dead at her feet.

"Darling, Hunter shot him!" she cried happily. "But you musn't feel badly because you didn't get him. We'll start out right now and find you another."

"Thank you very much," said the young man, wiping the sweat off his forehead with a shaking hand. "I only want to know one thing—how long will it take me to get back to Nairobi?"

Poor, gay little Fay. When all other thrills failed to satisfy her she took to drugs. What finally happened to her I have no idea. She was a girl of free morals, no doubt, but she was an excellent shot and a good companion. You can't expect to find everything in a woman.

I believe that most sportsmen's reluctance to use a heavy-caliber gun is responsible for the majority of hunting accidents. I admit this is a pet subject with me and I have had many an argument over it. I grant that if you hit an elephant, rhino, or buffalo in the correct spot, you can kill him with a light-caliber bullet. But if you are stopping a charge you must have a bullet with sufficient hitting force to knock the animal off his feet. Many a hunter has been killed by a "dead" buffalo or rhino that he has hit in a vital place; the impetus of the charge was sufficient to carry the animal onto the man with fatal results.

Unfortunately, very few sportsmen care to endure the punishment of a heavy gun's kick. After a few shots at target practice, the sportsman begins to flinch as he squeezes the trigger. Of course, this ruins his shooting and he turns to a lighter gun. The man forgets that in the excitement of a hunt he will not feel the kick.

I realize a sportsman has several problems when it comes to selecting his battery. Most men like to use their own weapon yet few own the heavy guns necessary for African big game. If the man rents a gun while in Africa, he cannot later show it to his friends as "the gun that shot that big bull." Also, many sportsmen have read accounts written by the old-time hunters who often used very light-caliber weapons. But in those days the game was so tame that a man could pick his shot, and the early hunters seldom bothered to venture into dense brush after a trophy.

Sportsmen's insistence on using light guns has given rise to a very miserable custom among some white hunters. When his client shoots the white hunter fires at the same moment with his heavy gun. The hunter cares not a jot whether his client hits the beast or simply fires into the air. The animal drops and the client can have the glory. The men I have guided like the McMartins, Commander Glen-Kidston or Major Bruce would have sent me packing back to Nairobi with a flea in my ear if I had tried any such tricks with them. Yet I understand the modern white hunter's motives. It is a law of the bush that you cannot leave an injured animal to die, so if your client wounds a dangerous beast, then the hunter must go into cover to get the animal. The client cannot go himself for the danger to him would be too great and also the hunter can do the job far better if he is alone.

I remember I was once hunting with a certain Continental prince and princess near Kasigau in the Voi area of Kenya. We saw a buffalo bull coming toward us and we lay down so he would come closer. He trotted up to within fifty yards or so. The princess was using a small-bore rifle and she was determined to kill the bull without any assistance. She fired, hitting him in the chest. With a heavy or even medium-caliber rifle this would have been a fatal shot, but the wounded bull was able to swing away and reach a dense thicket of thornless bush.

We checked the spoor. The tracks were spotted with minute blood drops. Part of a hunter's work is to be able to identify the different types of blood resulting from various wounds. Lung blood is light-colored and usually means a long hunt. Blood from the kidneys is very dark and means the animal is mortally wounded. Blood from the body and limbs is medium in color and generally means a superficial wound. This blood spoor was of the last type. So here was a wounded beast sound in limb and wind that would fight it out in cover of its own choosing—an unpleasant prospect.

The princess still insisted on following the wounded animal with her popgun. When I objected, her royal blood boiled and she gave me a fine tongue-lashing. These people who have never been crossed in their lives are apt to be difficult. I still refused to allow her to commit suicide. The prince, a clear-thinking young fellow, finally interfered and told me to go ahead and finish off the animal.

Taking my Walingulu tracker, I entered the bush. The Walingulu tribe are, in my opinion, the best trackers in Kenya and I had every confidence in the man. The ground was sandy soil and we could move quietly through the brush. It was very quiet and I knew that probably meant the bull was waiting motionless in ambush for us. Such knowledge serves to keep your mind alert.

We came to a spot where the blood spoor was very heavy. The

bull had stopped here for several minutes. He had heard the princess screaming at me and had paused to listen. When the argument stopped and we began trailing, he had moved on.

Suddenly we smelled the pungent odor of the bull. We both stopped. He must be only a few yards away. The Walingulu stood with his nostrils flaring, like a pointer trying to locate a covey of partridges. Then he pointed into the bush. I could see nothing. Thinking the bull was still a little distance off I motioned the man to toss something in the direction of the animal. He picked up a stone and flung it straight into the bush ahead of us. I heard the stone smack against the bull's horn. The animal was standing there in full view but his black hide blended so perfectly with the shadows that I had not seen him.

Instantly the bull charged. I had no time to aim. I flung my .500 d/b express to my shoulder and fired the rifle as though it were a shotgun. The bullet hit the buffalo below the left eye, killing him in his stride. If I had been using a lighter rifle, the animal would certainly have killed us before he died.

The most remarkable task a client ever asked me to perform was to crawl down a hole after a wounded warthog. I was guiding the Earl of Carnarvon when he shot and wounded a big boar warthog. The animal took refuge in a hole. When a warthog enters a hole, he always turns and backs in so as to have his tusks pointed in the direction of a possible pursuer. The earl wanted the animal badly but I could think of no way to get at him. We had no digging tools and there was no way of smoking the pig out.

I asked my scouts if they would go down the hole after the boar. They explained that they were all of the Islam faith and were forbidden to touch a pig, otherwise they would have been delighted. There was nothing for it but do the task myself. I peeled off my coat and after telling the boys to drag me out by the legs when I began to kick, I started down the burrow.

The hole was a fairly tight fit for my waistline and the stinking breath of the pig nearly stifled me. With my body blocking the entrance the hole was pitch dark. I wriggled along, feeling ahead with my right hand, until I touched the boat's snout. Then I grabbed him by the tusk. The boar promptly tried to jab my hand against the top of the burrow but I hung on, kicking madly. I was close to fainting from the lack of air and the heavy odor of the pig. The boys pulled me out and I dragged the smelly beast with me.

When I stood up, wiping my face, the earl said, "Splendid, Hunter. I don't want the boar as a trophy. I just want his hide for saddle leather. Are you sure you didn't damage it getting him out of that hole?"

I can only hope the earl got enough pleasure from his saddle to justify the agony I went through extracting that boar from his burrow.

ERNEST
HEMINGWAY

The Green Hills of Africa

Selecting a hunting tale by Ernest Hemingway that has not been reprinted in a half-dozen books, or served as a Hollywood vehicle, is difficult. The two-legged rather than the four-legged animal is the major character in the Hemingway story, but by going back to his *Green Hills of Africa* I found a chapter that stopped the search. In this book Hemingway was attempting to answer a self-imposed challenge, to "write an absolutely true book to see whether the shape of a country and the pattern of a month's action can, if truly presented, compete with a work of the imagination." This is something you can answer.

The road was only a track and the plain was very discouraging to see. As we went on we saw a few thin Grant's gazelles showing white against the burnt yellow of the grass and the gray trees. My exhilaration died with the stretching out of this plain, the typical poor game country, and it all began to seem very impossible and romantic and quite untrue. The Wanderobo had a very strong odor and I looked at the way the lobes of his ears were stretched and then neatly wrapped on themselves and at his strange un-negroid, thin-lipped face. When he saw me studying his face he smiled pleasantly and scratched his chest. I looked around at the back of the car. M'Cola was asleep. Garrick was sitting straight up, dramatizing his awakeness, and the old man was trying to see the road.

By now there was no more road, only a cattle track, but we were coming to the edge of the plain. Then the plain was behind us and ahead there were big trees and we were entering a country the

435

loveliest that I had seen in Africa. The grass was green and smooth, short as a meadow that has been mown and is newly grown, and the trees were big, high-trunked, and old with no undergrowth but only the smooth green of the turf like a deer park and we drove on through shade and patches of sunlight following a faint trail the Wanderobo pointed out. I could not believe we had suddenly come to any such wonderful country. It was a country to wake from, happy to have had the dream and, seeing if it would clown away, I reached up and touched the Wanderobo's ear. He jumped and Kamau snickered. M'Cola nudged me from the back seat and pointed and there, standing in an open space between the trees, his head up, staring at us, the bristles on his back erect, long, thick, white tusks upcurving, his eyes showing bright, was a very large warthog boar watching us from less than twenty yards. I motioned to Kamau to stop and we sat looking at him and he at us. I put the rifle up and sighted on his chest. He watched and did not move. Then I motioned to Kamau to throw in the clutch and we went on and made a curve to the right and left the wart-hog, who had never moved, nor showed any fright at seeing us.

I could see that Kamau was excited and, looking back, M'Cola nodded his head up and down in agreement. None of us had ever seen a wart-hog that would not bolt off, fast-trotting, tail in air. This was a virgin country, an un-hunted pocket in the million miles of bloody Africa. I was ready to stop and make camp anywhere.

This was the finest country I had seen but we went on, winding along through the big trees over the softly rolling grass. Then ahead and to the right we saw the high stockade of a Masai village. It was a very large village and out of it came running long-legged, brown, smooth-moving men who all seemed to be of the same age and who wore their hair in a heavy club-like queue that swung against their shoulders as they ran. They came up to the car and surrounded it, all laughing and smiling and talking. They all were tall, their teeth were white and good, and their hair was stained a red brown and arranged in a looped fringe on their foreheads. They carried spears and they were very handsome and extremely jolly, not sullen, nor contemptuous like the northern Masai, and they wanted to know what we were going to do. The Wanderobo evidently said we were hunting kudu and were in a hurry. They had the car surrounded so we could not move. One said something and three or four others joined in and Kamau explained to me that they had seen two kudu bulls go along the trail in the afternoon.

"It can't be true," I said to myself. "It can't be."

I told Kamau to start and slowly we pushed through them, they all laughing and trying to stop the car, making it all but run over them. They were the tallest, best-built, handsomest people I had ever seen and the first truly light-hearted happy people I had seen in Africa. Finally, when we were moving, they started to run beside the car smiling and laughing and showing how easily they could run and then, as the going was better, up the smooth valley of a stream, it became a contest and one after another dropped out of the running, waving and smiling as they left until there were only two still running with us, the finest runners of the lot, who kept pace easily with the car as they moved long-legged, smoothly, loosely, and with pride. They were running too, at the pace of a fast miler, and carrying their spears as well. Then we had to turn to the right and climb out of the putting-green smoothness of the valley into a rolling meadow and, as we slowed, climbing in first gear, the whole pack came up again, laughing and trying not to seem winded. We went through a little knot of brush and a small rabbit started out, zig-zagging wildly and all the Masai behind now in a mad sprint. They caught the rabbit and the tallest runner came up with him to the car and handed him to me. I held him and could feel the thumping of his heart through the soft, warm, furry body, and as I stroked him the Masai patted my arm. Holding him by the ears I handed him back. No, no, he was mine. He was a present. I handed him to M'Cola. 'Cola did not take him seriously and handed him to one of the Masai. We were moving and they were running again now. The Masai stooped and put the rabbit on the ground and as he ran free they all laughed. M'Cola shook his head. We were all very impressed by these Masai.

"Good Masai," M'Cola said, very moved. "Masai many cattle. Masai no kill to eat. Masai kill man."

The Wanderobo patted himself on the chest.

"Wanderobo—Masai," he said, very proudly, claiming kin. His ears were curled in the same way theirs were. Seeing them running and so damned handsome and so happy made us all happy. I had never seen such quick disinterested friendliness, nor such fine-looking people.

"Good Masai," M'Cola repeated, nodding his head emphatically. "Good, good Masai." Only Garrick seemed impressed in a different way. For all his khaki clothes and his letter from B'wana Simba, I believe these Masai frightened him in a very old place. They were our friends, not his. They certainly were our friends though. They had that attitude that makes brothers, that unexpressed but instant and complete acceptance that you must be Masai wherever it is you come from. That attitude you only get from the best of the English, the best of the Hungarians and the very best Spaniards; the thing that used to be the most clear distinction of nobility when there was nobility. It is an ignorant attitude and the people who have it do not survive, but very few pleasanter things ever happen to you than the encountering of it.

So now there were only the two of them left again, running, and it was hard going and the machine was beating them. They were still running well and still loose and long but the machine was a cruel pacemaker. So I told Kamau to speed it up and get it over with because a sudden burst of speed was not the humiliation of a steady using. They sprinted, were beaten, laughed, and then we were leaning out, waving, and they stood leaning on their spears and waved. We were still great friends but now we were alone again and there was no track, only the general direction to follow around clumps of trees and along the run of this green valley.

After a little the trees grew closer and we left the idyllic country behind and now were picking our way along a faint trail through thick second-growth. Sometimes we came to a dead halt and had to get out and pull a log out of the way or cut a tree that blocked the body of the car. Sometimes we had to back out of bush and look for a way to circle around and come upon the trail again, chopping our way through with the long brush knives that are called pangas. The Wanderobo was a pitiful chopper and Garrick was little better. M'Cola did everything well in which a knife was used and he swung a panga with a fast yet heavy and vindictive stroke. I used it badly. There was too much wrist in it to learn it quickly; your wrist tired and the blade seemed to have a weight it did not have. I wished that I had a Michigan double-bitted ax, honed razor-sharp, to chop with instead of this sabering of trees.

Chopping through when we were stopped, avoiding all we could, Kamau driving with intelligence and a sound feeling for the country, we came through the difficult going and out into another open-meadow stretch and could see a range of hills off to our right. But here there had been a recent heavy rain and we had to be very careful about the low parts of the meadow where the tires cut in through the turf to mud and spun in the slick greasiness. We cut brush and shovelled out twice and then, having learned not to trust any low part, we skirted the high edge of the meadow and then were in timber again. As we came out, after several long circles in the woods to find places where we could get the car through, we were on the bank of a stream, where there was a sort of brushy bridging across the bed built like a beaver dam and evidently designed to hold back the water. On the other side was a thorn-brush-fenced cornfield, a steep, stump-scattered bank with corn planted all over it, and some abandoned looking corrals or thorn-brush-fenced enclosures with mud and stick buildings and to the right there were cone-shaped grass huts projecting above a heavy thorn fence. We all got out, for this stream was a problem and, on the other side, the only place we could get up the bank led through the stump-filled maize field.

The old man said the rain had come that day. There had been no water going over the brushy dam when they had passed that morning. I was feeling fairly depressed. Here we had come through a beautiful country of virgin timber where kudu had been seen walking along the trail to end up stuck on the bank of a little creek in some one's cornfield. I had not expected any cornfield and I resented it. I thought we would have to get permission to drive through the maize, provided we could make it across the stream and up the bank and I took off my shoes and waded across the stream to test it underfoot. The brush and saplings on the bottom were packed hard and firm and I was sure we could cross if we took it fairly fast. M'Cola and Kamau agreed and we walked up the bank to see how it would be. The mud of the bank was soft but there was dry earth underneath and I figured we could shovel our way up if we could get through the stumps. But we would need to unload before we tried it.

Coming toward us, from the direction of the huts, were two men and a boy. I said "Jambo," as they came up. They answered, "Jambo," and then the old man and the Wanderobo talked with them. M'Cola shook his head at me. He did not understand a word. I thought we were asking permission to go through the corn. When the old man finished talking the two men came closer and we shook hands.

They looked like no negroes I had ever seen. Their faces were a gray brown, the oldest looked to be about fifty, had thin lips, an almost Grecian nose, rather high cheekbones, and large, intelligent eyes. He had great poise and dignity and seemed to be very intelligent. The younger man had the same cast of features and I took him for a younger brother. He looked about thirty-five. The boy was as pretty as a girl and looked rather shy and stupid. I had thought he was a girl from his face for an instant when he first came up, as they all wore a sort of Roman toga of unbleached muslin gathered at the shoulder that revealed no line of their bodies.

They were talking with the old man, who, now that I looked at him standing with them, seemed to bear a sort of wrinkled and degenerate resemblance to the classic-featured owner of the shamba; just as the Wanderobo-Masai was a shrivelled caricature of the handsome Masai we had met in the forest.

Then we all went down to the stream and Kamau and I rigged ropes around the tires to act as chains while the Roman elder and the rest unloaded the car and carried the heaviest things up the steep bank. Then we crossed in a wild, water-throwing smash and, all pushing heavily, made it halfway up the bank before we stuck. We chopped and dug out and finally made it to the top of the bank but ahead was that maize field and I could not figure where we were to go from there.

"Where do we go?" I asked the Roman elder.

They did not understand Garrick's interpreting and the old man made the question clear.

The Roman pointed toward the heavy thorn-bush fence to the left at the edge of the woods.

"We can't get through there in the car."

"Campi," said M'Cola, meaning we were going to camp there.

"Hell of a place," I said.

"Campi," M'Cola said firmly and they all nodded.

"Campi! Campi!" said the old man.

"There we camp," Garrick announced pompously.

"You go to hell," I told him cheerfully.

I walked toward the camp site with the Roman who was talking steadily in a language I could not understand a word of. M'Cola was with me and the others were loading and following with the car. I was remembering that I had read you must never camp in abandoned native quarters because of ticks and other hazards and I was preparing to hold out against this camp. We entered a break in the thorn-bush fence and inside was a building of logs and saplings stuck in the ground and crossed with branches. It looked like a big chicken coop. The Roman made us free of this and of the enclosure with a wave of his hand and kept on talking.

"Bugs," I said to M'Cola in Swahili, speaking with strong disapproval.

"No," he said, dismissing the idea. "No bugs."

"Bad bugs. Many bugs. Sickness."

"No bugs," he said firmly.

The no-bugs had it and with the Roman talking steadily, I hoped on some congenial topic, the car came up, stopped under a huge tree about fifty yards from the thorn-bush fence and they all commenced carrying the necessities in for the making of camp. My ground-sheet tent was slung between a tree and one side of the chicken coop and I sat down on a petrol case to discuss the shooting situation with the Roman, the old man, and Garrick while Kamau and M'Cola fixed up a camp and the Wanderobo-Masai stood on one leg and let his mouth hang open.

"Where were kudu?"

"Back there," waving his arm.

"Big ones?"

Arms spread to show hugeness of horns and a torrent from the Roman.

Me, dictionary-ing heavily, "Where was the one they were watching?"

No results on this but a long speech from the Roman which I took to mean they were watching them all.

It was late afternoon now and the sky was heavy with clouds. I was wet to the waist and my socks were mud soaked. Also I was sweating from pushing on the car and from chopping.

"When do we start?" I asked.

"Tomorrow," Garrick answered without bothering to question the Roman.

"No," I said. "Tonight."

"Tomorrow," Garrick said. "Late now. One hour light." He showed me one hour on my watch.

I dictionaried. "Hunt tonight. Last hour best hour."

Garrick implied that the kudu were too far away. That it was impossible to hunt and return, all this with gestures, "Hunt tomorrow."

"You bastard," I said in English. All this time the Roman and the old man had been standing saying nothing. I shivered. It was cold with the sun under the clouds in spite of the heaviness of the air after rain.

"Old man," I said.

"Yes, Master," said the old man. Dictionary-ing carefully, I said, "Hunt kudu tonight. Last hour best hour. Kudu close?"

"Maybe."

"Hunt now?"

They talked together.

"Hunt tomorrow," Garrick put in.

"Shut up, you actor," I said. "Old man. Little hunt now?"

"Yes," said old man and Roman nodded. "Little while."

"Good," I said and went to find a shirt and undershirt and a pair of socks.

"Hunt now," I told M'Cola.

"Good," he said. "M'uzuri."

With the clean feeling of dry shirt, fresh socks and a change of boots I sat on the petrol case and drank a whiskey and water while I waited for the Roman to come back. I felt certain I was going to have a shot at kudu and I wanted to take the edge off so I would not be nervous. Also I wanted not to catch a cold. Also I wanted the whiskey for itself, because I loved the taste of it and because, being as happy as I could be, it made me feel even better.

I saw the Roman coming and I pulled the zippers up on my boots, checked the cartridges in the magazine of the Springfield, took off the foresight protector and blew through the rear aperture. Then I drank what was left in the tin cup that was on the ground by the box and stood up, checking that I had a pair of handkerchiefs in my shirt pockets.

M'Cola came carrying his knife and Pop's big glasses.

"You stay here," I said to Garrick. He did not mind. He thought we were silly to go out so late and he was glad to prove us wrong. The Wanderobo wanted to go.

"That's plenty," I said and waved the old man back and we started out of the corral with the Roman ahead, carrying a spear, then me, then M'Cola with glasses and the Mannlicher, full of solids, and last the Wanderobo-Masai with another spear.

It was after five when we struck off across the maize field and down to the stream, crossing where it narrowed in high grass a hundred yards above the dam and then, walking slowly and carefully, went up the grassy bank on the far side getting soaked to the waist as we stooped going through the wet grass and bracken. We had not been gone ten minutes and were moving carefully up the stream bank, when, without warning, the Roman grabbed my arm and pulled me bodily down to the ground as he crouched; me pulling back the bolt to cock the rifle as I dropped. Holding his breath he pointed and across the stream on the far bank at the edge of the trees was a large, gray animal, white stripes showing on his flanks and huge horns curling back from his head as he stood, broadside to us, head up, seeming to be listening. I raised the rifle but there was a bush in the way of the shot. I could not shoot over the bush without standing.

"Piga," whispered M'Cola. I shook my finger and commenced to crawl forward to be clear of the bush, sick afraid the bull would jump while I was trying to make the shot certain, but remembering Pop's "Take your time." When I saw I was clear I got on one knee, saw the bull through the aperture, marvelling at how big he looked and then, remembering not to have it matter, that it was the same as any other shot, I saw the bead centered exactly where it should be just below the top of the shoulder and squeezed off. At the roar he jumped and was going into the brush, but I knew I had hit him. I shot at a show of gray between the trees as he went in and M'Cola was shouting, "Piga! Piga!" meaning, "He's hit! He's hit!" and the Roman was slapping me on the shoulder, then he had his toga up around his neck and was running naked, and the four of us were running now, full speed, like hounds, splashing across the stream, tearing up the bank, the Roman ahead, crashing naked through the brush, then stooping and holding up a leaf with bright blood, slamming me on the back, M'Cola saying, "Damu! Damu!" blood, blood, then the deep cut tracks off to the right, me reloading, we all trailing in a dead run, it almost dark in the timber, the Roman, confused a moment by the trail, making a cast off to the right, then picking up blood once more, then pulling me down again with a jerk on my arm and none of us breathing as we saw him standing in a clearing a hundred yards ahead, looking to me hard-hit and looking back, wide ears spread, big, gray, white-striped, his horns a marvel, as he looked straight toward us over his shoulder. I thought I must make absolutely sure this time, now, with the dark coming and I held my breath and shot him a touch behind the fore-shoulder. We heard the bullet smack and saw him buck heavily with the shot. M'Cola shouted, "Piga! Piga! Piga!" as he went out of sight and as we ran again, like hounds, we almost fell over something. It was a huge, beautiful kudu bull, stone-dead, on his side, his horns in great dark spirals, widespread and unbelievable as he lay dead five yards from where we stood when I had just that instant shot. I looked at him, big, long-legged, a smooth gray with the white stripes and the great, curling, sweeping horns, brown as walnut meats, and ivory pointed, at the big ears and the great, lovely heavy-maned neck, the white chevron between his eyes and the white of his muzzle and I stooped over and touched him to try to believe it. He was lying on the side where the bullet had gone in and there was not a mark on him and he smelled sweet and lovely like the breath of cattle and the odor of thyme after rain.

Then the Roman had his arms around my neck and M'Cola was shouting in a strange high sing-song voice and Wanderobo-Masai kept slapping me on the shoulder and jumping up and down and then one after the other they all shook hands in a strange way that I had never known in which they took your thumb in their fist and held it and shook it and pulled it and held it again, while they looked you in the eyes, fiercely.

We all looked at him and M'Cola knelt and traced the curve of his horns with his finger and measured the spread with his arms and kept crooning, "Oo-oo-eee-eee," making small high noises of ecstasy and stroking the kudu's muzzle and his mane.

I slapped the Roman on the back and we went through the thumb pulling again; me pulling his thumb too. I embraced the Wanderobo-Masai and he, after a thumb-pulling of great intensity and feeling, slapped his chest and said very proudly, "Wanderobo-Masai wonderful guide."

"Wanderobo-Masai wonderful Masai," I said.

M'Cola kept shaking his head, looking at the kudu and making the strange small noises. Then he said, "Doumi, Doumi, Doumi! B'wana Kabor Kidogo, Kidogo." Meaning this was a bull of bulls. That Karl's had been a little one, a nothing.

We all knew we had killed the other kudu that I had mistaken for this one, while this first one was lying dead from the first shot, and it seemed of no importance beside the miracle of this kudu. But I wanted to see the other.

"Come on, kudu," I said.

"He's dead," said M'Cola, "Kufa!"

"Come on."

"This one best."

"Come on."

"Measure," M'Cola pleaded. I ran the steel tape around the curve of one horn, M'Cola holding it down. It was well over fifty inches. M'Cola looked at me anxiously.

"Big! Big!" I said. "Twice as big as B'wana Kabor."

"Eee-eee," he crooned.

"Come on," I said. The Roman was off already.

We cut for where we saw the bull when I shot and there were the tracks with blood breast high on the leaves in the brush from the start. In a hundred yards we came on him absolutely dead. He was not quite as big as the first bull. The horns were as long, but narrower, but he was as beautiful, and he lay on his side, bending down the brush where he fell.

We all shook hands again, using the thumb which evidently denoted extreme emotion.

"This askari," M'Cola explained. This bull was the policeman or bodyguard for the bigger one. He had evidently been in the timber when we had seen the first bull, had run with him, and had looked back to see why the big bull did not follow.

I wanted pictures and told M'Cola to go back to camp with the Roman and bring the two cameras, the Graflex and the cinema camera and my flashlight. I knew we were on the same side of the stream and above the camp and I hoped the Roman could make a short cut and get back before the sun set.

They went off and now, at the end of the day, the sun came out brightly below the clouds and the Wanderobo-Masai and I looked at this kudu, measured his horns, smelled the fine smell of him, sweeter than an eland, even, stroked his nose, his neck, and his shoulder, marvelling at the great ears, and the smoothness and cleanness of his hide, looked at his hooves, that were built long, narrow, and springy so he seemed to walk on tip-toe, felt under his shoulder for the bullet-hole and then shook hands again while the Wanderobo-Masai told what a man he was and I told him he was my pal and gave him my best four-bladed pocket knife.

"Let's go look at the first one, Wanderobo-Masai," I said in English.

The Wanderobo-Masai nodded, understanding perfectly, and we trailed back to where the big one lay in the edge of the little clearing. We circled him, looking at him and then the Wanderobo-Masai, reaching underneath while I held the shoulder up, found the bullet hole and put his finger in. Then he touched his forehead with the bloody finger and made the speech about "Wanderobo-Masai wonderful guide!"

"Wanderobo-Masai king of guides," I said. "Wanderobo-Masai my pal."

I was wet through with sweat and I put on my raincoat that M'Cola had been carrying and left behind and turned the collar up around my neck. I was watching the sun now and worrying about it being gone before they got up with the cameras. In a little while we could hear them coming in the brush and I shouted to let them know where we were. M'Cola answered and we shouted back and forth and I could hear them talking and crashing in the brush while I would shout and watch the sun which was almost down. Finally I saw them and I shouted to M'Cola, "Run, run," and pointed to the sun, but there was no run left in them. They had made a fast trip uphill, through heavy brush, and when I got the camera, opened the lens wide and focused on the bull the sun was only lighting the tops of the trees. I took a half a dozen exposures and used the cinema while they all dragged the kudu to where there seemed to be a little more light, then the sun was down and, obligation to try to get a picture over, I put the camera into its case and settled, happily, with the darkness into the unresponsibility of victory; only emerging to direct M'Cola in where to cut to make a full enough cape when skinning out the head-skin. M'Cola used a knife beautifully and I liked to watch him skin-out, but tonight, after I had shown him where to make the first cut, well down on the legs, around the lower chest where it joined the belly and well back over the withers I did not watch him because I wanted to remember the bull as I had first seen him, so I went, in the dusk, to the second kudu and waited there until they came, with the flashlight and then, remembering that I had skinned-out or seen skinned-out every animal that I had ever shot, yet remembered every one exactly as he was at every moment, that one memory does not destroy another, and that the not-watching idea was only laziness and a form of putting the dishes in the sink until morning, I held the flashlight for M'Cola while he worked on the second bull and, although tired, enjoyed as always his fast, clean, delicate scalpeling with the knife, until, the cape all clear and spread back he nocked through the connection of the skull and the spine and then, twisting with the horns, swung the head loose and lifted it, cape and all, free from the neck, the cape hanging heavy and wet in the light of the electric torch that shone on his red hands and on the dirty khaki of his tunic. We left the Wanderobo-Masai, Garrick, the Roman, and his brother with a lantern to skin out and pack in the meat and M'Cola with a head, the old man with a head, and me with the flashlight and the two guns, we started in the dark back for camp.

In the dark the old man fell flat and M'Cola laughed; then the cape unrolled and came down over his face and he almost choked and we both laughed. The old man laughed too. Then M'Cola fell in the dark and the old man and I laughed. A little farther on I went through the covering on some sort of game pit and went flat on my face and got up to hear M'Cola chuckling and choking and the old man giggling.

"What the hell is this? A Chaplin comedy?" I asked them in

English. They were both laughing under the heads. We got to the thorn-bush fence, finally, after a nightmare march through the brush and saw the fire at the camp and M'Cola seemed to be delighted when the old man fell going through the thorns and got up cursing and seeming barely able to lift the head as I shone the flash ahead of him to show him the opening.

We came up to the fire and I could see the old man's face bleeding as he put the head down against the stick and mud cabin. M'Cola put his head down, pointed at the old man's face and laughed and shook his head. I looked at the old man. He was completely done-in, his face was badly scratched, covered with mud and bleeding, and he was chuckling happily.

"B'wana fell down," M'Cola said and imitated me pitching forward. They both chuckled.

I made as though to take a swing at him and said, "Shenzi!"

He imitated me falling down again and then there was Kamau shaking hands very gently and respectfully and saying, "Good, B'wana! Very good, B'wana!" and then going over to the heads, his eyes shining and kneeling, stroking the horns and feeling the ears and crooning the same, sighing, "Ooo-ooo! Eee-eee!" noises M'Cola had made.

I went into the dark of the tent, we had left the lantern with the meat bringers, and washed, took off my wet clothes and feeling in the dark in my ruck-sack found a pair of pajamas and a bath-robe. I came out to the fire wearing these and mosquito boots. I brought my wet things and my boots to the fire and Kamau spread them on sticks and put the boots, each one, leg-down, on a stick and back far enough from the blaze where the fire would not scorch them.

In the firelight I sat on a petrol box with my back against a tree and Kamau brought the whiskey flask and poured some in a cup and I added water from the canteen and sat drinking and looking in the fire, not thinking, in complete happiness, feeling the whiskey warm me and smooth me as you straighten the wrinkled sheet in a bed, while Kamau brought tins from the provisions to see what I would eat for supper. There were three tins of Christmas special mince meat, three tins of salmon, and three of mixed fruit, there were also a number of cakes of chocolate and a tin of Special Christmas Plum Pudding. I sent these back wondering what Kati had imagined the mince-meat to be. We had been looking for that plum pudding for two months.

"Meat?" I asked.

Kamau brought a thick, long chunk of roast Grant gazelle tenderloin from one of the Grant Pop had shot on the plain while we had been hunting the twenty-five-mile salt lick, and some bread.

"Beer?"

He brought one of the big German liter bottles and opened it.

It seemed too complicated sitting on the petrol case and I spread my raincoat on the ground in front of the fire where the ground had been dried by the heat and stretched my legs out, leaning my back against the wooden case. The old man was roasting meat on a stick. It was a choice piece he had brought with him wrapped in his toga. In a little while they all began to come in carrying meat and the hides and then I was stretched out drinking beer and watching the fire and all around they were talking and roasting meat on sticks. It was getting cold and the night was clear and there was the smell of the roasting meat, the smell of the smoke of the fire, the smell of my boots steaming, and, where he squatted close, the smell of the good old Wanderobo-Masai. But I could remember the odor of the kudu as he lay in the woods.

Each man had his own meat or collection of pieces of meat on sticks stuck around the fire, they turned them and tended them, and there was much talking. Two others that I had not seen had come over from the huts and the boy we had seen in the afternoon was with them. I was eating a piece of hot broiled liver I had lifted from one of the sticks of the Wanderobo-Masai and wondering where the kidneys were. The liver was delicious. I was wondering whether it was worth while getting up to get the dictionary to ask about the kidneys when M'Cola said, "Beer?"

"All right."

He brought the bottle, opened it, and I lifted it and drank half of it off to chase down that liver.

"It's a hell of a life," I told him in English.

He grinned and said, "More beer?" in Swahili.

My talking English to him was an acceptable joke.

"Watch," I said, and tipped the bottle up and let it all go down. It was an old trick we learned in Spain drinking out of wine skins without swallowing. This impressed the Roman greatly. He came over, squatted down by the raincoat and started to talk. He talked for a long time.

"Absolutely," I told him in English. "And furthermore he can take the sleigh."

"More beer?" M'Cola asked.

"You want to see the old man tight I suppose?"

"N'Dio," he said, "Yes," pretending to understand the English.

"Watch it, Roman," I started to let the beer go down, saw the Roman following the motion with his own throat, started to choke, barely recovered and lowered the bottle.

"That's all. Can't do it more than twice in an evening. Makes you liverish."

The Roman went on talking in his language. I heard him say Simba twice.

"Simba here?"

"No," he said. "Over there," waving at the dark, and I could not make out the story. But it sounded very good.

"Me plenty Simba," I said. "Hell of a man with Simba. Ask M'Cola." I could feel that I was getting the evening braggies but Pop and P. O. M. weren't here to listen. It was not nearly so satisfactory to brag when you could not be understood, still it was better than nothing. I definitely had the braggies, on beer, too.

"Amazing," I told the Roman. He went on with his own story. There was a little beer in the bottom of the bottle.

"Old Man," I said. "Mzee."

"Yes, B'wana," said the old man.

"Here's some beer for you. You're old enough so it can't hurt you."

I had seen the old man's eyes while he watched me drink and I knew he was another of the same. He took the bottle, drained it to the last bit of froth and crouched by his meat sticks holding the bottle lovingly.

"More beer?" asked M'Cola.

"Yes," I said. "And my cartridges."

The Roman had gone on steadily talking. He could tell a longer story even than Carlos in Cuba.

"That's mighty interesting," I told him. "You're a hell of a fellow, too. We're both good. Listen." M'Cola had brought the beer and my khaki coat with the cartridges in the pocket. I drank a little beer, noted the old man watching and spread out six cartridges. "I've got the braggies," I said. "You have to stand for this, look!" I touched each of the cartridges in turn, "Simba, Simba, Faro, Nyati, Tendalla, Tendalla. What do you think of that? You don't have to believe it. Look, M'Cola!" and I named the six cartridges again. "Lion, lion, rhino, buffalo, kudu, kudu."

"Ayee!" said the Roman excitedly.

"N'Dio," said M'Cola solemnly. "Yes, it is true."

"Ayee!" said the Roman and grabbed me by the thumb.

"God's truth," I said. "Highly improbable, isn't it?"

"N'Dio," said M'Cola, counting them over himself. "Simba, Simba, Faro, Nyati, Tendalla, Tendalla!"

"You can tell the others," I said in English. "That's a hell of a big piece of bragging. That'll hold me for tonight."

The Roman went on talking to me again and I listened carefully and ate another piece of the broiled liver. M'Cola was working on the heads now, skinning out one skull and showing Kamau how to skin out the easy part of the other. It was a big job to do for the two of them, working carefully around the eyes and the muzzle and the cartilage of the ears, and afterwards flesh all of the head skins so they would not spoil, and they were working at it very delicately and carefully in the firelight. I do not remember going to bed, nor if we went to bed.

I remember getting the dictionary and asking M'Cola to ask the boy if he had a sister and M'Cola saying, "No. No," to me very firmly and solemnly.

"Nothing tendacious, you understand. Curiosity."

M'Cola was firm. "No," he said and shook his head. "Hapana," in the same tone he used when we followed the lion into the sanseviera that time.

That disposed of the opportunities for social life and I looked up kidneys and the Roman's brother produced some from his lot and I put a piece between two pices of liver on a stick and started it broiling.

"Make an admirable breakfast," I said out loud. "Much better than mince-meat."

Then we had a long talk about sable. The Roman did not call them Tarahalla and that name meant nothing to him. There was some confusion about buffalo because the Roman kept saying, "nyati," but he meant they were black like the buff. Then we drew pictures in the dust of ashes from the fire and what he meant were sable all right. The horns curved back like scimitars, way back over their withers.

"Bulls?" I said.

"Bulls and cows."

With the old man and Garrick interpreting, I believed I made out that there were two herds.

"Tomorrow."

"Yes," the Roman said. "Tomorrow."

" 'Cola," I said. "Today, kudu. Tomorrow, sable, buffalo, Simba."

"Hapana, buffalo!" he said and shook his head. "Hapana, Simba!"

"Me and the Wanderobo-Masai buffalo," I said.

"Yes," said the Wanderobo-Masai excitedly. "Yes."

"There are very big elephants near here," Garrick said.

"Tomorrow elephants," I said, teasing M'Cola.

"Hapana elephants!" he knew it was teasing but he did not even want to hear it said.

"Elephants," I said. "Buffalo, Simba, leopard."

The Wanderobo-Masai was nodding excitedly. "Rhino," he put in.

"Hapana!" M'Cola said shaking his head. He was beginning to suffer.

"In those hills many buffalo," the old man interpreted for the now very excited Roman who was standing and pointing beyond where the huts were.

"Hapana! Hapana! Hapana!" M'Cola said definitely and finally. "More beer?" putting down his knife.

"All right," I said. "I'm just kidding you."

M'Cola was crouched close talking, making an explanation. I heard Pop's title and I thought it was that Pop would not like it. That Pop would not want it.

"I was just kidding you," I said in English. Then in Swahili, "Tomorrow sable?"

"Yes," he said feelingly. "Yes."

After that the Roman and I had a long talk in which I spoke Spanish and he spoke whatever it was he spoke and I believe we planned the entire campaign for the next day.

ALEXANDER LAKE

Killers in Africa

Countless temporary residents of Hollywood have moved temporarily to the African bush, but few permanent residents of the African bush have moved permanently to Hollywood. That is only one of the reasons why Alexander Lake is different. The other is his ability to write about hunters and hunted. A professional "white hunter" for many years, Lake found that his ability to write about his clients and their quarry was more rewarding than serving as their mentor in the bush. His philosophy might be summed up in the subtitle of one of his books: "Or Animals That Lie in Wait, and Hunters That Lie in Print." Lake is a fine hunter, an excellent guide, and an extremely able writer. This chapter from *Killers in Africa* is proof of all three.

I know exactly what happened to twenty-three men in tragic encounters with African lions. Eight of those men were horribly mauled. Six of them lie buried in the cemetery at Nairobi. Graves of nine others are far scattered among the purple-and-silver silences of Africa.

Each man was mauled or killed through his own fault because he was ignorant, or careless, or reckless, or a poor shot, or hysterical, or dependent on native gunbearers for support. These are the six deadly shortcomings of lion hunting. Perhaps the best way to explain them is to take some of those twenty-three tragedies apart.

George Grey was the scion of a noble English family. He possessed all six of the deadly shortcomings. He was out after lions with Sir Alfred Pease, one of Africa's most publicized hunters. Six other men were also in the party. All were mounted. Now a horse is slow freight compared to a lion, which is just about the fastest animal on earth. Pease had warned all members of the party not to approach a lion closer than two hundred yards. But Grey was over-eager. He rode after a shaggy male who was ambling off about his own business.

The lion paid no attention to the pounding hoofs behind him until Grey was within ninety yards, when without warning, the lion whirled and charged. Ninety yards! A lion can do a hundred yards from a standing start in *four seconds* flat. I know. I've timed them. Martin Johnson, who has photographed more lions than any other wild-animal photographer, says that the lion can do a hundred yards from a running start in *three seconds*.

Grey's lion was coming at him at a speed of twenty-five yards every second. He was doing it in forty-five-foot jumps. Ninety yards —270 feet—six jumps! Grey leaped from his horse and let off his first shot at twenty-five yards. He let off his second shot at five yards. Figure it out. Less than four fifths of a second between shots. That means he was using a heavy-caliber double rifle. It also means that the second shot was a flash shot, for no human can recover from the recoil of one of those big rifles and let off a second *aimed* shot that fast.

Both shots hit, but the lion never faltered. One fifth of a second after Grey's last shot, the lion was tearing at him with claws and teeth. One minute later three of Grey's companions galloped up and each slapped a bullet into the lion from ten yards. They were close enough to have made successful brain shots, but because they were believers in the "shock treatment," they slammed their slugs into the beast's guts. Instead of slowing him, those shots increased his fury and he began mauling Grey unmercifully. Pease arrived in a rush, dismounted, placed the muzzle of his rifle against the side of the lion's head, and killed him.

The tragedy began as a simple situation. The lion had been ambling away. Any man who could shoot at all could have crippled, perhaps killed, the animal with a backside shot. The backside shot is one of the best. It often punctures the guts, liver, kidneys, lungs, and sometimes gets the heart. If it's a bit off and gets a back leg, it ties the lion down. It's true that lions can get along on three legs for a while, but their flashing speed is gone. Hit in a back leg, a lion may turn at bay or he may head for brush; but he won't attempt a charge until the hunter gets within leaping distance.

If he turns toward the hunter, he's wide open for a chest shot.

Aim an inch or two below the base of his throat. His heart is low in his chest. Of course you could make a head shot, but you'll probably want the head for a trophy, and it's a shame to damage it. Anyway, the head shot is a dangerous one for uncertain marksmen. Men have died because they thought there was some skull in that great mop of hair. There isn't. The lion has hardly any skull above the eyes.

Grey and his companions couldn't have made more mistakes if they'd held a conference for the purpose. And Grey might be alive today if his companions hadn't slapped those three useless shots into the lion. Up to that moment the lion was chewing on Grey's arm and shoulder. The chances are that he was about through with mauling, for a lion's anger ebbs quickly once his victim is down. Even when two of the beasts put on one of their earth-shaking battles over a female, the victor's rage vanishes instantly once his opponent is whipped.

However, those three gut shots made Grey's death certain. I wonder how many men must die before sportsmen learn that *you can't kill a lion with shock*. And I wonder how many men must die before hunters learn the anatomies of animals they're hunting; learn the location of the heart and brain, at least.

Not long ago I was sitting around a campfire with five deer hunters in California. They were talking about heart shots. I listened awhile, then asked: "Just where is a deer's heart?" All five told me, and all five were wrong. They all had the heart too high. A deer's heart is in the lower third of the chest, a good handbreadth back of the foreleg. Hearts of most other animals are in the same area.

Grey couldn't shoot accurately. He let off his first shot when the charging beast was twenty-five yards away. That means that it was in the middle of the lion's next to the last jump. Any man who can't put a bullet into a lion's chest at twenty-five yards when the animal's coming head on shouldn't be hunting big game. Grey's first slug went through the fleshy part of the lion's shoulder, expanded and tore a nasty furrow along the animal's side. The second shot, at five yards, got the beast as it reared high in its final leap. It entered the stomach just behind the breast-bone.

Now if Grey had fired his first shot at ninety yards and his second at sixty yards and they had done the same damage, Grey still would have died. For he had made another mistake. He had gone after lion with a double rifle and no second gun handy for emergency. Unless you're a whiz with a rifle, you need a minimum of five bullets in your gun if you're going to shoot at a lion. Only a few old professionals consistently drop a lion with a first shot. The average sportsman takes four shots before he gets one in that lays a lion low. And if he's wise, he has a support gunner beside him just in case.

Personally, I like a ten-cartridge magazine. That's one of the reasons I prefer a military Lee-Enfield .303. Ten cartridges in the magazine and one in the chamber. Eleven shots. And there have been times when I needed them all.

It's true that the double rifle is the fastest-shooting gun made— for two shots. But by the time you grab your second gun (if the gunbearer is still there) and let off two more shots, your four-shot total is slower than four shots with a bolt-action rifle.

How fast can a man shoot a bolt- or lever-action gun and still do an accurate job? Well, I held some snap-and-rapid African championships. My best work was eleven bull's-eyes at two hundred yards in thirty-six seconds. I used a Lee-Enfield .303 and worked the bolt without taking the butt from my shoulder. I used a wide V back sight.

There's no place in dangerous game shooting for telescope, small-peep, narrow, or buckhorn sights. I never could see why a man wanted a telescope sight unless his eyes were poor. Anyway, these sights catch in grass, twigs, vines, and everything else that scrapes along the barrel. On small game in open plain, there's no objection to them. The large peep sight is all right. A small peep blurs.

I've known the best lion men in Africa. Almost without exception they use a wide V back sight. Aiming with a wide V is as natural as pointing your finger. You merely see that the tip of the fore sight lines up level with the back-sight shoulders so that it makes a perfect W out of the V. Tilting the barrel is bad business, and a man simply can't tilt the barrel unknowingly with a wide V back sight.

Trigger squeeze is everything. The pull should be adjusted to the man. I like a three-pound pull for game. Some professionals like five pounds. That's too much for a light rifle. A hair trigger doesn't help a man's shooting and may kill someone.

It's possible that Grey waited until the last couple of jumps because he thought the lion was bluffing. Four times out of five a lion's charge is a bluff. He's not really angry, but trying to frighten you away. There's a difference in a lion's charges. When he means business, he comes full-tilt. He uses all of his terrific

speed. When he's trying only to scare you, he comes more leisurely
—at about one hundred yards in ten seconds.

Let's suppose you think a lion is bluffing and that you do not
want to kill him. Your best bet is to stand motionless until he's
about twenty-five yards from you. If he's bluffing, he'll stop about
there and switch his tail at you. If he doesn't stop, let him have it.
If you think he's bluffing and you don't feel like waiting to find
out, and if there's a bush handy, step behind it. Once you're out of
his sight, he'll probably be satisfied and forget you.

In any case, *do not talk*. There's something about the human
voice that stirs rage in the hearts of some lions. You may be standing watching a peaceful family group lying under a tree. They see
you, but except for an occasional lifting of their lips they ignore
you. You speak, and instantly one gets to his feet, stiffens his tail,
and rushes you. One of the problems of professional guides is how
to keep clients from speaking at wrong times.

Occasionally a lion that has stopped his rush and is staring at
the hunter will be goaded into a genuine charge because someone
starts talking. As for yelling at the brutes—well, I'll tell you about
Orlando.

Orlando was an American Portuguese. I took him into
Bechuanaland to the Okavango Swamp country for some big-game
shooting. Incidentally, if you want to save money, do your hunting
in Bechuanaland. You can bag the entire list of game, except
elephants, at a total cost of about six hundred dollars—licenses and
all—and there's no limit on lions and leopards.

Orlando was a short, dark, hard-talking hombre. His jaw stuck
out like a crag. He liked to talk about fist fights he'd had and
always ended his yarns by saying: "So I bopped him." On a rhino
and a buffalo he did all right, but at his first sight of a lion he
hurled his rifle at it. The beast was at least 150 yards away.

I said: "What's the matter? Snake bite you?"

He stared at me for a moment, turned to look at the lion, saw it
moving slowly in our direction, then grabbed me by the arms from
behind and started pushing. I jerked loose. He began yelling.

The lion, which I don't believe had seen us up to that time,
stopped, flipped his tail straight up three or four times, and came
a-barreling. As I lifted my rifle, Orlando grabbed me again and
began shaking me. So I bopped *him*.

The lion came within about fifty yards, then changed direction
and galloped toward some brush. I let him go. Orlando got to his
feet, a bit groggy but sane.

"Once when I was a kid," he said, "our cat scratched me and I got hysterical like this. Ever since, even a kitten gives me the willies."

"Well," I told him, "you can cure it. Just face up to the next lion. Better yet, let's go and get this one."

He shook his head. "Just get me back to Bulawayo."

So back to Bulawayo we went.

I've seen several men who had an unreasonable fear of one beast or another. Some of them acted every bit as hysterical as Orlando did. Most of them cured themselves by standing up to their particular *bête noire* the next time they had a chance. That takes guts.

Never run from a charging lion. If two men are facing a lion and one man runs, the lion will take after him, passing up the man who stands quietly. Four of the twenty-three died while running from charging lions. One of the four, an Irishman named Wisdom, had just seen his lion run down a bull giraffe. He knew that a giraffe does a hundred yards in five seconds. He knew that the lion had caught up with the bull in six or seven jumps. Yet when pressure was on, Wisdom ran. He didn't have a chance, of course. His partner, who'd stood his ground, got the lion, but not before the brute had broken Wisdom's neck with a sweep of his paw.

But let's get back to Grey. It's obvious that his troubles stemmed from the fact that he couldn't shoot straight. He wasn't in a panic. If he'd been in a panic, he wouldn't have waited until the lion was two jumps from him. He must have known he was no dead shot, otherwise why the big-caliber-rifle? No, he made the sad error of thinking that shock would kill a lion. I repeat: *It won't.* Neither will it kill a buffalo.

Grey's fatal encounter took place on open plain. The grass was short, so he could have shot at almost any distance. If the grass had been high, the lion would have stalked him to within fifteen or twenty yards before charging. That, of course, would have been an entirely different setup. Only a man with a suicide urge or one who is just plain nuts will hunt lion in shoulder-high grass. Two of the twenty-three made that mistake.

Those two were Englishmen of a type one often reads about but seldom sees. Thir names were St. Leger and Meagher, pronounced "Silinger" and "Mar." They were fine old fellows who wore wrapped cloth puttees, green riding pants, and pleated shooting jackets; they smoked big curved-stem pipes and drank great quaffs of whiskey which they called "nips."

The smallest guns they had were .450 Powells. In addition, each had a .510 Rigby and a .600 Express. Six gunbearers carried the rifles in green canvas cases.

St. Leger and Meagher wouldn't shoot standing beasts. "Not sporting, y'know. Must bag 'em on the wing."

When I explained that I thought it more sporting to be sure of killing rather than just wounding game, St. Leger said: "Do 'em in quickly. Elephant guns, y'know. Mustn't dispatch sitting beasts. Be like shooting sitting hares, what?"

I'd met the old codgers by appointment at their camp near Maun on the edge of the Okavango Swamp in Bechuanaland. This was in 1938. What a camp! They'd set up four large double tents of green canvas. They had deck chairs. They had bookcases. They had two tables to each tent, Aladdin lamps, cases of whiskey, and cases of square-face gin. They'd set up a Whymper tent as a kitchen and had stocked it with all sorts of canned goods. Under green tarpaulins wre parked two Chevrolet pickups and a Ford flat-bed.

They greeted me with grave dignity, poured me a whiskey-soda, made a few remarks about the weather, and lapsed into uneasy silence. They puffed at their pipes awhile, then Meagher said, waving his pipe at the camp: "This sort of thing won't do, y'know."

St. Leger nodded. "Want to rough it," he said. "Not these bally conveniences. Not hunting at all. Not Africa. Silly way to shoot."

I laughed. They looked so serious. I said: "I don't like this sort of thing either. How about getting an ox-wagon outfit together and foot-slogging it about the country?"

A load seemed to drop from their shoulders. They beamed. Said Meagher: "Sleep on the ground, what?"

"And live off the country," St. Leger added.

"Why not?" I said. "There's *hunting* and *hunting*. Too much rocking-chair shooting being done these days." Indicating the luxury of the camp with a sweep of my arm, I added: "Somebody sold you a bill of goods."

"Ha! Excellent way to put it," said Meagher. "Fast-talking chap at Pretoria outfitted us. Wouldn't stop talking, so we bought everything. Easiest way, y'know."

"Well," I said, "I'll go into Maun tomorrow and pick up a wagon outfit. It's too wet to go into the swamp. Rainy season's just ended. We'll go toward Daka, through grass, brush, and sand country. How many boys have you?"

"Twenty-eight."

"We'll leave twenty-four of them here. I'll bring a white man back from Maun to watch camp."

"Leave our gunbearers here?"

"Yes. And leave all the guns but your two .450s."

They took it on the chin like gentlemen.

Meagher got three water glasses from a cupboard. He poured them to the brim with Haig & Haig and handed them around. "Well," he said, downing half his glass, "cheer-o."

We loaded the ox wagon with plenty of blankets, corn meal, salt, sugar, milk, liquor, oil lanterns, pots, and camping odds and ends. I chose a Bantu cook, a camp boy, an ox driver, and a *voorlooper* to lead the span. I had my own trackers, the Zulu, Ubusuku, and a Bantu named Jantje. We started northeast at dawn of the third day after my arrival. St. Leger and Meagher paced gravely beside the wagon. They thought they were fooling me, but I knew they were as excited as Boy Scouts on their first weekend camp.

I learned to love those old rascals. The wagon did about twenty miles a day, but the three of us and the trackers prowled the veld in all directions, sometimes doing thirty miles before reaching the outspan at night.

Surprisingly, they could shoot. Steady, dogged, deliberate. They tossed a coin the first morning to see which of them would take the first shot at the first game. From then on each took his turn, the other beside him, acting as support gun.

For five days we passed through a game paradise. Not the overwhelming herds of East Africa, but small, more exciting herds of gemsbok, hartebeests, springbok, zebras, reedbuck, and duikers. Once or twice each day we spotted ostriches; and on the fifth day, beside a clear-flowing spruit, we found lion dung. That did it. The old devils got lion fever, and from that moment nothing else would do. We made our base camp right there.

It was almost two weeks before we got a lion. In the meantime I made St. Leger and Meagher responsible for getting meat for camp.

Long before sunrise, those two happy hunters had folded their blankets, piled them neatly on the wagon bed, and were cleaning overnight oil from their rifle barrels between sips of tea from great blue enamel mugs.

I had been teaching them a bit of spooring and they became fascinated with the stories told by sign. Spooring is not a difficult art to learn if one works at it. I've seen a greenhorn become the equal of the average native tracker in a few months.

While Ubusuku, Jantje, and I stood around the fire, St. Leger and Meagher would circle camp in the dim predawn light, looking for dark, dewless animal trails through the wet grass. Down they'd get on their hands and knees looking for dung, the best identification of an animal. They kept notes like these:

"*Springbok droppings*—about the shape and size of .500 slugs.

"*Reedbuck*—sometimes like small walnuts; sometimes like .600 bullets.

"*Bushbuck*—usually an oblong waffle-looking affair, but sometimes the waffle falls into pieces."

On the day we found the first lion dung they made this entry:

"*Lion*—looks like a hairy almond the size of a lemon."

Good descriptions to a man who's seen various dungs, but not much good to anyone else.

I taught them to watch for nibbled and crushed grass, for dropped chewings; to test the moisture in hoofprints; to note whether or not the cloven hoofprints of antelope were spread wide, indicating running; and to keep their eyes open for a hundred other signs that make the veld a book easily read—after one learns to read it. They developed fast, chiefly because they concentrated with single-minded intensity.

One midmorning Jantje grunted and pointed ahead to a group of three acacia thorn trees. A yellow-maned lion had just got to his feet and was stretching sleepily, mouth open in a wide yawn. The wind was toward us, so I said to St. Leger and Meagher: "There's a nice trophy. About 150 yards. One of you take him."

They looked hurt. Meagher said: "Can't be done, old chap. He's standing, y'see."

"Doggone it," I said, "then walk toward him, and if he charges, shoot fast and sure."

They moved ahead side by side, their .450s across their stomachs. The lion looked at them without interest and lay down again. Not so a female that had been hidden in the shade of a second tree. She came fast, leaping low, making no sound.

I held my sights on her—just in case. But St. Leger fired, kneeling. The big lioness turned a somersault, slapped her tail a few moments, and lay quiet. The male got to his feet and moved behind a third tree. I lost sight of him for a couple of minutes, then saw him high-tailing it toward brush a half mile away.

The lioness was still. St. Leger and Meagher looked at me. I said: "Move closer and put another slug in her. Can't ever tell."

A second shot wasn't needed. St. Leger's shot was one of the best I'd ever seen. Low in the chest, it got the lungs, heart, stomach, and liver. The old boy stood beside the dead beast, stroking his mustache with exaggerated calmness, but I noticed a trembling in his fingers.

Meagher filled and lighted his pipe. He took a few puffs, then said: "Well bowled, Topper, old boy."

I'd never heard St. Leger's nickname before. It showed that beneath his composure Meagher, too, was deeply moved. Disciplined old bluffers, they were, shy as schoolboys.

Meagher got his lion about a week later. A male with a skimpy mane. Meagher said ruefully that he'd have to buy it a wig before putting the head up in his den. He got the animal with a nice quartering shot through the shoulder blade into the chest.

By this time the two old fellows, who had been overweight and in poor condition when I met them, were lean and hard. They fiddled around the veld for the next two weeks, potting animals here and there. By the time the days got fiery hot and the grass got high and brown, they had collected one springbok, one reitbok, two buffalo, a small kudu, two zebras, and the two lions.

Then one morning in a soft spot where he had watered, a kudu bull left a clear, deep print of a hoof. It measured almost six inches from heel to points, a good one third larger than any kudu spoor I'd ever seen. Even I got excited. This could be a record bull, one with horns sixty-seven inches measured straight. With a foot that size, he would scale over five hundred pounds, I figured. His fresh trail was well marked through the grass. I let St. Leger and Meagher take the lead. They went ahead like bird dogs.

The bull was traveling upwind. As we advanced, the grass rose from knee height to hip height and finally to our shoulders. Lions could be bad here, but I figured the old kudu wouldn't be moving so leisurely if big cats were around. Yet I was uneasy.

Then out of nowhere came an earth-jarring roar, and a male lion, blood dripping from his mouth, leaped at St. Leger. It was the first time in years I'd heard a lion really roar. St. Leger threw himself sideways, and the enraged lion missed him by inches. I shot from the hip. Meagher's gun bellowed so close to my ear that I thought for a moment I'd been hit. The lion disappeared into tall, rough-edged grass.

St. Leger was unhurt, but for once his reserve was shattered. He kept repeating: "By Jove! Oh, by Jove!" About thirty feet away we found the lion-mangled body of the kudu bull. His horns were everything we had hoped they'd be. He hadn't been dead for more than a few minutes. Blood was still oozing from awful wounds.

I went back to where we'd shot at the big cat. Both bullets had evidently hit, for a splash of blood was foamy, indicating a lung puncture, and a second puddle of blood was normal red. I said: "While Jantje skins the kudu we'll take it easy and give the lion's wounds time to stiffen. Then Ubusuku and I'll go after him."

"It's our job," St. Leger said.

I grinned. "You'd be killed. Ubusuku'll go in on his belly. He can do it without rustling the grass. I'll follow the lion's trail. I'll be able to tell by the blood how fast he's losing strength. No— you men stay here and help Jantje with his kudu."

"It's our job," St. Leger repeated stubbornly.

"No, stay here. I don't want the reputation of having my clients killed."

They kept protesting. I said: "Listen. A white hunter friend of mine named Van der Wall let one of his sportsmen go into brush after a wounded lion. He'd told him how foolish it was. Begged him to wait at least until the animal had time to weaken from bleeding. Explained that a wounded lion lies down at the first opportunity and that wounds stiffen if given time. He said: 'When he hears you coming, he'll stop groaning. He'll know where you are, but you won't know where he is. He won't come at you running. He'll wait until you're within feet of him.'

"That guy wouldn't listen. Said he'd come to Africa for thrills and that this was a worth-while one. He stalked into the brush. He walked right past the lion as it lay close to the ground in heavy underbrush. The lion hit him from behind. Broke his neck, bit through his skull. Van der Wall dropped the lion on top of its victim, but that didn't do the dead man any good."

The sun was hot. Ticks were biting hard on my back. I said to Ubusuku: "Let's go over in the shade of that bush, and you can burn a couple of ticks off my back."

Ticks bury their heads deep. If you pull them off, the heads stay in the flesh and you have to dig them out with a knife. If you put the flame of a match to their backsides, they jerk their heads out in a hurry. Ubusuku got the ticks all right, and I was putting my shirt back on when Jantje yelled: "Old men go get lion, *Baas*."

I grunted in dismay. Ubusuku grabbed up his assagai and was gone like a flash. As I paused beside Jantje to pick up my .303, I saw Ubusuku dive headfirst into the grass. I checked the cartridges in the chamber and magazine and trotted along the lion's trail. My worry was that he would circle and, while the two men were following his spoor, would come up behind them.

The trail made a sweeping curve. Foamy blood spotted the

ground grass here and there. Higher up, red blood streaks showed the beast had been hit high, probably near his rear. The blood wasn't smeared as it would have been had it been a front shot and the lion's body had rubbed against the stains in passing.

I yelled two or three times for St. Leger and Meagher to wait for me. They didn't answer. Then it happened all at once. I heard Ubusuku yell. Heard the lion cough. Heard one of the old men scream. Saw a rifle go hurtling away like a helicopter propeller. I cut through the grass to the turmoil, and my heart went sick.

St. Leger, a bloody mass, lay broken. Meagher was under the lion, and the lion, with Ubusuku's assagai sticking out like a second tail, was coughing great bubbly gobs of blood. With three shots I made a mess of that lion's head.

St. Leger had a broken collarbone, a compound fracture of the ulna, and several broken ribs. The blood on him proved to be the lion's blood. Meagher, when we got him from under the carcass, was claw-torn from shoulder to ankle. His clothes were ripped off. Terrible foreleg swipes had struck like bolts of lightning. Had the lion been an inch closer when he struck, he'd have disemboweled Meagher.

Well, we got Meagher's bleeding stopped after a while, and he cursed as I poured iodine in his wounds. I took the first-aid kit over to St. Leger and bandaged him as well as possible. It took seven days to get the old gentlemen to Maun, where a private plane took them to Livingstone. Two weeks later I visited them in the hospital. As I walked into their room I heard Meagher calling St. Leger a brittle-boned old female. St. Leger grinned at me and said:

"Toss a coin, will you, old chap? Tails I get that bunged-up lion's head and Scar-bottom over there gets the kudu."

I tossed a coin.

It came down tails.

Venator

Although Izaak Walton is the prophet of the angler, he did not completely ignore hunting, as Venator's defense—or perhaps justification—of his sport clearly shows.

Well, Sir, and I will now take my turn, and will first begin with a commendation of the Earth, as you have done, Auceps, of the Air; the earth being that element upon which I drive my pleasant, wholesome, hungry trade. The earth is a solid, settled element; an element most universally beneficial both to man and beast; to men who have their several recreations upon it, as horse-races, hunting, sweet smells, pleasant walks; the earth feeds man, and all those several beasts that both feed him and afford him recreation. What pleasure doth man take in hunting the stately Stag, the generous Buck, the Wild-Boar, the cunning Otter, the crafty Fox, and the fearful Hare. And if I may descend to a lower game, what pleasure is it sometimes with gins to betray the very vermin of the earth, as namely, the Fitchet, the Fulimart, the Ferret, the Polecat, the Mouldwarp, and the like creatures that live upon the face and within the bowels of the Earth. How doth the earth bring forth herbs, flowers, and fruits, both for physic and the pleasure of mankind! And above all, to me at least, the fruitful vine, of which when I drink moderately it clears my brain, cheers my heart, and sharpens my wit. How could Cleopatra have feasted Mark Antony with eight wild-boars roasted whole at one supper, and other meats suitable, if the earth had not been a bountiful mother? But to pass by the mighty Elephant, which the earth breeds and nourisheth, and descend to the least of creatures, how doth the earth afford us a doctrinal example in the little Pismire, who in the summer provides and lays up her winter provision, and teaches man to do the like. The earth feeds and carries those horses that carry us. If I would be prodigal of my time and your patience, what might not I say in commendations of the Earth? That puts limits to the proud and raging sea, and by that means preserves both man and beast that it destroys them not, as we see it daily both those that venture upon the sea, and are there shipwrecked, drowned, and left to feed haddocks; when we that are so wise as to keep ourselves on earth, walk, and talk, and live, and eat, and drink, and go ahunting: of which recreation I will say a little, and then leave Piscator to the commendation of Angling.

Hunting is a game for princes and noble persons; it hath been highly praised in all ages; it was one of the qualifications that Xenophon bestowed on his Cyrus, that he was a hunter of wild beasts. Hunting trains up the younger nobility to the use of many exercises in their riper age. What more manly exercise than hunting the Wild-Boar, the Stag, the Buck, the Fox or the Hare. How doth it preserve health, and increase strength and activity.

And for the dogs that we use, who can commend their excellency to that height which they deserve? How perfect is the Hound at smelling, who never leaves or forsakes his first scent, but follows it through so many changes and varieties of other scents, even over and in the water, and into the earth. What music doth a pack of dogs then make to any man, whose heart and ears are so happy as to be set to the tune of such instruments. How will a right Greyhound fix his eye on the best Buck in a herd, single him out, and follow him, and him only, through a whole herd of rascal game, and still know and then kill him. For my Hounds, I know the language of them, and they know the language and meaning of one another, as perfectly as we know the voices of those with whom we discourse daily.

I might enlarge myself in the commendation of Hunting, and of the noble Hound especially, as also of the docileness of dogs in general; and I might make many observations of land creatures, that for composition, order, figure, and constitution approach nearest to the completeness and understanding of man; especially of those creatures which Moses in the Law permitted to the Jews, Lev. 9:2-8, which have cloven hoofs and chew the cud, which I shall forbear to name, because I will not be so uncivil to Piscator as not to allow him a time for the commendation of angling, which he calls an Art; but doubtless 'tis an easy one; and, Auceps, I doubt we shall hear a watery discourse of it, but I hope it will not be a long one.

ROBERT SURTEES

John Jorrocks

In the English-reading world of yesterday the name Jorrocks was synonymous with the so-called "blood sports." This creation of Surtees moved more in the huntin' rather than the shootin' circles, but his tribulations when he turned to the fowling pieces are not lacking in interest. It may be that Surtees's not-so-soft satire has less effect today than it had when participation in these sports was more strictly regulated, but Jorrocks still remains one of the great characters of sport fiction. These experiences of the Cockney sportsman have been selected as typical. Some of our own laws of trespass and game regulation are as complicated today as they were when Jorrocks took to the field.

One of Mr. Jorrocks's earliest recorded adventures proclaims him as a devotee of the gun, and the story may therefore be quoted in full:

Our fox-hunting friends, we are sure, will allow him to be an enthusiastic member of the brotherhood, and though we do not profess to put him in competition with Musters, Osbaldeston, or any of those sort of men, yet we mean to say that had his lot been cast in the country instead of behind a counter, his keenness would have rendered him as conspicuous—if not as scientific—as the best of them.

For a cockney sportsman, however, he is a very excellent fellow —frank, hearty, open, generous, and hospitable, and with the exception of riding up Fleet Street one Saturday afternoon, with a cock pheasant's tail sticking out of his red coat pocket, no one ever saw him do a cock tail action in his life.

The circumstances attending that exhibition are rather curious. He had gone out as usual on a Saturday, to have a day with the Surrey, but on mounting his hunter at Croydon, he felt the nag rather queer under him, and thinking he might have been pricked in the shoeing, he pulled up at the smith's at Addington to have his feet examined. This lost him five minutes, and unfortunately when he got to the meet, he found that a "travelling fox" had been tallied at the precise moment of throwing off, with which the hounds had gone away in their usual brilliant style, to the tune of "Blue bonnets are over the border." As may be supposed, he was in a deuce of a rage; and his first impulse prompted him to withdraw his subscription and be done with the hunt altogether, and he trotted forward "on the line," in the hopes of catching them up to tell them so. In this he was foiled, for after riding some distance, he overtook a string of Smithfield horses journeying "foreign for Evans," whose imprints he had been taking for the hoof-marks of the hunters. About noon he found himself dull, melancholy, and disconsolate, before the sign of the "Pig and Whistle," on the Westerham road, where, after wetting his own whistle with a pint of half-and-half, he again journeyed onward, ruminating on the uncertainty and mutability of all earthly affairs, the comparative merits of stag, fox, and hare-hunting, and the necessity of getting rid of the day somehow or other in the country.

Suddenly his reverie was interrupted by the discharge of a gun in the field adjoining the hedge along which he was passing, and the boisterous *whirring* of a great cock-pheasant over his head, which caused his horse to start and stop short, and to nearly pitch Jorrocks over his head. The bird was missed, but the sportsman's dog dashed after it, with all the eagerness of expectation, regardless of the cracks of the whip—the "comes to heel" and "downs to charge" of the master. Jorrocks pulled out his hunting telescope, and having marked the bird down with the precision of a billiard-table keeper, rode to the gate to acquaint the shooter with the fact, when to his infinite amazement he discovered his friend, Nosey Browne (late of "The Surrey"), who, since his affairs had taken an unfortunate turn, had given up hunting and determined to confine himself to shooting only. Nosey, however, was no great performer, as may be inferred, when we state that he had been in pursuit of the above-mentioned cock-pheasant ever since day-break, and after firing thirteen shots at him had not yet touched a feather.

His dog was of the right sort—for Nosey at least—and hope deferred had not made his heart sick; on the contrary, he dashed after his bird for the thirteenth time with all the eagerness he displayed on the first. "Let *me* have a crack at him," said Jorrocks to Nosey, after their mutual salutations were over. "I know where he is, and I think I can floor him." Browne handed the gun to Jorrocks, who, giving up his hunter in exchange, strode off, and having marked his bird accurately, he kicked him up out of a bit of furze, and knocked him down as "dead as a door nail." By that pheasant's *tail* hangs the present one.

Now Nosey Browne and Jorrocks were old friends, and Nosey's affairs having gone crooked, why of course, like most men in a similar situation, he was all the better for it; and while his creditors were taking twopence-halfpenny in the pound, he was taking his diversion on his wife's property, which a sagacious old father-in-law had secured to the family in the event of such a contingency as a failure happening; so knowing Jorrocks's propensity for sports, and being desirous of chatting over all his gallant doings with "The Surrey," shortly after the above-mentioned day he despatched a "twopenny," offering him a day's shooting on his property in Surrey, adding, that he hoped he would dine with him after. Jorrocks being invited himself, with a freedom peculiar to fox-hunters invited his friend the Yorkshireman, and visiting his armoury, selected him a regular shot-scatterer of a gun, capable of carrying ten yards on every side.

At the appointed hour on the appointed morning, the Yorkshireman appeared in Great Coram Street, where he found Mr. Jorrocks in the parlour in the act of settling himself into a new spruce green cut-away gambroon butler's pantry-jacket, with pockets equal to holding a powder-flask each, his lower man being attired in tight drab stocking-net pantaloons, and Hessian boots with large tassels—a striking contrast to the fustian pocket-and-all-pocket jackets marked with game-bag strap, and shot-belt, and the weather-beaten many-coloured breeches and gaiters, and hob-nail shoes that compose the equipment of a shooter in Yorkshire. Mr. Jorrocks not keeping any "sporting dogs," as the tax-papers call them, had borrowed a fat house-dog—a cross between a setter and a Dalmatian—of his friend Mr. Evergreen the greengrocer, which he had seen make a most undeniable point one morning in the Copenhagen fields at a flock of pigeons in a beet-root garden. This valuable animal was now attached by a trash-cord through a ring in his brass collar to a leg of the sideboard, while a clean-licked dish at his side showed that Jorrocks had been trying to attach him to himself, by feeding him before starting.

"We'll take a coach to the Castle," said Jorrocks, "and then get a 'go-cart' or a cast somehow or other to Streatham, for we shall have walking enough when we get there. Browne is an excellent fellow, and will make us range every acre of his estate over half a dozen times before we give in." A coach was speedily summoned, into which Jorrocks, the dog Pompey, the Yorkshireman, and the guns were speedily placed, and away they drove to the Elephant and Castle.

There were short stages about for every possible place except Streatham. Greenwich, Deptford, Blackheath, Eltham, Bromley, Footscray, Beckenham, Lewisham—all places but the right. However, there were abundance of "go-carts," a species of vehicle that ply in the outskirts of the Metropolis, and which, like the watering-place "fly," take their name from the contrary—in fact, a sort of *lucus a non lucendo*. They are carts on springs, drawn by one horse (with curtains to protect the company from the weather), the drivers of which, partly by cheating, and partly by picking pockets, eke out a comfortable existence, and are the most lawless set of rascals under the sun. Their arrival at the Elephant and Castle was a signal for a general muster of the fraternity, who, seeing the guns, were convinced that their journey was only what they call "a few miles down the road," and they were speedily surrounded by twenty or thirty of them, all with "excellent osses, vot vould take their honours fourteen miles an hour." All men of business are aware of the advantages of competition, and no one more so than Jorrocks, who stood listening to their offers with the utmost *sang froid*, until he closed with one to take them to Streatham church for two shillings, and deliver them within the half-hour, which was a signal for all the rest to set-to and abuse them, their coachman, and his horse, which they swore had been carrying "stiff-uns" all night, and "could not go not none at all." Nor were they far wrong; for the horse, after scrambling a hundred yards or two, gradually relaxed into something between a walk and a trot, while the driver kept soliciting every passerby to "ride," much to our sportsmen's chagrin, who conceived they were to have the "go" all to themselves. Remonstrance was vain, and he crammed in a master chimney-sweep, Major Ballenger the licensed dealer in tea, coffee, tobacco, and snuff, of Streatham (a customer of Jorrocks), and a wet-nurse; and took up an Italian organ-grinder to ride beside himself on the front, before they had accomplished Brixton Hill. Jorrocks swore most lustily that he would fine him, and at every fresh assurance, the driver offered a passer-by a seat; but having enlisted Major Ballenger into their cause, they at length made a stand, which unfortunately for them, was more than the horse could do, for just as he was showing off as he thought, with a bit of a trot, down they all soused in the mud. Great was the scramble; guns, barrel-organ, Pompey, Jorrocks, driver, master chimney-sweep, Major Ballenger, were all down together, while the wet-nurse, who sat at the end nearest the door, was chucked clean over the hedge into a dry ditch. This was a signal to quit the vessel, and having extricated themselves the best way they could, they all set off on foot, and left the driver to right himself at his leisure.

Ballenger looked rather queer when he heard they were going to Nosey Browne's, for it so happened that Nosey had managed to walk into his books for groceries and kitchen-stuff to the tune of fourteen pounds, a large sum to a man in a small way of business; and to be entertaining friends so soon after his composition seemed curious to Ballenger's uninitiated suburban mind.

Crossing Streatham Common, a short turn to the left by some yew-trees leads, by a near cut across the fields, to Browne's house; a fiery-red brick castellated cottage, standing on the slope of a gentle eminence, and combining almost every absurdity a cockney imagination can be capable of. Nosey, who was his own "Nash," set out with the intention of making it a castle and nothing but a castle, and accordingly the windows were made in the loop-hole fashion, and the door occupied a third of the whole frontage. The inconveniences of the arrangements were soon felt, for while the light was almost excluded from the rooms, "rude Boreas" had the complete run of the castle whenever the door was opened. To remedy this, Nosey increased the one and curtailed the other, and the Gothic oak-painted windows and door flew from their positions to make way for modern plate-glass in rich pea-green casements and a door of similar hue. The battlements, however, remained, and two wooden guns guarded a brace of chimney-pots and commanded the wings of the castle, one whereof was formed into a green, the other into a gig-house.

The peals of a bright brass-handled bell at a garden gate, surmounted by a holly-bush with the top cut into the shape of a fox, announced their arrival to the inhabitants of "Rosalinda Castle," and on entering they discovered young Nosey in the act of bobbing for gold fish, in a pond about the size of a soup-basin; while Nosey, senior, a fat, stupid-looking fellow, with a large corporation and a bottle nose, attired in a single-breasted green cloth coat, buff waistcoat, with drab shorts and continuations, was reposing, *sub tegmine fagi*, in a sort of tea-garden arbour, overlooking a dung-heap, waiting their arrival to commence an attack upon the sparrows which were regaling thereon. At one end of the garden was a sort of temple, composed of oyster-shells, containing a couple of carrier-pigeons, with which Nosey had intended making his fortune, by the early information to be acquired by them; but "there is many a slip," etc., as Jorrocks would say.

Greetings being over, and Jorrocks having paid a visit to the larder, and made up a stock of provisions equal to a journey through the Wilderness, they adjourned to the yard to get the other dog, and the man to carry the game—or rather, the prog, for the former was but problematical. He was a character, a sort of chap of all work, one, in short, "who has no objection to make himself generally useful;" but if his genius had any decided bent, it was, perhaps, an inclination towards sporting.

Having to act the part of groom and game-keeper during the morning, and butler and footman in the afternoon, he was attired in a sort of composition dress, savouring of the different characters performed. He had on an old white hat, a groom's fustian stable-coat cut down into a shooting jacket, with a whistle at the button hole, red plush smalls, and top-boots.

There is nothing a cockney delights in more than aping a country gentleman, and Browne fancied himself no bad hand at it; indeed, since his London occupation was gone, he looked upon himself as a country gentleman in fact. "Vell, Joe," said he, striddling and sticking his thumbs into the arm-holes of his waistcoat, to this invaluable man of all work, "we must show the gemmen some sport to-day; vich do you think the best line to start upon—shall we go to the ten h'acre field, or the plantation, or Thompson's stubble, or Timms' turnips, or my meadow, or vere?" "Vy I doesn't know," said Joe; "there's that old hen-pheasant as we calls Drab Bess, vot has haunted the plantin' these two seasons, and none of us ever could 'it (hit), and I hears that Jack, and Tom, and Bob, are still left out of Thompson's covey; but, my eyes! they're 'special vild!" "Vot—only three left? vere is old Tom, and the old ramping hen?" inquired Browne. "Oh, Mr. Smith, and a party of them ere Bankside chaps, com'd down last Saturday's gone a week, and rattled nine-and-twenty shots at the covey, and got the two old uns; at least it's supposed they were both killed, though the seven on 'em only bagged one bird; but I heard they got a goose or two as they vent home. They had a shot at old Tom, the hare, too, but he is still alive; at least I pricked him yesterday morn across the path into the turnip-field. Suppose we goes at him first?"

The estate, like the game, was rather deficient in quantity, but Browne was a wise man and made the most of what he had, and when he used to talk about his "manor" on 'Change, people thought he had at least a thousand acres—the quantity a cockney generally advertises for, when he wants to take a shooting place. The following is a sketch of what he had:—The east, as far as the eye could reach, was bounded by Norwood, a name dear to cockneys, and the scene of many a furtive kiss; the hereditaments and premises belonging to Isaac Cheatum, Esq. ran parallel with it on the west, containing sixty-three acres, "be the same more or less," separated from which, by a small brook or runner of water, came the estate of Mr. Timms, consisting of sixty acres, three roods, and twenty-four perches, commonly called or known by the name of Fordham; next to it were two allotments in right of common, for all manner of cattle, except cows, upon Streatham common, from whence up to Rosalinda Castle, on the west, lay the estate of Mr. Browne, consisting of fifty acres and two perches. Now it so happened that Browne had formely the permission to sport all the way up to Norwood, a distance of a mile and a half, and consequently he might have been said to have the right of shooting in Norwood itself, for the keepers only direct their attention to the preservation of the timber and the morals of the visitors; but since his composition with his creditors, Mr. Cheatum, who had "gone to the wall" himself in former years, was so scandalized at Browne doing the same, that no sooner did his name appear in the Gazette than Cheatum withdrew his permission, thereby cutting him off from Norwood and stopping him in pursuit of his game.

Joe's proposition being duly seconded, Mr. Jorrocks, in the most orthodox manner, flushed off his old flint and steel fire-engine, and proceeded to give it an uncommon good loading. The Yorkshireman, with a look of disgust mingled with despair, and a glance at Joe's plush breeches and top-boots, did the same, while Nosey, in the most considerate sportsman-like manner, merely shouldered a stick, in order that there might be no delicacy with his visitors, as to who should shoot first—a piece of etiquette that aids the escape of many a bird in the neighborhood of London.

Old Tom—a most unfortunate old hare, that what with the harriers, the shooters, the snarers, and one thing and another, never knew a moment's peace, and who must have started in the world with as many lives as a cat—being doomed to receive the first crack on this occasion, our sportsmen stole gently down the fallow, at the bottom of which were the turnips, wherein he was said to repose; but scarcely had they reached the hurdles which divided the field, before he was seen legging it away clean out of shot. Jorrocks, who had brought his gun to bear upon him, could scarcely refrain from letting drive, but thinking to come upon him again by stealth, as he made his circuit for Norwood, he strode away across the allotments and Fordham estate, and took up a position behind a shed which stood on the confines of Mr. Timms' and Mr. Cheatum's properties. Here having procured a rest for his gun, he waited until Old Tom, who had tarried to nip a few blades of green grass that came in his way, made his appearance. Presently he came cantering along the outside of the wood, at a careless, easy sort of pace, betokening either perfect indifference for the world's mischief, or utter contempt of cockney sportsmen altogether.

He was a melancholy, woebegone-looking animal, long and lean, with a slight inclination to grey on his dingy old coat, one that looked as though he had survived his kindred and had already lived beyond his day. Jorrocks however saw him differently, and his eyes glistened as he came within range of his gun. A well-timed shot ends poor Tom's miseries! He springs into the air, and with a melancholy scream rolls neck over heels. Knowing that Pompey would infallibly spoil him if he got up first, Jorrocks, without waiting to load, was in the act of starting off to pick him up, when, at the first step, he found himself in the grasp of a Herculean monster, something between a coal-heaver and a game-keeper, who had been secreted behind the shed. Nosey Browne, who had been watching his movements, halloaed out to Jorrocks to "hold hard," who stood motionless on the spot from whence he fired, and Browne was speedily along side of him. "You are on Squire Cheatum's estate," said the man; "and I have authority to take up all poachers and persons found unlawfully trespassing; what's your name?" "He's not on Cheatum's estate," said Browne. "He is," said the man. "You're a liar," said Browne. "You're another," said the man. And so they went on; for when such gentlemen meet, compliments pass current. At length the keeper pulled out a foot-rule, and keeping Jorrocks in the same position he caught him, he set-to to measure the distance of his foot from the boundary, taking off in a line from the shed; when it certainly did appear that the length of a big toe was across the mark, and putting up his measure again, he insisted upon taking Jorrocks before a magistrate for the trespass. Of course, no objection could be made, and they all adjourned to Mr. Boreem's, when the whole case was laid before him. To cut a long matter short—after hearing the pros and cons, and referring to the act of parliament, his worship decided that a trespass had been committed; and though, he said, it went against the grain to do so, he fined Jorrocks in the mitigated penalty of one pound one.

This was a sad damper to our heroes, who returned to the castle with their prog untouched and no great appetite for dinner. Being only a family party, when Mrs. B. retired the subject naturally turned upon the morning's mishap, and at every glass of port Jorrocks waxed more valiant, until he swore he would appeal against the "conviction"; and remaining in the same mind when he awoke the next morning, he took the Temple in his way to St. Botolph Lane and had six-and-eightpence worth with Mr. Capias the attorney, who very judiciously argued each side of the question without venturing an opinion, and proposed stating a case for counsel to advise upon.

As usual, he gave one that would cut either way, though if it had any tendency whatever it was to induce Jorrocks to go on; and he not wanting much persuasion, it will not surprise our readers to hear that Jorrocks, Capias, and the Yorkshireman were seen a few days after crossing Waterloo Bridge in a yellow post-chaise, on their way to Croydon sessions.

After a "guinea" consultation at the Greyhound, they adjourned to the Court, which was excessively crowded, Jorrocks being as popular with the farmers and people as Cheatum was the reverse. Party feeling too running rather high at the time, there had been a strong "whip" among the magistrates to get a full attendance to reverse Boreem's conviction, who had made himself rather obnoxious on the blue interest at the election. Of course they all came in new hats, and sat on the bench looking as wise as gentlemen judges generally do.

One hundred and twenty-two affiliation cases (for this was in the old poor law time) having been disposed of, about one o'clock in the afternoon, the chairman, Mr. Tomkins of Tomkins, moved the order of the day. He was a perfect prototype of a county magistrate —with a bald powdered head covered by a low-crowned broad-brimmed hat, hair terminating behind in a queue, resting on the ample collar of a snuff-brown coat, with a large bay-window of a corporation, with difficulty retained by the joint efforts of a buff waistcoat, and the waistband of a pair of yellow leather breeches. His countenance, which was solemn and grave in the extreme, might either be indicative of sense or what often serves in the place of wisdom—when parties can only hold their tongues—great natural stupidity. From the judge's seat, which he occupied in the centre of the bench, he observed, with immense dignity, "There is an appeal of Jorrocks against Cheatum, which we, the bench of Magistrates of our Lord the King, will take if the parties are ready," and immediately the Court rang with "Jorrocks and Cheatum! Jorrocks and Cheatum! Mr. Capias attorney at law! Mr. Capias answer to his name! Mr. Sharp attorney at law! Mr. Sharp's in the jury room.—Then go fetch him directly," from the ushers and bailiffs of the court; for though Tomkins of Tomkins was slow himself, he insisted upon others being quick, and was a great hand at prating about saving the time of the suitors. At length the bustle of counsel crossing the table, parties coming in and others leaving court, bailiffs shouting, and ushers responding, gradually subsided into a whisper of "That's Jorrocks! that's Cheatum!" as the belligerent parties took their places by their respective counsel. Silence having been called and procured, Mr. Smirk, a goodish-looking man for a lawyer, having deliberately unfolded his brief, which his clerk had scored plentifully in the margin, to make the attorney believe he had read it very attentively, rose to address the court—a signal for half the magistrates to pull their newspapers out of their pockets, and the other half to settle themselves down for a nap, all the sport being considered over when the affiliation cases closed.

"I have the honour to appear on behalf of Mr. Jorrocks," said Mr. Smirk, "a gentleman of the very highest consideration—a fox-hunter—a shooter—and a grocer. In ordinary cases it might be necessary to prove the party's claim to respectability, but in this instance, I feel myself relieved from any such obligation, knowing, as I do, that there is no one in this court, no one in these realms— I might also add, no one in this world—to whom the fame of my most respectable, my most distinguished, and much injured client is unknown. Not to know Jorrocks is indeed to argue oneself unknown.

"This is a case of no ordinary interest, and I approach it with a deep sense of its importance, conscious of my inability to do justice to the subject, and lamenting that it has not been entrusted to abler hands. It is a case involving the commercial and the sporting character of a gentleman against whom the breath of calumny has never yet been drawn—of a gentleman who in all the relations of life, whether as a husband, a fox-hunter, a shooter, or a grocer, has invariably preserved that character and reputation, so valuable in commercial life, so necessary in the sporting world, and so indispensable to a man moving in general society. Were I to look round London town in search of a bright specimen of a man combining the upright, sterling integrity of the honourable British merchant of former days with the ardour of the English fox-hunter of modern times, I would select my most respectable client, Mr. Jorrocks. He is a man for youth to imitate and revere! Conceive then the horror of a man of his delicate sensibility—of his nervous dread of depreciation—being compelled to appear here this day to vindicate his character, nay more, his honour, from one of the foullest attempts at conspiracy that was ever directed against any individual. I say that a grosser attack was never made upon the character of any grocer, and I look confidently to the reversion of this unjust, unprecedented conviction, and to the triumphant victory of my most respectable and public-spirited client. It is not for the sake of the few paltry shillings that he appeals to this court— it is not for the sake of calling in question the power of the constituted authorities of this county—but it is for the vindication and preservation of a character dear to all men, but doubly dear to a grocer, and which once lost can never be regained. Look, I say, upon my client as he sits below the witness-box, and say, if in that countenance there appears any indication of a lawless or rebellious spirit; look, I say, if the milk of human kindness is not strikingly portrayed in every feature, and truly may I exclaim in the words of the poet—

> If to his share some trifling errors fall,
> Look in his face, and you'll forget them all.

I regret to be compelled to trespass upon the valuable time of the court; but, sir, this appeal is based on a trespass and one good trespass deserves another."

The learned gentleman then proceeded to detail the proceedings of the day's shooting, and afterwards to analyse the enactments of the New Game Bill, which he denounced as arbitrary, oppressive, and ridiculous, and concluded a long and energetic speech by calling upon the court to reverse the decision of the magistrate, and not support the preposterous position of fining a man for a trespass committed by his toe.

After a few minutes had elapsed, Mr. Serjeant Bumptious, a stiff bull-headed little man, desperately pitted with the small-pox, rose to reply, and looking round the court, thus commenced:

"Five-and-thirty years have I passed in Courts of Justice, but never, during a long and extensive practice, have I witnessed so gross a perversion of that sublimest gift called eloquence, as within the last hour"—here he banged his brief against the table, and looked at Mr. Smirk, who smiled.—"I lament, sir, that it has not been employed in a better cause—(bang again—and another look). My learned friend has, indeed, laboured to make the worse appear the better cause—to convert into a trifle one of the most outrageous acts that ever disgraced a human being or a civilized country. Well did he describe the importance of this case!—important as regards his client's character—important as regards this great and populous county—important as regards those social ties by which society is held together—important as regards a legislative enactment, and important as regards the well-being and prosperity of the whole nation—(bang, bang, bang). I admire the bombastic eloquence with which my learned friend introduced his *most distinguished client*—his *most* delicate-minded—sensitive client! Truly to hear him speaking I should have thought he had been describing a lovely, blushing, young lady, but when he comes to exhibit his paragon of perfection, and points out that great, red-faced, coarse, vulgar-looking, lubberly lump of humanity (here Bumptious looked at Jorrocks as though he would eat him) sitting below the witness-box, and seeks to enlist the sympathies of your worships on the Bench—of *you, gentlemen,* the high-minded, shrewd, penetrating judges of this important cause (and Bumptious smiled and bowed along the bench upon all whose eyes he could catch) on behalf of such a monster of iniquity, it does make one blush for the degradation of the British bar—(bang bang bang—Jorrocks here looked unutterable things). Does my learned friend think by displaying his hero as a fox-hunter, and extolling his prowess in the field, to gain over the sporting magistrates on the bench? He knows little of the upright integrity—the uncompromising honesty—the undeviating, inflexible impartiality that pervades the breast of every member of this tribunal, if he thinks for the sake of gain, fear, favour, hope, or reward, to influence the opinion, much less turn the judgment of any one of them." (Here Bumptious bowed very low to them all and laid his hand upon his heart. Tomkins nodded approbation.) "Far, far be it from me to dwell with unbecoming asperity on the conduct of any one—we are all mortals—and alike liable to err; but when I see a man who has been guilty of an act which has brought him all but within the verge of the prisoners' dock; I say, when I see a man who has been guilty of such an outrage of society as this ruffian Jorrocks, come forward with the daring effrontery that he has this day done, and claim redress where he himself is the offender, it does create a feeling in my mind divided between disgust and amazement" (bang).

Here Jorrocks's cauldron boiled over, and rising from his seat with an outstretched shoulder-of-mutton fist, he bawled out, "D——n you, sir, what do you mean?"

The Court was thrown into amazement, and even Bumptious quailed before the fist of the mighty Jorrocks. "I claim the protection of the Court," he exclaimed. Mr. Tomkins interposed, and said he should certainly order Mr. Jorrocks into custody if he repeated his conduct, adding that it was *"most* disrespectful to the justices of our Lord the King."

Bumptious paused a little to gather breath and a fresh volume of venom wherewith to annihilate Jorrocks, and catching his eye, he transfixed him like a rattlesnake, and again resumed.

"How stands the case?" said he. "This cockney grocer—for after all he is nothing else—who I dare say scarcely knows a hawk from a hand-saw—leaves his figs and raisins, and sets out on a marauding excursion into the county of Surrey, and regardless of property—of boundaries—of laws—of liberties—of life itself—strides over every man's land, letting drive at whatever comes in his way! The hare he shot on this occasion was a *pet* hare! For three successive summers had Miss Cheatum watched and fed it with all the interest and anxiety of a parent. I leave it to you, gentlemen, who have daughters of your own, with pets also, to picture to yourselves the agony of her mind in finding that her favourite had found its way down the throat of that great guzzling, gormandizing, cockney cormorant; and then, forsooth, because he is fined for the outrageous trespass, he comes here as the injured party, and instructs his counsel to indulge in Billingsgate abuse that would disgrace the mouth of an Old Bailey practitioner! I regret that instead of the insignificant fine imposed upon him, the law did not empower the worthy magistrate to send him to the treadmill there to recreate himself for six or eight months, as a warning to the whole fraternity of lawless vagabonds." Here he nodded his head at Jorrocks as much as to say—"I'll *trounce* you, my boy!" He then produced maps and plans of the different estates, and a model of the shed to show how it had all happened, and after going through the case in such a strain as would induce one to believe it was a trial for murder or high treason, concluded as follows.

"The eyes of England are upon us—reverse this conviction, and you let loose a rebel band upon the country, ripe for treason, stratagem, or spoil—you overturn the finest order of society in the world; henceforth no man's property will be safe, the laws will be disregarded, and even the upright, talented, and independent magistracy of England brought into contempt. But I feel convinced that your decision will be far otherwise—that by it you will teach these hot-headed, rebellious, radical grocers that they cannot offend with impunity, and show them that there is a law which reaches even the lowest and meanest inhabitant of these realms, that amid these days of anarchy and innovation you will support the laws and aristocracy of this country, that you will preserve to our children, and our children's children, those rights and blessings which a great and enlightened administration have conferred upon ourselves, and raise for Tomkins of Tomkins and the magistracy of the proud county of Surrey a name resplendent in modern times and venerated to all eternity."

Here Bumptious cast a parting frown at Jorrocks, and banging down his brief, tucked his gown under his arm, turned on his heel and left the Court to indulge in a glass of pale sherry and a sandwich, regardless which way the verdict went, so long as he had given him a good quilting. The silence that followed had the effect of rousing some of the dosing justices, who nudging those who had fallen asleep, they all began to stir themselves, and having laid their heads together, during which time they settled the dinner hour for that day, and the meets of the stag-hounds for the next fortnight, they began to talk of the matter before the Court.

"I vote for reversing," said Squire Jolthead, "Jorrocks is such a capital fellow." "I *must* support Boreem," said squire Hicks, "he gave me a turn when I made the mistaken commitment of Gipsey Jack." "What do you say, Mr. Giles?" inquired Mr. Tomkins. "Oh anything *you* like, Mr. Tomkins." "And you, Mr. Hopper?" who had been asleep all the time. "Oh! *guilty*, I should say—three months at the treadmill—privately whipped if you like," was the reply. Mr. Petty always voted on whichever side Bumptious was counsel—the learned sergeant having married his sister—and four others always followed the chair.

Tomkins then turned round, the magistrates resumed their seats along the bench, and coming forward he stood before the judge's chair, and taking off his hat with solemn dignity and precision, laid it down exactly in the centre of the desk, amid cries from the bailiffs and ushers for "*Silence*, while the Justices of the Peace of our Sovereign Lord the King, deliver the judgment of the Court."

"The appellant in this case," said Mr. Tomkins, very slowly, "seeks to set aside a conviction for trespass, on the ground, as I understand, of his not having committed one. The principal points of the case are admitted, as also the fact of Mr. Jorrocks's toe, or a part of his toe, having intruded upon the respondent's estate. Now, so far as that point is concerned, it seems clear to myself and to my brother magistrates, that it mattereth not how much or how little of the toe was upon the land, so long as any part thereof was there. '*De minimis non curat lex*'—the English of which is 'the law taketh no cognizance of fractions'—is a maxim among the salaried judges of the inferior courts in Westminster Hall, which we the unpaid, the in-cor-rup-ti-ble magistrates of the proud county of Surrey, have adopted in the very deep and mature deliberation that preceded the formation of our most solemn judgment. In the present great and important case, we, the unpaid magistrates of our Sovereign Lord the King, do not consider it necessary that there should be 'a toe, a whole toe, and nothing but a toe,' to constitute a trespass, any more than it would be necessary in the case of an assault to prove that the kick was given by the foot, the whole foot, and nothing but the foot. If any part of the toe was there, the law considers that it was there in *to-to*. Upon this doctrine, it is clear that Mr. Jorrocks was guilty of a trespass, and the conviction must be affirmed. Before I dismiss the case I must say a few words on the statute under which this decision takes place.

"This is the first conviction that has taken place since the passing of the Act, and will serve as a precedent throughout all England. I congratulate the country upon the efficacy of the tribunal to which it has been submitted. The Court has listened with great and becoming attention to the arguments of the counsel on both sides: and though one gentleman with a flippant ignorance has denounced this new law as inferior to the pre-existing system, and a curse to the country, we, the Magistrates of the proud county of Surrey, must enter our protest against such a doctrine being promulgated. Peradventure, you are all acquainted with my prowess as a shooter, I won two silver tankards at the Red House, Anno Domini, 1815. I mention this to show that I am a practical sportsman, and as to the theory of the Game Laws, I derive my information from the same source that you may all derive yours—from the bright refulgent pages of the *New Sporting Magazine.*"

This lengthy extract proclaims Mr. Jorrocks not only as a devotee of the gun but also as a convicted poacher. Throughout his career we repeatedly come across evidence that shooting was a sport which he regarded as a fit and proper pastime but, although a self-confessed "martyr to fox-hunting," Mr. Jorrocks was with difficulty persuaded to attend a race-meeting at Newmarket:

"What in the name of all that's impure, have you to do at Newmarket?" he exclaimed. "Why nothing in particular," replied his *fidus Achates* the Yorkshireman, "only when there's neither hunting nor shooting going on, what is a man to do with himself? —I'm sure you'd despise me if I were to go fishing." "True," observed Mr. Jorrocks somewhat subdued, and jingling the silver in his breeches-pocket. "Fox 'unting is indeed the prince of sports. The image of war without its guilt and only half its danger."

H. C. WATSON

The Muckle Hart of Benmore

Having tasted of deer stalking in the modern manner, it seemed appropriate to devote a short space to the same activity in the earlier style. Watson, who collected and compiled stories of the chase for his own amusement but now, we understand, to his profit, considered this offering to be authentic. Apparently there were, in those days, a few individuals who found the wilds of the Highlands suitable for the distillation of tax-free spirits, just as the modern hunter finds similar havens in the more heavily wooded sections of our own southland. The modern guide and the old Scottish gillie have quite a bit in common.

S t. John's "Wild Sports of the Highlands," is a work peculiarly attractive, by the unaffected simplicity and honest cordiality which pervade it. The author's hand is evidently more familiar with the rod and rifle than with the pen—he gives a blunt country gentleman sort of detail of Highland sport by field and flood, and has an observant eye to the habits of the lower animals, and a kindly regard withal to the objects of the chase, which is ever characteristic of the legitimate sportsman. We extract, with slight abridgment, one of the most stirring incidents in the volume, the stalking of "The Muckle Hart of Benmore."

"Malcolm, the shepherd of the sheiling at the foot of Benmore, reported his having crossed in the hill a track of a hart of extraordinary size, and guessed it must be 'the muckle stag of Benmore.' This was an animal seldom seen, but which had long been the talk and marvel of the shepherds for its wonderful size and cunning. They love the marvellous, and in their report 'the muckle stag' bore a charmed life; he was unapproachable and invulnerable. I had heard of him too, and, having got the necessary information, resolved to try to break the charm, though it should cost me a day or two.

"*Monday*.—This morning, at sunrise, Mr. St. John with his rifle, Donald, an eccentric gillie, carrying his double-barreled gun, and Bran, his deer-hound, took their way up the glen to the sheiling at the foot of Benmore. After a fruitless beating of the glen, we turned, at nightfall, to the sheiling, rather disheartened; but the shepherd cheered us by the assurance that the hart was still in the district, and describing his track, which he said was like that of a good-sized heifer. Our spirits were quite restored by a meal of fresh caught trout, oat-cake, and milk, with a modicum of whiskey, which certainly was of unusual flavor and potency.

"*Tuesday*.—We were off again by daybreak. I will pass by several minor adventures, but one cannot be omitted. Malcolm went with us to show us where he had last seen the track. As we crossed a long reach of black and broken ground, the first ascent from the valley, two eagles rose out of a hollow at some distance. Their flight was lazy and heavy, as if gorged with food; and on examining the place, we found the carcass of a sheep half eaten, one of Malcolm's flock. He vowed vengeance; and merely pointed out to us our route, returned for a spade to dig a place of hiding near enough to the carcass to enable him to have a shot at the eagles if they should return. We held on our way, and the greater part of the day, without any luck to cheer us, my resolution 'not to be beat,' being, however, a good deal strengthened by the occasional grumbling of Donald. Towards the afternoon, when we had tired ourselves with looking with our glasses at every corrie in that side of the hill, at length, in crossing a bare and boggy piece of ground, Donald suddenly stopped, with a Gaelic exclamation, and pointed —and there, to be sure, was a full fresh footprint, the largest mark of a deer either of us had ever seen. There was no more grumbling. Both of us were instantly as much on the alert as when we started on the adventure. We traced the track as long as the ground would allow. Where we lost it, it seemed to point down the little burn, which soon lost itself to our view in a gorge of bare rocks. We proceeded now very cautiously, and taking up our station on a concealed ledge of rocks, began to search the valley below with our telescopes. It was difficult ground to see a deer in, if lying; and I had almost given up seeking, when Donald's glass became motionless, and he gave a sort of grunt as he changed his posture, but without taking the glass from his eye. "Ugh! I'm thinking yon's him, sir, I'm seeing his horns." I was at first incredulous; but the doubt was short. While we gazed, the stag rose and commenced feeding; at last I saw the great hart of Benmore! He was a long way off, perhaps a mile and a half, but in excellent ground for getting at him. Our plan was soon arranged. I was to stalk him with the rifle, while Donald, with my gun and Bran, was to get round, out of sight, to the pass by which the deer was likely to leave the valley. My task was apparently very easy. After getting down behind the rock, I had scarcely to stoop my head, but to walk up within shot, so favorable was the ground and the wind. I walked cautiously, however, and slowly, to give Donald time to reach the pass. I was now within three hundred yards of him, when, as I leant against a slab of stone, all hid below my eyes, I saw him give a sudden start, stop feeding, and look round suspiciously. What a noble beast! what a stretch of antler! with a mane like a lion! He stood for a minute or two, snuffing every breath. I could not guess the cause of this alarm; it was not myself; the light wind blew fair down from him upon me; and I knew Donald would give no inkling of his whereabouts. He presently began to move, and came at a slow trot towards me. My pulse beat high. Another hundred yards forward, and he is mine! But it was not so to be. He took the top of a steep bank which commanded my position, saw me in an instant, and was off, at the speed of twenty miles an hour, to a pass wide from that where Donald was hid. While clattering up the hill, scattering the loose stones behind him, two other stags joined him, which had evidently been put up by Donald, and had given the alarm to my quarry. It was then that his great size was conspicuous. I could see with my glass they were full-grown stags, and with good heads, but they looked like fallow deer as they followed him up the crag. I sat down, disappointed for the moment, and Donald soon joined me, much crestfallen, and cursing the stag in a curious variety of Gaelic oaths. Still it was something to have seen 'the muckle stag,' and *nil desperandum* was my motto. We had a long and weary walk to Malcolm's sheiling; and I was glad to get to my heatherbed, after arranging that I should occupy the hiding-place Malcolm had prepared near the dead sheep next morning.

"*Wednesday.*—After dispatching the plundering eagles in fine style, our hero and his redoubted gillie again set forth in quest of 'the muckle hart.' Our line of march today was over ground so high, that we came repeatedly into the midst of ptarmigan. On the very summit, Bran had a rencontre with an old mountain fox, toothless, yet very fat, which he made to bite the dust. We struck at one place the tracks of the three deer, but of the animals themselves we saw nothing. We kept exploring corrie after corrie till night fell; and as it was in vain to think of returning to the sheiling, which yet was the nearest roof, we were content to find a sort of niche in the rock, tolerably screened from all winds; and having almost filled it with long heather, flower upwards, we wrapped our plaids around us, and slept pretty comfortably.

"*Thursday.*—A dip in the burn below our bivouac renovated me. I did not observe that Donald followed my example in that; but he joined me in a hearty attack on the viands which still remained in our bag, and we started with renewed courage. About midday we came on a sheiling beside a long narrow loch, fringed with beautiful weeping birches, and there we found means to cook some grouse, which I had shot to supply our exhausted larder. The shepherd, who had 'no Sassenach,' cheered us by his report of 'the deer' being lately seen, described his usual haunts. Donald was plainly getting disgusted and homesick. For myself, I looked upon it as my fate that I must have that hart; so on we trudged. Repeatedly that afternoon we came on the fresh tracks of our chase, but still he remained invisible. As it got dark, the weather suddenly changed, and I was glad enough to let Donald seek for the bearings of a 'whisky bothy,' which he had heard of at our last stopping-place. While he was seeking for it, the rain began to fall heavily, and through the darkness we were just able to distinguish a dark object, which turned out to be a horse. 'The lads with the still be no far off,' said Donald. And so it turned out. But the rain had increased the darkness so much, that we should have searched in vain, if I had not distinguished at intervals, between the pelting of the rain and the heavy rushing of a black burn that ran beside us, what appeared to me to be the shrill treble of a fiddle. I could scarcely believe my ears. But when I communicated the intelligence to Donald, whose ears were less acute, he jumped with joy. 'It's a' right enough, sir; just follow the sound. It's that drunken deevilish Sandy Ross; ye'll never haud a fiddle frae him, nor him frae a whisky-still.' It was clear that the sound came from across the black stream, and it looked formidable in the dark. However, there was no remedy. So grasping each other's collar, and holding our guns high overhead, we dashed in, and staggered through in safety, though the water was up to my waist, running like a mill-race, and the bottom was of round stones. Scrambling up the bank, and following the merry sound, we came to what seemed a mere hole in the bank, from which it proceeded. The hole was partially covered by a door woven of heather; and, looking through it, we saw a sight worthy of Teniers. On a barrel in the midst of the apartment —half hut, half cavern—stood aloft, fiddling with all his might, the identical Sandy Ross, while round him danced three unkempt savages; and another figure was stooping, employed over a fire in the corner, where the whisky-pot was in full operation. The fire, and a sliver or two of lighted bog-fir, gave light enough to see the whole, for the place was not above ten feet square. We made our approaches with becoming caution, and were, it is needless to say, hospitably received; for who ever heard of Highland smugglers refusing a welcome to sportsmen? We got food, rest, and fire—all that we required—and something more; for long after I had betaken me to the dry heather in the corner, I had disturbed visions of strange orgies in the bothy, and of sober Donald exhibiting curious antics on the top of a tub. These might have been the productions of a disturbed brain; but there is no doubt that, when daylight awoke me, the smugglers and Donald were all quiet and asleep, far past my efforts to rouse them, except one, who was still able to tend the fire under the large black pot.

"*Friday.*—From the state in which my trusty companion was, with his head on a heap of ashes, I saw it would serve no purpose to awake him, even if I were able to do so. It was quite clear that he could be good for nothing all day. I therefore secured some breakfast and provisions for the day, (part of them oat-cake, which I baked for myself,) tied up Bran to wait Donald's restoration, and departed with my rifle alone. The morning was bright and beautiful; the mountain streams overflowing with last night's rain. I was now thrown on my own resources, and my knowledge of the country, which, to say the truth, was far from minute or exact. 'Benna-skiach' was my object today, and the corries which lay beyond it, where at this season the large harts were said to resort. My way at first was dreary enough, over a long slop of boggy ground, enlivened, however, by a few traces of deer having crossed, though none of my 'chase.' I at length passed the slope, and soon topped the ridge, and was repaid for my labor by a view of glen, and wood, and water so beautiful, that I sat down to gaze at it, though anxious to get forward.

"While I lay above the lake, the day suddenly changed, and heavy wreaths of mist came down the mountain sides in rapid succession. They reached me soon, and I was inclosed in an atmosphere through which I could not see twenty yards. It was very cold, too, and I was obliged to move, though scarcely well knowing whither. I followed the course of the lake, and afterwards of the stream which flowed from it, for some time. Now and then a grouse would rise close to me, and, flying a few yards, light again on a hillock, crowing and croaking at the intruder. The heron, in the darkness, came flapping his great wings close past me; I almost fancied I could feel the movements they caused in the air. Nothing could be done in such weather, and I was not sure that I might not be going away from my object. It was getting late, too, and I had made up my mind that my most prudent plan was to arrange a bivouac before it became quite dark. My wallet was empty, except a few crumbs, the remains of my morning's baking. It was necessary to provide food; and just as the necessity occurred to me, I heard, through the mist, the call of a cock grouse as he lighted close to me. I contrived to get his head between me and the sky, as he was strutting and croaking on a hillock close at hand; and aiming at where his body ought be, I fired my rifle. On going up to the place, I found I had not only killed him, but also his mate, whom I had not seen. It was a commencement of good luck. Sitting down, I speedily skinned my birds, and took them down to the burn to wash them before cooking. In crossing a sandy spot beside the burn, I came upon—could I believe my eyes?—'the track.' Like Robinson Crusoe in the same circumstances, I started back, but was speedily at work taking my information. There were prints enough to show the hart had crossed at a walk, leisurely. It must have been lately, for it was since the burn had returned to its natural size, after the last night's flood. But nothing could be done till morning, so I set about my cooking; and having, after some time, succeeded in lighting a fire, while my grouse were slowly broiling, I pulled a quantity of heather, which I spread in a corner, a little protected by an overhanging rock; I spread my plaid upon it, and over the plaid built another layer of heather. My supper ended, which was not epicurean, I crawled into my nest under my plaid, and, in spite of a rapid change from a dull foggy sky to a clear keen frost, was soon sound asleep.

"*Saturday.*—Need I say my first object was to go down and examine the track anew. There was no mistake. It was impossible to doubt that 'the muckle hart of Benmore' had actually walked through that burn a few hours before me, and in the same direction. I followed the track and breasted the opposite hill. Looking round from its summit, it appeared to me a familiar scene, and, on considering a moment, I found I overlooked, from a different quarter, the very same rocky plain and the two black lochs where I had seen my chase three days before. I had not gazed many minutes, when I saw a deer lying on a black hillock which was quite open. I lay down immediately, and with my glass made out at once the object of all my wandering. My joy was somewhat abated by his position, which was not easily approachable. My first object, however, was to withdraw myself out of his sight, which I did by crawling backwards down a little bank, till only the tips of his horns were visible, and they served to show me that he continued still. As he lay looking towards me, he commanded with his eye three-fourths of the circle; and the other quarter, where one might have got in upon him under cover of the little hillock, was unsafe, from the wind blowing in that direction. A burn ran between him and me, one turn of which seemed to come within two hundred yards of him. It was my only chance; so, retreating about a half a mile, I got into the burn in hidden ground, and then crept up its channel with such caution, that I never allowed myself a sight of more than the tips of his horns till I reached the nearest bend to him. There looking through a tuft of rushes, I had a perfect view of the noble animal, lying on the open hillock, lazily stretched out at length, and only moving now and then to scratch his flank with his horns. I watched him for fully an hour, the water up to my knees all the time. At length he stirred, gathered his legs together, and rose; and arching his back, he stretched himself just as a bullock does when rising from his night's lair. My heart throbbed, as turning all round he seemed to try the wind for his security, and then walked straight to the burn, at a point about one hundred and fifty yards from me. I was much tempted, but had resolution to reserve my fire, reflecting that I had but one barrel. He went into the burn at a deep pool, and, standing in it up to his knees, took a long drink. I stooped to put on a new copper cap and prick the nipple of my rifle; and on looking up again, he was gone! I was in despair, and was on the point of moving rashly, when I saw his horns again appear a little farther off, but not more than fifty yards from the burn. By and by they lowered, and I judged he was lying down. 'You're mine at last,' I said; and I crept cautiously up the bed of the burn till I was opposite where he had lain down.

"I carefully, and inch by inch, placed my rifle over the bank, and then ventured to look along it. I could see only his horns, but within an easy shot. I was afraid to move higher up the bed of the burn, where I could have seen his body; the direction of the wind made that dangerous. I took breath for a moment, and screwed up my nerves; and then with my cocked rifle at my shoulder, and my finger on the trigger, I kicked a stone, which splashed into the water. He started up instantly; but exposed only his front towards me. Still he was very near, scarcely fifty yards, and I fired at his throat just where it joins the head. He dropped on his knees to my shot; but was up again in a moment, and went staggering up the hill. Oh for one hour of Bran! Although he kept on at a mad pace, I saw he was becoming too weak for the hill. He swerved, and turned back to the burn, and came headlong down within ten yards of me, tumbling into it apparently dead. Feeling confident, from the place my ball had taken effect, that he was dead, I threw down my rifle, and went up to him with my hunting knife. I found him stretched out, and, as I thought, dying; and I laid hold of his horns to bleed him. I had scarcely touched him when he sprang up, flinging me backwards on the stones. It was an awkward position. I was stunned by the violent fall; behind me a steep bank of seven or eight feet high; before me was the bleeding stag, with his horns levelled at me, and cutting me off from my rifle. In desperation I moved, when he instantly charged, but fortunately tumbled ere he quite reached me. He drew back again like a ram about to butt, and then stood still with his head lowered, and his eyes bloody and swelled, glaring upon me. We stood mutually at bay for some time, till, recovering myself, I jumped out of the burn so suddenly, that he had not time to run at me, and from the bank above I dashed my plaid over his head and eyes, and threw myself upon him. I cannot account for my folly, and it had nearly cost me dear. The poor beast struggled desperately, and his remaining strength foiled me in every attempt to stab him in front; and he at length made off, tumbling me down, but carrying with him a stab in the leg which lamed him. I ran and picked up my rifle, and then kept him in view as he rushed down the burn on three legs towards the loch. He took the water, and stood at bay up to his chest in it.

"As soon as he halted, I commenced loading my rifle, when, to my dismay, I found that all the balls I had remaining were for my double-barrel, and were a size too large for my rifle. I sat down and commenced scraping one to the right size, an operation that seemed interminable. At last I succeeded; and having loaded, the poor stag remaining perfectly still, I went up within twenty yards of him, and shot him through the head. He turned over and floated, perfectly dead. I waded in and towed him ashore, and then had leisure to look at my wounds and bruises, which were not serious, except my shin-bone, which was scraped from ankle to knee by his horn. I soon had cleaned my quarry, and stowed him away as safely as I could, and then turned down the glen at a gay pace. I found Donald, with Bran, reposing at Malcolm's sheiling; and for all reproaches on his misconduct, I was satisfied with sending him to bring home 'the muckle hart of Benmore,' a duty which he performed before nightfall."

PAUL A. CURTIS

Connemara Nellie

No one has presented a more typical picture of the rough shooting in Ireland than Paul A. Curtis, who, at the same time, provides a central character such as many of us have met and remembered. Countless Nellies are scattered through the shooting world and doing much to make the sport what it is.

My wife and I sat on the hotel porch absorbing the mellow glow of an Irish evening. To the westward a great orange sun suffused the peaceful waters of Cashel Bay with a benediction.

The tide was coming in and the shore folk were restless; curlews cried mournfully as they collected to fly off to the hills, while knot and dunlin skitted about over the slob, eager to obtain the last mouthful before being driven from the feast. The blue smoke of peat fires rose from many a whitewashed shabeen where the evening meal was being prepared, on the slopes below Cashel Mountain and the lower ground across the bay where the snipe bogs lay.

The letter had said that we were too early for good shooting, as the snipe and the 'cock would not be in till November—still, there were a few grouse about if one would walk for them, and, with the odd snipe, they would do their best to show me sport.

We were well pleased with the prospects as we sat in the sun digesting an excellent supper, and our mood was receptive when our host joined us, followed by an ancient dog.

"Ye'll be liking it, perhaps?"

"Yes," I agreed, "we will be well pleased if the sport is a match for your fare and scenery."

He nodded. "I've eleven thousand acres that haven't had a gun on them this year—and didn't the O'Flaherty brothers take four-teen brace off of it the first day last season?"

O'Neil's tongue was a little thick and there was a bleary look in his eyes that betokened a long farewell with some recently de-parted guests, but his words were pleasing because they were what I wanted to hear.

"That's splendid!" I said. "And you have a man with a good dog to take me out?"

"Oh!" he answered with a maudlin grin, "there's Nellie." He nodded at the poor old wreck that sat at his feet and looked adoringly at him out of eyes as befogged as his own. My heart sank in one shattering plunge to my boots—and the spell of Conne-mara was broken. This, then, was what I had crossed Ireland for —to shoot over a dog that a kinder master would have destroyed three years gone by.

"Yes," continued O'Neil, "there's not a setter from Galway to Malin Head that's a match for her at holding the grouse. Isn't it so, Nellie?"

The old bitch made an effort and, after a couple of ineffectual starts, got to her feet and wobbled to her master. I have seen all kinds of dogs, but never one as decrepit as Nellie. She was an undersized red setter with a lusterless coat, faded to yellow where the ends of the hair were dead. Her body, wracked by an excessive bearing of puppies, was like a misshapen sack, and like most old dogs, she was broken down behind so that her hind legs appeared ready to give way under her at the next effort to move. Poor old thing, she had not even the marks of good breeding to redeem her. Her head was too short and her toothless jaws were too light.

Her master bent to give her a careless pat, and she tottered over to sniff my tweeds. I glanced at my wife, who, reading my thoughts and pitying me, held her peace—she knew what a disappointment our outing was apt to be.

"Will Mrs. Curtis be shooting with you?" O'Neil asked.

She shook her head. "I think I shall try the river—I do so want to kill a salmon." Trust a woman to be diplomatic in a crisis—and to make the best of it.

O'Neil agreed. The river was right and some fine creels had been brought in, as indeed we knew to be the case. By that time I had overcome my first shock of disappointment.

"But, O'Neil," I said, "surely you don't expect this old bitch to hunt again this season? It will kill her!"

"Ah, no fear! Sure, Nellie has looked like that for three or four years. Have you not?" And he looked towards her for agreement. " 'Twill do her good; takes the rheumatism out of her bones. Let her go easy at first and she will be better than ever by the end of the week."

"How old is she?"

"Fifteen," said O'Neil.

The following morning O'Neil introduced me to Joe Rudge, who came forward from a bunch of gillies who were gathered in back of the hotel waiting for their "gentlemen" to come forth.

"Good marrnin', surrh!" he said with a tip of his dilapidated hat, and that was all. Joe was in type similar to Nellie. His eyes had that same rheumy, far-away look, as if casting back into the past with little hope in the future. His gaunt six-foot frame was encased in a neat suit of homespun, and he wore a huge pair of brogans. Joe Rudge was sixty-four, although he looked older, but if anyone thought that he could beat him bogtrotting or climbing mountains, he was badly fooled.

"It's a fine morning," I said.

"It is, surrh, a fine marrnin'." He went in and got the lunch, shouldering my cartridge bag, and called to Nellie, saying briefly that we would start out through the barnyard and out over a shoulder of Cashel to the moor that lay behind. Nellie wagged her tail and looked at my gun, but she held back; she did not seem very keen, for the best dog in Connemara.

Eventually, and with much blandishment, Joe got her out of the yard and though she turned back several times, eventually coaxed her on to the goat path which led up the mountain. For that, at least, I was thankful. I need not be shamed by marching through the village with such a pair of companions—like the last of the Grand Army.

I was getting leary of this Irish grouse shooting before I was fairly started. The fishermen at the hotel had wished me luck with much the same spirit they would have used to the leader of a forlorn hope.

I was truly heartsick when we reached the top of the ridge and saw the great lonely expanse of moor stretching before us. How was I going to cover that with such a dog? I hardly cast an eye back at the glorious panorama of wild Irish loveliness. It was dark as twilight where we stood with the mist swirling about; and the sky was menacing, blue-gray as an old slate roof, and the somber mountains seemed ready to topple over and crush us. But away off in the direction of Ballyconneely the sun had pierced the clouds and struck the low ground with a glare of light, so that the green spots stood out like emeralds against the granite boulders which angry gods had tossed about all over the land—and the blue sea beyond.

We took a beat along the top of the ridge to the eastward, old Nellie trotting on ahead as we left the path, nosing here and there.

Occasionally she would break into an ambling gallop, but she was never more than twenty paces in front. We swung back low down on the far side without a sign of game, the silent Rudge paralleling on my left hand, and headed towards the mountains. The moor was silent as the grave, except for the squelching of our shoes in the boggy ground. A wet mist blew in our faces.

Turning, I was surprised to find old Nellie standing on the edge of a clump of bracken. One could not call it a point: she did not stretch out, tail like a poker, one foot raised in the conventional pose. She simply stopped and stayed put, head sunk between her shoulders, as ludicrous a figure as a dog could present, staring into the bracken. Thinking that it was only a rabbit, I stepped in, thrashing about, and with a rasping protest, a snipe sprang from a muddy rill, hurtling down the mountain to tumble headlong when the nitro broke the stillness.

Nellie fetched it back and Rudge slipped it into a pocket; he seemed to brighten perceptibly and couched the remark that " 'Twas a good shot, whatever." We continued around the base of the mountain and conditions looked better; here and there on the rougher ground of the north slope the heather had withstood the ravages of the shepherds; great masses of fine old bush were a lovely purple in the mist. Twice I saw old droppings, and once a feather.

Old Nellie stopped again, standing just as she had before, looking straight ahead at a huge outcropping of granite some twenty yards in front. Gun ready, I passed her, and a single grouse hurtled into the mist and came down in a smother of feathers just as it passed over the rock.

I felt better as old Nellie brought the fine bird to me. Maybe it wouldn't be so bad, after all. We put out another single at long range and continued on across a long flat moor that was lifeless. It was heavy going and I sank in the water above the tops of my low shoes at every step, but its coolness was pleasant on my feet. Nellie was well out in front now, wasting her meager energy in a fruitless attempt, where anyone could see that there would be no birds, but she was too deaf to come in to a whistle.

Away across the moor there was another range of low hills, purple with heather, towards which we were making, with a hope of better luck. As we reached the base of them, the old setter showed signs of interest and went slowly. Directing our course with silent signals of the arm, Rudge led me sweating to the top.

"We should do this bit again, surrh; they are here somewhere."

I nodded and we tried back. The slope was a series of ledges and we worked each one carefully in turn. Nellie pointed, and I walked in. Nothing happened, and I went ahead until I could look down onto the lower shelf, thinking that it was but another false point, and then something really happened. A covey of nine or ten birds took the air. I missed with my first barrel, clipped a tail feather with my second, and watched them swoop down the slope, only to zoom again on the far side and disappear in the mist with the protesting *Grrrrr-beck! Grrrrr-beck!* of the old cock in my ears. It was just as if he were growling, "Go back! Go back!" like some choleric old gentleman who hated being disturbed.

I looked at Joe Rudge with mingled pleasure at finding the birds and disgust at my poor shooting.

"Thim downhill shots are the very divil, surrh," he said cheerfully. "Maybe we will be finding them again."

But we found only one lying where we thought the rest of them had gone, and I added it to my bag. Then we sought a sheltered spot for lunch. Joe Rudge had a special one for Nellie, but the old fool would not touch it. She threw herself down on her broad, fat back and wriggled about in the grass with grunts of pleasure, trying to dry herself, as agile as a pup, and then wandered off to sniff about, despite our efforts to make her rest. She did take a bit of hard-boiled egg and a lobster claw that I offered, but plainly she was not hungry and wanted to continue the hunt.

On the way home we took another bird to which Nellie's unfailing nose led us, and then, striking the low ground, we tried several rushy places and picked up a couple of snipe. It was a very stiff and tired old setter that reached the hotel, where she was quickly rubbed down with a wisp of straw under the watchful eye of O'Neil, given a spoonful of brandy in a saucer of milk at the bar, and hustled off to the kitchen to rest in her favorite place by the fire. Yet that evening, when over the coffee I was telling the surprised fishermen that we actually had taken some birds, the old girl wandered out and pushed her white muzzle into my hand.

The next day was disappointing. We went to a distant moor by car, far back in the mountains where another man who was supposed to know the land met us at a wayside tavern. It was a sparkling day and Nellie was, as O'Neil had predicted, a different dog. She was still wobbly on her old pins, but she got well out in front and ambled along at a shuffling canter. We skirted a low moor that held no more heather than I could carry in my hat, and came back to the tavern having raised one lone grouse which got up hundreds of yards in front of us. I did not mind so much for myself, bad as it was, but I did hate to see that poor old setter work so hard for nothing when I might have been saving her up for the following day.

The indefatigable Irishman who was guiding us had all kinds of reasons why the birds had shifted, but Joe Rudge remained silent and I knew that the only shifting they had done was into the pocket of some local poacher. The guide wanted to work the other side of the same ground in the afternoon, but I vetoed that, so we walked the edge of a marshy pond where I picked up a couple of snipe, and as our car was not expected for hours, we decided to walk towards home till we met it. Time and again the old dog quit the road to hunt ahead of us. Four times in an hour she pointed and I had to shoot at snipe she was holding, two of which I added to the meager bag. It was dawning upon me that O'Neil was right. Despite her wobbly legs, dimmed vision, and deafness, her decrepit old hulk held a heart that never said quit. There was no doubt about it—Nellie was one of the greatest grouse dogs that I had ever seen, and I had shot over Brodick Castle Brigadier when he was the champion of all Scotland and the North of Ireland.

We sat down on the bank of the road and I looked back towards the mountain as we smoked our pipes.

"A grand sight, that, Rudge," I said.

"It is, surrh," he agreed. " 'Tis the Twelve Pins of Connemara—you can count them all from here. I'm sure it's one of the most beautiful spots in the world."

"That's where the leprechauns live, I suppose," I hazarded.

"Oh, it is, surrh. But shure, they do you no harm!"

I was silent for a while digesting that one—there could be no doubt about it, the old man honestly believed in them, God bless him! and I wished that I did, too. And there was that old fool of a Nellie pointing again across the road! I would have to wade out in another bog to satisfy her. Well—let her wait.

"Did you ever see one?" I asked Rudge, knocking out my pipe.

"No, surrh," he answered solemnly. "I never did—though I have seen strange lights at night on the moor. But I know people who have," he added hopefully.

"I'd like to get one to take to America," I said, for the want of something else to say.

"Ah, shure you couldn't ever see one, surrh. 'Tis only an Irishman with the sight that can—they don't take kindly to strangers."

I got up and went out to Nellie to kill the snipe.

The following morning was my last chance. I had to be back by two at the latest, as we were going down into the south to visit friends at Ballybrittas. When I went out back I found Joe Rudge and old Nellie—tail awag—waiting for me. Actually, that old fraud was getting younger. Rudge explained that we could not do better than try Cashel Mountain again. He was sure that we had not put up all the birds there and anyway, we might relocate the big covey. But first, we were to go down the road to the shores of a little lake where the returing fishermen and their gillie had put up a strong covey the evening before. The gillie had told Rudge right where they were. "They're off our land, surrh," he said, "but we'll push them back across the road before we shoot into them."

Reaching the little lake, we skirted the shore unsuccessfully and decided that the birds had moved, so we struck out in the direction of our own moor, crossing a nasty bit of bog where the ground shook like jelly at every step. I was scared, but Rudge assured me that it was all quite safe so long as one did not go through the top crust. That was a comfort! I suppose that if one did he would have gone right down to China! Certainly I was not thinking of birds at the moment and a more unlikely place for them could not be imagined. Yet, there they were. With a loud cackling from the old cock they flushed in front of us, and forgetting the evil footing I cut loose, bringing down one with my left barrel at long range.

We watched them settle half a mile away behind some low hillocks, and took up the pursuit. Old Nellie trotted ahead, and we made two or three unsuccessful casts before she found them to the left of where I expected. I hurried over the intervening space between us and settled down to a walk; as I drew abreast of her the covey sprang, and again I missed with my first and scored with the second, bringing down the old hen of the covey. I loaded my gun and turned to send Nellie after the bird when I noticed that she was still holding her point.

"Hello!" I thought. "There's a single that hasn't got up," and

I worked forward. Then another covey took the air and that time a brace hit the turf. The first covey had led us straight to a second one, and now we had two nice lots spread out before us about another half mile away. We watched them winging swiftly, low over the next ridge, like tiny black spots before one's eyes the morning after a bad night, but Rudge was sure that we would find them.

Picking up the birds, we went on and Nellie found them again. The first bird got up wild, carrying several others with it that apparently had had enough and were going to cross Ireland, but as we topped a knoll, she pointed. A single got up and I downed it; fifty yards from it I grassed another and going to pick it up, flushed two more.

O'Neil was waiting for me when I got back to the hotel. "It's luck you've been having," he declared with an appreciative eye, seeing Rudge with the birds.

"It is," said I.

"How did Nellie do today?"

"Fine," said I, "except that the old fool took after a hare on the way home and chased it halfway back to the Twelve Pins."

"She would," said he. "Sure, before the season is over she will be out of control entirely. There's no holding her!"

And I believed him.

RAYMOND R. CAMP

Hunting Terms

For those hunters who tend to describe bird or animal groups as a "bunch," "herd" or "flock" this is presented as a vocabulary aid. While some of the terms may be obsolete, and others employed primarily in England, Scotland and Ireland, no one can criticize you on the basis of accuracy for their use.

During the earlier days of sports hunting, the fowler, wild-fowler and big game hunter participated in an activity that was formal and formalized. In writing or discussing his sport the individual showed his knowledge, or lack of it, by his use of terms. To some degree, this is true even today. The experienced angler winces when he hears a rod described as a "pole," and the knowing shooter frowns when a rifle is referred to as a "gun."

For more than thirty years I conducted a somewhat desultory research in the formal terms employed in hunting and fishing, a pursuit in which I was assisted by interested readers of the "Wood, Field and Stream" column of *The New York Times*. Many of the terms that emerged from obscurity are obsolete, which in no sense detracts from their interest and color. Some of the early terms were onomatopoetic, others descriptive of the nature or character of the bird or beast, and still others merely dramatic. This is especially apparent in the terms applied to groups of both birds and animals.

Bitterns	Siege
Bustards	Flock or Carry
Capercailzies	Tok
Coots	Covert or Fleet

Cranes	Herd
Crows	Murder
Curlews	Herd
Doves	Flight or Pitying
Ducks	Paddling, Brace, Team or Sore
Eagles	Convocation
Finches	Charm
Geese	Gaggle or Skein
Goldfinches	Charm or Trembling
Grouse	Covey or Pack
Gulls	Colony
Herons	Siege
Jays	Band
Lapwings	Deceit
Larks	Exaltation
Mallards	Sord or Flush
Nightingales	Watch
Peacocks	Ostentation or Pride or Muster
Pheasants	Nide, Nie or Bouquet
Plovers	Congregation
Pochard (Redhead)	Rush
Quail	Bevy or Covey
Ravens	Unkindness
Rooks	Building
Shelldrakes	Dopping or Trip
Snipe	Wisp, Leash or Walk
Sparrows	Host
Starlings	Chattering or Murmuration
Swans	Herd, Wedge
Teal	Spring, Coil or Knob
Thrush	Mutation
Turkeys	Rafter
Widgeon	Company
Woodcock	Fall or Flight
Woodpeckers	Descent
Storks	Mustering
Apes	Shrewdness
Badgers	Set
Bears	Sloth
Boars	Sounder
Camels	Flock

Cats	Clowder, Glaring or Destruction
Chamois	Herd
Colts	Rag
Cur Dogs	Cowardice
Elk	Gang
Ferrets	Business
Foxes	Skulk
Goats	Trip
Hares	Trip, Husk or Drove
Kangaroos	Troop
Leopards	Leap
Lions	Pride
Martens	Richness
Moles	Labor
Monkeys	Troup
Rabbits	Bury
Rhinoceros	Crash
Squirrels	Dray
Wolves	Pack or Route